139341

j917.1 Putnam, Donald Fulton, 1903-
 Put      Canadian regions; a geography of Canada.
       Editor, Donald F. Putnam.   [8th ed.]
       Toronto, Dent, 1968.
          601 p. illus., maps.

       Includes bibliography.


       1. Canada - Descr. & travel.
    I. Title.
                              H-6129
                              20977

# CANADIAN REGIONS

## A Geography of Canada

# Contributors

**DONALD F. PUTNAM,** B.S.A., PH.D. (Toronto)
*Department of Geography,*
*University of Toronto.*

**BENOIT BROUILLETTE,** B.A., M. COM., D.PH. (Sorbonne)
*Faculty of Commerce,*
*University of Montreal.*

**DONALD P. KERR,** M.A., PH.D. (Toronto)
*Department of Geography,*
*University of Toronto.*

**J. LEWIS ROBINSON,** M.A., PH.D. (Clark)
*Department of Geology and Geography,*
*University of British Columbia.*

# CANADIAN REGIONS

## A Geography of Canada

Editor
### DONALD F. PUTNAM

## J. M. DENT & SONS (CANADA) LIMITED
### TORONTO   —   VANCOUVER

*Printed and bound in Canada*
*by*
MARACLE PRESS LIMITED
This book is set in 10 on 11 Baskerville and Bodoni Types

# Publisher's Foreword

The Publishers present CANADIAN REGIONS as an authoritative and up-to-date geographical description of Canada from a Canadian point of view. The authors are native Canadians with lifetimes of experience and personal knowledge of the regions about which they have written. They are all members of university faculties with years of experience in the teaching of Canadian geography.

Professor Brouillette has written the chapters on Quebec; Professor Kerr has written those on British Columbia, and Professor Robinson has dealt with the Canadian Northland. The introductory and concluding chapters, as well as those dealing with the other regions, are the work of Professor Putnam, who has also assumed the task of editing the complete volume. Most of the maps and diagrams have been drawn by R. E. Thornhill from sketches and materials supplied by the authors and the editor. Other figures have been contributed by Mrs. L. J. Wonders, Miss Kate Moore, and Mr. John Crosby.

# Editor's Preface

CANADIAN REGIONS is a geography of Canada. Its purpose is to provide a balanced and up-to-date treatment of the available geographic information. It has been written in the hope that it will prove useful alike to the outsider who wishes to learn about Canada and to the Canadian who wishes to develop a better understanding of his own country.

CANADIAN REGIONS is the work of four authors. By combining the results of their personal observations, researches, and teaching experiences, they have produced a well-rounded and authoritative book. Editorial efforts have been directed mainly toward preserving balance insofar as possible, without disturbing the style, organization, or emphasis in the various sections.

The statistics are as up to date as it was possible to make them at the time of going to press. Some of the data are from the reports of the census of 1941, some from government publications issued at various times during the past decade, and population figures from the preliminary bulletins of the census of 1951 have been inserted during proofreading. The student, the teacher of geography, or the man of affairs will always have available the latest edition of the *Canada Year Book* and will be able to make his own revisions. While accurate data constitute an essential part of geography, it is more important to make correct interpretations and correlations.

This book could not have been compiled without the co-operation and goodwill of numerous persons and organizations in all parts of the country. Among these may be mentioned officials in various departments of the governments of Canada and all ten provinces, municipal officials, boards of trade and chambers of commerce in many towns and cities. Numerous photographs were made available by the National Film Board; the Royal Canadian Air Force; the Photographic Survey Corporation Limited, Toronto, Ontario; Photographic Surveys (Quebec) Limited, Montreal; Canadian National Railways; Canadian Pacific Railways; Experimental Farms Services; Provincial Publicity Bureau, Quebec; British Columbia

Travel Bureau, and others. Figures 233, 234, and 235 are included by kind permission of Dr. W. A. Mackintosh and the Macmillan Company of Canada; figures 46-56, 289, 291, and 294 are used by courtesy of the *Canadian Geographical Journal* and the diagrams in figure 15 are reprinted from *Scientific Agriculture*.

To all who have given us help, we wish to express our sincere thanks and appreciation.

DONALD F. PUTNAM

*Toronto, Ontario*
August, 1952

## Preface to the Second Edition

The widespread acceptance of the first edition of CANADIAN REGIONS having necessitated a second printing, the authors have taken advantage of this opportunity to effect extensive revisions. During the past year the results of the ninth census of Canada, taken in 1951, have become more fully available and they have been used wherever possible in place of older figures. It has not been possible however, to bring up to date all the various graphs throughout the book. Considerable new textual and statistical materials have been inserted in various parts of the book because of the rapid developments taking place in many parts of Canada. The authors hope, therefore, that this edition will prove to be even more useful than its predecessor. To the many friends who have provided materials, checked errors and proffered constructive criticisms we again extend our deepest thanks and appreciation.

DONALD F. PUTNAM

*Toronto, Ontario*
March, 1954

# Contents

Lockwood Survey Corporation Ltd.

*Ottawa, the Capital City of Canada*

*The view includes the Houses of Parliament and Confederation Square. In the background are the Ottawa River and the industries of Hull.*

# CHAPTER 1

# Physical Background

C ANADA is third in size among the countries of the world. Only the U.S.S.R. and China have larger areas. Canadian territory covers 3,845,000 square miles, one-fifteenth approximately, or 6.8%, of the land surface of the globe. This huge area is inhabited by about 16,000,000 people, giving a population density of four and one-seventh per square mile. Only Antarctica, Greenland, Alaska and Australia have lower population densities. The geographer's problem may be stated very simply, it is to explain why one-fifteenth of the world should contain only one one-hundred-and-fiftieth of its total population. This small population is by no means uniformly distributed over the entire area. Less than 500,000 square miles in a narrow band along its southern border may be said to be effectively occupied and even here there are many areas of considerable size which have no inhabitants.

## Global Position

Canada comprises the northern half of the continent of North America, with the exception of Alaska, and all the adjacent islands. Canada looks out upon three oceans. On the west Canada is bounded by the Pacific Ocean and by Alaska, which belongs to the United States; from ocean to ocean the southern boundary, also, is formed by the territory of the United States; on the east lie the Atlantic Ocean, Davis Strait, Baffin Bay and the waters separating Ellesmere Island from Greenland; on the north is the Arctic Ocean, over an appropriate segment of which Canada exercises jurisdiction as far as the North Pole. Middle Island in Lake Erie, north latitude 41° 41', is the southernmost point. From east to west, Canada extends from Cape Spear, west longitude 52° 37', to west longitude 141°, on the Alaskan boundary.

## Political Divisions

The global grid, or graticule, provides a means of precise location for any geographic feature, unit area or point upon the earth's surface. Beyond that, however, it is rather an unimaginative frame of reference. Natural earth features have names, of course, and so do cultural features resulting from the activity of man. Most universally recognized by the map makers are the areas under the control of individual governments or political administrations. The political map depicts one factor only, but it is usually most easily comprehended and most often used.

The common atlas or wall map of Canada shows the country divided into political divisions. Such a map is undoubtedly already familiar to the reader and his attention is for a few moments redirected toward it. (Figure 1). The southern part of Canada is composed of ten provinces,

1

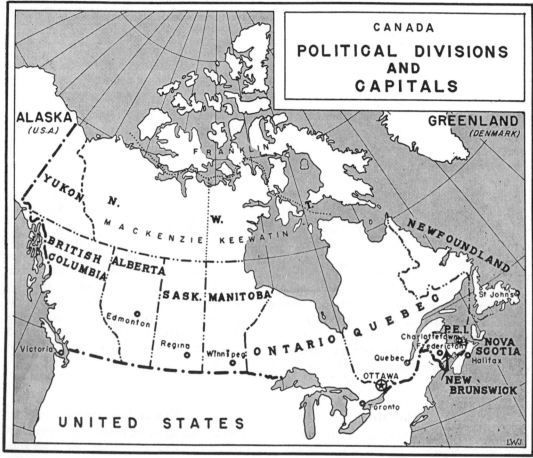

Figure 1. *The Political Divisions of Canada with their capitals.* Canada is composed of ten provinces: British Columbia, Alberta, Saskatchewan, Manitoba, Ontario, Quebec, New Brunswick, Nova Scotia, Prince Edward Island, and Newfoundland; Yukon Territory and the Northwest Territories (Mackenzie, Keewatin and Franklin). Each of the provinces has its own local seat of self government while the territories are administered from the national capital at Ottawa.

each of which enjoys local self government. Reading from west to east, that is from left to right on the conventional map, the provinces are British Columbia, Alberta, Saskatchewan, Manitoba, Ontario, Quebec, New Brunswick, Prince Edward Island, Nova Scotia and Newfoundland. They comprise three-fifths of the total area. The northern two-fifths is made up of the district of Yukon and the Northwest Territories which are subdivided into the districts of Mackenzie, Keewatin and Franklin.

The provinces with their areas and populations, their capital cities and their populations are given in table I, as are also the areas of the northern territories and current estimates of their populations.

Although they carry no political significance there are two well known names which are applied to groups of provinces. They are the Prairie Provinces, including Manitoba, Saskatchewan and Alberta, and the Maritime Provinces, including Nova Scotia, New Brunswick and Prince Edward Island. As we shall see later, however, these areas are not only convenient but fairly logical geographical regions.

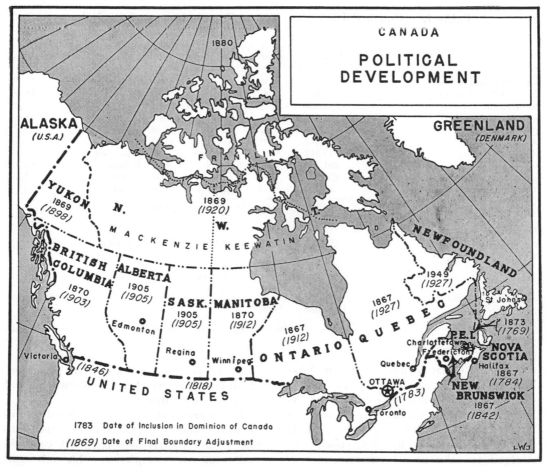

Figure 2. *Political Development and Boundary Adjustments.* Confederation took place in 1867, but the final delimitation of the various units took place at various times, some long before, and some, long after that date. Canada reached its most northerly extent in 1880, when given jurisdiction as far as the North Pole, but it attained its maximum area, only in 1949, with the inclusion of its most easterly province, Newfoundland.

The political map of Canada has undergone many changes, the last one taking place in 1949 when Newfoundland and its Labrador dependency became the tenth province. Our sketch map, figure 2, shows the present administrative divisions, their names and dates of their establishment in their present form.

The Dominion Government was established under the British North America Act in 1867. It was a confederation of three of the scattered British Colonies, Nova Scotia, New Brunswick, and the province of Canada. Since the name, Canada, was chosen for the whole country, Lower Canada and Upper Canada, respectively, became the provinces of Quebec and Ontario. In 1869, the Hudson's Bay Company relinquished its territorial rights and a government was provided for the Northwest Territories. In 1870, the province of Manitoba was established and admitted to confederation and the Northwest Territories transferred to the Dominion. In 1871, British Columbia became a province, followed by Prince Edward Island in 1873. In 1880, the Northwest Territories were enlarged to include all land to the north,

## Table I.   Political Divisions, Areas, Populations and Capitals

| Provinces | Area in Square Miles | Per cent of total area | Population (Census 1956) | Per Cent of total pop. | Capital | Population * |
|---|---|---|---|---|---|---|
| Newfoundland | 154,734 | 4.02 | 415,074 | 2.60 | St. John's | 77,991 |
| Prince Edward Island | 2,183 | 0.06 | 99,285 | .62 | Charlottetown | 16,707 |
| Nova Scotia | 21,068 | 0.55 | 694,717 | 4.35 | Halifax | 164,200 |
| New Brunswick | 27,985 | 0.70 | 554,616 | 3.45 | Fredericton | 18,303 |
| Quebec | 594,860 | 15.47 | 4,628,378 | 28.80 | Quebec | 309,959 |
| Ontario | 412,582 | 10.73 | 5,404,933 | 33.50 | Toronto | 1,358,028 |
| Manitoba | 246,512 | 6.41 | 850,040 | 5.30 | Winnipeg | 409,121 |
| Saskatchewan | 251,700 | 6.54 | 880,665 | 5.48 | Regina | 89,755 |
| Alberta | 255,285 | 6.64 | 1,123,116 | 7.00 | Edmonton | 251,004 |
| British Columbia | 366,255 | 9.52 | 1,398,464 | 8.70 | Victoria | 125,447 |
|  | 2,333,165 | 60.64 | 16,049,288 | 99.80 |  |  |
| *Territories* |  |  |  |  |  |  |
| Yukon | 207,076 | 5.39 | 12,190 | .08 | Whitehorse | 2,570 |
| Northwest Territories |  |  |  |  |  |  |
| Mackenzie | 527,490 | 13.72 | } 19,313 | .12 |  |  |
| Keewatin | 228,161 | 5.93 | 31,503 |  |  |  |
| Franklin | 549,253 | 14.02 |  |  |  |  |
|  | 1,511,980 | 39.36 |  | .20 |  |  |
| CANADA | 3,845,145 | 100.00 | 16,080,791 | 100.00 | Ottawa | 345,460 |

*Suburbs included

over which Great Britain had any jurisdiction. After several shifts in district boundaries, the present provinces of Alberta and Saskatchewan were constituted in 1905. In 1912, the provinces of Manitoba, Ontario and Quebec were enormously enlarged to take in all territory west of Hudson's Bay and south of 60° N. latitude and all of the territory east of the bay which was formerly known as Ungava. The boundary between Quebec and Labrador was fixed by a decision of the British Privy Council in 1927.

Newfoundland, although represented at the first discussion on Confederation in 1864, remained apart from it until after World War II when, as the result of a plebiscite in 1948, it became a part of Canada in March, 1949.

The Northwest Territories, as defined in 1869 and in 1880, have undergone considerable revision apart from the area lost through provincial expansion. The district of Yukon, as it exists on present day maps, was defined in 1897 and, in 1920, the present outlines of the provisional districts of Mackenzie, Keewatin and Franklin came into force.

The consolidation of a scattered group of thinly populated British colonies into one great country has required only 82 years for its completion. Though still underpopulated and underdeveloped, its trading capacity, its proven military might in two world wars, and its political influence are far greater than might be expected of a nation of fourteen millions. Such achievements attest the wisdom of the Fathers of Confederation as well as the ability of the people.

## Geomorphology

According to geological theory the continents are masses of lighter rock floating upon the heavier deep seated rocks of the earth's crust which underlie the floors of the ocean basins. Basically the land mass or continent of North America has a three-part structure. The northeastern portion consists of hard old rocks, once strongly folded and altered, former mountain ranges long since completely worn down, now constituting a stable land mass or Shield. The mid-portion of the continent consists of vast plains underlain by later beds of rock which have departed little from their original horizontal position because they rest upon the ancient Shield. The western margin of the continent is a zone of high and rugged young mountains which were raised up in comparatively recent geological periods and have not yet been worn down. Apparently this is a belt of weaker rocks which has been crumpled between the Shield and the resistant rocks of the floor of the Pacific basin. The eastern margin of the continent also has a mountain belt but it is older and considerably worn down.

Canada, the northern half of the continent, has nearly all of the exposed area of the ancient Shield, hence the interior lowlands are considerably less than those of the United States. Canada also has a very irregular coastline and many large islands. Much of the lower marginal area of the continental mass is flooded and the higher parts protrude while great bays invade the heart of the country. The drowned portion of the mass is known as the continental shelf.

Figure 3 is a map of Canada showing the natural physiographic regions into which the country may be divided.

(1) The *Appalachian Region,* comprising the Maritime Provinces, the island of Newfoundland and the hilly portion of Quebec south of the St. Lawrence River.

(2) The *Canadian Shield,* a vast, rough area of very old Precambrian rocks surrounding Hudson Bay and comprising the northeastern one-third of the country.

(3) The *Interior Lowlands,* underlain by almost undisturbed Paleozoic rocks. These small northern extensions of the great central plains of the United States are found along the St. Lawrence, the Great Lakes and in southern Manitoba.

(4) The *Great Plains,* a vast area extending from western Manitoba to the Rocky Mountains and northward into the

Figure 3. *Physiographic Regions of Canada.* The eastern and western regions are portions of very large natural units which include large areas in the United States as well. The central and northern areas have no counterparts to the south.

Plate 1. The Donjek River is fed by the Glaciers of the St. Elias Mountains.

Mackenzie Valley. It is underlain by gently dipping beds of Mesozoic and Tertiary age. This is the northern half of a physiographic province which extends south to the Rio Grande.

(5) The *Cordilleran Region,* extending from Western Alberta to the Pacific Ocean. It may be divided into the Rocky Mountains, the Interior Plateaus and the Coast and Insular Ranges.

(6) The *Hudson Bay Lowland,* an area of flat-lying paleozoic rocks much like those of the interior lowlands farther south.

(7) The *Arctic Archipelago,* a composite area of many large islands of Northern Canada, resting upon the continental shelf which borders the Arctic Ocean. The ten largest islands range from 10,000 to 200,000 square miles in area.

Figure 4 is a much generalized contour map of Canada which needs to be studied in conjunction with the preceding map in order to gain a full appreciation of the pattern. Only a small portion of the country, practically all located in the Cordilleran region, is above 4,000 feet in eleva-

tion. More than 70 named peaks exceed 11,000 feet in elevation. The highest peaks are in the St. Elias Mountains in the southwestern corner of Yukon where Mount Logan reaches 19,850 feet above sea level. Mount Robson (12,972 feet) is the highest peak in the Rocky Mountains and Mount Waddington (13,260 feet) is the highest of the coast mountains. In eastern Canada, the Torngats of Labrador rise to about 5,500 feet while the summit of Mount Jacques Cartier, the highest peak in the Shickshocks of the Gaspé Peninsula, is 4,160 feet above sea level.

The Great Plains are, for the most part, above or very close to the 2,000 foot level while the Canadian Shield, with the exception of some parts of Quebec and Labrador, is less than 2,000 feet in elevation. Baffin Island, Devon Island and Ellesmere Island also have considerable areas above 2,000 feet in elevation. These high areas carry extensive ice fields.

The Hudson Bay Lowland and adjoining portions of the Canadian Shield appear as an enormous basin surrounded by an upland rim. A somewhat similar but much smaller basin contains the Gulf of St. Lawrence. A third great depression is found in the northwest, between the Shield and the Rocky Mountains. Unlike the other two, it is not low enough to be invaded by the sea but it does contain several very large lakes. These major depressions, sometimes called *geosynclines*, exert a controlling influence upon the drainage pattern of the country.

## Natural Drainage

Some of the more important river systems are shown in figure 5. Here the controlling influence of the Hudson Bay depression is seen for it receives the water from 1,400,000 square miles, almost half of the mainland of Canada. The Nelson River system drains 368,000 square miles,

exclusive of a small area in the United States. From the head of the Bow River in the Rocky Mountains, its total length is 1,600 miles. Other important rivers entering Hudson Bay are the Churchill, 1,000 miles; Severn, 610 miles; Albany, 610 miles; Dubawnt, 580 miles; Eastmain, 510 miles; and the Moose 340 miles in length. The Koksoak River flowing into Ungava Bay is 660 miles long.

An area of over 900,000 square miles drains to the Arctic Ocean, more than half of it by way of the Mackenzie. This river is the longest in Canada measuring 2,635 miles to the head of the Finlay, its most distant source. Its drainage basin contains some very large lakes including Great Bear, 12,000 square miles; Great Slave, 11,170 square miles; and Athabaska, 3,058 square miles in area. From Fort Smith on

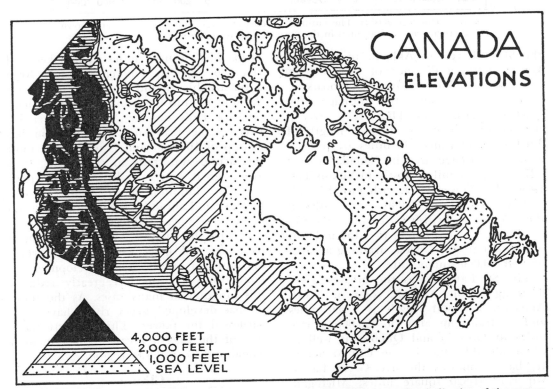

Figure 4. *Elevations.* This much generalized contour map of Canada gives a first indication of the nature of the various physiographic regions. The western mountains contain the only large area of really elevated land.

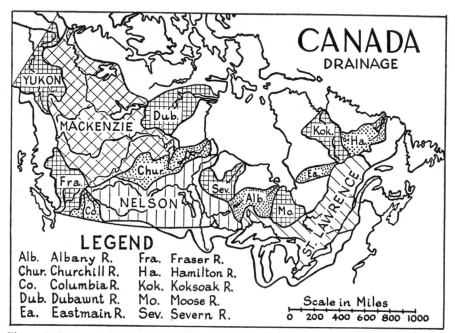

Figure 5. *Drainage Basins.* The outlines of fourteen large drainage basins are shown, but there are many small ones in the unshaded areas of the map.

the Slave River, to Aklavik in the Mackenzie delta, a distance of nearly 1,300 miles is navigable for large river boats.

The Pacific receives the drainage from 400,000 square miles. The largest river is the Yukon which has a total length of 1,979 miles of which 714 miles are in Canada. Its drainage area in Canada is over 127,000 square miles, mostly in Yukon Territory. The Fraser River, with a total length of 850 miles, drains 80,000 square miles in the interior of British Columbia. The Columbia has a total length of 1,150 miles of which 459 are in Canada, draining an area of over 40,000 square miles.

The St. Lawrence is the greatest river draining to the Atlantic coast of North America. Its total length is 1,900 miles and it drains an area of 359,000 square miles in Ontario and Quebec as well as a considerable area in the United States. Its basin contains the five Great Lakes: Superior 31,820 square miles; Michigan, 22,400 square miles; Huron, 23,010 square miles; Erie, 9,940 square miles and On-

tario, 7,540 square miles. The lakes and rivers of the St. Lawrence system form a remarkable inland waterway for nearly 2,000 miles into the heart of the continent. Niagara Falls on the Niagara River between Lake Erie and Lake Ontario has a drop of 160 feet and is one of the most spectacular waterfalls in the world. It is also a great source of hydro-electric power. The Hamilton River drains a great plateau in Labrador, the Grand Falls on this river are over 300 feet high.

During the early history of the country its rivers and lakes were very important as routes of travel. The development of land transportation has greatly reduced this function in many cases. As the country has developed many rivers have been harnessed for power. This is particularly true of the rugged areas of the Canadian Shield and Cordilleran region.

## Climate

Canadian territory extends 42° to 83° N. latitude, almost half way from the equator to the North Pole, and a slightly greater distance from east to west. Consequently the climate of Canada is one of great variation. While this variation will be treated in considerable detail in subsequent regional studies it will be necessary in this introduction to show the relationship to the general world pattern and to draw in some regional outlines.

## Temperature

All differences in climate from place to place on the earth's surface are due to the unequal distribution of the radiant energy of the sun and its resultant redistribution and loss. Other factors being equal, we expect temperature to decrease from the equator to the pole because of the difference in the angle with which the sun's rays strike the surface of the earth. The angle changes with the seasons since in June the overhead sun is 23½° north

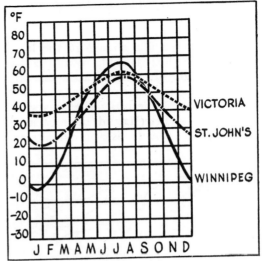

Figure 6. *The Influence of Continental Position on the Temperature Regime.* Victoria, B.C.; Winnipeg, Manitoba; and St. John's, Newfoundland; all have practically the same latitude. The differences in their temperature curves must be attributed to their positions in west coast, central continental and east coast locations.

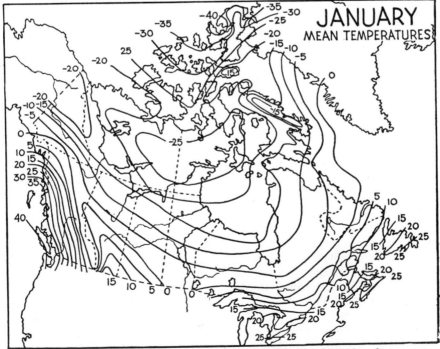

Figure 7. *January Mean Temperatures.* Midwinter in Canada is cold, only a narrow band on the west coast remains above freezing. Note the extremely cold 'loop' in the north central portion.

of the equator while in December it is 23½° south.

Coincident with the shift of the overhead sun there is a change in the length of day. In low latitude countries this change is of little significance but in a northern country such as Canada its effect is great. Thus while the longest day (June 21) on Pelee Island, the most southerly part of Canada, is approximately 15

the Arctic circle. The corresponding lack of daylight makes the northern winter indescribably bitter.

Another important factor in temperature distribution is the difference between land and water. Land heats up more quickly and cools off more rapidly than water. In the summer the interior of a large land mass such as North America gets much warmer than its coastal areas.

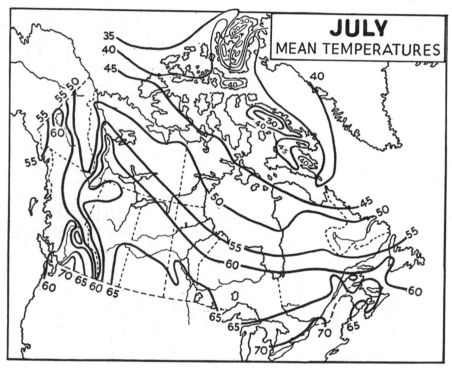

Figure 8. *July Mean Temperatures.* Midsummer temperatures are much more uniform than those of midwinter, the north-south gradient is very gradual. Note the warm 'loop' extending down the Mackenzie Valley.

hours, it is 16 hours at the 49th parallel and 24 hours at Great Bear Lake which is on the Arctic Circle (66½° N. Latitude). Northward the period of daylight lengthens rapidly and at Canada's most northerly point of land the midnight sun is visible for approximately five months. This extra length of day in some measure compensates the lower intensity of the sun's rays in northern latitudes and permits the growth of some crop plants even within

In winter the opposite is the case and interiors are colder than the coasts. Large water surfaces act as great equalizers of temperature and coastal places have narrow ranges of temperature. Because of the prevailing winds and the pattern of ocean currents this effect is greater on the west coast of Canada than it is on the east. This can readily be seen in a comparison of the temperature records of Victoria, B.C. and St. John's, Newfoundland.

The effect of a continental position is shown by the record for Winnipeg, Manitoba. (Figure 6).

Still another factor affecting the temperature pattern is the elevation of the land, but because of the complexity of mountainous regions its effect cannot be shown accurately upon small scale maps. It is often stated that a difference of 1,000 feet in elevation makes a difference of 3° F.

## Air Masses

Air which remains for a long time in one position or travels for a long time over

in summer a large part of the interior of the continent may become occupied by a mass of warm dry air. The climate of Canada is also greatly influenced by air masses which receive their characteristic properties in areas at a considerable distance. We will, therefore, briefly discuss the major air masses which affect the continent of North America. The general locations of these masses are shown in the accompanying chart (Figure 9).

Polar continental air masses accumulate over northern Canada. In winter they become intensely cold. They are protected

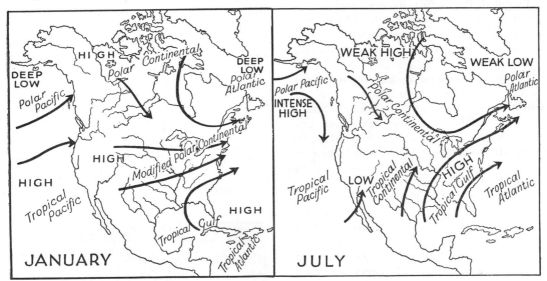

Figure 9. *Air Masses Affecting the Climate of Canada.* (a) In January the polar air mass is greatly enlarged influencing the whole of Canada. Warm air affects only the southern and coastal margins. (b) In July warm air covers the whole country as far as the Arctic Sea.

the same kind of surface tends to take on qualities characteristic of its environment. Thus polar air masses tend to be cold, tropical air masses tend to be warm, those conditioned by a long sojourn over land are dry and those remaining for a long time over the sea take on a great deal of moisture. Air masses are affected by seasonal temperature regimes so that in winter a great deal of cold dry air tends to accumulate over northern Canada and at times may spread over a great deal of the continent. On the other hand,

by the mountains of the Cordilleran region against the invasion of moist air from the Pacific, hence they are also dry. In summer the lower layers of air become somewhat warmed by contact with the earth but there is always plenty of cold air aloft with a tendency to settle earthward. When air from this region spreads over the country, either in winter or summer it brings lowered temperatures and typically cloudless weather.

Polar Pacific air masses originate over the north Pacific Ocean. It is warmer than polar continental air because of its contact with the water but it is still moderately cool. It is also moist. The west coast is under the influence of this air mass during most of the year.

Polar Atlantic air gets its characteristics from contact with the Atlantic, north of the Gulf Stream drift. It is cold and has less moisture content than other marine air masses. From time to time this air invades Newfoundland and the Maritime Provinces. In spring and summer it is a source of cold air accompanied by cloudy unsettled weather.

Tropical Pacific air masses originate in the warm part of the Pacific Ocean and sometimes invade the continent but seem to have little direct effect on the Canadian climate.

Tropical continental air becomes differentiated in Northern Mexico and the southwestern part of the United States. Being an elevated region, it is cool and dry in winter and its atmosphere is hardly to be differentiated from Polar continental air. In summer it is warm and exceedingly dry and may at times move north as far as the Prairie Provinces.

Tropical Gulf and Tropical Atlantic air masses are of extreme importance in central and eastern North America including the southern part of Canada. Summer is the season of greatest effect for these air masses. The interior of the continent develops a low pressure while the western Atlantic becomes a high pressure area. Warm moist air therefore, invades the eastern part of the continent, becoming even warmer until it reaches the region of the Great Lakes. This extra heat generates thunderstorms which are accompanied by precipitation. In fact most of the summer precipitation is of this type.

In winter the Tropical Gulf air encounters the polar continental mass in the region between the Gulf of Mexico and the Great Lakes and, being warmer and lighter, tends to override it causing heavy precipitation which is usually rain in the Southern States and snowfall in Southern Canada. The source of most of the moisture of the Humid East of North America, then, is in the great expanse of warm water in the Caribbean Sea and Gulf of Mexico.

**Fronts**

'Front' is the term given to the zone of contact between two air masses of different qualities. Since air is extremely fluid, fronts are zones of mixing and of unsettled weather. There are two main types of frontal formations. Cold fronts occur when a cold air mass advances into or underruns a warm one, while a warm front is formed when a warm air mass is forced to rise over the edge of a cold air mass. The sinuous fluctuating zone which crosses North America from west to east dividing the polar air masses from those of tropical origin is usually known as the Polar front.

Other fronts may also develop as, for instance, between the Polar Pacific and Polar continental air masses or between a fresh outbreak of polar air and the now modified polar continental air of a previous outbreak.

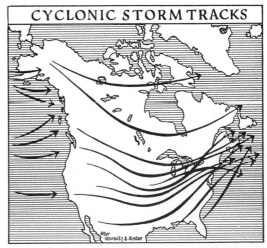

Figure 10. *Generalized Map of Cyclonic Storm Tracks Across North America.* Note that most of these routes converge on the Great Lakes and leave the continent by way of the Maritime Provinces.

## Cyclonic Storms

Southern Canada is often stated to be in the belt of westerly winds and cyclonic storms. Long before the days of air mass studies it was known that our weather was characterized by the passing of alternate high and low pressure areas from west to east across the country. The low pressure areas or cyclones are gigantic eddies in the atmosphere into which air currents spiral from all directions. Precipitation usually accompanies these storms. On the other hand the winds spiral outward from the high pressure areas or anticyclones, the passing of which occasions periods of clear dry weather. This type of weather is more noticeable in the cool half of the year when the cyclonic belt lies farther south. Regardless of where they may first appear on the continent these storms usually leave it by way of eastern Canada.

## The Effects of Surface Relief

Compared with the sea the surface of the land is rough and offers considerable resistance to the free passage of air masses. This is, of course, particularly true of western Cordilleran region, but Atlantic air masses also find difficulty in invading the continent beyond the Appalachians.

The Cordilleran region has a great effect upon the climatic pattern. The temperature variations due to elevation are alone enough to make it a distinct climatic region. There are two important results of its function as a barrier to the passage of air masses. In the first place, because the air must rise rapidly on reaching the mountains, with a great cooling and condensation of its moisture content, the West Coast is the area of greatest rainfall in Canada. Secondly, since this precipitation is withheld from the valleys and plains to the east of the mountains, the latter areas are correspondingly dry. Such areas in the lee of mountains are known as *rain shadows* and, in some parts of the earth, are occupied by extremely dry deserts.

The "chinook" is another striking effect of the mountain barrier. It is a warm dry wind which from time to time affects the area east of the mountains. In winter it may cause spectacular changes in the weather bringing temperatures of 50° F. or over to Calgary and Lethbridge in mid-winter. In winter, as we have noted, the interior of Canada is occupied by cold Polar continental air while warmer air is found

*Courtesy: Ont. Dept. Lands & Forests.*
Plate 2. Snow Scene in Eastern Canada.

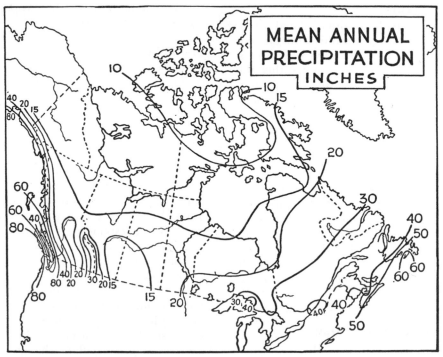

Figure 11. *Mean Annual Precipitation*. Only in the Pacific borderlands and in the extreme southeast is there heavy precipitation. It is much lighter in the central and northern parts.

on the West Coast. The passage of a pronounced cyclone across the midwestern States and Great Lakes will cause the cold air to be drawn off rapidly to the southeast. Its place will be taken by the upper levels of the Pacific air which is easily able to flow across the mountain barrier and is greatly warmed by compression as it glides down the eastern slopes. Since this air has been elevated over the mountain ranges it contains little moisture, and its power of evaporation is greatly increased by the rise of temperature during its descent.

Its most visible result, therefore, is a rapid removal of snow cover from the Prairies. This is of considerable value to the ranching districts of southern Alberta where it makes winter grazing possible. Measured from this point of view, the area of a "chinook" rarely extends beyond Swift Current but the whole Prairie region ex-

periences a spell of mild weather in sharp contrast with the "cold wave" which preceded it.

**Precipitation**

The map of mean annual precipitation (Figure 11) shows Canada, on the whole, to be a country of little rainfall. Most of the country has less than 20 inches per annum. Narrow wet belts appear along the western mountain ranges while a broader area with an adequate rainfall is found in the southeast from the Great Lakes to the Atlantic Ocean. The highest rainfall is found on the west coast of Vancouver Island where there are stations which have records of over 200 inches per year while 100 inches seems to be a general average for the coastal strip. The eastern margin of the island is a rain shadow where some stations have an average of less than 30 inches. The pattern is repeated on the coast of the mainland where most stations have over 60 inches per year and one has over 100 inches. The interior of B.C. has less than 15 inches and there are some stations with less than 10 inches per year on the average. The western slopes of Selkirks and Rocky Mountains are wet but not so rainy as the Coast Ranges. The Prairie areas have an average of less than 15 inches of rain per year, constituting a broad "rain shadow" of the Rocky Mountains, wherein a few stations receive even less than 10 inches. A belt in the central part of the Prairie Provinces receives a little over 15 inches per year while north of this lies about half of the area of Canada with less than 15 inches. There is a large area in the Arctic Archipelago and adjoining mainland which gets less than 10 inches. The record for least precipitation is held by Eureka (80° N), one of the most northerly weather stations in Canada, which receives less than 2 inches per year.

In a country such as Canada, with great temperature differences between summer and winter, the seasonal distribution of rainfall is highly important. In the high rainfall areas of the west coast the summers are relatively dry while the winters are wet. Many places on Vancouver Island and the north coastal area of B.C. receive more rain in a single winter month than Prairie stations get in a whole year. On the other hand the rainfall of the Prairies comes in the summer, some stations getting half the year's total in three summer months. The low rainfall of the interior of B.C., on the other hand, tends to be rather uniformly distributed but the winter maximum is again in evidence on the western slopes of the Rocky Mountains. Southeastern Canada is a region of uniform rainfall, with little difference from month to month except on the Atlantic coast where there is a tendency for a winter maximum. In the low rainfall

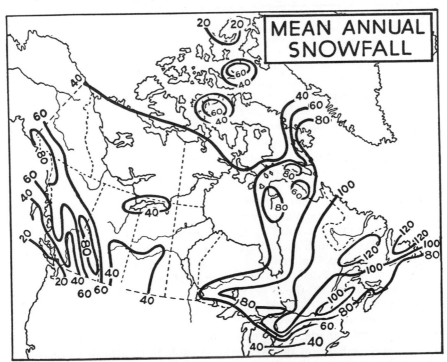

Figure 12. *Mean Annual Snowfall.* Southeastern Canada is the general region of heaviest snowfall, but much snow falls on the slopes of the western mountain ranges as well.

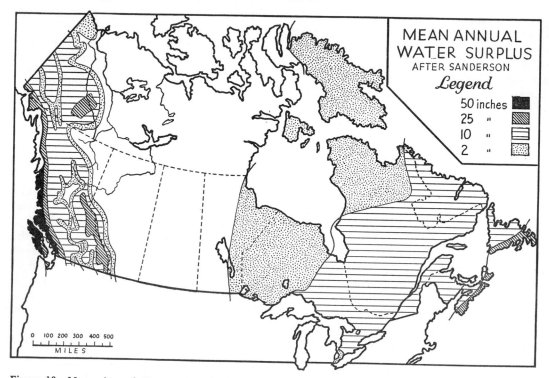

Figure 13. *Mean Annual Water Surplus in Canada*, according to the formula of Dr. C. W. Thornthwaite, (after Sanderson). The central and northern areas have little surplus moisture on an annual basis.

regions of the north the greatest precipitation occurs in late summer and autumn with very little in the winter.

Another result of seasonal temperature differences is that considerable precipitation occurs as snow. A generalized map of snowfall distribution is shown in figure 12. As might be expected, the areas of greatest snowfall lie in areas of great total precipitation but the agreement between the two maps is by no means complete. Vancouver Island, which has the greatest total rainfall, is too warm to receive much snow. The highest snowfall records in Western Canada are at Anyox on the border of Alaska (203 inches) and Glacier in the Rocky Mountains (390 inches per year). Much the largest area of land affected by heavy snowfall is located in Eastern Canada, in a great wedge extending from a base on the Newfoundland-Labrador coast to the district surrounding Georgian Bay. All of this re-

gion receives over 100 inches of snow per year, with some areas exceeding 120 inches. The record is held by Harrington Harbour in the eastern part of Quebec with 204 inches per year. The position of this wedge is, of course, very closely related to the usual tracks of winter cyclonic storms.

**Moisture Surplus and Deficiency**

Moisture derived from precipitation is disposed of in two ways. Either it is evaporated and transpired back to the atmosphere in the locality in which it fell or it runs away in the streams and eventually finds its way back to the ocean. The ability of the atmosphere to take up moisture is, of course, directly related to temperature. If at any season of the year the supply of moisture is greater than the capacity of the atmosphere to absorb it, there is a surplus to feed the streams. On the other hand, deficiencies occur when the climatic need

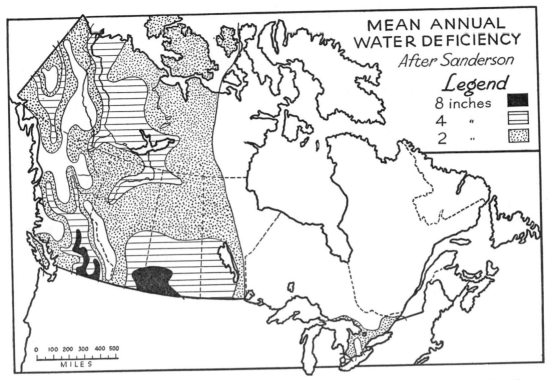

Figure 14. *Mean Annual Water Deficiency in Canada,* according to the formula of Dr. C. W. Thorn-thwaite, (after Sanderson). Note the contrast between this map and Figure 13. Note too, that some areas have both surplus and deficiency, but at different times of the year.

for water, that is the evaporating power of the atmosphere, is greater than the supply. If the deficiency is great and pro-longed then we call it a drought. In Can-ada, as a rule, surplus water comes during the winter when temperatures are very low. Much of it accumulates as snow which does not melt until spring thus not only completely saturating the soil but giving rise to floods as well. On the other hand during the summer season the climatic need is much greater than the rainfall, the soil dries out and a moisture defi-ciency results.

Many investigators have tried to meas-ure climatic moisture relations. The most recent attempt and the one which seems most adapted to Canadian conditions is that of the American climatologist, Dr. C. W. Thornthwaite. Using his formulae Mrs.

M. Sanderson has drawn up the maps re-produced herewith.

Figure 13 shows the distribution of an-nual water surplus. It is seen that the southeastern seaboard of Nova Scotia and Newfoundland has a surplus of more than 25 inches per year while the west coast has more than 50 inches. These, of course, are the areas of greatest rainfall. On the other hand the Prairie Provinces and Northwest Territories have a surplus of less than two inches and some small areas actually have none at all.

Water deficiency is shown in figure 14. Very large areas in the east have less than two inches while the same is true for the west coast and high mountain areas. The southern prairies and the interior of Brit-ish Columbia have annual deficiencies which may amount to more than eight inches.

When the two maps are compared it is evident that much of Canada experiences both surplus and deficiency. Southwestern Ontario, for instance, has a deficiency of four inches and a surplus of ten. These, of course, occur at different seasons giving that area a pronounced wet-and-dry climate. The same is true in varying degree for other parts of Canada as is shown by the station diagrams in figure 15.

While zero isopleths have not been drawn on the maps and, in fact, would be very hard to locate, it is evident that somewhere in western Ontario, or eastern Manitoba, very low deficiencies cancel out equally low surpluses. This is a very significant zone which separates the humid east coast climate from that of the interior. In the Cordilleran region a similar zone, which is even more difficult to indicate on a map, separates the interior from the moist west coast.

## Major Climatic Regions

The major climatic regions shown in the accompanying map have been drawn up with an eye to the realities of the pattern of natural vegetation and the needs of agriculture. From both points of view the length of the growing period and the availability of soil moisture are the most important criteria.

The experiments of botanists with ordinary mid-latitude crops such as cereals have indicated that a temperature of 42° or 43° F. is necessary for growth. The length of the summer growing period is conveniently measured in months, and, with less than six months of growing temperatures the variety of crops which may be grown is strictly limited. This limit also seems to fit the boundary between the hardwood and coniferous forests. With a growing season of less than five months, most agriculture is very difficult if not impossible. The northern limit of forests corresponds very closely to the isopleth of 50° F. for July mean temperature and it

is adopted as the southern limit of the Arctic climates.

The most significant moisture criteria seem to be those derived by C. W. Thornthwaite and applied to Canadian data by M. Sanderson. Along a line extending from Lake of the Woods to Churchill a balance is struck between water surplus and water deficiency thus dividing the humid east coast climates from the sub-humid interior types. This line continues north to divide the moist arctic from the dry arctic climatic regions. The critical limit in the Thornthwaite system which separates the subhumid from the semi-arid also conveniently outlines the driest parts of western Canada.

The use of the foregoing criteria enables us to outline ten major climatic regions which, of course, may be much further subdivided in the regional studies of this book.

1. Dry Arctic.
2. Moist Arctic.
3. Boreal Interior.
4. Boreal East Coast.
5. Cool Temperate Interior.
6. Semi Arid.
7. Cool Temperate East Coast with short summers.
8. Cool Temperate East Coast with long summers.
9. Cool Temperate West Coast.
10. Mountain Climates.

Arctic climates are those in which no month has a mean temperature above 50° F. Only a narrow southern border of this region has more than one month above 43° F. and much of the area none at all. There are significant moisture differences between the eastern and western regions, the western Arctic in general having less rainfall and an overall moisture deficiency. The eastern Arctic, parts of which have 15-20 inches of precipitation, has a moisture surplus. In this area too, the higher parts of Baffin Island, Devon Island and Ellesmere Island have permanent ice caps.

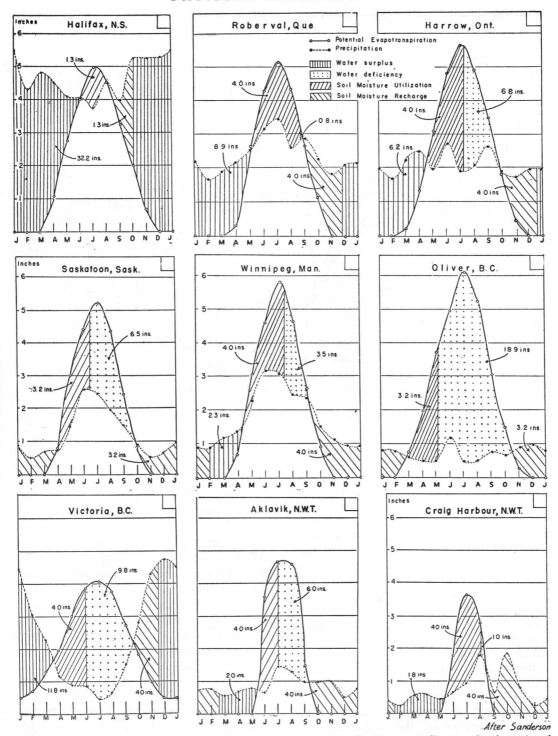

**Figure 15.** *Moisture Relations of Nine Representative Canadian Stations,* according to the formula of Dr. C. W. Thornthwaite. (Scientific Agriculture 28.)

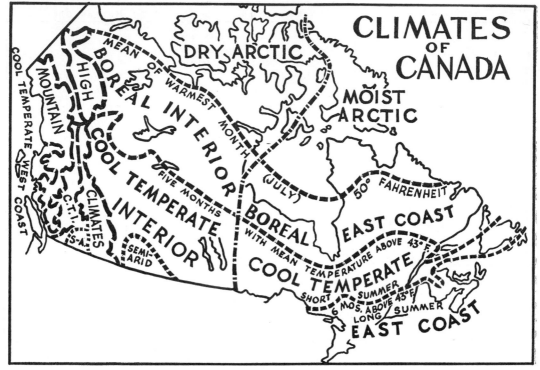

Figure 16. *Major Climatic Regions of Canada.*

Permafrost or permanently frozen ground is encountered everywhere.

Boreal, Subarctic or Cold climates extend from Alaska to Labrador. This region has less than five months with growing temperatures of 43° F. or higher. The southern boundary also corresponds very closely to the July isotherm of 60° F. mean temperature. This line marks the northern limits of commercial forests and is also the limit of successful agriculture. West of Hudson Bay the subhumid interior area gets from 10 inches to 15 inches of precipitation which is not enough to balance evaporation. The humid east coast Boreal climate, on the other hand, receives from 20 inches to 40 inches of precipitation and always has a water surplus.

The Cool Temperate climatic regions stretch across southern Canada from Atlantic to Pacific, interrupted only by the high mountains of the Cordilleran region. For the most part these regions have

from five to seven months of growing temperatures with the July means ranging from 60° F. to 70° F. It is important to note, however, that although not shown on the map, small areas in southern B.C., southern Alberta and southern Ontario have midsummer means above 70° F. On the other hand much of the west coast has midsummer mean temperatures between 55° F. and 60° F. The short summer phase and the long summer phase are separated by the line representing six months of growing temperatures. This division occurs only in the east since all stations on the west coast have more than six months growing season.

On the basis of moisture relations four divisions appear: the wet west coast, the subhumid interior, the semi-arid areas of southern B.C. and the southern Prairies, and the humid east coast. A narrow fringe of the Atlantic seaboard might also be classed as wet since it has over 25 inches of surplus water yearly.

The tenth division comprises the high mountain areas which are both cool and wet or snowy because of their great elevation.

## Vegetation

Because plant growth is so definitely under the influence of moisture supply and temperature, geographers have long recognized the importance of the pattern of natural vegetation. In fact the climatic types of some regions are more often known by the names of their associated types of vegetation as, for example, tundra, selva and savanna. In spite of this no full study of the plant geography of Canada has yet been undertaken. Adams' "Flora of Canada" gives useful information on a very broad regional basis. Halliday's "Forest Classification For Canada" is also most useful but it deals only with forest trees which, while the most noticeable, are not necessarily the most important elements of the plant cover. The exact relationships of forest distribution to various climatic factors are not yet completely understood and no maps have yet been drawn which show the exact climatic controls of the various forest types in Canada. Certain broad correlations, however, do appear.

The simplest concept is probably that of the climax association. Theoretically a particular climate favours the selection of certain species which tend to become a balanced and stable plant community. Thus a maple-beech-basswood hardwood forest characterizes a large part of southern Ontario while western hemlock and western red cedar dominate the forest of the Pacific coast. The vegetation region, however, is much more complex for it must take into consideration, also, all the various sub-climax association. The denudation of a forest area by fire is followed by an entirely different plant association. In certain parts of Nova Scotia, for instance, the burning of a mixed spruce, balsam fir, red maple stand is followed by blueberries, wire birch and

tamarack. In the Lake Superior region, mixed forests are followed by aspen and white birch in many cases.

Edaphic conditions also cause great variation in the forest cover. In eastern Ontario, the rolling hill lands of Glengarry carry an association of sugar maple, beech and white cedar, the adjoining clay plains are characterized by elm, ash and soft maple. Sand plains in the same locality originally had magnificent stands of white pine. All these variations must, of course, be comprehended within the same vegetation region.

Vegetation regions must take into account not only the plants which can be identified, but also the plant communities or associations, the density of the stand and type of growth, and the apparent adaptation of the various species to the environment. White spruce, for instance, is found from Nova Scotia to the Yukon and is characteristic of the great Boreal Forest which, in most geographies, stretches unbroken over most of the land mass of Canada. Balsam fir, tamarack, aspen and white birch are almost as widespread. The growth and appearance of these trees in the northern "land of little sticks", however, is very different from that in the southern part of the country.

Having in mind the foregoing points, the accompanying map of vegetation regions was drawn up (Figure 17). Its main boundaries are fairly close to those of Halliday, but it has not been possible to show all the small areas of different vegetation types which exist in the Cordilleran region. Fourteen vegetation regions, accordingly, will be discussed in the following paragraphs.

1. Arctic Tundra.
2. Subarctic or Transition Forest Region.
3. Boreal Forest Region or Taiga.
4. Pacific Coast Forest Region.
5. Rocky Mountain Forest Region.
6. Alpine Tundra.
7. Columbia Forest Region.

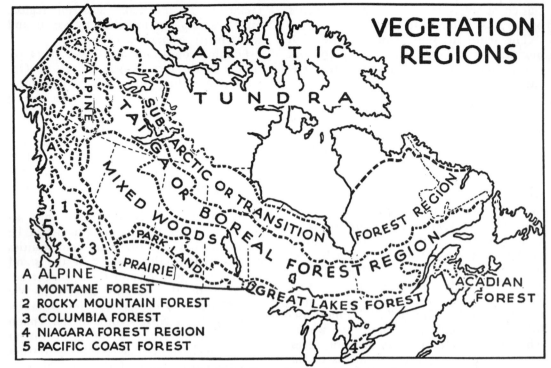

Figure 17. *Major Vegetation Regions of Canada.*

8. Montane Forest Region.
9. Central Mixed Woods Region.
10. Aspen Grove or Parkland Region.
11. Prairie Region.
12. Great Lakes—St. Lawrence Forest Region.
13. Niagara Forest Region.
14. The Acadian Forest Region.

### The Arctic Tundra

Treeless landscapes characterize the northern part of the mainland and the entire Arctic Archipelago comprising nearly one-third of the total area. The severe climate with its long, excessively cold winter and its low rainfall have already been described. Another important factor is the perpetually frozen subsoil, above which the ground thaws out to a depth of 2 or 3 feet annually.

The word *tundra* is derived from the Finnish "tundren" meaning a treeless rolling

plain. Treelessness was formerly thought to be due entirely to low temperatures but various investigators in recent years have indicated that lack of moisture is just as important. Some of the "barren ground" therefore may be regarded as Arctic steppe. Porsild states "So light indeed is the rainfall during the growing season that, were it not for the fact that the ground remains perpetually frozen a few inches below the surface thus preventing the surface water from penetrating to levels beyond the reach of the roots, most of the Arctic zone would be a lifeless desert." [1] On the other hand our climatic maps show that the extreme eastern part of the Arctic has an excess of moisture. It is evident then that there is no simple floral association that may be said to characterize the tundra. Rather it is a complex mosaic of associations.

The vegetation of drift covered plains consists of prairie and heath. In the Arc-

[1] *Canada's Western Northland.* p. 134. Ottawa. 1937.

tic prairies, grasses and sedges comprise the bulk of the cover forming a short dense sward. Arctic poppy, dandelion, Arctic wallflower and other flowering plants are found. Such meadows are very extensive in central Keewatin and along the Arctic coast. On the upland north of Great Bear Lake and in other places as well there are wide areas of Arctic heath. Here are found ground birch (*Betula glandulosa*), Labrador tea (*Ledum decumbens*), white heather (*Cassiope tetragona*), bilberry (*Vaccinium uliginosum* var. *alpinum*), Alpine cranberry (*V. Vitis-Idaea*), cotton grass (*Eriophorum vaginatum*), Arctic lupine (*Lupinus nootkatensis*), loco-weed (*Oxytropis*) and rhododendron (*Rhododendron lapponicum*).

The rocky areas have a much more scattered plant cover including rock lichen (*Gyrophora*), arctic ferns (*Woodsia glabella, W. ilvensis* and *Dryopteris fragrans*), saxifrages, crowberry (*Empetrum*) and vetch (*Astragalus alpinus*). The outstanding characteristics of arctic plants are their low cushion-like growth forms and the amazing rapidity with which they go through the annual cycle of growth. The small purple flowered saxifrage (*Saxifraga oppositifolia*); the yellow whitlow grass (*Draba alpina*) and the yellow Iceland poppy are able to mature seed within a month of commencing growth. However, very few plants are annuals and most of them have some vegetative means of reproduction, such as overwintering buds, and are not totally dependent upon seed production.

### The Subarctic or Transition Forest Region

The transitional zone between the tundra and the Boreal Forest stretches unbroken from the Mackenzie to the Strait of Belle Isle but reaches its greatest breadth in Ungava and Labrador. This is undoubtedly a response to the low summer temperatures of this region. From the standpoint of tree species this is part of Boreal Forest, the most common trees being white spruce (*Picea glauca*), black spruce (*P. mariana*), larch (*Larix laricina*) and white birch (*Betula papyrifera*). The trees of this zone are in scattered stands and stunted, very few attaining useful size, hence the popular designation, "land of little sticks". The creeping form of the common juniper (*Juniperus communis*) is also found as well as dwarf willow and ground birch.

This is a region of lakes and muskegs, the latter being undrained basins now filled with peat moss. Around the edges dense stands of tamarack and black spruce are found the trees being smaller and smaller toward the centre of the bog. In the central treeless area are found Labrador tea, leatherleaf (*Chamaedaphne calyculata*), bog rosemary (*Andromeda polifolia*) and cranberry.

### The Boreal Forest Region

The Boreal Forest or Taiga extends from Newfoundland to Alaska. The principal trees are white and black spruce, balsam fir (*Abies balsamea*), aspen (*Populus tremuloides*), large-toothed aspen (*P. grandidentata*), balsam poplar (*P. tacamahaca*), Balm of Gilead (*P. candicans*), paper birch and jack pine (*Pinus Banksiana*). In the far northwest, alpine fir (*Abies lasiocarpa*), lodgepole pine (*Pinus contorta*) and Alaska

Plate 3. A Plank Road in the Pulpwood Forests of the Northern Ontario Clay Belt.

D. F. Putnam

white birch (*Betula alaskana*) are found. The previously mentioned shrubs are found here together with others commonly found in more southern regions. Herbaceous plants of the forest floor include gold thread (*Coptis trifolia*), kidney-leaved violet (*Viola renifolia*), bunch-berry (*Cornus canadensis*), Coral root (*Corallorrhiza trifida*), Clintonia (*Clintonia borealis*) and twinflower (*Linnaea borealis*). There are also many ferns.

The eastern half of this forest belt, from Manitoba to Newfoundland is the great area of pulpwood exploitation.

## Pacific Coast Forest Region

In the mild and humid climate of the Pacific coast forest trees grow luxuriantly. The dominant species are conifers including western hemlock (*Tsuga heterophylla*) and western red cedar (*Thuja plicata*). Associated with these are Sitka spruce (*Picea sitchensis*) in the north and Douglas fir (*Pseudotsuga taxifolia*) in the south. Other conifers found here are western white pine (*Pinus monticola*), amabilis fir (*Abies amabilis*), alpine fir (*Abies lasiocarpa*), and mountain hemlock (*Tsuga Mertensiana*). Alluvial lands in the south are occupied by black cottonwood (*Populus trichocarpa*), red alder (*Alnus rubra*), broad-leaved maple (*Acer macrophyllum*) and grand fir (*Abies grandis*) In the dry summer area madrona (*Arbutus Menziesii*), cascara (*Rhamnus Purshiana*) and Garry oak (*Quercus garryana*) are characteristic species.

Among the characteristic shrubs of the coast are red-flowered currant (*Ribes sanguineum*), salmon berry (*R. spectabilis*), Indian plum (*Osmaronia cerasiformis*), salal (*Gaultheria Shallon*) and red billberry (*Vaccinium parvifolium*). Common herbaceous species include western buttercup (*Ranunculus occidentalis*), cut-leaved goldthread (*Coptis asplenifolia*), vanilla leaf (*Achlys triphylla*) and many-flowered Dutchman's breeches (*Dicentra formosa*).

## The Columbia Forest Region

The Columbia Forest is influenced by a belt of higher rainfall in the Selkirk and Monashee Mountains. It has some of the characteristics of the coastal forest but exhibits many of the features of its neighbours, the Montane forest and the Subalpine forest. The most important species are Engelmann spruce, western red cedar, western hemlock and Douglas fir. Western white pine, western larch and grand fir occur in the southern section. Lodgepole pine comes in after fires. Black cottonwood is common on river bottoms.

## The Montane Forest Region

The Montane Forest is found in the southern interior of British Columbia, often known as the Dry Belt. It occupies the plateaux and slopes as far north as the Skeena river but in the lowest and driest valleys gives way to open grassland. The outstanding tree of this region is the yellow or ponderosa pine (*Pinus ponderosa*). Toward the north however, ponderosa pine gives way to an association of Douglas fir and lodgepole pine while toward the northeast there is considerable admixture of Engelmann spruce and alpine fir. Aspen is important, also, toward the north. The most typical montane landscape however, is a scattered parklike stand of ponderosa pine amidst a steppe vegetation of bunch grass (*Agropyron spicatum*), spear grass (*Stipa columbiana*), balsam root (*Balsamorrhiza sagittata*), wild rose (*Rosa nutkana*), coral berry (*Symphoricarpos racemosus*) and, where overgrazed, wormwood (*Artemisia frigida*), yarrow (*Achillea millefolium*) and mullein (*Verbascum thapsus*).

## The Rocky Mountain Forest Region

This elongated but complex area comprises the subalpine forests of the foothills and lower mountain slopes from three thousand feet to the tree line. Beyond this are the alpine tundra and the areas of perpetual snow which cannot be differentiated on our small scale map. The dominant species are Engelmann spruce (*Picea Engelmanni*) and alpine fir (*Abies lasiocarpa*) while lodgepole pine and aspen comprise a sub-climax. Toward the south alpine larch (*Larix Lyallii*) and whitebark pine (*Pinus albicaulis*) are found.

Many of the plants of the alpine tundra are the same as those of the Arctic, others however are found only in the Cordilleran region, including alpine willow (*Salix nivalis*), red heather (*Phyllodoce empetriformis*), moss heather (*Cassiope Mertensiana*), alpine hairgrass (*Deschampsia alpicola*) white marsh-marigold (*Caltha leptosepala*) and mountain pink (*Douglasia nivalis*).

## The Mixed Wood Region

By some regarded as a subdivision of the Boreal Forest, this is a large area extending from the Manitoba lowland to the Rocky Mountains, including most of the commercial forests of the Prairie Provinces. White spruce is well developed in this area but aspen, Balm of Gilead and white birch are much more common than in the main Boreal forest belt.

## Aspen Grove or Parkland Region

This formation occupies a narrow zone between the open grassland and the mixed wood region. The landscape is dotted with "bluffs" or clumps of trees and the river valleys contain fairly continuous bands of forest. Aspen and black poplar are the common trees but, in the southeast, Manitoba maple (*Acer negundo*), bur oak (*Quercus macrocarpa*), elm (*Ulmus americana*) and green ash (*Fraxinus campestris*) may be found. Highbush cranberry (*Viburnum trilobum*) and Saskatoon berry (*Amelanchier alnifolia*) are common also. The tall prairie grasses of this belt include awned wheat grass (*Agropyron subsecundum*), slender wheat grass (*A. pauciflorum*), northern wheat grass (*A. dasystachyum*), fringed Brome grass (*Bromus ciliatus*), reedgrass (*Calamagrostis canadensis*) and Hooker's oatgrass (*Avena Hookerii*).

## The Prairie Region

The Prairies may be divided into a short grass zone and a mixed grass zone. These belts are climatically controlled by the available water supply. In southwestern Saskatchewan and southeastern Alberta, the driest section, the common grasses are: blue grama grass (*Bouteloua gracilis*), common spear grass (*Stipa comata*), western wheat grass (*Agropyron smithii*), June grass (*Koeleria cristata*) and blue grass (*Poa secunda*). Other common plants adapted to the dry habitat are: pasture sage (*Artemisia frigida*), hoary sage (*A. cana*), silver sage (*Eurotia lanata*) and pricklypear cactus (*Opuntia polyacantha*). Especially note-

*Courtesy Exp. Farms Service.*

Plate 4. The Valley of Maple Creek in Southwestern Saskatchewan. Only in the bottom of the valley is there enough moisture to support tree growth.

worthy are the saline sloughs and lakes around which salt tolerant plants are found such as spike grass (*Distichlis spicata*), salt grass (*D. stricta*), alkali grass (*Puccinellia Nuttalliana*), barley grass, (*Hordeum jubatum*), sea crowfoot (*Ranunculus cymbalaria*), seablight (*Suaeda erecta*) and samphire (*Salicornia rubra*).

In the mixed grass zone many of the same plants appear, as well as porcupine grass (*Stipa spartea*), green spear grass (*S. viridula*), rough fescue (*Festuca scabrella*) and, toward the moister margin, northern wheatgrass and others which are found in the parkland zone.

### The Great Lakes—St. Lawrence Forest Region

This forest formation extends from Lake of the Woods to Baie de Chaleur and is, essentially, a transition between the boreal coniferous forest and the deciduous forest of eastern North America. The dominant conifers are white pine (*Pinus strobus*), red pine (*P. resinosa*), hemlock (*Tsuga canadensis*) and white cedar (*Thuja occidentalis*); others, apparently invaders from the north, are jack pine, tamarack, balsam fir and white spruce. The dominant hardwood deciduous trees are: sugar maple (*Acer saccharum*), beech (*Fagus grandifolia*), yellow birch (*Betula lutea*), red oak (*Quercus borealis*), bur oak (*Q. macrocarpa*) and white oak (*Q. alba*) on upland soils; with red maple (*A. rubrum*), silver maple (*A. saccharinum*), white elm (*Ulmus americana*), white ash (*Fraxinus americana*) and black ash (*F. nigra*) on the low ground. This forest region has probably more species and a greater number of associations than any other in Canada. It is especially noted for the excellent pine timber and deals which for approximately a century were shipped from the St. Lawrence in great quantities.

The vegetation also includes many smaller plants, shrubs and herbaceous forms of the forest floor and the cleared lands. It is not possible to name them all but mention may be made of ground hemlock (*Taxus canadensis*), juniper (*Juniperus communis*), hazel (*Corylus rostrata*), witch hazel (*Hamamelis virginiana*), sumach (*Rhus typhina*), poison ivy (*R. toxicodendron*), service berry (*Amelanchier canadensis*), wild grape (*Vitis vulpina*), hawthorn (*Crataegus canadensis* and many others), raspberry (*Rubus idaeus*), blackberry (*Rubus canadensis*), thimbleberry (*R. occidentalis*) and honeysuckle (*Lonicera dioica*). While these may be found sparingly as rather slender stunted forms in the high forest, they show their best growth in cleared, uncultivated lands. Hawthorns have taken over many thousands of acres of pasture in southern Quebec and southern Ontario and large areas are occupied by almost impenetrable tangles of raspberries and brambles. The herbaceous flora of the deciduous forest floor is much richer than that of the boreal region. A few of the common species are mayapple (*Podophyllum peltatum*), herb Robert (*Geranium Robertianum*), Jack-in-the-pulpit (*Arisaema triphyllum*), lily of the valley (*Maianthemum canadense*), baneberry (*Actaea pachypoda*), white trillium (*Trillium grandiflorum*), enchanter's nighshade (*Corcaea lutetiana*), sarsaparilla (*Aralia nudicaulis*), blue wood aster (*Aster cordifolius*), Ontario aster (*A. ontarionis*), calico aster (*A. lateriflorus*), Canada fleabane (*Erigeron canadensis*) and Canada golden rod (*Solidago canadensis*). There are many species of aster and goldenrod, almost unnoticed in the forest, which take over large areas of unimproved, low pasture land. On drier sites there is sometimes an almost complete coverage of mullein (*Verbascum thapsus*) and blueweed (*Echium vulgare*). As a matter of fact, in most of settled Ontario and Quebec the natural vegetation of the roadsides, fence rows and old fields is more characteristic geographically than the once dominant, but now vanished, forest. Not many geographers, however, are qualified botanists. Nor is a once-over by a taxonomist sufficient. The scene changes from season to season, almost from week to week, from early spring with its faint green, through the succession of summer flowers to the colourful autumn. This is especially emphasized by Macoun and Malte in the following passage:

"Very characteristic of the zone is the autumnal colouring of the leaves of trees, shrubs, and herbaceous plants. This autumnal colouring lasts a comparatively long time, from about the first week in September to the second week in October, dependent upon the dryness of the season. During that period the most splendid display of colours is exhibited, especially in the open mixed woods where underbrush is well developed. Every shade of yellow, golden bronze, red and scarlet is mixed in a gorgeous symphony of colours generally most marvellously modulated by the somber dark green or bluish green of the conifers which are dotted among the deciduous trees. No such wealth of colour is ever met with in any other country." [1]

Add to this the lush green of the pastures, the blue of alfalfa in bloom, the changing tints of the ripening fields of wheat, oats and corn as well as the complete mosaic of other crops and it is little wonder that this region has developed a healthy school of landscape painting.

## The Niagara Forest Region

Much of what is written above concerning the composition and appearance of the vegetation of the larger Great Lakes region applies also to the much smaller strip along the northern shore of Lake Erie which Halliday calls the Niagara section of the deciduous forest region of North America. There are differences, however. Except for the pines of the sand plains there are few evergreens while, on the other hand, there are additional species of deciduous trees. Among the latter are chestnut (*Castanea dentata*), tulip tree (*Liriodendron tulipifera*), magnolia (*Magnolia acuminata*), Kentucky coffee tree (*Gymnocladus dioica*), mockernut hickory (*Carya alba*), black wal-

nut (*Juglans nigra*), sycamore (*Platanus occidentalis*) and sassafras (*Sassafras variifolium*) as well as others. The chestnuts, here as in the eastern states, were practically wiped out by the chestnut blight. In actuality the southern hardwoods form but a small portion of the standing forest which resembles its northern neighbour very closely. The area is also, of course, the habitat of many small plants not found farther north.

## The Acadian Forest Region

The Acadian Forest is the result of an adjustment of the forest to the slightly cooler and considerably more moist climate of the Maritime Provinces. In general appearance and composition, however, there is strong resemblance to the forests of the Great Lakes—St. Lawrence region. Hemlock, white pine and red pine that characterize that region are well represented here, as are also the characteristic hardwoods, beech, sugar maple and yellow birch. Here also are found white spruce, balsam fir and aspen, reminiscent of the boreal forest. The dominant and characteristic tree, however, is red spruce (*Picea rubra*) which is found throughout this region and, apparently, to no great extent anywhere else. This forest was early and most completely exploited. White pine especially was in demand for masts and spars. The old original stands are said to have contained trees six feet in diameter and more than 200 feet high. Lumbering followed, for much of the forest was within easy reach of the long indented coastline. Very large areas were burned over. Nevertheless, except for Prince Edward Island, most of the Acadian Forest remains, and will remain to produce lumber and pulpwood for the future.

The shrubs and herbaceous plants of this region show nearly as many affinities with the boreal region as with the St. Lawrence region. Areas of acid, sandy soils, especially, have rhodora (*Rhodora canadensis*), blueberry (*Vaccinium sp.*), lamb-

---

[1] Canada Year Book. 1915.

kill (*Kalmia angustifolia*), wintergreen (*Pyrola sp.*) and mayflower (*Epigaea repens*). The mayflower is the floral emblem of Nova Scotia. Bracken, sweetfern and raspberry are also common.

An important segment of this vegetation region is its sea coast margin, particularly along the Bay of Fundy and its headwaters where the tidal range is great, many salt tolerant plants are found which do not have extensive distribution elsewhere. Characteristic of this "salt marsh" are fox

colours and that there is a great difference between sand and clay, but few people are fully aware of the geographical distribution and significance of these differences. This is not surprising since it is only within recent years that soil scientists themselves have begun to study these matters intensively. As the results of their work unfold they are being adopted by geographers and used to amplify geographical description and provide further explanation of geographical problems.

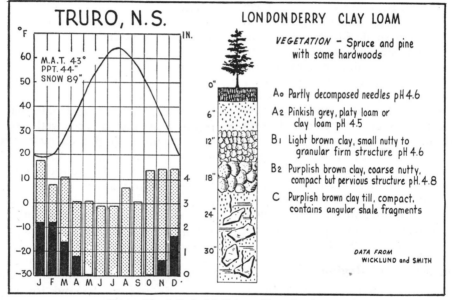

Figure 18. *A Podzol Soil from Nova Scotia.*

grass (*Spartina juncea*), black grass (*Juncus gerardii*), and marsh greens (*Plantago juncoides*). The latter, as its name implies, is commonly eaten in the same manner as spinach.

## Soils

The soil is the medium in which plants grow. It consists of mineral matter derived from the underlying rocks and organic matter mainly derived from the vegetative cover. The soil is not everywhere the same, its characteristics vary in both vertical and horizontal directions. Almost everyone is aware that soils have different

## The Soil Profile

All soil description is based upon observation of the soil *profile* which is the face of a vertical exposure from the surface down to the unaltered parent material. Such a face is seen to be composed of zones or *horizons* having different colours as well as other physical characteristics.

1. An accumulation of organic debris upon the surface, in various stages of decay. This is particularly noticeable in forest areas and usually absent in grassland. Soil scientists designate it as the $A_0$ horizon.

2. A dark coloured horizon usually containing a relatively high amount of organic matter. This is known as the $A_1$ and is well developed in grassland soils.

3. A light coloured, leached horizon, well developed under forest vegetation but obscure or lacking in grassland. It is designated $A_2$.

4. The B horizon in which the material leached from the upper horizons is deposited. It is usually some shade of brown in colour and is somewhat more compact than the A horizon.

tions. Figure 19 on the other hand is representative of the black grassland soils of Manitoba.

**Soil Geography**

Pedogeography or soil geography in its modern sense began with the observations of Dokuchaev, a Russian scientist who was sent out by the Imperial government in the 1870's to classify land for new settlement. He was impressed by the great regional differences in soil qualities throughout the empire. The great grasslands or

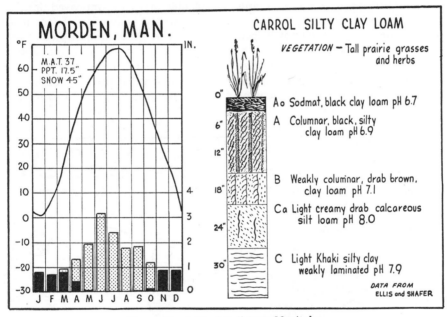

Figure 19. *A Black Soil from Manitoba.*

5. The C horizon or parent material.

Because of minor differences soil descriptions often record other horizontal subdivisions such as $A_3$, $B_1$, $B_2$, etc.

As an illustration of the strong contrasts in the appearance of soils from different geographical regions the reader should study the accompanying photographs and diagrams. Figure 18 represents a soil found in Nova Scotia in a moist climate under a forest vegetation composed of conifers and deciduous trees. It is representative of the *podzols* discussed in the following sec-

steppes of southern Russia were underlain by *chernozem*, rich black soil which when cultivated yielded good crops of wheat. The forests of the north, on the other hand, grew upon grey soil, *podzol*, which had little natural fertility and required a great deal of careful attention in order to produce rye and potatoes while wheat could not be grown successfully. Dokuchaev found that black soils were formed on many types of bedrock or parent material and that the same rocks might be found under the *podzols*. It was clear to him that soils were to be correlated with vegetation and climate rather than with bed rock. It was true, of course, that the mineral matter or skeleton of the soil was derived from the bed rock but, provided that enough time had elapsed, all soils formed under the same climatic influences eventually came to be much alike in colour, organic matter content, chemical reaction and natural fertility. This geographic theory of soil distributions was accepted and elaborated by a number of pupils and co-workers of Dokuchaev and has eventually become familiar to soils men and geographers the world over.

In North America the acknowledged leader was Curtis F. Marbut of the U.S. soil survey who obtained his knowledge of the Russian school from a book written by K. D. Glinka, a pupil of Dokuchaev. Translated into English by Marbut and

entitled "The Great Soil Groups of the World and Their Development", this book has had a great influence.

Soil surveys in Canada have been patterned after those in U.S.A. although the workers in each of the provinces have introduced various modifications into the system. In the years 1920-1950 about 215,000,000 acres have been surveyed and mapped. Of this about 135,000,000 acres are occupied and 77,000,000 acres are improved farm land. There remain over 35,000,000 acres of occupied land and 14,000,000 acres of improved land of which soil surveys have not been made. Thus while the great unoccupied area of Canada has not been surveyed and classified, we are, nevertheless, able to draw a generalized map of the soil zones of the country. This map, Figure 20, is seen to exhibit many close similarities to the generalized

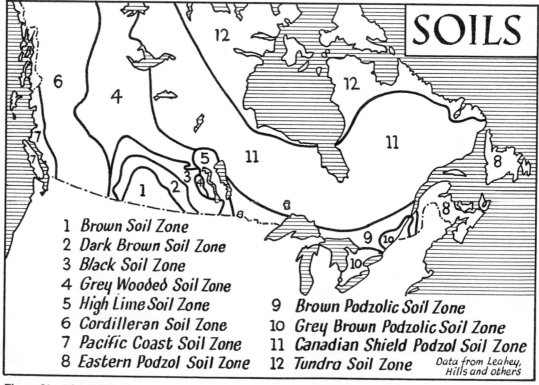

1  Brown Soil Zone
2  Dark Brown Soil Zone
3  Black Soil Zone
4  Grey Wooded Soil Zone
5  High Lime Soil Zone
6  Cordilleran Soil Zone
7  Pacific Coast Soil Zone
8  Eastern Podzol Soil Zone

9   Brown Podzolic Soil Zone
10  Grey Brown Podzolic Soil Zone
11  Canadian Shield Podzol Soil Zone
12  Tundra Soil Zone    Data from Leahey, Hills and others

Figure 20. *The Soil Zones of Canada.* This is an extremely generalized map. Within each zone there is great variety of soil, depending upon geological material, land form and drainage.

maps of climate and vegetation with which we are already familiar. Very brief notes on each soil zone will now be given in order to complete our survey of the natural geographical factors. Much further detail will be found in the various regional descriptions. For convenience the western and eastern sections of the country will be considered separately.

## Soil Zones of Western Canada

### The Brown Soil Zone

Brown soils and the associated characteristic short-grass vegetation have developed under the most arid climatic conditions in Canada. They are found in the southwestern part of Saskatchewan, the southeastern part of Alberta and in some of the valleys of the southern interior of British Columbia. In general, Brown soils have the shallowest profiles of the grassland soils. The brown top soil may be quite light in colour and it grades into a whitish calcareous horizon at a depth of one to two feet. Other salts may be present as well.

### The Dark Brown Soil Zone

The Dark Brown soils are found in a wide crescent extending through the three Prairie Provinces and also in the intermountain areas of British Columbia. The top soil is dark brown in colour and somewhat deeper than that of the Brown soil while the lime accumulation lies at a greater depth and is less concentrated. These are the fertile soils of the "Wheat Belt".

### The Black Soil Zone

The Black soils are found under a prairie vegetation of tall grasses and flowering plants interspersed here and there by small groves of aspen and other trees, often termed a "Park" landscape. The surface soil is deep, granular and black with a high content of organic matter. The whole profile is usually deeper than in the other grassland soils although there are marginal areas of "shallow black" soils.

Plate 5. A Chernozem developed on silty lacustrine sediments, South-Central Manitoba.

### The Grey Wooded Soils

Grey Wooded soils are found in a very large area of the Prairie Provinces and the interior of British Columbia. They have developed in a cooler and slightly more moist climate than that of the grasslands. In keeping with the forest vegetation these soils have grey-leached A horizons but the subsoil contains a zone of lime accumulation similar to that of the grasslands. This is apparently an adjustment in response to the influences of a climate which is alternately wet and dry. The natural fertility of these soils is lower than that of the dark coloured grassland soils. A mixed type of agriculture is therefore necessary. Because of surface configuration and the occurrence of swamps and bogs, only a small part of this area is potentially arable.

### The High Lime Soil Zone

The High Lime soils are found in the vicinity of Lake Winnipeg and Lake Manitoba in an area where climate and vegetation indicate the development of Grey Wooded soils. Highly calcareous parent material derived from Paleozoic limestones has inhibited the development of normal profiles. The dark surface soils may be highly alkaline and contain traces of unleached calcium carbonate. The profiles are quite shallow. Many areas are very stony and thus unsuitable for farming.

*D. F. Putnam*
Plate 6. Podzol Profile in Nova Scotia.

### The Soils of the Cordilleran Region

It is quite impossible to depict, on a small scale map, the complicated and imperfectly known soils pattern of this region. We have already noted the occurrence of Brown, Dark Brown, Black and Grey Wooded soils. There are also cool, moist mountain areas where true podzols have developed. Large areas, however, are so steep and rocky that normal soil development is impossible. Where it is, the mountain sides display soil zones, arranged vertically, in which there is a regular sequence from Brown soils in the valleys to mountain podzols and alpine tundra at the top.

### Soils of the Pacific Coast

The coastal margin of the Cordilleran region has specific climatic and vegetational characteristics and it also has soils which are quite different from those of the interior. With high humidity and a coniferous forest, its soils are subject to podzolic leaching but are classified as Brown Podzolic, rather than as Podzols. In the area with an almost Mediterranean type of summer dry climate, the subsoils have a reddish tinge indicating a relationship with the soils of California.

## Soil Zones of Eastern Canada

The soils of eastern Canada have all been developed under a humid climate and forest vegetation and are classified as Podzols, Brown Podzolic and Grey Brown Podzolic soils.

### The Eastern Podzol Zone

This is a large zone, the exact size and boundaries of which are yet undefined, although pedologists are quite familiar with the soils of its southern portion in the Maritime Provinces, Newfoundland, Quebec and Ontario. A division is usually made between the podzols of the Maritimes and Southern Quebec and those of the Canadian Shield. This is not only because of the difference in rock material but because the southeastern zone receives more rainfall and its soils are weathered more deeply and more completely than those of the northern region. In both areas, however, the soils are acid and in-fertile. Only a small area has been cleared for agriculture, except on Prince Edward Island which is the most completely oc-cupied and cultivated province in Canada.

### The Brown Podzolic Soil Zone

Brown Podzolic soils are to be regarded as a transition between true Podzols and the Grey Brown Podzolic soils. They are found on the southern fringe of the Ca-nadian Shield in Ontario and Quebec and, in the latter province, on a considerable portion of the Appalachian uplands as well. For the most part cool moist climates and forests of mixed conifers and decid-uous trees are found. The Brown Pod-zolic soil profile is much like that of the Podzol except that it does not have a pro-nounced $A_2$ leached horizon.

Such soils are not highly valued for agriculture but considerable acreages are farmed, often successfully. Some land now in farms will revert to forest but a mixed type of agriculture may be expected to maintain itself in the Eastern Townships, in the pockets of clay soils in the Nipissing lowlands, and in other such areas.

### The Grey Brown Podzolic Soil Zone

This is one of the smaller soil zones of Canada, being a northern outlier of the broad belt of temperate, forested lands of northeastern United States. The northern boundary of this zone in Southern Ontario is sharply demarcated by the geological boundary of the Canadian Shield although the hardwood forests are not so confined.

As in the western plains, the parent ma-terials are almost all glacial and derived from calcareous sedimentary rocks with an admixture of crystalline rock from the Shield. With a great wealth of land forms, drainage conditions vary and several dif-ferent soil profiles will be found associated on the same parent material. In all cases

with free drainage, however, the normal soil profile is that of the Grey Brown Pod-zolic soil. Apart from the forest litter and mould of the virgin soil, the profile is well differentiated into $A_1$, $A_2$ and B horizons. The $A_1$, or surface soil, is greyish brown in colour, slightly acid, and has a fair con-tent of organic matter well incorporated in it. The $A_2$, or leached horizon, is usually pale brown or brownish yellow in colour and not white or very light grey as in the podzol. The B, or horizon of accumula-tion is brown in colour, usually sharply differentiated, containing more clay than the A horizons and having a small blocky or nut-like structure. All the lime is leached from both A and B horizons but it is nearly always found in the upper part of the parent material; there seems, however, to be little accumulation as in the case of the grassland and Grey Wooded soils. Most profiles are of only moderate depth with few much more than 36 inches.

The normal soils of this zone are of moderate fertility and under a wisely con-ducted mixed type of farming maintain their productivity. Some of the associated intrazonal soils are even more productive, once artificial drainage has been estab-lished. For the most part, the soils of this zone have been cleared and very little land is left in forest. In some places there are pressing problems of soil erosion and wa-ter control which are beginning to receive attention. Though not by any means the largest area of agricultural land in Can-ada, it will continue to be one of the most important because of the variety of prod-ucts which may be produced.

### Soils of Northern Canada

The soils of the north have not yet been studied very fully but various obser-vations have been made in the Mackenzie valley. As might be expected, the presence of permafrost in most locations inhibits the development of a mature soil profile although not always bringing about the formation of peat on the surface. On the great Pleistocene terraces, there is sufficient drainage to induce a considerable degree of podzolization.

## Faunal Distribution

The presence, characteristics and distribution of animal populations constitute an important phase of systematic geography which is largely ignored by many regional geographers. In competition with advancing and increasing human populations wild life has had to give way, many species being exterminated or forced into the more inaccessible places where the scattered bands eke out a precarious existence. This is more especially true of the larger mammals, the grazing species of the plains such as buffalo and the antelope, and the larger carnivorous such as the bears and wolves. Bird life too has suffered through the destruction of their breeding and feeding grounds as well as through indiscriminate hunting. It is true, of course, that the destruction of one type of habitat cannot be accomplished without the creation of another. While the original bird life of southern Ontario departed with its primeval forests, an association of different species has taken its place. We now see clouds of starlings instead of passenger pigeons. Pigeons thrive in cities. The same principle applies to mammals; in the unbroken forest one sees very few woodchucks, but in old pastures they become plentiful.

Animal life is more, however, than a mobile feature of the landscape. It may be the basis of human occupance. Hunting and fishing provided and still do provide the means of existence for primitive peoples. The Plains Indian was a hunter of the buffalo, the Barren Ground Eskimo gets his living from the Barren Ground caribou and from fishing. The primitive way of life has given way to a curious hybrid civilization in the case of the forest dwelling Indian who has, for three centuries, been trapping furs for sale to the white man, but the basis of his existence is still the natural wild life.

A third phase of animal relations is the status of the predator. There are few animals in Canada from which man himself is in any danger and then only under special circumstances. But with the disappearance of natural prey, predators have developed a liking for domestic animals. Hawks and foxes take the farmers' chickens, wolves and coyotes pull down sheep and calves, to mention a few examples. Another type of predatory relationship is seen when rabbits destroy young fruit trees or when deer invade vegetable gardens.

Animals are subject to climatic influence, more particularly perhaps to temperature, and life zones have been drawn up on that basis. Water supply is important. The need for shelter and food relations, whether direct or through the medium of a food chain, imply a strong dependence upon vegetation. Although animals may run, swim or fly about, indeed they may migrate and vanish completely from a region for certain seasonal periods, yet for the most part faunal regions are nearly equivalent to vegetation regions.

### Arctic

It is somewhat remarkable to find the far north inhabited by large grazing animals. The muskox (*Ovibos moschatus*), one of the hardiest animals known, formerly ranged the Arctic from the tree line to the north part of Ellesmere Island. In 1930 it was estimated that less than 500 remained on the mainland and perhaps 12,000 on the islands. The Barren Ground caribou (*Rangifer arcticus*) is the most important game mammal of the mainland tundra area. The caribou of the northern islands are smaller and apparently intergrade with the polar caribou (*R. pearyi*) found on Ellesmere Island. The Dominion Government has introduced the reindeer (*Rangifer rangifer*) into the western mainland area. Carnivorous animals of the region include the polar bear (*Thalarctos maritimus*), the arctic wolf (*Canis*

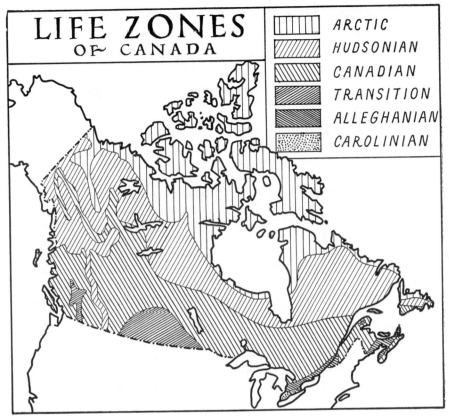

Figure 21. *Life Zones of Canada*, (Generalized from maps by Anderson and others).

*tundrarum),* the white fox *(Alopex lago-pus)* and the arctic weasel *(Mustela arc-tica).* The arctic hare *(Lepus arcticus),* the brown lemming *(Lemmus trimucronatus),* the white lemming *(Decrostonyx groenlan-dicus),* Parry ground squirrel *(Citellus par-ryii)* and various meadow mice *(Microtus sp.)* also inhabit the Barren Ground. Sea life is important in the Arctic Archipel-ago, the bowhead whale *(Balaena mysti-cetus),* the white whale *(Delphinapterus leucas)* and the narwhal *(Monodon mon-oceras)* were the subject of a short-lived whaling industry and are still taken by the Eskimos. The ringed seal *(Phoca his-pida),* harp seal *(Phoca groenlandica)* and the bearded seal *(Erignathus barbatus)* are the most common seals, while the Atlantic walrus *(Odobenus rosmarus)* ranges north

to Barrow Strait and Lancaster Sound. The most common food fish along the Arctic coast and islands is the Arctic char *(Salvelinus alpinus).* Whitefish *(Coregon-us),* lake trout *(Cristivomer namaycush),* grayling *(Thymallus signifer)* and pike *(Esox lucius)* are found in the mainland lakes.

While not by any means including all the birds to be seen in the Arctic the fol-lowing are typical. Willow ptarmigan *(Lagopus lagopus)* and rock ptarmigan *(L. rupestris)* are the only feathered game available in winter. Eider ducks *(Soma-teria spp.)* nest throughout the tundra re-gion. The Lapland longspur *(Calcarius lapponicus),* snow bunting *(Plectrophenax nivalis)* and the redpoll *(Acanthis horne-manni* and *A. linaria)* are representative

Arctic sparrows. Common birds of prey are the snowy owl (*Nyctea nyctea*) and the gyrfalcon (*Falco rusticolus*).

## Boreal

The Boreal Life Zone is often subdivided into Hudsonian and Canadian belts which are nearly coextensive with Subarctic and Boreal forest regions which have already been discussed. Zoologic associations are usually fairly constant throughout this vast area. There are some species, however, with a more restricted or even local habitat.

The moose (*Alces americana*) ranges north to the limit of trees and is found all the way from Yukon to Nova Scotia, but is not found in Newfoundland. Primarily a browser, its food is obtained from shrubs and low growing trees to a height of about seven feet. In summer they feed extensively upon aquatic vegetation in lakes, ponds and the stillwaters of northern streams. In winter they band together in "yards" where coniferous growth is plentiful. The woodland caribou (*Rangifer caribou*) was also originally found throughout these zones but is now found rather sparingly through the northern portion of the range. The wood buffalo (*Bison bison athabascae*) was formerly found as far north as Great Slave Lake but is now confined to the Wood Buffalo Park. Here also are large numbers of plains buffalo (*Bison bison*). The mule deer (*Odocoileus hemionus*) is also found in the park.

*Can. Gov. Photo.*
Plate 7. The Beaver—symbol of Canadian resources and industry.

The black bear (*Ursus americanus*), the timber wolf (*Canis lupus*), the coyote (*Canis latrans*), the Canada lynx (*Lynx canadensis*), the common fox (*Vulpes fulva*), are among the larger carnivorous animals. Smaller ones include the northern skunk (*Mephitis hudsonica*), the otter (*Lutra canadensis*), the marten (*Martes americana*), the fisher (*Martes pennanti*), the mink (*Mustela vison*) and various weasels (*Mustela spp.*)

The rodent population includes the porcupine (*Erethizon dorsatum*), the red squirrel (*Tamiasciurus hudsonicus*), the eastern chipmunk (*Tamias striatus*), the western chipmunk (*Eutamias minimus*) and the meadow mouse (*Microtus pennsylvanicus*). Two larger rodents of aquatic habitat characterize this zone almost as well as the moose and black bear: the beaver (*Castor canadensis*) and the muskrat (*Ondatra zibethica*). Badly depleted in many parts of its range, the beaver is now staging a comeback under present trapping regulations. The effect of the beaver upon the landscape is considerable; creating ponds, bogs and meadows throughout the northern forest, he maintains the habitat of his choice. The snowshoe rabbit or varying hare (*Lepus americanus*) in its various forms is found throughout the Boreal Forest. It is an important source of food for some of the valuable carnivorous furbearing animals and is also eaten by the Indians. The population of these animals shows great fluctuation during an approximate ten-year cycle, with a consequently similar effect upon the numbers of lynx and other furbearers which prey upon them.

Many species of fish inhabit the lakes throughout the glaciated Canadian Shield. Among them are several species of whitefish (*Coregonus*), pike (*Esox lucius*), yellow pickerel (*Stizostedion vitreum*), lake trout (*Cristivomer namaycush*) and tullibee (*Leucichthys lucidus*).

This is also the breeding ground of dozens of species of birds. Characteristic of the northern or Hudsonian zone are the fox sparrow (*Passerella iliaca*) and the pine grosbeak (*Pinicola enucleator*); the Canadian zone may be represented by the brownheaded chickadee (*Penthestes hudsonicus*), hermit thrush (*Hylacichla guttata*), Canada jay (*Perisoreus canadensis*) and the three-toed woodpecker (*Picoides trydactylis*). Around the lakes are found such fisheaters as the osprey (*Pandion haliaetus*) and the kingfisher (*Megaceryle alcyon*).

## Southeastern Canada

As a faunal region, southeastern Canada may be said to include a strip from the Great Lakes to the Atlantic including the southern parts of Ontario and Quebec and the Maritime Provinces. It includes those portions of the Alleghenian and Carolinian life zones which have been mapped in Canada, as well as the southern portion of the Canadian life zone. It is the region most altered by the hand of man, both in effect upon habitat and, more directly, upon the animals themselves.

Many of the animals of the northern forest are occasionally found in this transition zone. The moose is found in Nova Scotia, New Brunswick and Quebec, so also is the black bear and wolf. The large mammal which characterizes the region, however, is undoubtedly the white tailed deer (*Odocoileus virginianus*). It is not an inhabitant of the dense coniferous forest but rather of the cutover areas, forest borders and partially cleared areas. Deer are not so plentiful in Southern Ontario as they were during the period of early settlement when they fed on the second growth of the settlers clearings and formed an important source of meat. There are still many, however, in the swamps and wooded areas. They thrive in the "Near North" or border area of the Shield. Algonquin Park, which is a protected area, has a very high density of deer population. Nova Scotia, with an area of 20,000

square miles, has one of the greatest deer populations of the whole region. An annual kill of 30,000 is estimated to be only 20% of the total population. Here it is quite evident that deer and moose come into competition for food and the moose are losing ground in spite of their slightly higher reach for browse. In Algonquin Park a browse line is quite evident on white cedar and it is impossible to find a white cedar seedling in the southern part of the park. There are no cedars in Nova Scotia where studies in the Chignecto and Liscomb Game Sanctuaries have established that the important food plants are birches, red maple, mountain maple (*Acer spicatum*), poplars, withe-rod (*Viburnum cassinoides*), hazel, red-berried elder (*Sambucus pubens*), wild cherry and balsam fir.

The cottontail rabbit (*Sylvilagus floridanus*) was probably not indigenous but since its appearance has spread throughout Southern Ontario. The European hare or jack rabbit (*Lepus europaeus*) has like-

Can. Gov. Photo.

Plate 8. The White-tailed deer, the most important game animal in Eastern Canada.

wise spread over the same area since its introduction in 1912. Small rodents worth mention are the muskrat, black squirrel (*Sciurus carolinensis*) and woodchuck (*Marmota monax*). The latter tends to take possession of old pastures, especially on sandy and gravelly soils, and may even invade cultivated fields where its burrows and spoil heaps are an unmitigated nuisance. Field mice and other small rodents also abound. The skunk *(Mephitis mephitis)*, raccoon *(Procyon lotor)*, red fox, bobcat *(Lynx rufus)*, mink and weasel are found in various parts of the region.

Among the upland game birds are ruffed grouse *(Bonasa umbellus)* and bobwhite *(Colinus virginianus)*, the prairie chicken *(Tympanuchus cupido)* on Manitoulin Island, and the introduced pheasant *(Phasianus colchicus)*. The sea coast, the Great Lakes and many smaller lakes are frequented by gulls among which the herring gull *(Larus argentatus)* and ring-billed gull *(L. delawarensis)* are the most common. Among the many other birds which might be mentioned are the cardinal *(Richmondena cardinalis)*, catbird *(Dumtella carolinensis)*, robin *(Turdus migratorius)*, whip-poor-will *(Antrastomus vociferus)*, bobolink *(Dolichonyx orizivorus)*, meadowlark *(Sturnella magma)*, redwinged blackbird *(Agilaeus phoenicius)* and mourning dove *(Zenaidura macrouna)*. Two introduced nuisances are the English sparrow *(Passer domesticus)* and the starling *(Sturnus vulgaris)*.

The waters of Eastern Canada contain many species of fish, some of them valued by both anglers and commercial fishermen. The king of them all, probably, is the Atlantic salmon *(Salmo salar)* which formerly entered all rivers draining to the Atlantic, including the streams flowing into Lake Ontario. Its range is now greatly restricted. A landlocked form, the ouananiche is found in some Quebec lakes. All the species mentioned in the Boreal zone are found here and some others including the sturgeon *(Acipenser rubicundus)*, the muskellunge *(Esox obriensis)*, the small-mouthed black bass *(Micropterus dolomieu)* and the brook trout *(Salvelinus fontinalis)*.

## The Prairie

The Canadian Prairie is easily recognized as a separate faunal region, one which, of course extends some distance south of the international boundary. By zoologists it is labelled the Transition Zone as is also the grassland of the interior of British Columbia. The original grassland was inhabited by large grazing mammals, by many small burrowing spe-

C.P.R. Photo.

Plate 9. The Buffalo, formerly abundant on the Western Plains.

cies and by large and small carnivores which preyed upon them. There were also a great number of birds which preferred open country instead of forest, including those attracted to the edges of the "sloughs".

The buffalo or American bison *(Bison bison)*, a great shaggy horned beast, though slightly smaller than the wood buffalo, covered the plains in huge herds, numbering millions. They furnished meat and hides to the Indian, who, after he had acquired the horse and the rifle from the white man, was able to make a comfortable living. The coming of the railway and the white hunter who killed for the hides alone, soon reduced them to a pitful remnant. They are now increasing in National Park areas but their former range is now put to other uses and they will never again be a real geographic factor. Their total influence as such is rather hard to estimate for besides their usefulness to man, they must have exercised considerable influence upon the ecology of the grassland itself. It has been suggested that the borders of the prairie were considerably extended by grazing.

The prong-horned antelope (*Antilocapra americana*) and the elk or wapiti (*Cervus canadensis*) were also found in great numbers and have suffered almost the same fate as the buffalo. Other prairie mammals include the northern gopher (*Thomomys talmoides*), the pocket gopher (*Geomyx bursarius*), b a d g e r (*Taxidea americana*), coyote (*Canis latrans*) and the jack rabbit (*Lepus townsendii*).

Among the breeding birds of the prairie may be mentioned the upland plover (*Bartramia longicanda*), prairie chicken (*Tympanuchus cupido*), sharp-tailed grouse (*Pediocetes phasianellus*) cowbird (*Molothrus alter*), Brewer's blackbird (*Euphagus cyanocephalis*), western meadowlark (*Sturnella neglecta*), prairie falcon (*Falco mexicanus*), Swainson's hawk (*Buteo swainsoni*), gopher hawk (*Buteo regalis*), California gull (*Larus californicus*), Franklin's gull (*Larus pipixcan*), mallard (*Anas platyrhynchos*), black duck (*Anas rubripes*) and pintail (*Dafila acuta*). The sloughs of the Prairie region and the lakes to the north make ideal habitats for waterfowl hence they are more numerous in western Canada than in the east.

## The Cordilleran Region

The animal life of the northern part of British Columbia is much like that of the Boreal region already described while that of the Dry Belt resembles that of the Prairies. However, there are a considerable number of alpine species recorded, while quite a number of species common to the Pacific Northwest are not found east of Rocky Mountains. Among the alpine mammals are the Rocky Mountain sheep (*Ovis canadensis*), mountain goat (*Oreamnos montanus*), mountain caribou (*Rangifer montanus*), the hoary marmot (*Monax caligata*), and the grizzly bear (*Ursus horribilis*). In the very dry parts of the Okanagan there is a desert fauna including a pocket gopher (*Thomomys fuscus*), pock-

et mouse (*Perognathus lordi*), western white-tailed jack rabbit (*Lepus townsendii*), sage grouse (*Centrocerus urophasianus*), western lark sparrow (*Chondestes grammecus strigatus*), poor-will (*Phalaenoptilis nuttalli*), rock wren (*Salpincles obsoletus*) and rattlesnake (*Crotalus oreganus*).

## Pacific Coast

The Pacific coast with its mild humid climate and luxuriant forests is inhabited by still another group of animals. Here are the Sitka deer (*Odocoileus columbianus sitkensis*), the elk (*Cervus c. roosevelti*), the black bear and several types of grizzly bear, the northwest wolf (*Canis occidentalis gigas*), the northwest skunk (*Mephitis occidentalis*) and the Pacific raccoon (*Procyon psora*). Some birds of the coastal forest are: Sitka grouse (*Dendragapus fuliginosus*), red-breasted sapsucker (*Sphyrapicus ruber*), Oregon junco (*Junco oreganus*), lutescent warbler (*Vermivora celata*), varied thrush (*Ixoreus naevius*) and the russet-backed thrush (*Hylocichla ustulata*).

Marine mammals include the spotted harbour seal (*Phoca richardii*), northern sea lion (*Eumatopias jubata*) and various whales. Most notable among the fish are the salmon, including sockeye (*Onocorhynchus nerka*), spring or chinook(*O. tachawytscha*), coho (*O. kisutch*), pink (*O. gorbuscha*), chum (*O. keta*), and steelhead (*Salmo gairdneri*). The spring salmon sometimes attains a weight of 100 pounds but the others usually run from five to fifteen pounds.

Entering the west coast rivers to spawn they were caught in large numbers to form the chief food of the coast-dwelling Indians. The white man has made them the basis of the most valuable commercial fishery in Canada.

## Canadian Regions

The bulk of this book is given over to discussions of various Canadian Regions. Regions are necessities in the study of the world or of any large country such as Can-

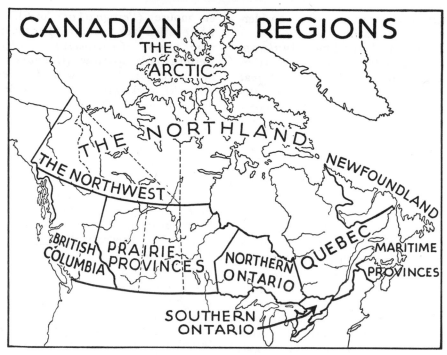

Figure 22. *Major Regions of Canada.* This map portrays the basic outline of the regional organization of this book. It represents integration and compromise involving the physical, political, economic and social factors of the geography of Canada.

ada. Remarkably little can be said about the whole area which would apply with equal validity to all of its parts. Geographers, therefore, have given much time and thought to the development of systems of regions. We have already in this introductory section presented regional divisions of the country on the bases of land form, climate, vegetation and soil. We have also glanced at the development of the political map of the country.

Climate, vegetation and soil are closely related. Any study of animal distribution would show a fairly similar pattern. If we superimposed this map upon one of land form regions we would get a fairly usable map of natural regions of Canada. Usable, that is, if we had no human populations with their different cultures, histories, political organizations and economic developments. Using these latter criteria we could delimit a whole series of human regions of

which we have presented only the political divisions.

It is fairly obvious that population distribution has some correlation with natural regions and that political boundaries, whether following natural features such as mountains and rivers, or laid out as astronomical lines, have some relationship to population clusters. It is also fairly obvious that geographical regions of any size cannot be delimited on the basis of homogeneity alone. Instead we must admit that relationships are often a more powerful regional cement than similarities. There is even a certain regional "impress of the central authority", although it must be admitted that provincial differentiation is often weak enough.

In the following chapters separate treatment is given to each of the following:

Newfoundland and its mainland dependency, Labrador.

The Maritime Provinces.
Quebec.
Southern Ontario.
Northern Ontario.
The Prairie Provinces.
British Columbia.
The Canadian Northland.

The reader will note immediately that these do not coincide with any of the regional patterns of land form, climate, vegetation and soils which have been observed. They are not regions which might be readily agreed upon from inspection of the map of population distribution. They are not even political divisions. They are admittedly regions of convenience and their boundaries are arbitrary. Yet they are realities, known, understood and accepted by most Canadians without question.

Within each of these regions we shall try to integrate location and area, land forms, climate, vegetation, soils, population, settlement patterns and economic activities. We want to know how many people live "where, why and what of it". For example, Montreal and Toronto together contain one-sixth of Canada's population. They are even more important in their respective regions, in each case forming a functional core or nucleus. Cities are the products of their regions but they also tend to dominate them. It is with such relationships that regional geography is most vitally concerned.

## Selected References

Adams, John. *The Flora of Canada.* Canada Year Book. pp. 30-59. Ottawa. 1938.

Alcock, F. J. *Geology.* Canada Year Book. pp. 19-29. Ottawa. 1947.

Anderson, R. M. *Faunas of Canada.* Canada Year Book. pp. 29-52. Ottawa. 1937.

Atwood, W. W. *The Physiographic Provinces of North America.* Ginn and Company. Boston. 1940.

Burpee, Lawrence J. *An Historical Atlas of Canada.* Thomas Nelson and Sons Limited. Toronto. 1927.

Connor, A. J. *The Climates of North America II. Canada.* Handbuch der Klimatologie. Band II. Teil J. pp. 332-424. 1938.

Connor, A. J. *The Climate of Canada.* Canada Year Book. pp. 41-62. Ottawa. 1948-49.

Glinka, K. D. *The Great Soil Groups of the World and Their Development.* Translated by C. F. Marbut. Edwards Brothers. Ann Arbour.

Halliday, W. E. D. *A Forest Classification for Canada.* Dominion Forest Service Bulletin 89. Ottawa. 1937.

Leahey, A. *The Agricultural Soil Resources of Canada.* Agricultural Institute Review 1· 285-289. 1946.

Macoun, J. M. and M. O. Malte. *The Flora of Canada.* Canada Year Book. 1915.

Moore, E. S. *The Mineral Resources of Canada.* The Ryerson Press. Toronto. 1933.

Putnam, D. F. *Soils and their Geographic Significance.* In *Geography in the Twentieth Century* pp. 221-247. Methuen and Company Ltd. London. 1951.

Putnam, D. F. *Pedogeography of Canada.* Geographical Bulletin No. 1, pp. 57-85. Ottawa. 1951.

Sanderson, Marie. *The Climates of Canada according to the new Thornthwaite Classification.* Scientific Agriculture 28: 501-517. 1948.

Taylor, G. *Canada.* Methuen and Company Limited. London. 1947.

# CHAPTER 2

# Newfoundland and the Coast of Labrador

Newfoundland, the newest and most easterly province of Canada, was actually the first to be discovered and settled. For several decades it ranked as one of the Dominions of the British Commonwealth but in 1934, because of economic difficulties, it reverted to the status of a British Colony. In 1949, Newfoundland became the tenth province in the Canadian Confederation. The Province consists of two main geographic units, the island of Newfoundland, itself, and the dependent mainland territory of Labrador, comprising a total area of about 155,000 square miles (Fig. 23). We shall deal with these two sections separately.

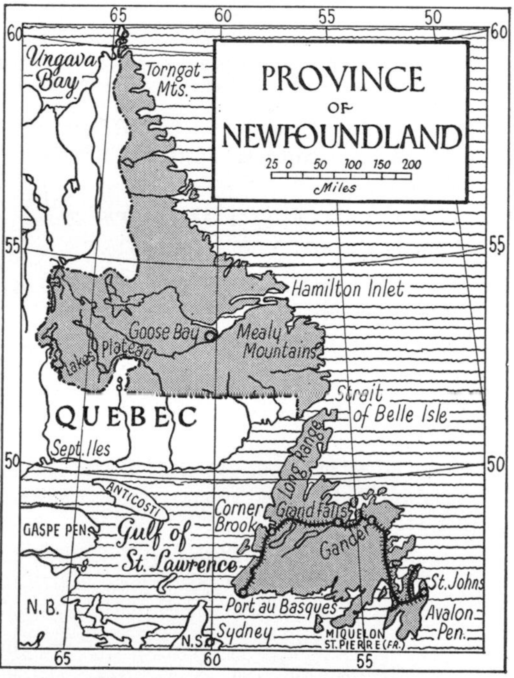

## NEWFOUNDLAND

### Position and Area

Newfoundland is a large island, having an area of 42,734 square miles and located between 46°36′ and 51°39′ north latitude and between 52°37′ and 59°24′ west longitude. It is separated from the Island of Cape Breton by Cabot Strait, about 60 miles in width, and from Labrador by the Strait of Belle Isle which is about 12 miles wide at its narrowest part. The island forms the eastern rim of the Gulf of Saint Lawrence and is normally the first landfall of navigators from Europe to North America.

### Structure and Relief

In general, the landforms of Newfoundland have much in common with those of the Maritime Provinces. Though rather rugged, the country possesses no areas of great relief except the Long Range parallel to the western coasts. Here the summits reach an elevation of more than 2,600 feet. As in Nova Scotia the major physiographic features are determined by a series of very old, worn-down fold-ridges with axes trending from northeast to southwest. This effect is suggested in the physiographic diagram

Figure 23. *The Province of Newfoundland.* It consists of the island of Newfoundland (area, 43,000 square miles) and the coast of Labrador (area, 112,000 square miles). The capital and largest city is St. John's.

shown in Fig. 25. Newfoundland is therefore to be regarded as a part of the Appalachian physiographic province of North America.

## Rocks

In common with Nova Scotia, also, Newfoundland is underlain by very old rocks. Fig. 24 is a much simplified geological map of the island. Rocks of Precambrian age are found in the Long Range and in the southeast corner of the island including the Avalon peninsula. In the west they are predominantly granites, schists and gneisses while in the east are great thicknesses of slates, quartzites, sandstones and conglomerates and a variety of volcanic rocks. The central part of the island is underlain by Paleozoic rocks which are for the most part of Ordovician age. Toward the north these are commonly sedimentary sandstones, shales and limestones, while toward the south these are wide-spread areas of such igneous rocks as granite and diorite. In the St. George's Bay and White Bay depressions, rocks of Carboniferous age are preserved. These also are sandstones, shales and limestones containing coal, gypsum and oil shale.

## Physiographic Development

Newfoundland was affected by three different mountain-building periods: the Taconic at the end of the Ordovician period, the Acadian foldings in Devonian time and the Appalachian folding and faulting during Permian time after the last of coal measures had been laid down.

The surface is a series of even-topped plateaus which are interpreted as old erosion surfaces similar to those found in the Maritime Provinces. Here, also, they are found to rise toward the north indicating that there has been a deformation of the earth's crust since these surfaces were cut. There seem to be three of these old erosion levels or *peneplains* as they are often called. The highest and oldest is represented by the flat top of the Long Range at about 2,200 feet, the second is

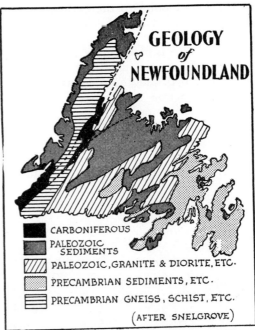

Figure 24. *A Simplified Geological Map of Newfoundland.* The largest areas are underlain by old, igneous and metamorphic rocks.

seen in the higher valleys at about 1,300 feet and on the residual hills or *monadnocks,* to the east of the range. The lowest and youngest of these erosion levels is the most widespread and comprises the most of the plateau-like surface of the island ranging from 500 to 1,000 feet in elevation.

## Glaciation

As in the neighbouring mainland, the surface of Newfoundland is covered by unconsolidated deposits of variable depth and great complexity. There seem to have been at least two periods of glaciation and may well have been more because the country has been very incompletely examined. There is some controversy among geologists as to whether the great continental ice caps extended far enough to cover the island or whether it had its own local glaciers. The ice-carved valleys, the numerous lakes in rock-basins on the plateau and the rounded shapes of the residual rock hills all point to the existence of an ice age in fairly recent time.

There have also been recent changes in sea level. This is particularly evident along the much indented northeast coast. This is similar to the southern coasts of Maine and Nova Scotia and is to be explained in much the same way, as the result of the recent drowning of river valleys which had become entrenched during the uplift of the old erosion surface. Some over-deepening may also be present due to the

*Courtesy L. G. Reeds.*

Plate 10. The Barren Rocky Surface of the Interior of Newfoundland.

work of the glaciers. There is also evidence of recent uplift of the land in the presence of raised marine beaches in various parts of the island.

### Drainage

Newfoundland possesses many rivers, but being a very irregularly shaped island, few of them are very long. Since the plateau of Newfoundland is tilted toward the northeast, most of the important rivers flow in that direction. Those draining to the south coast are short and rapid.

The largest river is the Exploits, 200 miles long, draining an area of about 4,000 square miles in the central part of the island. In its drainage basin are a number of lakes: Red Indian Lake, 37 miles in length,

is the largest. Exploits River empties into the Exploits Bay, a long arm of Notre Dame Bay. Farther east, Gander River, 100 miles long, and Terra Nova River, 70 miles in length, drain large areas. Gander Lake, drained by the river of the same name, is about 33 miles long. In the western part of the island, the largest river is the Humber, 80 miles in length. In its drainage basin are Grand Lake, about 56 miles long and 200 square miles in area, and Deer Lake which is about 15 miles long. There are many smaller river systems. These streams are important as sources of power, and as means of transporting pulpwood from the interior. In addition, they contain salmon and trout which are popular with visiting anglers.

### Coastline

The coastline of Newfoundland is estimated to be 6,000 miles long, very long indeed for its area of 43,000 square miles. From the map it is very noticeable that there are three distinct types of coastline:

1. Rectilinear coasts such as those along both sides of the Northern Peninsula and along the western part of the south shore. Such straight lines are probably related to major fault zones of the earth's crust. Good harbours are rather few.

2. The very much indented northeast facing coast from White Bay to Bonavista Bay. This coast is bordered by a great number of small islands. Between them and the mainland, and among the islands themselves, is a veritable maze of waterways to which Newfoundlanders have applied a number of curious geographic names such as "tickle", "run", "reach", "arm" and "sound".

3. The embayments of Eastern Newfoundland. The eastern part of the island is composed of a number of peninsulas between which are very large open bays such as Trinity Bay, Conception Bay, St. Mary's Bay, Placentia Bay and Fortune Bay. The shape of this coast suggests its origin in the drowning of a very old mountain range. For the most part, the shores are steep and

rocky but there are a few good pouch-shaped harbours, among them St. John's, the chief port of the island.

The coast is geographically the most important part of Newfoundland. Most of the people are settled along the bays and inlets and the interior of the country is practically empty.

## The Grand Banks

Newfoundland is surrounded by shallow seas covering the great submerged continental shelf of eastern North America. The 100-fathom contour is usually considered to mark the shoulder of the slope which leads to the ocean depths. Across this shelf there are a number of deep valleys, particularly the one which lies between Nova Scotia and Newfoundland and leads toward the mouth of the St. Lawrence River. It is apparent that the island is only the more elevated undrowned portion of a great eastern continuation of the mainland of North America. The "Banks" are the more elevated portions of this submerged plateau; the most noted of these, the "Grand Banks", lying southeast of Newfoundland, have an area as great as that of the island itself. (See Figure 70).

The shallow waters of the Banks are located in the area where the warm Gulf stream is met by the cold Labrador current. The continuous mixing which takes place creates conditions of temperature, salinity and nutrient supply which are most favourable to the development of the small floating plants upon which the food supply of the fish population ultimately depends. Consequently the Banks have, since their discovery, continued to be one of the greatest fishing grounds in the world.

## Physiographic Divisions

Although the island might for the sake of simplicity be regarded as a plateau sloping gently in a northeasterly direction it is divided naturally into three physiographic units; the Western Uplands, the Central Plateau and the Avalon Peninsula.

*The Western Uplands.* The Long Range Plateau includes the northern peninsula of Newfoundland which extends unbroken from Bonne Bay to the Strait of Belle Isle, together with the more isolated highland masses extending southward from Bonne Bay to St. Georges Bay. It is separated from the rest of the island by a down-faulted lowland, marked by St. Georges Bay, Grand Lake and White Bay. The summits of the Long Range are found along the western margin of the Upland, below which a steep escarpment falls to a narrow coastal plain along the Gulf of St. Lawrence. Gros Morne, 2,651 feet above sea level, overlooking Bonne Bay and the isolated Lewis Hills, 2,763 feet, are the highest points on the island. A steep scarp marks the eastern border of the plateau, especially along White Bay where rocky cliffs 300 to 500 feet high overlook the sea. The Anguille Mountains, flat topped uplands whose highest point is 1,759 feet above sea level, overlook St. Georges Bay from the Southeast. On the east of these hills lies the Codroy Valley, bordered by steep escarpments. It merges northward with the coastal plain of St. Georges Bay.

*The Central Plateau.* The western edge of the central plateau is a more or less continuous escarpment overlooking the down-faulted lowlands which extend from the Codroy Valley to White Bay. Composed of more resistant rocks, this part of the plateau has summits over 2,000 feet, constituting the Southern Long Range. East of the valley of the Exploits River the Annieopsquotch Mountains also have summits about 2,000 feet in elevation. The general level of the plateau, however, is about 1,000 feet, with a barren rocky surface marked by innumerable lakes and bogs. The southern margin of the plateau is steep and fairly regular, suggesting that it also is a fault zone. From the south and west the surface slopes gently toward the northeast where it dips below sea level. In Bonavista Bay and Notre Dame Bay particularly, there are a great number of is-

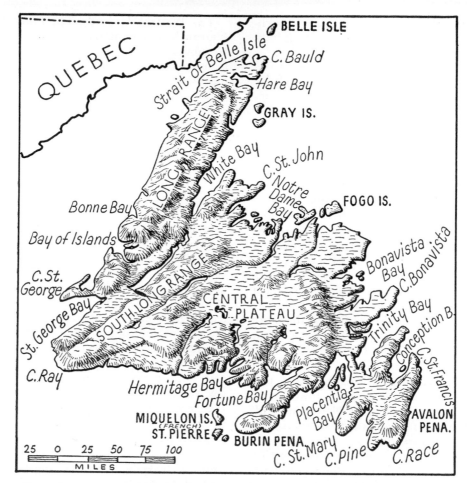

**Figure 25.** *Physiographic Diagram of Newfoundland.* The island consists of a series of large upland areas, the Long Ranges, the Central Plateau and the Avalon Peninsula, with a number of small, coast and valley lowlands.

lands and indentations corresponding to the irregularities of the old peneplain surface.

*Avalon Peninsula.* Almost separated from the main body of the island by Trinity Bay and Placentia Bay, the Avalon Peninsula is essentially part of the same plateau. Its outline is very irregular with deep bays separating the peninsulas. The surface is generally between 500 and 1,000 feet in elevation and very rocky and barren.

## Climate, Vegetation and Soils

*Climate.* Newfoundland has a humid climate with short, cool summers and cold, snowy winters. Because of its position on the eastern side of North America, it comes under the influence of continental air masses and experiences a great range between winter and summer temperatures. Although it lies in the same latitude, its climate is much less equable than that of Vancouver Island. The average July temperatures range from 50°F. to 63°F. but, as shown in figure 26, only a very small part of the island has mean July temperatures above 60°F. January mean temperatures range from 10°F. to 26°F. While the win-

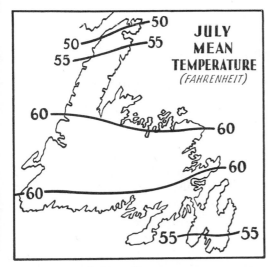

Figure 26. *July Mean Temperatures*—representative of midsummer conditions.

ters of the south coast are relatively mild, they are much more severe on the west coast and especially toward the north where they are affected by the cold polar continental air masses. The advent of spring is retarded and summer temperatures, especially on the northeastern coasts, are kept low by the ice laden Labrador current. The frost-free season is relatively short, the average length, in those sections which are consid-

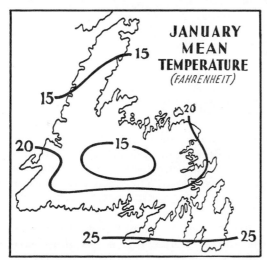

Figure 27. *January Mean Temperatures*—representative of midwinter.

ered to have agricultural possibilities, ranging from 108 to 140 days.

The island has abundant precipitation, having the equivalent of 30 to 55 inches of rainfall per annum. In general the amount is least in the northwest and greatest in the southeast, but everywhere there is a fairly uniform distribution from month to month. Snowfall is heavy with only a portion of the south coast receiving less than 80 inches per annum while a belt of heavy snowfall (120 inches per annum) covers the interior and the northeast coast.

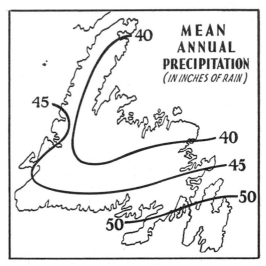

Figure 28. *Mean Annual Precipitation*. Snowfall is included in terms of rainfall equivalent.

The weather of Newfoundland is exceedingly variable being affected by the cyclonic storms which, every few days, leave the continent by way of the Gulf of St. Lawrence. They are more frequent during the winter months often being accompanied by very high winds. Ice storms, or freezing rain, occur when warm air masses from the Atlantic sweep over the frozen land.

The coasts of Newfoundland are foggy, although no more so than the southern coast of Nova Scotia. St. John's has an average of 37 foggy days per year, but the Grand Banks, to the east of the island, are known as one of the foggiest areas in the world. June and July are the foggiest

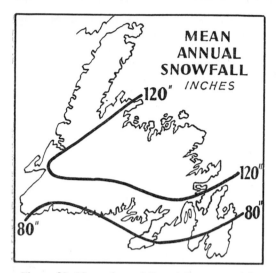

Figure 29. *Mean Annual Snowfall*—measured in inches of freshly fallen snow.

months while there is much less "thick weather" in the winter season. Fogs are caused by the warm moist air from the south mixing with the air which has been chilled by the Labrador current.

Closely related to the climate are the ice conditions of the sea surrounding the island (Figure 30). Early in December sea ice begins to form in the shallow bays of the northern peninsula. It gradually spreads southward during the winter reaching its greatest extent in March when only the

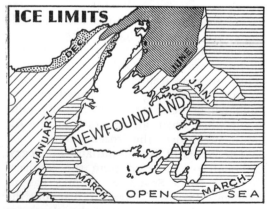

Figure 30. *The Limits of Sea and Land-fast Ice, at Different Seasons, Around Newfoundland.* (After Gutsell).

south coast is open. Normally ships can reach St. John's through a narrow coastal passage which, however, may be closed when the ice pack is driven on shore by a southeasterly wind. The Strait of Belle Isle is closed to navigation from December until June.

Besides the local ice, there is Arctic ice which drifts southward from Davis Strait. It also reaches its maximum extent in March covering the Grand Banks to latitude 45°. During the spring and summer, icebergs are also observed. They originate from land ice in the far north and usually

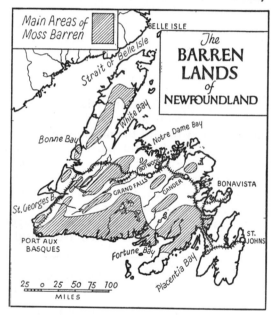

Figure 31. *The Barren Lands of Newfoundland.* (After Gutsell). Only part of Newfoundland is forested; the remainder, mostly cool upland, is moss-covered barren.

require about two years to reach the Grand Banks. Because of their great bulk which is mostly underwater, they are very dangerous to navigation. They melt rapidly when they reach the warm waters of the Gulf Stream.

*Vegetation.* Newfoundland lies within the Boreal Forest region, its short cool damp summers and long cold winters being unsuitable for the growth of most deciduous trees. There is, however, considerable variation in the vegetative pattern. Only two fifths of the area is covered with productive forest while one half is composed of barren lands, bogs and lakes. (Figure 31) The chief forest areas lie within the drainage basins of the large rivers, the Humber, the Exploits, the Gander and the Terra Nova. Good timber is also found along the rivers which drain into White Bay and St. Georges Bay.

Elevation and drainage are the principal factors affecting vegetation. The best forest growth is found on well drained slopes which support mixed stands of balsam fir (*Abies balsamea*), white spruce (*Picea glauca*), black spruce (*P. mariana*), white birch (*Betula papyrifera*) and even some white pine (*Pinus strobus*). On the forest floor are found pigeon-berry (*Cornus canadensis*), snake-berry (*Clintonia borealis*), blueberry (*Vaccinium sp.*), sheep laurel (*Kalmia angustifolia*) and feather moss (*Hypnum sp.*). This plant association characterizes most of the productive forest.

The St. Georges district in the southwest may be considered a small subregion in which the forest is somewhat akin to that of the Acadian region. Here the lower well drained slopes carry more hardwoods including red maple (*Acer rubrum*) and yellow birch (*Betula lutea*) as well as white spruce and balsam fir. The undercover may contain trillium (*Trillium sp.*), violet (*Viola sp.*) and wood-fern (*Aspidium sp.*).

In the poorly drained swamp forests of the valley bottoms, black spruce is the dominant tree with an undergrowth of labrador tea (*Ledum sp.*) and sheep laurel. At higher elevations also black spruce is the dominant tree, giving way on the plateau summits at about 1,200 feet to open barrens of reindeer moss (*Cladonia*) and lichens, with sometimes small stunted black spruce. Sphagnum bogs may be found in both upland and lowland locations.

*Soils.* Several factors tend to make the soils of Newfoundland a poor base for agriculture except in favoured localities. They are podzols. The humid climate and the coniferous forest cover produce highly leached, acid conditions while the hard old granite rocks have, at best, only a limited supply of the elements needed for plant growth. Only a few small areas have been examined by soil surveyors as yet, but from their reports it is evident that the best chances for agricultural development lie in the coastal plains and the alluvial bottoms of the larger valleys where the soils are deep and less severely weathered. Among the locations which may be mentioned are the upper Humber Valley, the Codroy Valley, the northwest coast, St. Mary's Bay and Grand Falls.

## History of Settlement

The discovery of Newfoundland is credited to Sir John Cabot who landed near Cape Bonavista in June 1497. On his return to England he reported the existence of great quantities of fish in the waters surrounding the new island. Within a few years fishermen from all the western European countries were making annual trips to Newfoundland. Although no permanent settlements were made, the temporary summer stations of these men are perpetuated in such names as English Harbour, Frenchman's Arm, Spaniard Bay, Portuguese Cove, Biscay Bay, Port aux Basques and Harbour Breton. Because of its harbour, St. John's very early became the principal fishing port.

For many years no country laid claim to territorial sovereignty but, gradually, the English became most numerous and on August 5, 1583, Sir Humphrey Gilbert took possession of the island in the name of the English crown. In the year 1600, there were about 10,000 fishermen and 200 ships from England engaged in the Newfoundland fisheries and the total catch was worth about $500,000. In 1610, the first permanent colony was established at Cupids in Conception Bay, by John Guy, a merchant from Bristol. Later this colony was governed by Captain John Mason. Other early attempts at settlement on the Avalon peninsula were the efforts of Sir William Vaughan at Trepassey (1617), Lord Falkland's colony at Renews and Sir George Calvert's (afterwards Lord Baltimore) establishment at Ferryland (1621). In 1622, many of Sir William Alexander's colonists, en route to Nova Scotia, joined the fishermen at St. John's. By 1629, there were about 350 English families resident between Cape Race and Bonavista. In 1638, the whole colony was given to Sir David Kirke who brought out a hundred colonists to Ferryland. By 1650, the colony contained a population of about 2,000. There were no further official attempts at colonization, in fact, permanent settlement was definitely discouraged because it was felt to be prejudicial to the interests of the fishing fleet from the homeland. This policy, known to historians as "the Old Colonial System", remained in vogue until the 19th century.

In 1662, French fishermen settled at Placentia, on the west side of the Avalon peninsula, where there was an excellent harbour. Here they built forts, maintained garrisons and, by times, waged war on the English colonists. The treaty of Utrecht, in 1713, gave the whole island to Britain and most of the French colonists were removed to Cape Breton. The French, however, retained the fishing rights on the northeastern and western shores, and by the treaty of Paris in 1763, they were given the islands of St. Pierre and Miquelon. The French rights to the fisheries were terminated in 1904, in return for territory in Africa, but the islands of St. Pierre and Miquelon still belong to France. The general effect of the French treaty rights was to discourage settlement in those parts of the island.

In spite of the early beginnings of colonization the growth of population was very slow and three hundred years after the discovery the island contained less than 25,000 people. The early colonists were mostly from the southwestern parts of England but during the eighteenth century a number of people from the south of Ireland were brought over. The number of Irish immigrants increased greatly during the next century when because of overcrowding and crop failure huge numbers left Ireland for the New World. There were also a few from other parts of the British Isles. Since the early part of the nineteenth century the population of Newfoundland has increased tenfold, but many people born on the island have emigrated to new homes in Canada and the United States.

## Population

At the census of 1956, Newfoundland had a total population of 415,074, of whom 10,800 were found in Labrador, thus leaving about 404,000 as the population of the island. Related to its area of 43,000 square miles, this means an average density of about 9 persons per square mile. Her neighbours, the Maritime Provinces, have a density about three times as great. The distribution, however, is far from uniform as may be seen by a glance at figure 32. For the most part, settlement is restricted to coastal areas and the interior is nearly as empty as on the day of Cabot's arrival. The island was settled by people who depended on the sea for a living, hence they occupied the small coves and bays which offered shelter for their boats and shore space for curing the catch. The most prolific fishing grounds lie to the southeast of the island and population has always been greatest in that sector. About 43% of the population live in the Avalon Peninsula while the capital city of St. John's contains one-sixth of the total population.

Most of the people live in some 1,300 small settlements along the coast. Only 26 centres have a population of more than 1,000; about 90 have between 500 and 1,000 and the remainder have less than 500 inhabitants. There is nothing resembling the great areas of dispersed agricultural settlement so common in other parts of North America.

Among the larger settlements might be mentioned St. John's (77,500), Corner

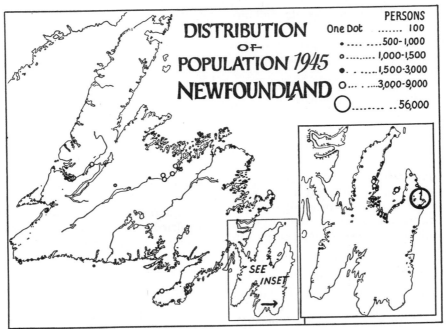

Figure 32. *The Distribution of Population in Newfoundland, According to the Census of 1945.* (After Gutsell). Note the coastal settlement and empty interior.

Brook (23,500), Bell Island (12,000), Grand Falls (4,500), Carbonear (4,000), Botwood (2,700), Windsor (4,500), Bishop's Falls (2,500), Grand Bank (2,400), and Harbour Grace (2,500).

Although not to the same extent as in other parts of Canada, a certain degree of population movement is taking place. This is indicated by the fact that among the important outposts in 1901 were Bay Roberts (2,226), Bonavista (3,696), Carbonear (3,703), and Harbour Grace (5,184). Only Carbonear now maintains anything like its old population. On the other hand some of the present day towns had not been founded or else were simply out-of-the-way hamlets untouched by modern development.

The small and scattered population presents difficulties in transportation and administration. For the coastal settlements the sea has been the highway and the island has no road net, except in the Avalon peninsula. In the northern settlements where the harbours are icebound from December to May, supplies must be laid in during the fall, and the people remain shut off from the world until spring. In some parts of the island, rough winter trails, passable by horse or dog-team, exist between settlements. As a result of this isolation, there has been little change in the way of living from generation to generation. Many obsolete words are still in use and the dialect remains much the same as in the early days. Isolation has also led to a considerable degree of intermarriage, so that, in some of the smaller settlements, most of the people answer to three or four family names.

By contrast, the living conditions in St. John's and in the paper and mining towns tend, more and more, to resemble conditions in similar communities in other parts of Canada.

Native born Newfoundlanders comprise 98.5% of the population. About 60% are of English and Channel Island stock, 25% are of Irish descent while French and Scotch make up 6% of the population.

About one third of the people embrace the Roman Catholic faith, one third are Anglican, one quarter belong to the United Church of Canada and the remainder to various other sects.

## Economic Geography of Newfoundland

Newfoundland has three chief sources of income which are directly based upon the utilization of natural resources, namely: the fisheries, the forests and the mines. The soil, which is a fourth great natural resource in the other provinces of Canada, does not contribute greatly to the wealth of Newfoundland for agriculture remains in an undeveloped condition.

## The Fisheries

Ever since its discovery, Newfoundland has been dependent upon its fisheries for the major portion of its wealth. The shallow waters of the Grand Banks simply team with fish and the ports of Newfoundland are closer than those of any other land. The cod is the most important fish, but other species including salmon, herring, halibut, turbot and lobsters add to the commercial catch while caplin and squid are taken for bait. Whaling and sealing are additional industries. The census of 1951 estimated that the fisheries employed over 18,000 men or about 20% of the gainfully employed males. In 1951 Newfoundland produced $29,000,000 in fish and fish products, accounting for 14% of the Canadian total.

### Codfishery

The codfishery of Newfoundland is divided into three branches: the inshore, the "Bank" or deep sea, and the Labrador fishery.

The shore fishery is carried on from all the small coves and harbours which indent the island. Normally it accounts for about three-fourths of the entire catch. Over a ten year period from 1938-48 it employed from 14,000 to 23,000 men while the catch varied from a low of 432,000 quintals of 112 lbs. dry weight, in 1942, to a peak of 835,000 quintals in 1947.

Inshore fishing is usually carried on within six miles of the shore by means of dories or small boats powered by 3 to 4 H. P. motors. The fish are caught by hand lines, trawl lines, "bulltows" or codnets. Larger boats, 25 to 28 feet long with 8 to 10 H.P. motors are used to operate cod traps. These are large square nets, set on the shoals near the headlands, capable of taking 60,000 pounds of fish at a single haul. The fish are split and cured on shore. The "flake", or rough platform upon which the fish are dried, is a familiar sight in every cove.

The Labrador fishery is carried on from June to October along the coast of Labrador. Each summer 15,000 people, 4,000 men with their families, migrate from Newfoundland. The migratory fishermen fall into two classes: the "stationers" who establish temporary quarters on shore, and the "floaters" who operate from their schooners and follow the fish from place to place. The permanent inhabitants of Labrador are known as "liveyers" (live-heres) to distinguish them from the summer fishermen. The Labrador fishery has also varied greatly within a ten-year period from a peak of 407,000 quintals in 1938 to a low of 167,000 in 1947. Labrador fish are soft-cured, the climate being unsuitable for the curing of the more valuable hard-dried product.

The Bank fisheries are those prosecuted on the Grand Banks and other fishing grounds on the Continental Shelf which lies to the south of Newfoundland and the Maritime Provinces. In company with those from the latter areas, as well as from the United States and some western European countries, Newfoundland sends a fleet of schooners and trawlers to the Banks. Newfoundland schooners range up to about 150 tons and make three voyages per year to the fishing grounds. Trawlers and auxiliary craft make much more frequent trips. In 1938 there were 236 vessels with 2,130 men in the "Bank" fishery. During the war the deep sea fishery fell off rather badly, as men joined the forces or were drawn into other employment. The catch, over a ten-year period, varied from a peak of 233,000 quintals in 1938 to a low of 62,000 in 1942. Since the war the government has been encouraging the use of trawlers or draggers by subsidizing the construction of larger vessels.

Dried salted cod is a staple in world markets and has long been the mainstay of Newfoundland's foreign trade. Recent shortage of foreign exchange, among other factors, has had an adverse effect; moreover, there has been a steady decline in the total demand since before World War I. To offset this there has been, during the past decade, a development of a fresh fish industry. In 1949, there were 13 quick freezing plants in operation at various places along the coast, including two at St. John's, with several refrigerator ships providing transportation for chilled and frozen fish from plant to market. During World War II, Great Britain provided the market for frozen fillets. With the post-war restriction of this market, an outlet is being found in the United States.

### Herring

The chief centre of the herring fishery is Bay of Islands on the west coast, where large pickling and canning plants are located. After a long decline the industry was revived and reached a peak in 1947, when 65,000,000 pounds, valued at $4,910,000, were exported.

### Salmon

Salmon are caught in May, June and July and are mainly marketed as frozen fish. The exports in 1948 amounted to $771,000.

### Lobsters

Lobsters are caught on the south and west coasts and in Notre Dame Bay. They are exported alive from the south and west coasts but in Notre Dame Bay and Fortune Bay several canneries are located. Some exporters have successfully operated an "airlift" of live lobsters to the United States.

### Whaling

The whale industry, always spasmodic, all but ceased in the 1930's. Since World War II, it has been revived. In the season of 1948, a record catch of 750 whales yielded approximately 5,000 tons of oil, valued at $2,000,000. The Norwegian method of hunting with harpoon-firing cannon is used and the oil is extracted at factories located on shore. In 1948, two factories were in operation, using six whale catching ships.

### Sealing

The hair seals of the North Atlantic annually migrate between the Arctic seas and the Grand Banks. In February the young are born on the floating ice fields off the coast of Newfoundland. For six or seven weeks they remain on the ice before taking to the water for the northward migration. At this time the young seal or "whitecoat" weighs about 50 pounds and has a two-inch layer of fat under its skin. The skin which is made into leather and the oil obtained from the fat are valuable commercial products.

The seal hunt is one of the most colourful and dangerous occupations of the Newfoundland seaman. It takes place during March and April. Formerly sailing vessels were employed but of late years specially constructed steamships have been used in the industry. Sailing from Saint John's with a crew of 100 to 150 men, each captain attempts to be the first to locate the ice floes with the herds of seals. Sometimes they are unsuccessful but usually they are found at about the same place each year. The men leave the ship and sometimes must travel several miles over the ice to reach the seals. The "whitecoats" are dispatched with a club and skinned immediately. The pelts are stacked in piles which are later picked up by the ship.

Sealing was almost a Newfoundland monopoly although in some years vessels from Nova Scotia and from Norway joined in the hunt. In 1938, eight steamers carrying 1,459 men brought in 226,747 seals valued at $490,664. During World War II the sealing fleet was entirely dispersed. Since the end of the war new ships have been built and sealing has revived. In 1949, fifteen vessels, including one from Halifax, took part in the hunt and 135,446 seals were caught having a value of $489,805.

## Forestry

Forestry has become an important source of income in Newfoundland, especially since the development of the pulp and

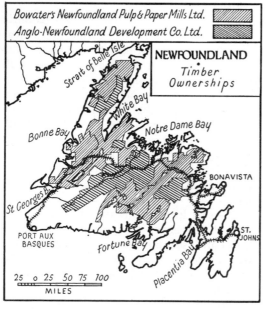

Figure 39. *Timber Ownership in Newfoundland.* (After Gutsell). Most of the timber limits on the island are controlled by two large pulp and paper companies.

paper industry to make use of the small coniferous trees which clothe nearly half of the island.

### Pulp and Paper

There are two very large pulp and paper concerns operating in Newfoundland; the Anglo-Newfoundland Development Company and the Bowater's Newfoundland Pulp and Paper Mills Limited. The former

concern which began operations in 1909 has plants at Grand Falls and Bishop's Falls. It controls approximately 7,500 square miles of forest land. The Bowater's plant is located at Corner Brook. It was begun in 1923 and is now one of the largest pulp and paper mills in the world. The wood is obtained from about 11,000 square miles of holdings. In 1938, these two concerns produced more than $12,000,000 worth of newsprint. Production dropped somewhat during World War II, but rose to its former level of 300,000 tons on the cessation of hostilities, with a value in excess of $30,000,000 in 1948.

The pulp and paper industry, in 1948, employed 9,400 men in the woods and 4,550 in the mills, paying salaries and wages amounting to $26,000,000. The average income is thus much more than that of the fisherman and the standard of physical well-being in the clean well-planned company towns is much above the Newfoundland average.

### Lumbering

There are about 1,000 small sawmills in Newfoundland which produce for the local market, only ten of which had an annual production of over 500,000 f.b.m. in 1947. Lumbering has increased in recent years; in 1938 about 30,000,000 f.b.m. of sawn lumber was produced, in 1943, 54,000,000 f.b.m. and, in 1947, the total was about 68,000,000 f.b.m. Most of the lumber is used in local construction, boat building and the manufacture of various fishing equipment. About 2,000 square miles of forest are held under lease by sawmill companies.

Other forest products include pit props and fuel wood. The government reserves a three mile strip of forest around the coast for the use of local inhabitants, but it has become largely depleted.

Since 1910, about 13% of the productive forest has been cut over. It is estimated that the reserves are sufficient to permit cutting at the present rate until 2040 without making inroads on the second growth. Since

1930, forest products have been more valuable than fish, but many more people depend upon the sea for a living.

## Mining

Many mineral occurrences have been found in the old rocks of Newfoundland. Silver, gold, nickel, chromium, antimony, asbestos and vanadium have all been reported but not in deposits capable of exploitation. Coal of good quality is reported near St. Georges Bay but the rock structure is unfavourable to mining. Nevertheless mining has become one of Newfoundland's three major industries. Two main developments, the Wabana iron mine on Bell Island and the copper-zinc-lead mine at Buchans, account for 90% of the output. The remainder is made up of limestone and fluorspar with small quantities of sand and gravel, brick clay, talc, quartzite and structural sandstone. The value of mineral production reached an all-time peak of $28,000,000 in 1949.

### Iron

Bell Island, about six miles long and two miles wide, lies in Conception Bay, a few miles northwest of St. John's. It is a tabular mesa of Ordovician sandstone and shale whose strata dip gently to the northwest beneath the waters of the bay. Interbedded and outcropping on the island are three

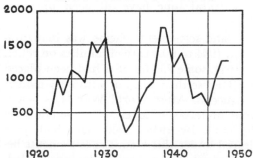

# NEWFOUNDLAND IRON ORE PRODUCTION 1921-1948

Figure 34. *Newfoundland Iron Ore Production.* (Shown in thousands of tons per annum).

beds of red hematite, said to contain at least 2,500 million tons within the limits of submarine mining. The ore is of good quality but rather high in silica and phosphorus. The hematite was identified in 1892 and the first cargo was shipped in 1895. Since 1899, the mines have been operated by the Dominion Steel and Coal Company and more than half the production has gone to the steel works at Sydney, N.S. During the interwar years, Germany was a big importer while small amounts went to the United Kingdom and the United States. Production in recent years has varied between a peak of 1,788,000 tons in 1951, and a low of 578,000 tons in 1945. In 1948, production amounted to 1,260,000 tons valued at $5,164,000. Of this, 47% was imported by the United Kingdom and the remainder went to Nova Scotia.

Because of the fluctuating market for iron ore, the town of Wabana has not been as prosperous as the pulp mill towns.

### Copper, Lead and Zinc

Ore outcrops containing copper, lead and zinc were discovered near Red Indian Lake in 1907, but it was not until 1925 that an economic process of concentrating the ore was discovered. The mill went into operation in 1927 with a capacity of about 500 tons per day, which has since been increased to about 1,200 tons. The concentrates are sent by rail to Botwood and shipped to the United States, Belgium, France, Norway and the United Kingdom. Several hundred men are employed and the town of Buchans had a population of 1,395 in 1945. Production in 1950 was valued at $15,000,000.

### Other Mines

Fluorspar has been mined at St. Lawrence on the south coast of Burin Peninsula since 1933. It is used as a substitute for cryolite in the smelting of aluminum and was in great demand during the Second World War, when the shipping of cryolite from Greenland was seriously curtailed. About 200 men were employed in 1948, and the value of fluorspar shipped was over $1,250,000.

Limestone is quarried at a number of places in Newfoundland. The largest quarry is that at Aguathuna, operated by the Dominion Iron and Steel Company. The limestone from this quarry is used as a flux in the steel furnaces at Sydney, Nova Scotia. One hundred and twenty-five men are employed and the annual production varies from 100,000 to 300,000 tons. The Humbermouth quarry produces limestone for use in the pulp and paper industries of Corner Brook and Grand Falls.

## Agriculture

Agriculture ranks fourth among the basic industries of Newfoundland and plays a minor part in the economy. An extensive commercial development such as is found in other parts of Canada does not exist and practically all the farms are of a part time and subsistence nature. The general trend, in recent decades, has been toward an overall decrease of cultivated land as increased transportation facilities have enabled the people to secure more of their needs from better agricultural regions. This trend is shown in the accompanying table.

### Table 2    Agricultural Statistics

| | Farmers | | | Farm Land | |
|---|---|---|---|---|---|
| Census Year | Full Time | Part Time | Total | Area Occupied (acres) | Area Improved (acres) |
| 1891 | 1,547 | 36,303 | 37,850 | | |
| 1901 | 2,475 | 40,438 | 42,913 | | |
| 1911 | 2,915 | 40,880 | 43,795 | 233,320 | 112,604 |
| 1921 | 3,227 | 34,979 | 38,206 | 188,136 | 89,287 |
| 1935 | 4,226 | 35,582 | 39,808 | 215,462 | 71,697 |
| 1945 | 2,809 | 32,765 | 35,574 | 137,275 | 62,642 |

A further light on the status of agriculture is given by the size of farms. In 1945, of the 35,574 farms, 15,909 were under one acre, 14,523 from 1 to 4 acres, 3,106 from 5 to 10 acres, 1,700 from 11 to 50 acres, and only 336 held more than 50 acres of land.

18,195 cultivators had more than one acre of improved land, of these 15,489 had from 1 to 4 acres, 2,201 had from 5 to 10, 498 had from 11 to 50, and only 7 had more than 50 acres. Nearly one quarter of all the improved land and two thirds of all the large farms are found in the St. Georges-Port-au-Port district in the southwest of the island. Most of the remaining agriculture is found on the Avalon peninsula, although the soil and climate are not so favourable, since this is the area of densest population. Near St. John's, especially, there are a number of dairy and other specialty farms. Dairy farms are also found near other large towns.

Apart from these areas, agriculture is confined mainly to kitchen gardens. Even these are operated under great difficulty along the rocky coasts where the fishing villages are located. The common vegetables are potatoes, turnips, cabbages, carrots, parsnips and beets. Small fruits such as strawberries, gooseberries, raspberries and currants are grown and, in favourable locations, tree fruits such as apples and plums.

The Newfoundland government has tried to encourage agriculture. It operates a demonstration farm of 192 acres near St. John's where ten students per year are given practical instruction in modern methods of producing crops and livestock products. Purebred animals are also imported in order to improve the local livestock. Soil surveys and soil testing programs, bonuses for land clearing and subsidies for agricultural lime have all been put into effect.

A land settlement scheme was inaugurated in 1934 to take care of families on relief. By 1944, some 236 families had been placed in 8 land settlements, but with only moderate success. After World War II, schemes were undertaken to establish veterans on the land. By 1948, 2,000 acres had been cleared under this plan, the settlements being located in the Avalon Peninsula, Codroy Valley and the Deer Lake area.

*National Film Board.*
Plate 11. A Kitchen Garden in the Settlement of La Scie, White Bay District, Newfoundland.

Agriculture on the island must always face two major physical handicaps: a short, cool growing season, with danger from frost, in the growing season, and a lack of any large area of fertile soil. It is probable that, in many areas, agriculture will always remain part time and supplementary to the other primary industries. The development of full scale commercial farming will depend very closely upon local needs.

According to the census of 1956, Newfoundland had about 2,400 farms, occupying obout 72,000 acres, approximately one-third of which was classed as improved land. These figures are not comparable with those of table 2 since they ignore many thousands of fishermen's gardens which formerly were counted. The farms of Newfoundland, however, are decreasing in number but growing in size.

## Water Power

The high rainfall, high humidity and low evaporation tend to make river volumes fairly uniform, but, in addition, the valleys cut in the plateau provide numerous power sites so that potential development is great. The largest hydro-electric installations are those of the two great pulp and paper companies, totalling 220,000 H.P. on the Humber and Exploits Rivers. Smaller developments supply St. John's and other towns in the southeast part of the island. The total installation on the island, in 1951, was 279,160 H.P.

## Transportation and Communications

The Newfoundland railway system comprises a main trans-island line and four branch lines making up 705 miles of narrow gauge track. The main line was completed in 1896, extending in an irregular semicircle from St. John's to Port Aux Basques by way of Grand Falls and Corner Brook. Since 1897 it has been linked to the Canadian National System (formerly the Intercolonial Railway) by a steamship service between Port Aux Basques and North Sydney, Nova Scotia. Since Newfoundland has entered confederation the railway has become part of the Canadian National Railways.

The most important means of transportation is still by sea, for many of the coastal towns have neither road nor rail connections. The Newfoundland Railway operates a fleet of coastwise steamers and a group of vessels between the island and Canadian ports. Ferry service from North Sydney, N.S. to Port aux Basques takes nine

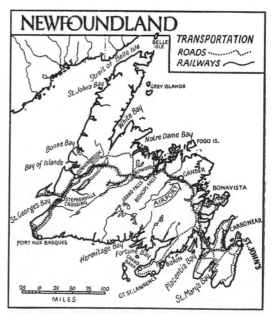

Figure 35. *Transportation in Newfoundland.* Most of the coastal settlements can only be reached by boat.

hours and the rail trip across the island to St. John's takes about twenty-six hours. In normal times a number of passenger ships make regular calls at St. John's while freight is shipped also from Botwood, Corner Brook and Port Aux Basques. Iron ore is shipped direct from Bell Island, thus making it also an important shipping point.

The highway system of Newfoundland is, as yet, very incomplete. In 1949, there still remained about 225 miles of road to build on the trans-island route, which will eventually be the eastern link of the Trans-Canada Highway. A fairly adequate road net, although with some unfilled gaps, is found on the Avalon Peninsula. Some roads also exist on the Burin and Bonavista Peninsulas and in the Exploits, Humber and Codroy Valleys. Elsewhere single short roads join settlements to railway stations. In 1954, there were, altogether, about 6,600 miles of roads of all types; eighty miles from St. John's to Carbonear being the main stretch of paved highway. There were about 20,000 cars and 9,000 trucks on the island.

The global position of Newfoundland has given it a prominent place in air transportation. Gander Airport, established by the United Kingdom and Newfoundland Governments before the Second World War, is the base for transatlantic flight and was extremly useful during the war. It is now administered by the federal Department of Transport. Around it a self contained community of about 2,000 people has grown up. Botwood was developed as a seaplane base, also before the war, but it is closed by ice for about five months each winter. During the war, the United States constructed air bases at Argentia and Stephenville, while Canada built a fighter base at Torbay north of St. John's. The latter field has, since the war, been a civil airfield and the terminus of Trans-Canada Airlines domestic service. Buchan's is an emergency field in the interior near the mining settlement of the same name.

Newfoundland is the landing place for 14 transatlantic cables, the first having been laid to Heart's Content in 1873. Telegraph and telephone service has linked up many out of the way places as well as all the settlements along the railway. Since 1939 a public broadcast system has been operated for sending messages to fishing vessels at sea and to remote areas.

## The Tourist Traffic

Newfoundland naturally expects that its 43,000 square miles of untamed wilderness will provide great attraction for tourists. Before the war tourist travel was chiefly confined to cruise passengers arriving at St. John's and Corner Brook and a few anglers who visited west coast streams.

About one fifth of the area of the island is occupied by lakes and there are countless streams containing brook trout, sea trout and salmon. Tuna fishing and even the taking of cod under the guidance of expert fishermen provide thrills for the sportsman.

For the hunter, the forests and barrens contain moose and caribou, while partridge, wild ducks, geese and other game birds are plentiful.

Even plain sightseeing among the picturesque coastal settlements and in the rugged interior has its attractions. At all events, the tourist trade has been of great value to scenic parts of the Canadian Provinces, and equal possibilities are present in Newfoundland.

## Manufacturing

The manufacturing industries of Newfoundland are chiefly concerned with the bulk processing of raw materials. Of this type are pulp and paper making, fish curing, and the extraction of by-products. There are, however, a number of small local plants making consumers goods. Most of these are located in St. John's, but a few are found in smaller places. Among the secondary products made by local manufacturers are oiled clothing for fishermen, boots and shoes, marine cordage, bedding, marine engines, stoves, nails, paint, hardware, furniture, bricks and wooden building materials, ice cream, confectionery, processed meats, cigarettes and paper goods. In 1954, 9,900 people were employed in manufacturing, producing goods worth $110,000,000 (net value $47,000,000).

Union with Canada has caused some readjustment since goods from the other provinces no longer have to pay import duties. Dealers in outports find it more profitable to buy in the Maritime Provinces than in St. John's. On the other hand, Newfoundland cordage can be sold in the Maritime Provinces.

St. John's is the location of most of the secondary industries, but a few are located in Corner Brook, Harbour Grace, Carbonear, Bay Roberts and Spaniard's Bay.

## Shipbuilding

The Newfoundlanders have long built their own fishing boats and vessels. In the first world war some larger ships of about 300 tons were constructed. During World War II, a number of 200 ton wooden mine sweepers and 300 ton wooden freighters were built. Shipyards are located at Port Union and Clarenville, the latter being a government establishment. Marine engines are manufactured in St. John's. The government pays bounties, both for the construction of vessels and, for the installation of motors.

## Trade and Commerce

Newfoundland exports the products of its fisheries, forests and mines and its trade has been very sensitive to changes in worldwide economics. The depression of the early 1930's was severe. Exports gradually increased during the prewar years to over $30,000,000; by 1945 they amounted to $46,000,000 and reached a total of $78,000,000 in 1948. Pulp and paper, dried codfish, cod fillets, herring, iron ore, lead, zinc and copper concentrates, fluorspar and limestone constitute the largest items. In recent years, the best customers have been the United States, the United Kingdom, Canada, the West Indies, Spain and Portugal.

Imports into the country have also greatly increased. From $24,000,000 in 1939, they reached over $65,000,000 in 1945. A further increase in the post-war period brought the total to $78,000,000 in 1948.

During World War II, the imports included large amounts for the use of the Canadian and American armed forces stationed on the island. Among the important items brought in were flour, sugar, confectionery, boots and shoes, feeds for livestock, hats and caps, leather, beer, furniture, soap and fertilizers. Canada ranked first among the source of supply, followed by the United States and the United Kingdom, with small amounts from the West Indies and many other countries.

As a Canadian province, Newfoundland will become even more dependent upon the other provinces for goods which she does not produce for herself, while the addition of Newfoundland's fish and newsprint to the exports statistics of Canada gives undisputed leadership in these items.

Even with Confederation, the economics of "the oldest colony" are still in the exploitive stage and therefore very much at the mercy of world conditions.

## Towns and Cities of Newfoundland

The ancient fishing economy gave rise to many small seaside villages in addition to the single seaport town of St. John's. The establishment of the mining and pulp and paper industries, within the first part of the 20th century, has brought about the growth of a number of fair sized towns in various parts of the island. The urban geography of these places is thus an important phase of the geographic study of the island.

### St. John's

St. John's, the capital and most populous settlement in the island, is located on the east coast of the Avalon peninsula. Its name commemorates the discovery of the island by John Cabot on St. John's Day 1497, although his landfall was at Cape Bonavista many miles to the north. The excellence of its sheltered harbour made it a favoured fishing station as early as 1502 although there was no permanent settlement before 1583. The population was estimated at 43,000 in 1939 but, in January 1944, there were 58,000 civilian ration cards in use. In 1956 the city had 57,078 and there were 77,553 in the St. John's area.

Drydock, established in 1926 and capable of caring for vessels up to 570 feet in length. The southeast side of the harbour is closely rimmed by the precipitous slopes of the Southside Hills, leaving only a narrow shelf at the bottom for wharves and warehouses.

To the northwest, the land slopes more gently to a low ridge about 300 feet high, about a mile from the shore. To the north

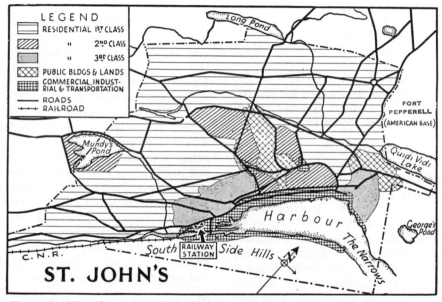

Figure 36. *The City of St. John's.* St. John's is an old city; built without plan, it developed first along the Waterfront, with newer sections stretching up the slopes.

## The Harbour and City Site

St. John's harbour is a small enclosed bay about 1¼ miles in length, from southwest to northeast, and ½ mile in width but with a depth of more than 15 fathoms. It is connected with the sea by way of the "Narrows", a channel about half a mile in length and about 200 yards in width, between steep rocky slopes 500 feet high. A heavy chain was stretched across this entrance to protect the harbour from attack during the wars with the French. It is an almost perfect haven for all small ships but too constricted for large modern liners. The water's edge is almost completely covered by wharves and quays, while at the head of the harbour is the Newfoundland

a low saddle, not over 125 feet in elevation, gives access to another valley in which lies Quidi Vidi Lake. This body of water empties into a narrow rocky inlet, Quidi Vidi Harbour, which lies north of Signal Hill. The older part of the city, and present business centre, lies along the northwestern shore of the harbour while the residential areas climb the hill to the north and northwest and extend along the lowland stretching southwestward from the head of the harbour.

## The Urban Landscape

St. John's has been cited as a city entirely without plan. It "just grew", and its growth has been almost entirely controlled by the

*National Film Board.*

Plate 12. Part of the Waterfront of St. John's Newfoundland.

topography of its site. Originating as a fishing station, the first buildings were located along the waterfront. Wharves were essential and each merchant built his own with a warehouse above it. In this way the main street, Water Street, developed and it is still the chief business section of the city. In the early days all buildings were of wood but a series of disastrous fires in 1816, 1846 and 1892 practically wiped out all the old buildings. City by-laws now require brick or stone construction in the business area. Apart from this, there are a

few scattered public buildings of fireproof materials, but the residential sections are built entirely of wood.

The Roman Catholic Cathedral, with its attendant group of convents, colleges and parish hall, occupies a prominent site on the central part of the ridge. Somewhat lower down the slope stands the Anglican Cathedral, a fine example of Gothic architecture, while near it are the spires of other Protestant churches. Toward the eastern end of the city are the Colonial Building (Legislature), Government House, the

*National Film Board.*

Plate 13. Fort Pepperell, the American Army Base near St. John's, Newfoundland.

Newfoundland Hotel, the Penitentiary and the General Hospital.

The terminus of the Newfoundland Railway lies to the southwest, adjacent to the dockyard at the upper end of the harbour. Here, also, are coal docks, lumber yards and the gas works.

Within the city are two parks, Bannerman's Park, adjoining the Colonial Building in the east, and Victoria Park in the southwest. Two miles outside the city, to the southwest, is Bowring Park, an area of 50 acres, well laid-out to provide all sorts of recreational facilities.

About a mile beyond the city, to the north and overlooking Quidi Vidi Lake, was located the American military camp during the war. Known as Fort Pepperell, it was completely planned and built along modern lines and contrasts strongly with the crowded and unplanned condition of St. John's itself. The airport is located about five miles to the north of the city on the road to Torbay.

### The Functions of the City

Since the earliest days, St. John's has been primarily a port and a fishing station. It is the administrative centre of the island and the chief commercial depot. The manufacturing industries include fish packing, processing and bi-products, shipbuilding and repairing, cordage, cooperage, woodworking, clothing, beverages, food products and many other lines for local consumption.

Apart from the export of the products of the sea, and some paper during the winter, the trade of St. John's is mostly one of imports. These include flour, fruit, sugar, tea, meats, tobacco, coal, gasoline, machinery and textiles. The forest products and minerals, which constitute the bulk of the exports of the island, are shipped chiefly from other ports. This, of course, is because the city, located on the Avalon peninsula, is more or less isolated from the main body of the island. This was not a handicap in the days when all traffic moved by

sea but it is so now, when interior mines and forests are being developed.

## Grand Falls

Grand Falls is a "company town", begun in 1909 to house the employees of the Anglo-Newfoundland Development Company. This concern, established by the Northcliffe interests of London, controls 7,442 square miles of pulpwood forests in Newfoundland. Grand Falls was selected as the site of the mill because of the power

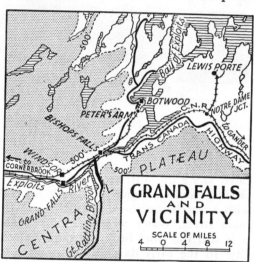

Figure 37. *Grand Falls and Vicinity.* Grand Falls, Windsor, Bishop's Falls and Botwood are the chief towns of the Exploits Valley.

possibilities of the river which at this point provides a "head" of 125 feet. Other points in its favour are its accessibility to the main line of the Newfoundland Railway and to ocean shipping a few miles away at Botwood. Another power site is found at Bishop's Falls where a subsidiary pulp mill is located. The pulp is pumped to the paper mill at Grand Falls through a pipeline eleven miles in length. Over 70,000 horsepower is developed at the two sites and another 70,000 horsepower is available. The company also operates its own railway connecting Grand Falls, Bishop's Falls and Botwood, a distance of 22 miles. The town of Grand Falls has a population of 5,000 while the district, including Windsor (4,500), Bishop's Falls (2,500), Millertown and Botwood (2,700), has about 20,000.

## The Urban Landscape

The focal point is the mill, with its nearby wood piles, paper sheds and power house. This industrial section occupies a terrace to the north of the river gorge. On the slopes behind it, the town is built. The plan has been adapted to the site, the roads curve around the hills in response to the contours, while the highest land has been left in woods. To the east is the civic centre containing the post office, a small hotel and several shops while, at intervals, to the west stand four imposing churches. Other prominent buildings are the centrally located staff house, and the hospital located at the extreme west. There is no very marked zonation of residences, some fairly large houses are found near the staff house and also at the base of the wooded ridge, smaller workmen's homes are located near the mill and also some distance away to the north. A terrace, to the northeast of the civic centre, is mainly occupied by houses of an intermediate type. Most of the houses are built of wood, but there are buildings of stone, brick and concrete. The town has its own water and electric system. The whole urban area occupies about one-half square mile of land.

## Corner Brook

Corner Brook, a town of 23,500, is the site of Bowater's Newfoundland Pulp and Paper Mill. This mill was built in 1925, and has a capacity of 665 tons of newsprint and 130 tons of sulphite pulp per day. The company has control of 11,000 square miles of forest on the Humber, White Bay, Bonavista Bay and St. George's Bay. About 2,000 men are employed in Corner Brook and about 5,000 in logging operations. The power is supplied from the Deer Lake hydro-electric plant, also in the valley of the Humber, which delivers 150,000 horsepower.

The location at Corner Brook combines the advantages of several geographic factors. It is on deep water and also on the main line of the Newfoundland Railway,

*National Film Board.*

Plate 14. Corner Brook is the Largest Settlement on the West Coast of Newfoundland.

thus facilitating transportation of both raw material and finished product. When the bay is frozen over during the winter, paper is shipped to Port Aux Basques which remains ice-free. The river furnishes power and transports pulpwood from the forests. Even the wood from the east coast areas is towed to Hampden in White Bay and loaded on trucks for a short portage to Sandy Lake, which is part of the Humber system. Wood from west coast points can be towed directly to the plant.

Corner Brook is the centre of a fairly densely populated district. To the west is the village of Curling while two miles to the east is the railway divisional point of Humbermouth. Including Deer Lake, the village at the power plant, and the scattered population along the Bay, the Humber District numbers 35,000 people and is the greatest concentration of settlements outside the Avalon Peninsula.

*The Urban Landscape.* Corner Brook lies on the south bank of Humber Arm at the point where it is entered by the small stream of the same name. The mill with its attendant paper sheds and woodpiles is

located on the delta at the mouth of the little stream, while the railway passes along the foot of the slope to the south, while just above it runs the main road. The docks and railway station lie to the east. The town is built on the higher ground to the east of the stream. About an open square are located a hospital, an inn and a moving picture theatre. Between this and the main road to the south lies a row of shops, while to the east, in a shallow tributary valley are found most of the "company houses". They are neat two-story wooden buildings with small gardens. Still farther up the slope along the road leading to the "company farm" are a number of larger houses. Adjoining the town is the suburb of West Corner Brook. It contains a number of small shops, a theatre, and several streets of small houses. A woodworking factory, furniture factory and a small foundry complete the scene.

## Wabana—Bell Island

Bell Island is a rock mesa or tableland, about six miles long and two and one half miles wide, rising from the waters of Conception Bay. It is surrounded by almost continuous cliffs from 100 to 200 feet in height. In general the surface of the island slopes gently toward the northeast being influenced by the dip of the rock strata.

Formerly the home of a few fishermen, Bell Island is now the location of one of the important iron mines in the world. It began operations in 1895 and, up to 1951, has produced about 50,000,000 tons of high grade iron ore, more than half of which has gone to the smelters at Sydney, Nova Scotia.

Three workable seams, or beds, of iron ore outcrop near the northwestern shore. The pit heads are located here but the mine levels run far out under the water. Four slopes varying in length from one to two and one-half miles are in operation. Cable cars carry the ore across the island to the southeast side. Here, there are two piers at which vessels can moor in deep water, while the ore is loaded by endless bucket-convey-

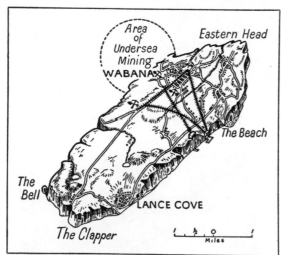

Figure 38. *Wabana—Bell Island.* Bell Island is a small rocky mesa in Conception Bay, on which three rich beds of iron ore outcrop. The pit heads are on the north side of the island but most of the Wabana ore production comes from the undersea workings.

ors from the top of the cliff at the rate of 3,000 tons per hour. During the winter the ore is stored in stockpiles. The mines are operated almost entirely by electricity which is transmitted to the island by two submarine cables from plants of the Newfoundland Light and Power Company.

*The Urban Landscape.* In general Wabana is older than the pulpmill towns and has more weatherbeaten appearance. It is a town of over 8,000 inhabitants, but its built-up areas are rather scattered and seem entirely without plan. The landscape may

suitable for the use of the largest air-liners. The administration and services are housed in temporary type buildings which are gradually being converted for permanent occupation.

An isolated and necessarily self-contained town, most of its 2,000 more or less permanent inhabitants also live in converted wartime buildings. New construction, however, will eventually give it a more permanent appearance. It may be cited as an example of a settlement completely dominated by air transportation.

*Courtesy R. C. A. F.*

Plate 15. Gander Airport.

be said to be dominated by the mine buildings, and to some extent the houses of the workmen are grouped near them. This may, in part, be due to the fact that the mines were formerly operated by two separate companies. Scattered settlement also occurs along the roads leading toward the pier.

### Gander Airport

A settlement of another type is found at Gander, developed during World War II as an important transatlantic airport and retaining much of that importance for peacetime traffic. Somewhat enlarged, its runways in 1950 contained over 10,000,000 square feet. The longest of them are 6,000 feet and

### The Fishing Villages

The typical Newfoundland settlement pattern, however, is not its larger or newer towns but its string of fishing villages along the shore, many of them more than two centuries old. The usual site is at the head of some cove where more gently sloping land gives space for the houses and fish flakes or drying platforms. In some places, however, the settlements cling precariously to rocky cliffs. The villages are entirely planless yet a rough pattern of functional zones is often apparent. The places of business, fishing rooms, stages and flakes are close along the water's edge separated from the houses by a narrow, winding and often rough and grassgrown road which, however, does not extend beyond the settlement. Somewhere along the uneven line of houses there may be a small church or school building. Adjoining each house is a small kitchen garden and perhaps a small weatherbeaten shack which protects the family cow from the winter weather. Farther back, if surface configuration and soil permit, there may be small fields of hay and patches of cabbage, turnips, carrots and potatoes. Such fields may not adjoin the village, however, but be located in a clearing a mile or so away in some spot where easily tilled soil has been discovered.

The place names of Newfoundland are as distinctive and quaint as its scenery and settlements. European origins are commemorated by English Bay, French Bay, Portugal Cove and Jersey Harbour. Early hardships are recalled by Famish Cove, Empty Basket and Bleak Point while success and satisfaction are reflected by Heart's Content, Safe Harbour and Little Paradise. Other unusual names include Main Topsail, Maggoty Cove, Noggin Cove, Blow-me-down, Juniper Stump and Horse Chops.

## Labrador

The Labrador dependency of Newfoundland comprises an area of 110,000 square miles. It stretches from the Strait of Belle Isle, latitude 51°20'N; to Cape Chidley, 60°20'N; a distance of 600 miles. It adjoins the province of Quebec along a boundary which in the south follows the 52nd parallel of latitude and in the west follows "the crest of the watershed of the rivers flowing into the Atlantic Ocean until it reaches Cape Chidley". Long in dispute this boundary was fixed by a decision of the Privy Council in March, 1927.

### Physiography

Labrador is part of the upraised Canadian Shield, underlain by hard, old Precambrian rocks. Its general form is that of a rough plateau, the summits of which represent the remnants of an ancient pene-

plain or surface of erosion. The plateau is tilted, presenting a bold escarpment toward the northeast along an old fault zone. It is highest in the north, where the Torngat Mountains have summits over 5,000 feet above sea level. The Mealy Mountains, south of the Hamilton River, attain heights of over 4,000 feet. The edge of the plateau is deeply cut by the valleys of rapid rivers draining into the Atlantic. The southwest part is known as the "plateau of the lakes" because here drainage has not been fully established and there are many lakes both large and small.

There is marked evidence of Pleistocene glaciation. The Torngat Mountains have many cirques, U-shaped valleys, sharp peaks and ridges cut by mountain glaciers. The seaward escarpment is indented by many ice scoured valleys now invaded by the sea to form fjords like those of Norway. While the eastern border shows the work of ice-scour, the inland area has many land forms produced by glacial deposition such as moraines, kames, eskers and outwash plains. There are large areas of till plains including many drumlins and in these areas there are few outcropping bedrock hills. The largest river is the Hamilton, which drains much of the Lake Plateau. Grand Falls, twice as high as Niagara, is a reserve of untamed power.

### Climate and Life Zones

Generally speaking, the climate of Labrador is harsh, the yearly average temperature for the whole country being below freezing. The summer is short and cool, exposed coastal stations having July mean temperatures below 50°F. Winters are extremely cold, especially on the interior plateau.

Precipitation ranges from about 40 inches per year in the south, to 20 inches in the north, with heavy snowfall. For much of the plateau, summer is less than three months in length. Snow begins to fall in September and does not disappear until the following June. On some of the higher mountains, small patches of snow may remain all summer.

The coast of Labrador may be regarded as an extension of the fog zone of the Grand Banks although, toward the north, fogs are not so frequent as they are in the Strait of Belle Isle.

The northern part of Labrador has little vegetation and may be regarded as a southern extension of the Arctic tundra. In the south, particularly at the lower elevations, there are coniferous forests which eventually may be worth economic exploitation. Spruce and balsam fir are the important trees.

Most of the valuable fur-bearing animals of eastern North America are found in Labrador, including the beaver, muskrat, mink, otter, martin and fox. The arctic hare is found in the northern barrens while the varying hare inhabits the southern forests. Both woodland and barren land caribou formerly were found in fair abundance but are now rather scarce. The coastal waters are frequented by arctic marine animals including various seals, the walrus and polar bear. Whales also come from the north and are caught some distance from the coast. Coastal waters also abound in cod, haddock and herring. The evidence of all observers indicates that the larger animals are disappearing. This is especially true of the land inhabiting forms. Fish, however, continue to be plentiful.

## History

The coast of Labrador has a long history having, apparently, been visited by the Norsemen in the tenth century. In 1534 parts of the coast were charted by Jacques Cartier who designated it "the land that God gave Cain". Almost from its discovery it was visited by fishermen each summer but permanent settlement was not attempted until after 1763. Since then, the isolated coastal settlements have been part of the colony of Newfoundland and, in 1927, the claim to the interior was confirmed also.

## Population and Economic Activity

The population is very small and grows very slowly. In 1857, there were about 1,650, by 1921 there were 3,774, in 1935, over 4,700 and, in 1956 there were 11,814. People of British origin predominate but other Europeans are represented also. The aborigines included 700 Eskimos, 800 Indians and 150 persons of mixed blood.

The Eskimo people inhabit the coast from Hamilton Inlet north to Cape Chidley, although it is probable that they once ranged farther south. Their chief occupations are sealing, fishing, caribou hunting and trapping arctic foxes.

The Indians are of two chief groups: the Naskaupi of the Barren Lands and the Montagnais of the forested south. Both tribes are of Algonquin origin. The Indians are nomadic hunters and trappers of the interior with no permanent encampments, but most of them pay an annual visit to some coastal settlement in order to trade.

The earliest white settlers in Labrador were fur traders. These were followed by fishermen who decided to remain overwinter in the north rather than to return to Newfoundland. These people became known as "Liveyeres" to distinguish them from the migratory fishermen. The chief economic enterprises of the settled white population are fishing and seal hunting with a winter sideline of fur trapping. There are also many who are mainly trappers, who have displaced the Indians from some of the best fur producing lands.

Moravian missionaries have ministered to the people of northern Labrador since 1752. Around their missions important villages such as Nain, Hopedale, Hebron and Makkovik have been built up. Nain has been called the capital of Eskimo Labrador. The village consists of a trim white mission house and church and a long line of grey Eskimo huts fronting the main street which follows the waterline.

The life of the southern Labrador people is probably best known from the work of Sir Willfred Grenfell. Dr. Grenfell, an Englishman, began medical work in Labrador in 1892. Aided by funds from the United States and Canada, he established a hospital at St. Anthony and secured a small ship to carry medical services to the coastal settlements. The Grenfell mission (now carried on by the International Grenfell Association) has been of great benefit to these isolated people.

Only in some of the southern settlements have fishermen's co-operatives and a few independent traders offered any competition.

## Resources and Future of Labrador

The present economy of Labrador is based entirely upon fishing and trapping. The latter, of course, can never be expected to support a large population and, while

Plate 16. Northwest River, Labrador.        *Courtesy R. C. A. F.*

## Trade

Most of the trade of Labrador has been in the hands of the Hudson's Bay Company since about 1830. It founded important villages such as Battle Harbour, Cartwright, Rigolet, Northwest River and Davis Inlet. In northern Labrador it has also operated in the mission villages. The company's neat white buildings with their red roofs stand out among the drab shacks which comprise the usual Labrador village while their well stocked shelves provide virtually all the necessities of life.

there is no evidence that the deep sea fishes are being unduly exploited, it does not seem that the market for Labrador fish can be greatly expanded. The southern part of the country contains large stands of pulpwood which await the erection of pulp mills. In recent years, mining geologists have proven that a great body of iron ore is located on the Lake Plateau, partly in Quebec and partly in Labrador. Exploitation of this resource required that a railway 360 miles in length be built from the port of Seven Islands on the north shore

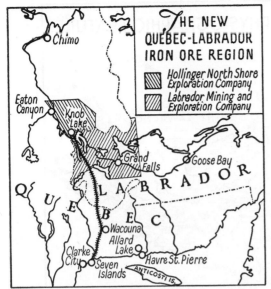

Figure 39. *The New Quebec—Labrador Iron Ore Region.* Newfoundland and Quebec share the great wealth of the iron beds of the Lake Plateau. A railway from Knob Lake will carry the ore to Seven Islands. Power is available at Eaton Canyon and at Grand Falls.

of the Gulf of St. Lawrence. Grand Falls on the Hamilton river has a power reserve of over 1,000,000 H.P. but the first project is the development of 12,000 H.P. on the Ashuanipi River. It is probable therefore that in the future Labrador may have an industrial population greater than its present total supported by fishing and trapping.

There are no good areas awaiting agricultural development but a certain amount of farming, even under great difficulties, may be expected in places where growing populations provide good markets. Potatoes, short season vegetables and grass will be the chief crops. The latter will make possible a limited livestock industry.

During World War II, the Canadian Government spent many millions of dollars on the construction of a great airport at Goose Bay. It still remains as an important defence outpost and is an alternative western base for commercial transatlantic air traffic. The importance of Labrador to the province of Newfoundland, and indeed to Canada, is bound to be greater as time goes on.

## Selected References

Government of Canada. *Province of Newfoundland. Statistical Background.* Dominion Bureau of Statistics. Ottawa. 1949.

Government of Canada. *Newfoundland—An Introduction to Canada's New Province.* Ottawa. 1950.

Gutsell, B. V. *An Introduction to the Geography of Newfoundland.* Department of Mines and Resources. Geographical Bureau. Information Series. No. 1. Ottawa. 1949.

Mackay, R. A. (Ed.) *Newfoundland.* Oxford University Press. Toronto. 1946.

Middleton, W. E. K. *The Climate of the Gulf of Saint Lawrence and the Surrounding Regions in Canada and Newfoundland as it affects Aviation.* Canadian Meteorological Memoirs No. 1. pp. 1-40. Ottawa. 1935.

Snelgrove, A. K. *Mines and Mineral Resources of Newfoundland.* Newfoundland Geological Survey. Information Circular No. 4. 162 pp., maps. St. John's 1930.

Tanner, V. *Outlines of the Geography, Life and Customs of Newfoundland—Labrador.* 2 Vols. Cambridge University Press. Cambridge. 1947.

Taylor, G. *Newfoundland—a study of Settlement with maps and illustrations.* Canadian Institute of International Affairs. Toronto. 1946.

Temple, W. B. and L. J. Harnum. *Information Booklet of Newfoundland and Labrador.* Newfoundland Industrial Development Board. St. John's. 1946.

Twenhofel, W. H. and P. MacClintock. *Surface of Newfoundland.* Bull. Geol. Soc. Am. Vol. 56: 1655-1728. 1940.

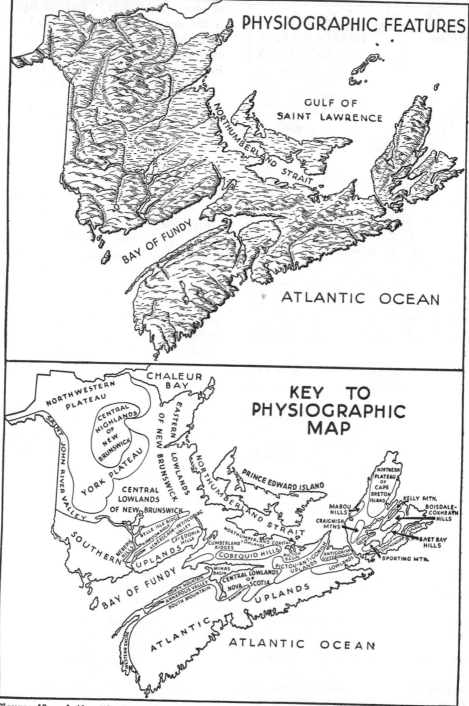

**Figures 40 and 41.** *Physiography of the Maritime Provinces.* The physiographic features of the Maritime Provinces occur in a rather complicated pattern of uplands and lowlands, shown and named in these maps.

# CHAPTER 3

# The Maritime Provinces
# Physical and Human Backgrounds

THE traditional Maritime Provinces of Canada lie on the Atlantic seaboard between 43° and 48° north latitude. An association of islands and peninsulas, possessed of an extremely long, sinuous and indented coastline, most of the area is within 30 miles of the sea while no part is more than 100 miles from salt water. The three provinces vary in size; New Brunswick, the largest and most northerly, has an area of 27,985 square miles; Nova Scotia, 21,068 square miles; and Prince Edward Island, 2,184 square miles. The total, 51,237 square miles, is less than 1.4% of the national area, although occupied by 9% of the Canadian people.

Historically, the outlook of the people of this area has been seaward; their trade with foreign countries rather than with central Canada. Among the first to enter Confederation, they have tended to adopt a sectional attitude which serves, at least, to bring them recognition as a group. In this they will in future be linked with Newfoundland. Thus in spite of the contrasts to be noted in both the physical and human aspects of geography, the Maritime Provinces deserve treatment as a region.

## Land Forms, Relief and Structure

Although the Maritime Provinces exhibit no great amplitude of relief — the highest point being only 2,700 feet above sea level — they possess a great variety of land forms. In a much simplified and generalized fashion, the physiographic diagram (Fig. 40) attempts to portray the earth sculpture of the region. In spite of the absence of high mountains, it can be divided into definite areas of greater and lesser relief, or in other words, into highlands and lowlands. By comparison with a contoured map it is seen that, in general, the boundary between these natural divisions of the land surface is approximately along the five hundred-foot contour.

Diversity of land forms must be explained in terms of the underlying rock structure. Figure 42 is a simplified geological map, in which is summarized the findings of many years of investigation by the workers of the Canadian Geological Survey. Generalizing somewhat, the central Maritime region is an ancient basin of deposition, or *geosyncline* as it is sometimes called, between the very ancient "oldland" of the Canadian Shield in Quebec and the hard old rocks of southern Nova Scotia. Both are of Precambrian age, and in the great depression between were laid down the various systems of Paleozoic rocks, including the Carboniferous which outcrops so widely around the Gulf of St. Lawrence. At various times, this mass of rock has been folded so that the exposures

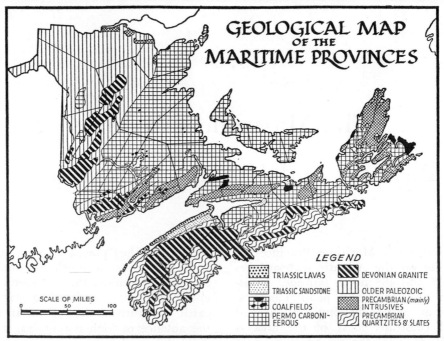

Figure 42. *A Simplified Geological Map of the Maritime Provinces,* based on maps of the Canadian Geographical Survey. Note the correlation between the major rock areas and the major physiographic divisions.

now consist of long belts running from N.E. to Southwest in the same general direction as the mountains of the rest of eastern North America. The youngest formations of all are the Triassic rocks of the Bay of Fundy region. In addition to the folding, the beds of sedimentary rock were intruded by molten magma. The most widespread of these rocks are the granites of Devonian age which now form the Central Highlands of New Brunswick and the central axis of the peninsula of Nova Scotia.

The province of New Brunswick may be divided into four great physiographic regions: the Northwestern Plateau, the Central Highlands, the Cental and Eastern Lowlands, and the Southern Uplands. In Nova Scotia, the upland areas include: the North Mountain, the Cobequid Mountains, the Uplands of Pictou and Antigonish, the extensive Atlantic Uplands, the various hilly regions of the southern

part of Cape Breton Island and the great Cape Breton Plateau which comprises the highest land in the province. The lowlands include: the Annapolis-Cornwallis Valley, the Hants-Colchester or Central Lowland, the North Shore or Northumberland Coastal Lowlands (actually an eastward extension of the Central and Eastern Lowlands of New Brunswick), the Antigonish-Guysborough Lowland and the Cape Breton Lowlands. No part of Prince Edward Island is more than 500 feet above tide, hence it may be regarded as a single lowland region.

## The Upland Areas

The great *Northwestern Plateau of New Brunswick* with a general level of about 1,000-1,500 feet above tide, is developed upon the folded calcareous or lime-containing slates of the Devonian period, and is part of an even larger region including much of the adjoining portions of Quebec and Maine. The area is deeply dissected by valleys tributary to both the St. John and Restigouche rivers.

The *Central Highlands* of New Brunswick consist of a dissected plateau having a skyline at above 2,000 feet A.T., surmounted by numerous monadnocks or relic mountains, the highest of which is

The *Southern Uplands* of New Brunswick are made up of several widely separated areas. Largest and highest of these is the great upland ridge along the Bay of Fundy east of the St. John River, comprising the Caledonia Hills, the Kent Hills, etc., with a maximum elevation of about 1,400 feet A.T. In structure it is a long oval

Courtesy Exp. Farms Service.

Plate 17. The Uplands of the Aroostook District in New Brunswick are noted for the production of potatoes.

Mount Carleton (2,700'). Numerous river valleys have deeply trenched the plateau to a depth of 1,000 feet or more below the summit level. The underlying rock of this highland area is an immense granite mass or batholith which was intruded into the stratified rocks in Devonian times. Hardened and folded sedimentary rocks around the edges of the batholith also take part in the formation of the plateau.

The *Central* or *York Plateau* laps around the southern and eastern edges of the highland. Its elevation averages about 1,000 feet A.T. and it is developed in part on the Devonian granite batholith and in part on hard metamorphosed Paleozoic sedimentaries. The Saint John River cuts directly across it from west to east in a rather deep and narrow valley to debouch on the Central Lowlands.

dome or arched ridge, with a core of Pre-Cambrian volcanic and intrusive rocks, pitching toward the northeast where it is overlapped by a fringe of the Lower Carboniferous system containing oil shales. To the north, across the Kennebecasis valley, is the long low ridge of the Kingston Hills, also with a Precambrian core which is exposed toward the west but covered by Carboniferous limestones and sandstones toward the northeast. Another narrow longitudinal valley intervenes between the Kingston Ridge and the Belle Isle Ridge to the north. Here the hard Precambrian outcrops give rise to numerous rounded summits, among these Bull Moose Hill is about 800 feet A.T. West of the St. John River lies another rugged area formed partly upon similar hard ancient rocks and partly upon another immense granite batholith of Devonian age. Although much of this area is below 500 feet A.T., large areas are above 1,000 feet in elevation, Mt. Champlain in the Nerepis Hills being 1,462 feet A.T. and Mt. Pleasant, thirty miles further west, is 1,175 feet A.T.

The *Cobequid Mountains* in Nova Scotia, although appearing as a sharp ridge from both north and south, in reality form a plateau with a skyline at about 900 feet A. T., on top of which rest a few low rounded remnants from 100 to 200 feet higher. This upland, which is from 8 to 12 miles wide and eighty-five miles long, is underlain by a complex of igneous and altered sedimentary rocks ranging in age from Precambrian to Devonian.

The *Pictou-Antigonish* uplands extend completely across both counties—from eastern Colchester to Cape George. They also are developed upon hard old rocks—Precambrian and older Paleozoic, igneous and metamorphic—and in part upon hard sandstones of the Carboniferous system. The highest point, McNeil Mountain (1,010 feet A.T.), is a volcanic plug.

The *North Mountain* which separates the Bay of Fundy from the Annapolis Valley is an inclined sheet of lava or trap rock, dipping northwestward beneath the Bay in a dish-like fold. Seen from the south it presents a long, steep escarpment, the top of which has an elevation of 500-700 feet A. T.

The *Atlantic Upland* comprises more than half the area of the Nova Scotia mainland. It also is an inclined surface rising northward at the rate of about 15 feet per mile to the brow of the South Mountain — a northfacing escarpment (600-700 feet A. T.) overlooking the Annapolis Valley. The surface is extremely irregular, yet the skyline is flat except for a few residual hills or monadnocks a hundred feet above the general level. In the eastern part of the mainland the upland ends in an abrupt escarpment overlooking the valley of the St. Mary's River. The highest parts of this upland are developed

upon enormous granite batholiths of Devonian age, while between them and the Atlantic Ocean the country is underlain by Precambrian rocks, — the folded slates and quartzites (whin) of the Gold Bearing Measures. The latter, having been strongly folded, are exposed in long narrow alternate belts parallel with the main axis of the province. Drainage is immature in the interior but the valleys become deeper and better developed southward although the mouths of all the rivers are drowned.

On Cape Breton Island there are several upland ridges trending from southwest to northeast, all on hard Precambrian crystalline rocks. The *Southeastern Upland* rises gradually from the water's edge to an elevation of about 400 feet on the brow of the escarpment overlooking Salmon River. The *East Bay Hills* and *Sporting Mountain* are from 500 to 600 A. T. The *North Mountains, Boisdale* and *Coxheath Hills* are from 600 to 700 feet A. T. Further northward the *Craignish Hills, Kelly Mountains* and *Mabou Highlands* are all more than 1,000 feet high.

The *Northern Tableland,* much of which is now included in the Cape Breton National Park rises abruptly from the narrow coastal lowlands to an elevation of 1,200 feet A.T., and reaches 1,500-1,700 feet A.T. in the interior. Poor drainage characterizes much of the upland surface but the edges of the plateau are scarred by deep V-shaped valleys.

## The Lowland Areas

It has been emphasized that the uplands are all underlain by hard crystalline rocks. The lowlands, on the other hand, are found on the weaker sandstones, shales and limestones; sedimentaries in large part belonging to the Carboniferous system.

The *Chaleur Bay* region was a basin of deposition as far back as Devonian and Carboniferous times. The present lowland, developed on these rocks, consists of a narrow coastal strip both north and south of the Bay.

The *Maritime Basin*. The central feature of the structure of the Maritime Provinces is, of course, the broad syncline or depositional basin in which the great areas of Carboniferous or coal-bearing rocks were laid down. It underlies the whole southwestern part of the Gulf of St. Lawrence as well as the whole of the Province of Prince Edward Island, nearly one half the area of New Brunswick, and the *Northumberland Coastal Lowlands* of Nova Scotia. The most prevalent rocks in the *Central* and *Eastern Lowlands* of New Brunswick are the Millstone Grits, sterile sandstones of the Pennsylvanian or Upper Carboniferous system. Coal is found in the central portion near Minto, and a few thin seams are also known along the shore of Chaleur Bay. Much of the area is flat and swampy, the drainage having been deranged by glaciation. Much of the plain is covered with deep sandy drift, but in places the rock lies almost at the surface over broad areas. In general, the plain is below 500 feet A. T., but around the edges of the basin the limestones of the Lower Carboniferous system come to the surface in ranges of rocky hills, 500-600 feet A. T. More or less to be considered an outlier of this system, is the *Petitcodiac-Kennebecasis* valley carved in Carboniferous rocks preserved in the syncline between the Kingston Hills and the Southern Uplands.

The eastern end is floored by Pennsylvanian sandstones while the western end is underlain by Mississippian limestones.

The *North Shore* or *Northumberland Coastal Lowland* of Nova Scotia is the eastward extension of the Carboniferous lowland of New Brunswick. Here, however, the beds are of slightly different character. While the Millstone Grits still appear in the crests of the long low anticlines, which cross the country in a direction slightly north of east, the coal measures occupy the synclines, giving rise to the productive mines at Joggins, Springhill and Stellarton. Gypsum, salt and oil shales are found in the Windsor beds of the Carboniferous system. By far the greatest area, however, is underlain by the red beds of Permian age which characterize the northern part of the coastal plain and the whole of Prince Edward Island where boreholes have proven them to be more than 2,000 feet thick.

The *Antigonish-Guysborough Lowland* is also underlain by Pennsylvanian or Upper Carboniferous rocks, mainly sandstones, shales and conglomerates. In the lowest part of this basin around Antigonish, however, are found the Windsor beds containing limestones and gypsum.

*Cape Breton Lowlands*, involving almost half the area of the island, are also developed upon Carboniferous rocks, both

Courtesy Exp. Farms Service.

Plate 18. The Tantramar Marsh. Dyked for protection against the high tides of the Bay of Fundy, these meadows have provided hay and grain for centuries.

Plate 19. The Plateau of Northern Cape Breton, bordered by an abrupt escarpment, below which the settlement of Cheticamp nestles on a narrow coastal plain.

the sandstones and the gypsum-bearing limestone beds being in evidence. The coal measures are preserved only in broad, pitching synclines with outcrops near the shore in the Port Hood, Inverness and Sydney areas so that the greater part of the coal reserve lies beneath the sea.

The last system of lowlands, with which we must deal, is that connected with the Bay of Fundy and its head waters. Here again, we have a great syncline in which are preserved rocks of Triassic age, the youngest rocks in Eastern Canada. While the outcrop of Triassic lava stands out as the North Mountain ridge, the underlying red shales and sandstones are eroded to form the *Annapolis-Cornwallis Valley, Annapolis Basin* and *St. Mary's Bay*. This long lowland is generally known as the *Annapolis Valley*. Further east the syncline contains Minas Basin and the red sandstones outcrop around the shores of Cobequid Bay. The greater part of the *Hants-Colchester Lowland*, however, is developed upon rocks of Carboniferous age, the limestone and gypsum beds in the

vicinity of Windsor being extensively worked.

## Development of Present Land Forms

In the preceding paragraphs, it has been shown that the land surface of the Maritime Provinces is readily divisible into systems of uplands and lowlands; moreover, on looking at the maps, we see that the grain of the country, that is, the direction of the rock strikes, is mostly in a N. E.-S. W. direction. The long axes of the basins or synclines, already mentioned, are similarly oriented. Examination of a physiographic map of North America, shows that a similar condition prevails over the whole eastern margin of the continent. The Maritime Provinces form part of the folded Appalachian Mountain region which has undergone modification during several mountain building epochs. Faulting as well as folding has had important effects. The scarps bordering the Cobequid Mountains, the Pictou-Antigonish Uplands and the Cape Breton Plateau indicate some of the important fault lines.

The present surface, however, does not bear a great deal of resemblance to the old folds, it truncates or cuts straight across them all. How was it developed? Why do we see such long level skylines on the North Mountain, the Cobequids, the Cape Breton Plateau, or the various uplands in New Brunswick?

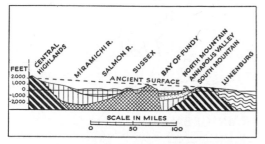

Figure 43. *Profile and Geological Section Across the Maritime Provinces.* This simplified diagram shows the facets of the tilted ancient peneplain preserved by the harder rock formations.

In Figure (43) is presented a profile or section from north to south across the area. Starting at sea level on the south shore of Nova Scotia it rises steadily to the crest of the South Mountain (600 feet A. T.). Across the Annapolis Valley the North Mountain reaches 700 feet A. T.; the Advocate Mountains are between 800 and 900 feet high. The Southern Uplands of New Brunswick are about, 1,200 feet A.T. Further north and fully 200 miles from the Atlantic we encounter a skyline slightly above 2,000 feet A.T. in the Central Highlands. In other words, the general elevation of the uplands increases at the rate of about 10 feet per mile. A similar section may be drawn from south to north on Cape Breton Island.

## Old Erosion Surfaces

The logical explanation is that these uplands are the remnants of an old erosion surface preserved on the harder rocks. The mountains, mentioned in a previous paragraph, were, over a long period of time, completely eroded by rain and rivers and reduced almost to sea level. This condition was very widespread, pieces of this erosion surface or peneplain (almost a plain) being found all the way from Georgia to Northern Labrador. This immense lowland did not, however, remain at or near sea-level. A new cycle of mountain building was initiated and the peneplain was raised and warped. The rivers on its surface took on a new lease of life and began to cut down their valleys, erosion being most effective on the belts of weaker rocks. It would seem that a second base-level was also established, since the great plateau of northwestern New Brunswick is about 1,000 feet below the skyline of the Central Highlands. It too was raised and a third cycle of erosion has carved out the present lowlands while still more recent tilting has allowed the sea to advance over large areas that were once dry land.

## Glaciation

The last major event in the shaping of the surface features of the Maritime Provinces, as in most of Canada was the Ice Age of the Pleistocene period. Great ice sheets spread over the land, and, when they melted, a great mixture of unconsolidated material was left upon the bed rock.

The wooded nature of the Maritime landscape has prevented complete systematic mapping of the glacial features but they are known to include moraines, drumlins, kames and eskers similar to those described in detail for other parts of Canada. In particular it is worth noting that there are many hundreds of drumlins in Nova Scotia. Halifax, Chester, Mahone Bay, Guysborough County and the interior of Queen's county all have these oval hills of drift in abundance.

Glaciation has completely disarranged most of the previously established drainage patterns causing the country to be dotted with swamps and lakes. Rivers, forced to carve new courses, have many interruptions in the form of rapids and waterfalls. Both the Reversing Falls and Grand Falls on the St. John River are of this type.

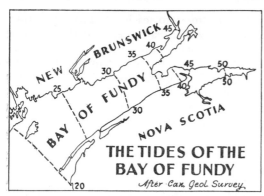

Figure 44. *The Tides of the Bay of Fundy.* The mean range between high and low water varies from 20 feet at Brier Island and Grand Manan, to 50 feet in Cobequid Bay.

## Tides

The tides of the Bay of Fundy and its headwaters are among the highest in the world. Twice each day the waters of this funnel-shaped basin rise and fall. The variation in water level is greatest in the narrow headwaters where the normal range is from 30 to 40 feet, but at high tide it may be from 50 to 60 feet between high and low water. Along the protected parts of the shoreline, and in the river estuaries, extensive deposits of silt were laid down

similar to deltas and flood plains. These wide alluvial lowlands, protected by dykes, now form some of the best farm lands of the region.

Tides occur on all coasts in the Maritimes but those of the Gulf of St. Lawrence and the Atlantic coasts do not have a range of more than ten feet.

Figure 45. *The Saint John River Drainage Area.* It includes 20,000 square miles in Quebec, New Brunswick and the State of Maine.

## Drainage

Compared with those in other provinces, the rivers of the Maritime region are rather small. The heavy rainfall and wooded

Plate 20. A newly built dyke on the tidal marshes in Nova Scotia.

character of their drainage areas give them a more reliable flow, however, and many of them are harnessed for the development of hydro-electric energy.

The St. John River, rising in the state of Maine, has a length of 400 miles and a drainage basin of over 20,000 square miles in Maine, Quebec and New Brunswick. Draining a forested country, this river and its tributaries have long been used for the transportation of timber. The lower course of the river, between St. John and Fredericton is navigable for small steamers. A large power generating station is located at Grand Falls.

Other rivers in New Brunswick include the Restigouche, Nipisiguit, Miramichi, Petitcodiac and St. Croix.

In Nova Scotia there are many short rivers, including the Annapolis, Tusket, Liverpool, Lahave, Musquodoboit, Sheet Harbour, St. Mary, Pictou and Shubenacadie.

## Climate, Vegetation and Soils

### Climate

Having an east coast mid-latitude location, the Maritime Provinces have a strongly continental climate with considerable variation in the seasonal temperature regime. Nearness to the ocean, however, modifies the continental influence and the Atlantic shores have lower summer temperatures and greater rainfall than inland areas.

At most stations January is the coldest month and July is the warmest, although in some parts of Nova Scotia February and August hold the honours, the reason being nearness to the ocean whose waters are slower to take on or give up heat than is dry land. The average temperatures for the months of January and July are seen in Figures 46 and 47, while the mean annual temperature is given in Figure 48. Two important facts stand out. One is the great cooling effect of the elevation of the New Brunswick Highlands upon summer temperatures, the other is the moderating in-

fluence of the Atlantic Ocean upon its shores in the winter. In Figures 49 and 50 are shown the distributions of the extreme high and extreme low temperature records. In general, August 1935 was the warmest month on record and February 1934, the coldest. Another function of temperature which is of importance, particularly to the farmer, is the occurrence of frosts. Figure 51 shows the average length of the frost-free period in days. Notice how short it is in Northern New Brunswick. In fact, in the Central Highlands, frost may be expected in any month in the year. On the other hand, the Bay of Fundy, the Gulf of St. Lawrence and the Atlantic Ocean, by minimizing the difference between night and day temperatures, serve to prolong the frost-free season along their shores.

Turning now to the moisture factor, we find that Figure 52 shows us the distribution of the average total precipitation for the year. There is over twenty inches difference between the wettest and driest localities, the South Shore of Nova Scotia receiving more than 55 inches per year, while Northern New Brunswick receives only 35 inches or less. Part of this precipitation is made up of snow and Figure 53 shows the average distribution of snowfall. Here, the effect of the oceanic influence is just the reverse, the South Shore of Nova Scotia gets only 70 inches or less while Northern New Brunswick gets more than 110 inches of snow. As a rule, ten inches of snow is counted as the equivalent of one inch of rain; therefore, in Northern New Brunswick over 30% of the precipitation falls as snow, whereas in Southern Nova Scotia only about 12% is snow, with a resulting very great difference in winter conditions. It is worth mentioning here, although no corresponding map is shown, that, in Northern New Brunswick, slightly more than half the yearly total falls in the warmer six months of the year, while, in Nova Scotia, the cooler half of the year is wetter. Worth noting too, is the number of rainy days per year, shown in Figure 54; on the South Shore, it

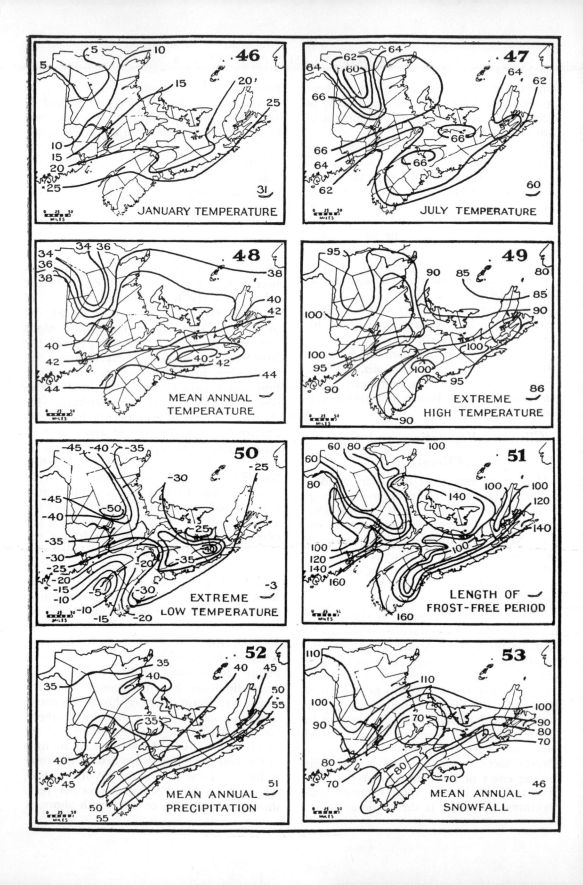

**46** JANUARY TEMPERATURE

**47** JULY TEMPERATURE

**48** MEAN ANNUAL TEMPERATURE

**49** EXTREME HIGH TEMPERATURE

**50** EXTREME LOW TEMPERATURE

**51** LENGTH OF FROST-FREE PERIOD

**52** MEAN ANNUAL PRECIPITATION

**53** MEAN ANNUAL SNOWFALL

rains on two out of every five days, while, in the interior of New Brunswick, the proportion is one out of three. Moisture deficiencies may occur in the central and northern regions but seldom on the South Shore.

Figure 55 shows the average number of foggy days per year. The Bay of Fundy and the South Shore are among the foggiest coasts on earth, while the Strait of Northumberland is relatively free from fogs. In the south and west most of the fogs occur in the summer, every other day in July usually being foggy. Toward the northeast, and especially in the Gulf of St. Lawrence, more fogs occur in the spring months.

From a study of these charts, the Maritime Provinces can be divided into eleven minor climatic regions which are shown in Figure 56. Two areas, the Central Highlands of New Brunswick and the Plateau of Northern Cape Breton, are elevated enough to warrant their separation as distinct climatic regions, although systematic data as to their characteristics are not available.

The peculiar location of the Maritime Provinces is the cause of considerable regional variation. The weather is controlled by cyclonic storms which in winter tend to pass along the southern border, inducing invasions of cold polar air, while in summer they pass to the north, drawing in warm air from the south and west. It is worth noting, too, that landward regions usually enjoy an earlier spring than marine locations, while the latter have a more prolonged and open autumn. In general, New Brunswick may be said to have a continental climate, while marine influence, in particular a much higher rainfall, charac-

terizes Nova Scotia. Prince Edward Island, though surrounded by water, is more continental than marine.

## Vegetation

The natural vegetation of the Maritime Provinces is forest. As might be expected from the variation in rocks, land forms and climate which have been discussed, the forest cover also shows considerable variation. W. E. D. Halliday of the Dominion Forest Service has published "A Forest Classification of Canada" and Figure 57 presents the forest regions into which he has divided the Maritime Provinces.

The forests of the higher parts of the Gaspé Peninsula are essentially like those of the northern parts of Quebec and Ontario, spruce and balsam being the dominant trees. The higher parts of the Northern Plateau of New Brunswick have similar forests, (Section 1 on the map.)

The forests of Section 2, or the Restigouche Forests, are also similar to those of large areas in the province of Quebec. The area contains a mixture of hardwoods and softwoods, although the latter dominate over large areas. Cedar, white spruce, balsam fir, black spruce, tamarack, red and white pines occur in the order given. White cedar reaches its best development on the continent in this area. The chief hardwoods are sugar maple and yellow birch.

The forests of the New Brunswick Uplands, Section 3, are essentially coniferous; balsam fir, black spruce, and red spruce are the leading trees with some white pine and cedar; the hardwoods are represented by sugar maple and yellow birch. Swampy areas contain tamarack and black ash.

Figure 46. *January Mean Temperature.* Midwinter in the New Brunswick uplands is much more severe than on the Atlantic coast. Figure 47. *July Mean Temperature.* The central and Gulf regions are warmer than the highlands or the Atlantic coast. Figure 48. *Mean Annual Temperature.* A range of more than 10°F. clearly indicates the influence of land and sea in this area. Figure 49. *Occurrence of Extremely High Temperatures.* This pattern shows the influence of land and sea as well as upland and lowland. Figure 50. *Occurrence of Extremely Low Temperatures.* The greatest contrast, in this map, lies between Central New Brunswick and the Western Shore of Nova Scotia. Figure 51. *Length of the Frost-Free Period.* Ranging from less than 60 to more than 160 days, the frost free period also shows the influence of land and sea. Figure 52. *Mean Annual Precipitation.* Ranging from 35 to 55 inches per annum, precipitation is fairly evenly distributed throughout the year. Figure 53. *Mean Annual Snowfall.* From one-fifth to one-third of the precipitation occurs as snow.

The Miramichi forests, Section 4, occupy the drainage basin of the Miramichi River and its tributaries. The sandy soils, derived from the Millstone Grits, are highly podzolized. Red and black spruce, balsam fir, aspens, white and wire birches, white pine,

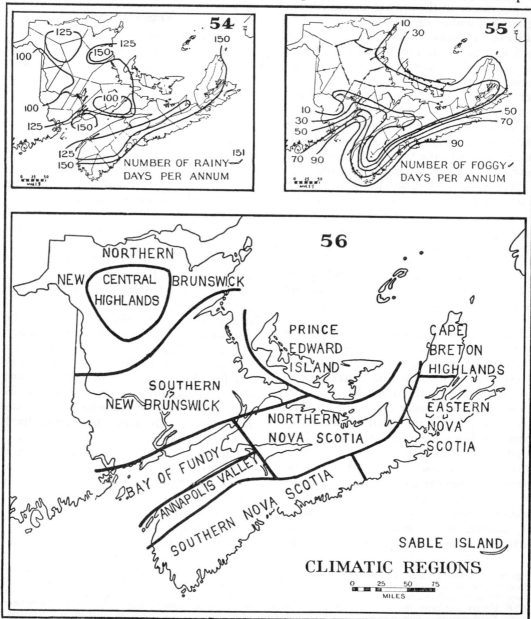

Figure 54. *Number of Precipitation Days per Annum.* Coastal locations average about three days of rain or snow per week.

Figure 55. *Number of Foggy Days per Annum.* The Bay of Fundy and the South Shore of Nova Scotia are very foggy in the early summer.

Figure 56. *Climatic Divisions of the Maritime Provinces.* Statistics differ sufficiently to allow separation of ten climatic sub-divisions, approximately as shown on this map.

and hemlock are found. It is probable that hemlock was much more plentiful in the area before the Miramichi fire which swept it more than one hundred years ago. White and wire birches and jack pines are trees which tend to occupy burned areas.

Section 5, the Northeast Coastal Forest occupies an area of sandy, and often poorly drained, soils. Peat bogs and barrens are common. Poorly drained areas carry black spruce, cedar and tamarack; white and wire birches and jack pines occupy the sand flats. Better sites carry a well developed forest of red spruce, yellow birch, beech and sugar maple.

The St. John Valley, Southern New Brunswick, Northern Nova Scotia and Prince Edward Island are all included in the central section, No. 6. Here the mixed forest of the Acadian type attains its fullest development. Sugar maple, yellow birch, beech, red maple, elm, black and white ash, are all common or abundant, while red oak, basswood, ironwood and butternut are found in some localities. This is the area in which red spruce reaches its greatest development, but white spruce, white pine, balsam fir and hemlock are also found. This is the area too, in which agriculture has made greatest progress and, even where not cleared, the forests have suffered severe culling. Prince Edward Island is practically all occupied by farms and no extensive tracts of forest remain.

Section 7, the Atlantic Slopes, includes not only the southern half of the mainland of Nova Scotia from Cape Sable to Cape Canso, but the southern shore of Cape Breton Island as well, which, like the mainland, is situated on the hard granites and Precambrian metamorphic rocks. Climatically much more moist than any other area, and with a drainage system still suffering from derangement during the glacial period, we are not surprised to find many bogs in this section. Many of these are treeless and are locally known as "savannas". Black spruce bogs are common, so also are swamps containing red maple, black ash,

Figure 57. *Forest Regions of the Maritime Provinces.* 1, Gaspé Forest; 2, Restigouche Forest; 3, Central Uplands Forest; 4, Miramichi Forest; 5, Northeast Coastal Forest; 6, Central Mixed Forest; 7, Atlantic Forest; 8, Cape Breton Lowland Forest; 9, Cape Breton Plateau Forest.

tamarack and black alder. The hard rocks such as granite and quartzite often have little or no soil covering, consequently rocky barrens, either natural or induced by fire, cover very large areas in the interior. Where soils are sufficiently deep, however, red spruce, hemlock and white pine grow well, while to the northward considerable balsam fir occurs.

In Cape Breton balsam fir is the predominant species, but in the central lowlands, Section 8, some red spruce occurs together with such hardwoods as yellow birch, sugar maple, elm and red oak. The Cape Breton Plateau, Section 9, is elevated, cold and wet. The dominant tree is the balsam fir in almost pure stands, but in some locations white and black spruce, paper birch and mountain ash are found. A large part of the plateau (some 300-400 square miles according to B. E. Fernow, "Forest Conditions of Nova Scotia") consists of barrens with heath or bog vegetation. Raised bogs are common here, as in other wet districts.

Sable Island is cited as possessing a rather unique type of climate. It is also

Plate 21. The Acadian Mixed Forest produces both softwood and hardwood lumber.

unique in that it possesses no forest growth, the extremely sandy soils and high winds being inimical to tree growth, beach grass being the most abundant plant.

## The Soils

Practically all of the maturely developed soils of the Maritime Provinces are *Podzols,* similar to those of Scandinavia, Northern Russia and the northern parts of Quebec and Ontario. The environmental factors favouring the formation of Podzols are: abundant precipitation; long, cold winters; short, cool summers; a natural forest vegetation composed largely of coniferous trees such as pine, spruce and balsam fir. In addition, as has already been pointed out, the surface geological deposits of much of the area have been derived from sandstones or from acidic crystalline rocks such as granite. Consequently, the soils tend to be acid, leached and infertile.

The characteristics of the Podzol environment are shown in Figure 58, which represents conditions in the Annapolis Valley. Under the dark coloured, partly decomposed forest litter which is designated as the $A_0$ horizon, the mineral soil is slightly darkened by an admixture of organic matter to form a shallow $A_1$ horizon. Below this is a white, or very light grey horizon of variable depth which is known as the $A_2$. These horizons constitute the portion of the soil from which the mineral nutrients such as calcium, magnesium and potassium have been leached by action of the acids released from the decomposing forest litter. Along with these, other substances, particularly the oxides of iron and aluminum are carried downward to be redeposited in the subsoil. The material left in the upper horizons, which often has the appearance of white sand, is, in fact, quite largely composed of quartz or silica ($SiO_2$), and therefore of very limited fertility.

The B horizon, or zone of accumulation, is usually reddish or brownish in color from the iron oxide which it contains. Sometimes it is somewhat compact and even cemented by iron and humus compounds.

Not only is the surface soil usually quite acid, but an acid reaction persists throughout the whole of the weathered soil profile.

It is not yet possible to present a complete regional summary of the soils of the Maritime Provinces because, to date, only five soil survey reports are available. They cover the Fredericton and Woodstock sections of the St. John Valley in New Brunswick and the Annapolis Valley, Cumberland and Colchester counties of Nova Scotia. From them some ideas of the variation in soil from place to place may be obtained.

In the Woodstock section, almost nine-tenths of the area is covered by till derived from sandstones and calcareous shales or slates of Paleozoic age. On the well-drained upland areas, the soil is weathered to a depth of 18 to 24 inches. In spite of the high percentage of lime in the parent material, the surface soils are acid (pH 4.00 to 5.00) and a leached horizon 2-4 inches deep has developed. The potato is the dominant crop. By the use of large amounts of commercial fertilizer, often a ton per acre, potatoes are made to yield about one hundred barrels per acre. This is the best yield in Canada, and the adjoining section of Maine holds the record in U.S.A. The upland ridges are separated by low areas of the same material. These soils are not nearly so acid and have a much greater natural fertility but they are usually left uncleared because of poor drainage.

In the Annapolis valley, only about half the area is based upon glacial till, and water deposited materials are widespread. Moreover, both classes of material are pre-

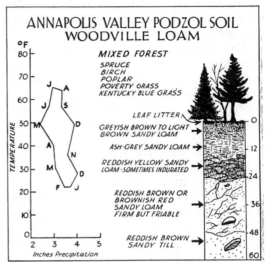

Figure 58. *An Annapolis Valley Podzol.* Climatic conditions are here presented in the form of G. Taylor's *hythergraph.* Note the depth and characteristics of the various soil horizons.

dominantly sandy, because of their derivation from the underlying Triassic sandstones and, in spite of the fact that this type of rock contains a certain amount of calcareous cement, all parent materials of the soils are distinctly acid. The soils themselves are much more so, ranging from pH 4.00 to 5.00. It is notable that in this area, with its abundance of water-worked drift, that there are a very large number of soil types so that soils vary greatly in productive capacity even on the individual farm. As a rule, the loams and sandy loams are rated best for orchards and potatoes, while the clay loams are rated best for hay and pasture. Careful soil management is necessary, the natural fertility of the Podzols is low and the orchardists of the Annapolis Valley are nearly as heavy users of commercial fertilizers as the potato growers of the St. John Valley.

Northern Nova Scotia, as represented by Cumberland and Colchester counties, has considerable contrast in soils. The lowlands, derived in large measure from Carboniferous sandstones and shales, have typical Podzols developed under coniferous woodland. The process of leaching has affected both sands and clays and, especially in imperfectly drained areas, the grey $A_2$ horizon is quite pronounced.

The soils of the Cobequid uplands, on the other hand, developed from harder igneous and metamorphic rocks under mixed deciduous forest, are not so highly leached. Nevertheless, since they are shallow and stony, they are of little value for agriculture.

The soils with the greatest natural fertility in both New Brunswick and Nova Scotia are those of the river bottoms or "intervales" and of the dyked marshes bordering the headwaters of the Bay of Fundy. The fertility of the latter was thought to be inexhaustable and they have been cropped continuously for two or three centuries without the addition of fertilizer. Needless

to say, they now show signs of exhaustion. Under a recently instituted program of marshland rehabilitation, dykes are being rebuilt, drainage improved and the fertility of the soil is being restored. In the past many thousands of tons of mud from the tidal flats were hauled and spread upon the upland fields of adjoining farms, but this practice is now too expensive.

## Population

Probably the most significant geographical facts concerning any area are the numbers, density and distribution of its human inhabitants; while a study of the historical factors of its development proves to be a most interesting investigation. The population of the Maritime Provinces, according to the census of 1941, is shown in Figure 59 by means of the dot and circle method. In it an attempt has been made to place the dots within the areas which are actually occupied rather than to scatter

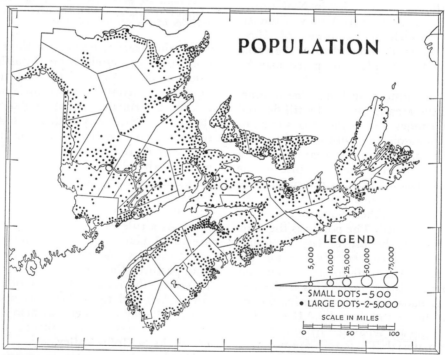

Figure 59. *Population Distribution in the Maritime Provinces.* Except on Prince Edward Island, the settlements are all in sea coast or valley locations, and there is much unoccupied land.

them indiscriminately throughout political divisions.

Several striking facts emerge from this study. In the first place, much of the area is still unoccupied. Prince Edward Island, only, can be said to be uniformly populated. Secondly, the populated regions of New Brunswick and Nova Scotia are chiefly peripheral. Thirdly, almost all of the urban centres, in all three provinces, are in sea coast locations or upon navigable waterways. There are good geographical and historical reasons for these patterns. The empty areas are those of the more rugged uplands or those underlain by hard igneous rocks. The granite batholiths of Central New Brunswick and Southwestern Nova Scotia are conspicuously devoid of population, so also are the higher plateaux of Cape Breton and Northern New Brunswick. Urban locations are explainable by the fact that the Maritimes were settled in an era when water transport was the only means of communication. The few inland towns owe their growth, if not their origins, to the coming of the railroads.

The total population of the Maritime Provinces in 1956 was 1,350,000, an increase of 34% since 1931. In the same period the population of Canada increased about 50%. Recent growth in the towns and cities has raised the proportion of urban dwellers to 43% of the total population. Nova Scotia is the most urbanized of the Maritime Provinces, while Prince Edward Island is the most rural province in Canada.

English speaking people number four-fifths of the total, while one-fifth is French. The proportions vary in the different provinces, New Brunswick's population is 36% of French origin, this group predominating in the upper St. John Valley and along the northern and eastern coasts. French people are numerous in the western end of Prince Edward Island, while in Nova Scotia they are found in Digby, Inverness, Richmond and Antogonish counties. In Nova Scotia about 7% of the population are of Dutch and German descent, found chiefly in Lunenburg county. People of Scottish descent are most abundant in Cape Breton Island and the eastern mainland of Nova Scotia and in the eastern end of Prince Edward Island. Persons of English descent comprise two-thirds of the population, they are found everywhere, but more particularly in the St. John Valley and in Western Nova Scotia. It is worth noting that at the present time 95% of the population of the Maitime Provinces consists of native Canadians. The Indians number about 4,200.

## Settlement — Periods and Patterns

The scattered settlements of the French regime in Acadia, at their climax held about 15,000 people; but, a great number of these settlements were dispersed and the

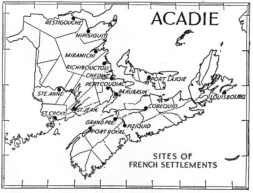

Figure 60. *Sites of some of the more important settlements in the French colony of l'Acadie.*

people removed to other territories as a defence measure in 1755, hence they have little significance in the present day pattern. Port Royal (1604) was the first settlement. The densest Acadian population was found in the vicinity of Minas Basin, Cobequid Bay and Chignecto Basin, where the presence of tidal marshes formed the basis of the agricultural economy. Other settlements existed on the St. John River, on Prince Edward Island and on Cape Breton Island where the fortress of Louisbourg afforded protection. Prince Edward Island and Cape Breton remained French until

1758, but the mainland was ceded finally to the English in 1713.

During the first decades of English rule no new settlements were founded, the only English in the land being the garrison, governing officials and a few traders at Annapolis Royal and a summer colony of New England fishermen at Canso.

Halifax was founded on Chebucto Bay by Lord Cornwallis in 1749, to offset the growing power of the French at Louisbourg. In 1750-2 some German immigrants, together with some French and Swiss Huguenots, came to Halifax but, in 1753, they removed to Lunenburg to found a settlement of their own.

After the final capture of Louisbourg in 1758, many settlers came from New England. Fishermen and whalers established colonies at Yarmouth, Barrington, Port

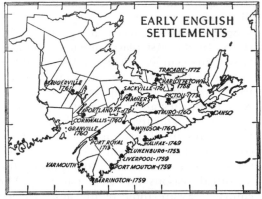

Figure 61. *Locations of Some Early English Settlements.* The settlement pattern of Nova Scotia was pretty well established before 1775.

Mouton, Liverpool and other South Shore points in 1759. The "Planters" established agricultural colonies in 1760-1 at Truro,

*Courtesy N.S. Bureau of Information.*

Plate 22. Grand Pré Memorial Park. The stone church of St. Charles stands on the site of the original Acadian church and contains a museum collection from the days of early settlement.

Onslow, Newport, Falmouth, Windsor, Horton, Cornwallis, Annapolis, Granville, Amherst and Sackville, for the most part on lands formerly occupied by the exiled Acadians. New Englanders also established settlements around Passamaquoddy Bay, at Portland Point in St. John Harbour and at Maugerville on the St. John River.

Other early settlers were the Yorkshiremen who came to Sackville and Amherst, the Ulstermen of Londonderry and the English settlers of Gagetown, Miramichi and Restigouche. Scottish Highlanders settled in Pictou and Prince Edward Island in 1773.

Within a few years the government of Nova Scotia granted over 18,000,000 acres, more than six times the present total of improved land.

In 1767 Prince Edward Island became a separate province and in 1769 it was divided into 67 townships of 20,000 acres each and granted to persons who had claims on the home government. This system of landlordism persisted until Prince Edward Island became a Province of the Dominion of Canada.

During this period, also, many Acadians returned and established the settlements in which their descendants still live.

At the close of the American War of Independence, more than 30,000 Loyalists

came to Nova Scotia. Many of them went to previously established settlements, but the majority established new ones in the territory north of the Bay of Fundy. This was the origin of the Passamaquoddy Bay parishes including St. Andrews, St. George, Black's Harbour, Grand Harbour and Lepreau. Saint John was founded in 1783 as two settlements, Parrtown and Carleton, but by Royal Charter became the city of Saint John in 1785. Other settlements along the St. John river and its tributaries included Rothesay, Hampton, Sussex, Kingston, Gagetown, Oromocto, Cambridge, Marysville, Federicton, Kingsclear and Woodstock. So great was the influx of new settlers, and so far did they feel themselves to be from the capital at Halifax, that, in 1784, a new province called New Brunswick was established and Fredericton was chosen as the capital.

The Loyalists founded new settlements at Clementsport, Digby and Weymouth in Western Nova Scotia, Wallace on the North Shore, Sydney on Cape Breton Island and Shelburne on the South Shore. These latter form an interesting contrast.

Sydney, first settled in 1784, soon had a population of about 4,000. Land was cleared by community effort and a townsite laid out, lots being given to those who had helped clear it. Agriculture was begun immediately and in addition Governor De Barres caused the opening of coal mines nearby which brought in large revenues to the colony. On that beginning the region around Sydney has grown to contain about 20% of the population of the whole province.

In 1783 there arrived at Shelburne about 10,000 Loyalists from New York to found a new town under the British flag. Some of them engaged in lumbering, shipbuilding and fishing, but in this rocky region extensive agriculture was out of the question. The region could not support so large a population and most of the inhabitants soon moved away. Shelburne, today, is a village of about 2,000 people.

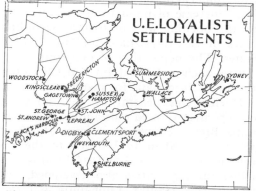

Figure 62. *Location of Some of the More Important Settlements of the United Empire Loyalists.* Most of the loyalists settled north of the Bay of Fundy, where they established a new province named New Brunswick.

There could be no better object lesson in the importance of geographical control upon the development of human enterprise.

The pattern of settlement in the Maritime Provinces crystallized fairly early in the nineteenth century. Many immigrants arrived, but the process of settlement, in the main, consisted in the expansion of the earlier sites, and, with the exception of a few places in the interior of New Brunswick, no new ones were established. Among the newcomers were a great many Scottish people who settled in Cape Breton Island and the eastern parts of Prince Edward Island and the Nova Scotian mainland. There were also many Irish who came to the southern part of New Brunswick and to Prince Edward Island.

During this period lumbering, shipbuilding and fishing became major industries. Eastern Canada had the highest *per capita* tonnage of merchant shipping on earth. Coal mining expanded with consequent increase of population at Joggins, Springhill, New Glasgow and, above all, in the Sydney area. Except in certain favoured localities, agriculture did not expand very rapidly but became a subsidiary or part-time occupation. Thus New Brunswick developed a race of farmer-lumbermen, and a race of farmer-fishermen arose in Nova Scotia.

The first railway in the Maritime Provinces was a short line from Albion Mines to Pictou Harbour opened in 1839 to provide for the increasing export of coal. Other lines followed and in 1876 the Intercolonial was completed to River du Loup, thus linking the Maritime Provinces to Canada.

In 1840, also, Samuel Cunard, a native of Halifax, inaugurated his transatlantic steamship service. Henceforth the wooden sailing vessel was rapidly displaced.

These changes in transportation had a profound effect upon population. Seaport sites declined in favour of locations upon the railway. Halifax and Saint John, rival outlets for overseas trade, especially in the

winter months, grew rapidly. Charlottetown, as the chief port and trade centre as well as the capital, maintained its ascendancy in Prince Edward Island.

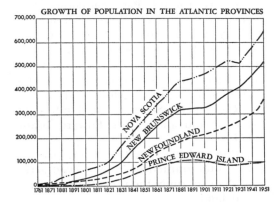

Figure 63. *One hundred and ninety years of population growth in the Atlantic Provinces.* Population has grown slowly, there have never been periods of rapid increase, such as those experienced in the newer parts of Canada.

Many areas, counties and smaller divisions alike, reached their maximum population figures in 1881 but the linking up of railway lines to central Canada and the building of the C.P.R. to the west put a definite check upon the growth of the Maritime Provinces. Prince Edward Island, with its greater dependence upon agriculture underwent serious decline. The natural increase of population was attracted by the opening west or to the expanding cities of Central Canada and the United States. The population of even important centres such as Saint John and Charlottetown remained static for many years.

During this general decline, however, certain areas showed outstanding increases. Cape Breton county grew from 31,000 in 1881 to 73,000 in 1911 owing to the development of the coal and steel industries. Other mining centres also developed, but more slowly. Halifax, Lunenburg and Yarmouth had notable increases which can, in part, be attributed to developments in the fishing industry. Large increases took place in the northern counties of New Brunswick which began to develop its forest resources. The Acadians of this region had a high birthrate and were disinclined to join the migration to the Prairies. In contrast, the southern part of New Brunswick lost population except for Moncton which continued to grow because of its importance as a railway centre.

Recent tendencies are somewhat conflicting. Prince Edward Island continued to lose population until the depression of the 1930's forced her people to remain at home. New Brunswick has never in any decade actually lost population, but Nova Scotia sustained a slight decrease in the 1921-31 period; both provinces registered gains in the following ten years. The centres of growth remain much as they were. Population continues to expand in northern New Brunswick while in Nova Scotia important increases have occurred in the Cape Breton coal fields and the Halifax harbour area. The fruit-growing area of the Annapolis Valley and the railway centres of Truro and Moncton continued to grow. World War II caused considerable shifts

in population. Wartime Halifax with more than 100,000 people was most overcrowded, but Truro, Sydney, Charlottetown, and other centres showed notable increases. At the close of the war many people who had crowded into these places, returned to homes in other parts of Canada. The cessation of wartime employment induced many natives of the Maritime Provinces, also, to migrate to Central and Western Canada at this time.

During the 1950's, Prince Edward Island's population has shown little growth, but there has been a significant increase in both New Brunswick and Nova Scotia. Rural populations nearly everywhere continue to decline while the larger urban centres continue to expand.

The Halifax Harbour area is an outstanding case. Having grown more than 40% during the intercensal period of 1941-51, it increased by nearly 20% in the next five years to reach 160,000 in 1956. Much of the new population is found on the eastern side of the Harbour which has been made much more accessible by the building of the Angus L. Macdonald bridge.

## Selected References

Alcock, F. J. *New Brunswick — Past and Present.* Canadian Geographic Journal 27:64-83. 1943.

Fernow, B. E. *Forest Conditions of Nova Scotia.* Canada Commission of Conservation. Ottawa. 1912.

Ganong, W. F. *Origins of Settlements in the Province of New Brunswick.* Transactions of the Royal Society of Canada. Section II. pp. 3-185. 1904.

Goldthwaite, J. W. *Physiography of Nova Scotia.* Canada Department of Mines. Geological Survey Memoir 140. Ottawa. 1924.

Halliday, W. E. D. *A Forest Classification for Canada.* Canada Department of Mines and Resources. Forest Service Bulletin 89. pp. 1-50. 1937.

Middleton, W. E. K. *The Climate of the Gulf of Saint Lawrence and Surrounding Regions in Canada and Newfoundland as it affects Aviation.* Canadian Meteorological Memoirs No.1. pp. 1-40. 1935.

Morrison, M. B. *The Forests of New Brunswick.* Canada Department of Mines and Resources. Forest Service Bulletin 91. 1938.

Putnam, D. F. *The Climate of the Maritime Provinces.* Canadian Geographical Journal 21: 134-147. 1940.

Roland, A. E. *Flora of Nova Scotia.* Proceedings of the Nova Scotian Institute of Science XXI. pp. 7-552. 1944-45.

# CHAPTER 4

# The Economic Geography
# of the Maritime Provinces

THE resources of the Maritime Provinces are quite diversified. The primary industries of agriculture, forestry, fishing and mining all produce large shares of the total wealth and in some areas manufacturing is also well developed. The three provinces vary considerably, however. Prince Edward Island depends upon agriculture for nearly two-thirds of her total income; New Brunswick gets more than half her wealth from forestry and agriculture; while Nova Scotia has four primary industries: agriculture, forestry, fishing and mining which are almost equally important. In Prince Edward Island secondary industries are rather weakly developed whereas in both Nova Scotia and New Brunswick they provide half of the total wealth.

## Agriculture

The Maritime Provinces do not constitute an outstanding agricultural region, but, since agriculture accounts for about 20% of the average annual production, it must be regarded as a major industry. Moreover, its distribution and adjustments show a large measure of response to geographical controls.

There is great variation in its importance, as it accounts for about 60% of the wealth of Prince Edward Island but only 13% in Nova Scotia, and about 18% in New Brunswick. There are other differences; both Prince Edward Island and

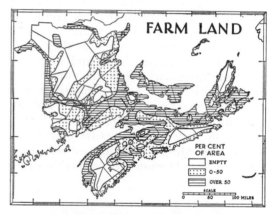

Figure 64. *Occupied Farm Land in the Maritime Provinces,* according to the Census of Agriculture, 1941. Note the large empty areas.

New Brunswick rely heavily upon field crops while there is more diversity in Nova Scotia where dairying and fruit-growing are more important. These differences are given graphical emphasis in the accompanying series of isopleth maps plotted from statistical data.

*Occupied land.* The farm land of the Maritime Provinces is strikingly localized. Only Prince Edward Island is uniformly occupied, many townships having over 90% in farms. On the other hand, large areas in Northern New Brunswick and Southern Nova Scotia have no farms at all.

*Improved land.* The distribution of improved land is even more strikingly lo-

### Table 3.   Net Values of Production in the Maritime Provinces

**Prince Edward Island**

| | 1939 $000 | 1939 Per Cent | 1945 $000 | 1945 Per Cent | 1951 $000 | 1951 Per Cent |
|---|---|---|---|---|---|---|
| Agriculture | 6,768 | 64.6 | 13,377 | 66.1 | 21,403 | 62.2 |
| Forestry | 126 | 1.3 | — | — | 24 | 0.1 |
| Fisheries | 683 | 7.0 | 2,309 | 11.4 | 2,240 | 6.5 |
| Trapping | 4 | — | 14 | 0.1 | 7 | — |
| Mining | — | — | — | — | — | — |
| Electric Power | 266 | 2.8 | 384 | 1.9 | 865 | 2.5 |
| Manufactures | 1,244 | 12.8 | 3,178 | 15.8 | 5,047 | 14.7 |
| Construction | 1,117 | 11.5 | 939 | 4.7 | 4,830 | 14.0 |
| Totals | 9,709 | 100.0 | 20,151 | 100.0 | 34,416 | 100.0 |

**Nova Scotia**

| | 1939 $000 | 1939 Per Cent | 1945 $000 | 1945 Per Cent | 1951 $000 | 1951 Per Cent |
|---|---|---|---|---|---|---|
| Agriculture | 15,421 | 15.7 | 24,171 | 13.5 | 38,279 | 12.8 |
| Forestry | 3,818 | 3.9 | 5,470 | 3.0 | 9,958 | 3.3 |
| Fisheries | 5,308 | 5.4 | 19,223 | 10.7 | 21,398 | 7.2 |
| Trapping | 180 | 0.2 | 231 | 0.1 | 285 | 0.1 |
| Mining | 22,953 | 23.3 | 23,175 | 12.9 | 46,958 | 15.7 |
| Electric Power | 5.072 | 5.1 | 6,963 | 3.9 | 11,750 | 3.9 |
| Manufactures | 35,886 | 36.5 | 84,358 | 47.0 | 119,486 | 39.9 |
| Construction | 9,787 | 9.9 | 15,954 | 8.9 | 51,253 | 17.1 |
| Totals | 98,425 | 100.0 | 179,545 | 100.0 | 299,366 | 100.0 |

**New Brunswick**

| | 1939 $000 | 1939 Per Cent | 1945 $000 | 1945 Per Cent | 1951 $000 | 1951 Per Cent |
|---|---|---|---|---|---|---|
| Agriculture | 14,790 | 21.7 | 31,021 | 23.4 | 44,216 | 17.1 |
| Forestry | 7,688 | 11.3 | 16,224 | 12.2 | 36,387 | 14.1 |
| Fisheries | 2,186 | 3.2 | 5,477 | 4.1 | 7,588 | 2.9 |
| Trapping | 755 | 1.1 | 382 | 0.3 | 38 | — |
| Mining | 3,390 | 5.0 | 3,312 | 2.5 | 7,378 | 2.9 |
| Electric Power | 3,594 | 5.3 | 4,870 | 3.7 | 8,581 | 3.3 |
| Manufactures | 27,041 | 39.8 | 63,380 | 47.8 | 120,595 | 46.7 |
| Construction | 8,554 | 12.6 | 8,035 | 6.0 | 33,482 | 13.0 |
| Totals | 67,998 | 100.0 | 132,701 | 100.0 | 258,265 | 100.0 |

D.B.S. 1953.

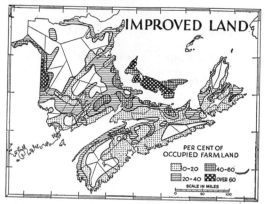

Figure 65. *Distribution of Improved Farm Land.* Census of Agriculture, 1941.

calized. Not all the occupied areas are uniformly improved. The most intensively cleared areas are located in the central part of Prince Edward Island, the St. John Valley, the Kennebecasis Valley, the shores of Northumberland Strait and the Annapolis Valley.

*Field Crops.* In no part of Nova Scotia is more than 40% of the farm area devoted to field crops; indeed, only in the Annapolis Valley, at the head of Cobequid Bay and along the North Shore, can they be said to be at all important. They are much more widely grown in Prince Edward Island and the St. John Valley. In all three provinces hay and oats rank first and second in area occupied; while in

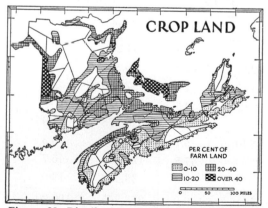

Figure 66. *Distribution of Crop Land.* Densities plotted as per cent of occupied farm land, according to the Census of Agriculture, 1941.

Prince Edward Island, generally, and in the St. John Valley and Baie de Chaleur areas of New Brunswick, potatoes are an important cash crop.

*Dairy Cows.* Dairying is the second great source of income for the farmers of the Maritime Provinces. There are several very definite centres of specialization. In New Brunswick, the long valley from Moncton to St. John, with well developed transportation systems, is the source of fluid milk for city consumption, in addition to supplying local dairy plants. In Nova Scotia, dairying is important in the Annapolis Valley, in the area around Truro, near

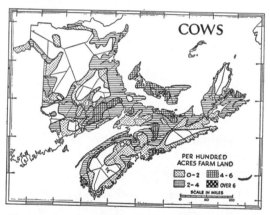

Figure 67. *Distribution of Dairy Cows in the Maritime Provinces,* according to the Census of Agriculture, 1941.

Amherst, in Pictou county and in the Cape Breton industrial region. On Prince Edward Island, there is a greater concentration of dairying in the central portion, particularly near Charlottetown.

## Agricultural Regions

The discontinuous, uneven, patchy distribution of agricultural activity can be summarized by a regional map which indicates the small nuclear areas of intensive agricultural development surrounded by areas of sparse agricultural occupance.

On the basis of location and statistical differences, seventeen areas can be delimited.

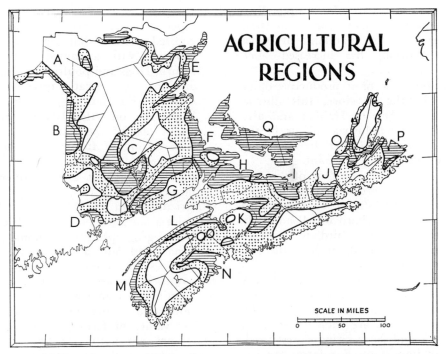

**Figure 68.** *Agricultural Regions.* **The seventeen small agricultural districts, outlined on this map, are primarily small natural units, but they also have different agricultural patterns.**

A. *Northwestern New Brunswick.* This is an area of fairly large farms and a generalized type of farming with potatoes as an important cash crop. It has an important group of pioneer settlements on the plateau.

B. *The St. John Valley.* This is a specialized potato producing region with considerable livestock farming as well.

C. *Fredericton.* A rather scattered settlement along the St. John and its tributaries, this is a general farming area with dairying, potatoes and some fruits and vegetables as sources of cash income.

D. *St. Croix,* Discounting the pioneer fringe with its large dependence upon forest products, this small region may be classed as a dairy area.

E. *Northeastern New Brunswick.* In the main, this is a coastal fringe with small farms and a part-time system of agri-

culture. There are a number of important inland pioneer settlements.

F. *Southeastern New Brunswick.* This is a general farming area with a fair dependence upon livestock. Some potatoes are grown as a cash crop and there is much part-time agriculture.

G. *Kennebecasis.* The valley areas lying between the cities of St. John and Moncton constitute one of the outstanding dairy regions in the Maritime Provinces.

H. *Cumberland.* This is a general farming area with emphasis on field crops with dairying in some localities.

I. *Pictou.* This is an outstanding dairy region which in addition to supplying its urban demand for fluid milk produces a large amount of creamery butter.

J. *Antigonish.* This is largely an area of subsistance and part-time farming with

a fair degree of dependence upon livestock. Sheep are more numerous than
elsewhere on the mainland of Nova
Scotia. Dairying has increased since
World War II.

K. *Colchester.* The most productive dairy
region in the province, this district
sends fluid milk to Halifax and also
supplies large industrial plants in the
town of Truro. Other livestock enterprises are also important.

L. *The Annapolis Valley.* One of the outstanding fruit growing areas of the
Dominion, "The Valley" contains about
35,000 acres of orchard which normally
produces from one-third to one-half
the commercial apple crop of the Dominion of Canada.

M. *The Western Shore.* A narrow fringe
along the shore, this area is characterized by subsistence and part-time agriculture. There are some commercial
live stock and dairy farms. Forest products are important. Fur farms are numerous.

N. *Lunenburg.* Live stock, dairy products
and forest products are the important
sources of farm income here. Many
farms are of small size and subsistence
and part-time agriculture is dominant.

O. *Inverness.* To a large degree this is a
subsistence and part-time farming area.
Forest products are important, there
is some dairying and more sheep are
raised than in any other area in the
province.

P. *Sydney.* The agriculture of this region
is completely overshadowed by heavy
industry, farming is largely on a part-
time or subsistence basis. Nevertheless
there is a fairly high development of
dairying to supply nearby urban markets.

Q. *Prince Edward Island.* Being almost
fully occupied and intensively cleared
this is probably the most important
region of all. It has nearly as much
improved land as the whole of Nova
Scotia. It is sometimes called "the mil-

lion-acre farm". The central portion is
especially well developed, being specialized toward dairying and potato-
growing, with a consequently higher
return. Hogs and poultry are important
and increased greatly under war-time
demand. Fur farming, which had its
beginning on "the Island", provides
about 5% of the total farm income.
The raising of fur-bearing animals is
an extremely specialized type of farming which is not attempted by most
farmers.

Agriculture in the Maritime Provinces
occupies a marginal position both economically and geographically. Its home markets
are small and only a few products, such
as potatoes and apples have been able to
find outside markets. Large quantities of
feed grain and commercial fertilizers must
be purchased to maintain production.

The values of farm production in the
Maritimes are extremely low, and only
those areas with an important special
source of income can maintain an adequate standard of living by agriculture
alone. Those areas are the dairy sections
in all three provinces, the Annapolis Valley
fruit-growing area, and the potato-growing
regions of the St. John Valley and Prince
Edward Island. In 1954, the cash income
from the sale of agricultural products
amounted to about $115,000,000. Farm
population has been steadily decreasing for
many years and there are many abandoned
farms.

## Forest Industries

Although most of Prince Edward Island
has been cleared, both Nova Scotia and
New Brunswick have nearly four-fifths of
their land area in forest. Owing to the
early policy of disposal of public land,
much of it is now in private hands. However, New Brunswick still has about 7,500,-
000 acres of Crown Land and Nova Scotia
over 2,000,000 acres. Current estimates
place the total forest resources at about 13,-
000,000,000 cubic feet of standing timber,

**Plate 23. Loading Christmas trees for Florida at Newcastle, N.B.** *National Film Board.*

two-thirds of which are in New Brunswick, where about 50% of the forest area is reported to carry merchantable stands, while one-third is found in Nova Scotia. The percentage of unproductive land is greater in the latter province, 20-25% being classified as barrens. Northern and Central New Brunswick are the most heavily forested areas but good forests are also found on Cape Breton Island and in Western Nova Scotia.

Forest exploitation began in the eight-

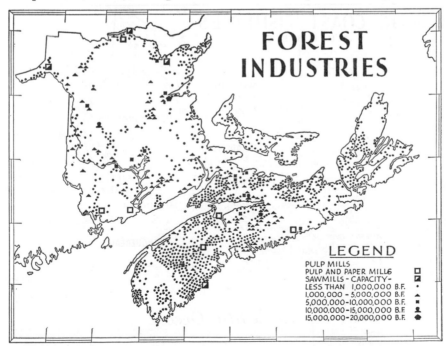

FOREST INDUSTRIES

LEGEND
PULP MILLS
PULP AND PAPER MILLS
SAWMILLS - CAPACITY-
LESS THAN 1,000,000 B.F.
1,000,000 - 5,000,000 B.F.
5,000,000 - 10,000,000 B.F.
10,000,000 - 15,000,000 B.F.
15,000,000 - 20,000,000 B.F.

Figure 69. *Forest Industries in the Maritime Provinces.* Note the peripheral distribution of larger establishments in New Brunswick.

eenth century with the production of masts
and spars for the Royal Navy. Later it was
closely linked with the shipbuilding industry, providing the raw materials from
which the ships were fashioned as well as
the most important cargoes which they
carried from their home ports. The coming of the railroad and the steamship led
to still further exploitation of the forests
and during the latter part of the nineteenth
century the trade in sawn lumber became
all-important. In the twentieth century
the production of pulpwood has become
the dominant phase of forest exploitation.

There are some differences to be noted
in the methods of forest exploitation in
Nova Scotia and New Brunswick. Operations in the former are usually on a smaller
scale, logging and sawing being carried on
by small crews with a portable mill. There
are few forest areas not within hauling
distance of a railway siding or a wharf.
New Brunswick has large interior tracts
which are not served by transportation facilities. There is, however, a wonderful
system of rivers which the lumbermen
make use of to bring their logs to the
huge mills which are located either upon
navigable water or upon a railway.

In New Brunswick the more important
areas for the production of both sawlogs
and pulpwood are in the north; in Nova
Scotia the sawn lumber comes mainly
from a centrally located group of counties
including Colchester, Cumberland, Hants,
Halifax and Pictou, while the cutting of
pulpwood is more closely restricted to the
counties along the Atlantic coast. In 1947
forestry provided a net income of about
$99,000,000 for the people of the Mari-
time Provinces.

## Fisheries

Fishing is the oldest industry in the
Western Hemisphere, having been carried
on continuously since the days of discov-

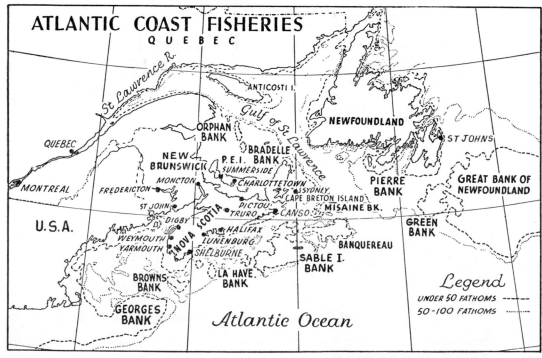

Figure 70. *Atlantic Coast Fisheries.* The shallow waters of the Atlantic Coastal Shelf are among the most
**imp**ortant fishing grounds in the world.

ery. The indented coastline of the Maritime Provinces is admirably suitable for fishing ports, while offshore lie 200,000 square miles of shallow sea comprising the greatest fishing grounds on the earth. The shallower areas of these surrounding seas are known as *banks,* the largest of which is the Grand Bank of Newfoundland, with an area of 36,000 square miles. In addition to the banks, there are several thousand square miles of *inshore* fishing grounds within fifteen miles of land.

The great food fish of the North Atlantic is the cod which, together with the closely allied haddock, hake and pollock, dominated the deep sea fishing for centuries. Herring and sardines are also important. In recent years, however, the lobster fishery has been the most valuable one in the Maritime Provinces, and holds second place to the British Columbia salmon, only, in the whole Dominion.

Deep sea fishing is carried on by schooners, trawlers and draggers. The chief ports engaged in deep sea fishing are: Lunenburg, Halifax, Lockeport, Yarmouth, Canso and North Sydney, all of them on, or not far from, the Atlantic coast of Nova Scotia. Lunenburg and Halifax greatly outrank all others, the former on account of the famous Lunenburg fishing fleet, the latter because of the rise of trawlers.

The fishing schooner, of the type made famous by the "Bluenose", is a two-masted vessel of about 135 tons, equipped with auxiliary oil-burning engines. Each schooner carries seven to ten dories, each manned by two fishermen who catch fish by means of hand lines. In addition to the dorymen, each vessel carries a captain, a salter, throater, header and cook, a total complement of nineteen to twenty-five men. At one time there were more than 140 vessels sailing to the banks from Lunenburg county ports, but in recent years the schooner fleet has declined greatly.

The trawler is a power driven, steel ship ranging in length from 130 to 250 feet. It catches fish by towing a large cone-shaped net or trawl. Previous to World War II three trawlers operated from the port of Halifax carrying a complement of about 75 men and landing an average annual catch of about 200,000 hundredweights of fresh fish, most of which was marketed in the cities of Quebec and Ontario.

Since the close of World War II the trawler fleet has been increased, with trawlers being operated out of Lunenburg as well as Halifax. Another type of fish catching vessel, the dragger, has also made its appearance in Nova Scotia. A typical dragger is a diesel-powered vessel of about one hundred tons, 85 feet in length, 20 feet beam and drawing about nine feet of water. It can ice down about 125,000 pounds of fresh fish.

In Gloucester county, New Brunswick, a somewhat smaller dragger with a capacity

Plate 24. Lobster fishermen setting traps in Northumberland Strait.       *National Film Board.*

of about 60,000 pounds of fresh fish is used on the Baie de Chaleur; 12 of these trawlers in one year captured 10,000,000 pounds of cod, about 45% of the total for the province.

Inshore fishing is carried on within twelve or fifteen miles of the home dock by means of small motor-boats. Hand lines similar to those of the deep sea fishermen are employed, and herring is ordinarily used as bait. Shore fish are landed daily and a great deal goes into the fresh and frozen fish trade although quantities are cured in the time honoured way.

The annual catch of lobsters amounts to about 300,000 cwt. worth about $4,000,-000, most of which is taken by Nova Scotian fishermen from the waters of Northumberland Strait. About 125 lobster canneries take care of the catch. Many lobsters are shipped alive in refrigerator cars and motor trucks to distant markets in Canada and the United States. Pictou is considered the centre of the industry and each year stages a "lobster carnival".

Sardines, "the little fish smothered in oil", takes second place to lobsters among the canned fish of the Atlantic coast. All the canning is done at Black's Harbour, N.B., although some of the fish are caught elsewhere.

Oysters are found in coastal waters of all three provinces but are taken chiefly in Prince Edward Island. Scallops from the Bay of Fundy are landed at Digby.

Markets for fish are continually changing. Not many years ago about 60% of the catch of cod and related species was sold as dried fish, 10% as fresh fish and the remainder in other forms. Recently about one-third of the total has been dried, one-third fresh and one third in other forms. The chief buyers of dried fish have been the United States, British West Indies, Cuba, Puerto Rico and Brazil, but in steadily declining quantities. In some years markets have been found in Italy and other Mediterranean countries. Fresh and frozen fish are marketed in central Canada.

During World War II there were great changes in the market situation. The chief European competitors were eliminated from the Latin American trade and Canadian exports of dried fish increased. Britain furnished a market for frozen cod fillets while canned lobster, which formerly went overseas, had to be marketed in North America. Since the war the markets in Britain and other "Sterling" countries have taken much smaller quantities of Canadian fish.

In the immediate prewar period, the total value of the fish caught annually in the Maritime Provinces varied in the neighbourhood of $12,000,000 annually and gave employment to about 15,000 persons. Since the war the value of the fisheries has increased to about $70,000,000 annually.

## Mining

Mining accounts for about one-eighth of the net income of the people of the Maritime Provinces, its relative importance in both pre-war and post-war periods being about the same. In 1954, mineral production was valued at over $85,000,000. Six-sevenths originates in Nova Scotia and one-seventh in New Brunswick, Prince Edward Island being so poor in minerals that

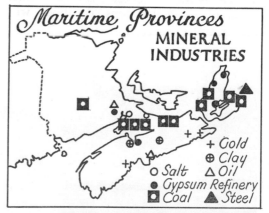

Figure 71. *The Locations of the Major Mines and Mineral Industries in the Maritime Provinces.*

even the gravel used in road construction is imported. The important minerals are coal, gold, gypsum, salt and structural materials.

*Coal.* The Maritime Provinces have extensive areas of Carboniferous rocks but only comparatively small areas have workable beds of coal. The known reserves, estimated at about 10,000,000,000 tons are insignificant when compared with the western coalfields, nevertheless, they continue to furnish nearly half of the coal mined in Canada.

There are four chief coal fields in Nova Scotia. They are located in the Counties of Cape Breton and Inverness on Cape Breton Island, and Pictou and Cumberland on the mainland. There are approximately 80 mines in the province, some of which have been discontinued, and about twenty different companies are operating. However, about two-thirds of the production is in the hands of the Dominion Coal Company, Limited, and three-quarters of the total is mined in the Cape Breton field.

The Cape Breton field extends for about thirty miles along the shores of the Atlantic Ocean and from one-half to two-thirds of the coal mined comes from submarine workings which extend as much as two and one-half miles from shore. The production of the field is distributed about as follows: the Glace Bay area produces nearly 3,000,000 tons per year from seven collieries; the New Waterford district raises about 1,500,000 tons from three pits; North Sydney and Sydney Mines have about ten pits in operation, three of which produce most of the total of 800,000 tons.

The Inverness field, on the north side of the island, produces about 100,000 tons per year, much of which also comes from beneath the sea.

The Pictou coal field comprises an area eleven miles long and two and one-half miles wide, which has been separated by faulting into three distinct areas. Some of the coal seams in this field are over thirty feet thick. The production of the Pictou

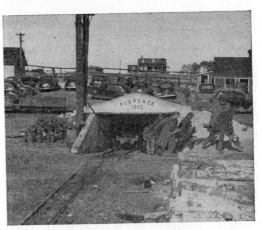

National Film Board.

Plate 25. The entrance to a submarine coal mine in Cape Breton.

field is as follows: Westville, with three mines operating, produces 200,000 tons; Stellarton with three mines, about 460,000 tons; Coalburn, with two pits, raises about 50,000 tons per annum. The mines formerly operated at Thorburn have been exhausted.

The Cumberland coalfields lie along the edges of a large trough or syncline which contains a great deal of hidden coal. Along the northern limb of the syncline five pits are in operation: two at Joggins, two at River Hebert and one near Maccan. The production is about 200,000 tons per annum. The shore cliffs cut in the coal measures near Joggins are remarkable for the upright fossil tree trunks embedded in the sandstone.

The Springhill mines are on the southern margin of the basin. Over 500,000 tons per annum are produced by three mines in the town of Springhill.

The Minto-Chipman field, or Grand Lake Basin produces practically all the coal mined in New Brunswick. An area of more than 100 square miles is underlain by a single coal seam 18 to 30 inches in thickness. In part it is operated by stripping from the surface and in part from underground workings, none of which is more than 125′ deep. The production is about 500,000 tons per annum.

Coal is important in the Maritimes, and particularly in Nova Scotia. Over 14,000 men find work in the mines and they form the basis for the prosperity of several of the important urban centres. The total output ranges around seven million tons per year. However, labour costs are high in the deep Nova Scotian mines, the average output per man per day is only a little over two tons, or about half as much as in the United States. The coal reaches a variety of markets. Normally about one-third is shipped to St. Lawrence ports while large amounts are taken by the railways and by the iron and steel industries. The remainder goes toward the domestic requirements of the Maritime Provinces and Newfoundland and to supply steamship bunkers.

The only *salt* mines in Canada are at Malagash in Nova Scotia. About 40,000 tons are extracted per annum from workings which now extend to a depth of 1200 feet. Beds of salt over 800 feet thick are known to lie under Amherst and brine wells have been put into operation nearby.

*Gypsum* is obtained from the Carboniferous rocks of both Nova Scotia and New Brunswick. The largest amounts come from the quarries near Windsor, N.S., where it is loaded directly in ocean steamers for transportation to the United States. Hillsborough in New Brunswick has been a producer for a long time. Recently a large new mine was opened near Milford; its shipping facilities are located on Bedford Basin near Halifax. The total annual production is over four million tons.

*Oil* and *gas* are obtained in small quantities at Stony Creek, south of Moncton, N.B.

*Gold* is mined from the Precambrian rocks of southern Nova Scotia, most of the production ($1,000,000 in 1939) from Caribou, Goldenville, Oldham and Seal Harbour. Small quantities of silver, copper, lead, zinc and manganese are reported in

some years. Iron was formerly obtained at Londonderry and Nictau.

Other mineral products included structural materials such as stone, sand and gravel, clay for bricks, sewer pipe and pottery, limestone for use in building, pulp manufacture and as a corrective for soil acidity, five-grained sandstone for use as grindstones, and silica for the manufacture of silica brick used in steel furnaces.

Raw materials of mineral origin imported into the Maritime Provinces include large quantities of iron ore and limestone from Newfoundland for use in the steel industry at Sydney and crude oil from South America which is refined in the Halifax Harbour industrial area.

## Manufacturing

The Maritime Provinces do not constitute a great manufacturing region, yet, even in peace time, manufacturing was in second place as a producer of wealth. In 1938 these industries accounted for 21% of the total production. There are great differences in the manufacturing capacities of the different provinces, in Prince Edward Island, only 6.6% of the total wealth came from this source, 20% in New Brunswick and 23% in Nova Scotia. The gross value in that year amounted to $137,000,-000, Nova Scotia leading with $75,000,000 and Prince Edward Island accounting for about $3,500,000.

During the war the relative position of manufacturing changed somewhat. In 1953 the percentage of the total net production attributable to manufacturing was 39% in Nova Scotia, 45% in New Brunswick, and 17% in Prince Edward Island; the net value of manufactures was $335,000,000 while the gross value had increased to $610,000,000. The distribution of net production by counties is shown in figure 72.

The leading industries in 1938 were pulp and paper, two-thirds of the production originating in New Brunswick, and primary iron and steel produced entirely in Nova Scotia. Other leading industries were fish

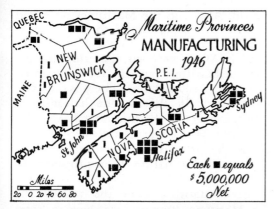

Figure 72. *Distribution of Manufacturing in the Maritime Provinces,* in terms of net value of production per county in 1946. (Data from D. B. S.)

curing and packing, saw-milling, petroleum refining, sugar refining, railway rolling stock and various food products. During the war shipbuilding and repairs became very important, but have since declined somewhat.

The manufactures of the Maritime Provinces fall into two rather important classes; (1) those based on local raw materials such as lumber, pulp and paper, fish curing and packing, processing of agricultural products, etc. which are based upon local raw materials and located mainly near the sources of supply; (2) those based on imported raw materials including: iron and steel, petroleum products, sugar and coffee, tea and spices. The second class of industry is usually found in the seaport cities. In the case of iron and steel the location of the coalfields determine which port shall be used.

The distribution of manufacturing activity corresponds fairly well with that of urban population, although in some cases important plants are located in rural areas.

The Halifax Harbour area, including the city of Halifax, the town of Dartmouth and the adjoining areas of Woodside and Imperoyal, is the most important. In 1938, this area produced goods to the value of about $25,000,000 and about double this amount in 1942. In 1954 the gross production was $95,000,000, with a net value of

$45,000,000. The most important industries are petroleum refining, shipbuilding and repairs, baking, confectionery and the processing of imported tropical products.

The Saint John Harbour area is nearly as important as the Halifax Harbour area, producing goods worth about $19,000,000 in 1938 and $44,000,000 in 1942. Gross value in 1954 was $85,000,000, with a net value of $35,000,000. The major industries of Saint John are sugar refining, shipbuilding, pulp and paper, the processing of coffee, tea, spices, bakery products and confectionery.

The Sydney area constitutes the third major manufacturing centre. Primary iron and steel normally account for nearly all of its output, which in 1938 was about $15,000,000. Wartime activity increased the value to $33,000,000 in 1942, and a total of $58,000,000 was reached in 1954.

Less important areas include the New Glasgow area (steel, rolling stock), Moncton (railway shops, textiles, biscuits, meat packing, sugar, oil) Truro (textiles, dairy products) and Charlottetown (dairy).

Large pulp and paper mills are found at Edmundston, Dalhousie and Bathurst in New Brunswick, and at Liverpool in Nova Scotia.

Fish curing and packing is an extremely decentralized industry with over 350 plants scattered along many hundreds of miles of coastline. Digby, Shelburne, Lunenburg, Halifax, Canso, North Sydney, Pictou and Black's Harbour are among the more important.

There are hundreds of small sawmills in Nova Scotia and New Brunswick, and a few fairly large ones in the latter province.

Included in the manufacturing industries we must also consider the many hundreds of small plants for the manufacture of butter and other dairy products, bread and other bakery products, aerated waters, feeds and flour, meats and wooden building supplies, all of which find a local market. The larger industries such as iron and steel, fish products, pulp and paper, lumber, textiles and sugar refining depend mainly upon markets in other Canadian provinces, the United States or overseas.

## Power Supply

Manufacturing industries depend upon a reliable power supply. There are few large rivers in the Maritime Provinces but since the good rainfall of the region provides a reliable flow, a number of small ones have also been harnessed. The St. John River in New Brunswick is a large source of power, the Grand Falls site being very important. The Nipisiguit and Musquash in New Brunswick, and the Tusket, Nictau, Avon, Mersey and Sheet Harbour rivers in Nova Scotia, also have important installations.

The earliest development of electrical power in the Maritimes was by means of coal-burning steam engines. Small plants for lighting purposes were set up in many towns. At present a large part of the electrical energy used is thermally produced at large central stations located in the coalfields of Cape Breton, Pictou county, Chignecto and Grand Lake, N.B. Coal burning stations are also operated outside of the coalfields. Practically all of the electrical power used in Prince Edward Island is produced by thermal engines.

The capacity of water power installations is about 280,000 h.p. (1953 data) and that of thermal engines amounts to nearly 375,-000 h.p., making a total of 655,000 h.p. Approximately one-third of this is developed by pulp mills and other power using industries.

Rural electrification programs are proceeding in all three provinces.

## Transportation and Communications

Early transportation depended upon the sea and shipping is still important. St. John, Halifax and Sydney are seaports of national importance, but there are many smaller ports from which lumber, pulp, fish, gypsum and other local products are shipped abroad. Although the Maritimes once had more shipping per capita than any other country, only 160,000 tons are now registered in Maritime ports. The shipping entered at Maritime ports in 1951 amounted to nearly 12,800,000 tons. There is only one short canal, St. Peter's, one half-mile in length connecting the Bras d'Or Lakes with St. Peters Bay. A marine railway was built across the isthmus of Chignecto but was never used. A canal has been proposed for this location.

Recent statistics show the railways of the Maritime Provinces to have a total length of 3,500 miles with lines connecting most of the important settlements. The first railway, a short line from Albion Mines to Pictou Harbour was built in 1839, but is not an important link in the present rail net. Both the C.N.R. and the C.P.R. have lines in Nova Scotia and New Brunswick but only the C.N.R. operates in Prince Edward Island. Both Prince Edward Island and Cape Breton Island are connected to the mainland by large modern ferries. The effect of the railways has been to emphasize the development of Halifax and St. John as ports and to curtail the growth of most others. The concentration of rail traffic at the junction points of Truro and Moncton has materially aided their growth. The railways also function as a large employer of labour and as customers of the coal mines.

Early overland roads connected Halifax with Annapolis and Amherst and gradually other roads were cut through the forest until all settlements in the Maritimes were connected. The effect of railway building was to turn the road net into a system of feeders focused on railway stations. After World War I, however, provincial governments tackled the problem of through highways. Much remains to be done but, on the whole, the highways of the Maritimes are not inferior to those of other parts of Canada. There are over 32,000 miles of road, approximately half of which is surfaced and trunk lines are rapidly being paved. Motor vehicle registrations in 1951 totalled 255,000, about 170,000 being passenger cars. Modern bus lines maintain schedules over all the main highways and a number of important freighting companies have grown up. Highway routes are, largely, parallel to rail routes and focus on the same centres. Truro and Moncton have thus benefited greatly from the trucking business.

The first airplane flight in the British Empire was made at Baddeck in 1909. Trans Canada Airlines maintain services to Moncton, Halifax, Yarmouth and Sydney while there are lines to Prince Edward Island and Central and Northern New Brunswick. Small airports are found in a number of places and there are several large R.C.A.F. airfields as well.

Electrical communications are well developed. In general railway lines are paralleled by telegraph lines and highways by telephone lines. There are over 170,000 telephones, one for each eight persons. The Canadian Government Telegraph and Telephone service maintains lines to scattered settlements along the coast of Cape Breton Island, and cables to Campobello, Grand Mannan and other islands of the Bay of Fundy, and to Prince Edward Island. Transoceanic cables focus on Nova Scotia; Canso, Halifax and North Sydney being the important terminals.

There are about a dozen broadcasting stations in the Maritime Provinces, located in the vicinity of the larger towns and cities. There are approximately 16 receiving sets per 100 population. The CBC international service transmitters are located on dyked marshland near Sackville, N.B.

## Selected References

Colby, C. C. *The Apple Industry of the Annapolis-Cornwallis Valley*. Economic Geography 1, pp. 337-55. 1925.

Gosselin, A and G. P. Boucher. *Settlement Problems in Northern New Brunswick*. Canada Department of Agriculture. Publication 764. Ottawa. 1944.

Grant, R. F. *The Canadian Atlantic Fishery*. Ryerson Press. Toronto. 1934.

Gray, F. W. *The Future of the Sydney Coal Field*. Dalhousie Review 21, pp. 178-83. 1941.

Hoyt, H. H. *Forests and Forestry in New Brunswick. A special report to the British Empire Forestry Conference. London, England*. N.B. Department of Lands and Mines. Fredericton. 1947.

Jenkins, H. P. *Nova Scotia at Work*. Ryerson Press. Toronto. 1940.

Keirstead, B. S. *The Economic Effects of the War on the Maritime Provinces*. Institute of Public Affairs. Dalhousie University. Halifax. 1944.

Lewis, J. N. and S. C. Hudson. *Land Use and Part-time Farming in Cape Breton County, Nova Scotia*. Canada Department of Agriculture. Ottawa. 1942.

Longley, W. V. and W. F. Chown. *Antigonish County*. Nova Scotia Department of Agriculture Bulletin 118. Halifax. 1936.

Putnam, D. F. *Farm Distribution in Nova Scotia*. Economic Geography 15, pp. 43-54. 1939.

Putnam, D. F. *Agricultural Development in New Brunswick*. Economic Geography 15, pp. 408-20. 1939.

*Proceedings of the Nova Scotia Fisheries Conference*. Nova Scotia Economic Council. Halifax. 1938.

Saunders, S. E. *Economic History of the Maritime Provinces*. Royal Commission on Dominion Provincial Relations. Ottawa. 1940.

Since the situation with respect to the various productive industries and other economic phases changes from year to year, the only reliable sources are the latest issues of the Canada Year Book and other publications of the Dominion Bureau of Statistics together with the annual reports of the various departments of the provincial governments.

# CHAPTER 5

# The Regions and Cities of The Maritime Provinces

Wᴴɪʟᴇ the Maritime Provinces constitute a separate region which may be distinguished from the rest of Canada, there are many internal contrasts which enable us to distinguish sub-regions. Their boundaries are not distinct and definite in every case but in each there is either a core area or a dominant characteristic which gives a semblance of unity. The cities and towns are part of the regional pattern.

## I. Prince Edward Island

Being a separate land mass with no pronounced upland and completely surrounded by water, Prince Edward Island has comparative uniformity of landforms, climate, soil and vegetation. It is also the most completely and uniformly settled area in the Maritime Provinces. Its present population is almost completely native born and the population density has not in-

Figure 73. *Geographic Regions of the Maritime Provinces.*

creased for nearly three-quarters of a century. The population (99,000) is predominantly rural and its economy largely dependent upon agriculture.

The low rolling hills covered with large fields of grass, grain and potatoes, the neatly painted farm buildings, spruce hedgerows, red roads and winding tidal

## Charlottetown

Charlottetown, like other cities of the Maritime Provinces, came into existence because of its harbour. This is a well protected basin about two miles in width, accessible from the sea through a short strait with a navigable channel over 30' in depth. From the basin three saltwater

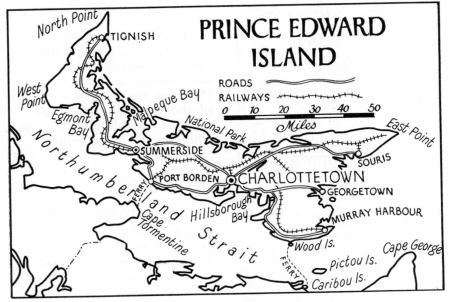

Figure 74. *Prince Edward Island.*

inlets combine to form an appealingly unique landscape. The sand beaches, dunes and red sandstone cliffs of the Prince Edward Island National Park have an unrivalled beauty.

There is only one large urban centre, Charlottetown, which is the administrative, commercial and cultural centre of the whole island. Next in size is Summerside, "the western capital", and a number of smaller centres including Souris, Montague, Georgetown and Kensington. Much of the appealing charm of Prince Edward Island lies in its rural hamlets such as Rustico, New Glasgow, Murray River, Hunter River, Crapaud, and New London, to mention only a few.

estuaries extend for many miles dividing the island into a number of peninsulas.

The first settlement was made across the harbour from the present city. Overlooking the entrance, the French in 1722 established Fort Lajoie. It consisted of an earthwork, a governor's house, barracks for a company of marines, a storehouse and a church named after St. John the Evangelist. A later settlement known as Port Lajoie was placed on the point of land opposite the harbour entrance. It was occupied by the British in 1758. In 1765 the site was selected as the future capital of the island and in 1768 the town of Charlottetown was surveyed into lots.

There are several well marked functional zones within the city. First of all is the

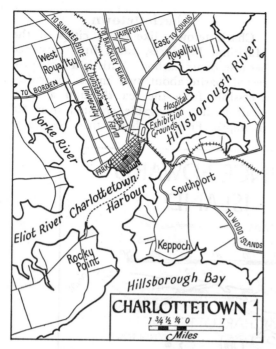

Figure 75. *Charlottetown and vicinity.* The only city of Prince Edward Island, Charlottetown, is centrally located on a protected harbour.

dock area with its array of warehouses and the immediately adjoining, small industrial area. The rather compact downtown commercial and administrative area is concentrated about the square which contains the historic Legislative building in which was held, in 1864, the first meeting which led to the Confederation of Canada. Surrounding this are various residential areas, interspersed with schools and churches. On the outskirts one finds a number of public institutions including hospitals, an orphanage, the Dominion Experimental Farm and St. Dunstan's University. Many of the former open fields of this peripheral zone have since World War II been filled with new sub-divisions. The Exhibition Grounds and Victoria Park occupy waterfront sites to the northeast and southwest of the city. With the exception of the central area, where many brick and a few stone structures are found, Charlottetown is a wooden city. Its resi-

dences are well placed and its streets pleasantly shaded.

As a manufacturing centre Charlottetown ranks well behind most other cities of similar size, but it accounts for nearly half the production of the Province. For the most part its industry consists of processing agricultural products and the making of small articles. Fish curing, printing and publishing and the baking industry are important.

The city has nearly half the retail trade of the Island and two-thirds of the wholesale trade and is thus one of the important distributing centres of the Maritime Provinces. Charlottetown is also the centre of the Island's tourist trade since many delightful seaside resorts are to be found within a few miles radius.

The city had a population of 14,821, according to the census of 1941, and had grown to 16,707 in 1956.

## Other Centres

*Summerside* (7,250) is the most important town in the western part of "the Island". Picturesquely located on Bedeque Bay it is a smaller edition of Charlottetown with a more compact business section and without the public buildings that mark the provincial capital. The harbour was once important as an export shipping port but is now used chiefly by fishing craft. Bedeque Bay is important for its oyster fishery. On the outskirts of Summerside is located the Dominion Government Experimental Fox Ranch where problems of the fur-breeding industry are investigated.

*Port Borden*, eighteen miles south of Summerside, is the point from which the C.N.R. ferry ships depart for Cape Tormentine, N.B. Here, since 1917, Prince Edward Island's newest town has developed, almost entirely in the service of transportation.

## II. Cape Breton

Like Prince Edward Island, Cape Breton is also a separate land mass, but somewhat

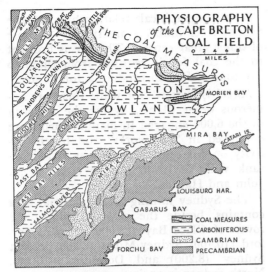

Figure 76. *Physiography of the Cape Breton Coal Field*. The Cape Breton Lowland is underlain by a tilted basin of Carboniferous rocks, most of which have no coal. The coal measures outcrop just behind the eastern shoreline and most of the coal lies under the Atlantic.

larger and possessing greater physical diversity, being dominated by rugged uplands. Its settlements are mainly along its

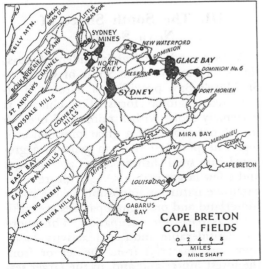

Figure 77. *The Mines and Settlements of the Cape Breton Coal Fields*. Glace Bay and the smaller mining towns are in close proximity to the mines, but Sydney with its huge steel works is localized by the harbour. Louisburg is an alternative port when Sydney Harbour is ice-bound.

shores leaving the interior almost empty. The population is further nucleated, 70% of the total being found in the Sydney industrial and mining area.

The areas suitable for agriculture are small and scattered and consequently, in the main, underdeveloped. Farming is largely a part-time occupation.

Cape Breton has great scenic resources which have attracted many tourists. The establishment of the Cape Breton National Park and the building of the Cabot Trail have made accessible vistas of breath-taking grandeur. Another point of interest is the centre of Gaelic culture which has been established at St. Anns. Many people on the island still speak Gaelic. There are also important areas around Arichat and Cheticamp where French is spoken.

The transportation system of the island is tied to the mainland by the Canadian National ferry service for railway cars and by the Nova Scotia Department of Highways ferry, both of which operate between Mulgrave and Port Hawkesbury, across the Strait of Canso. It has for decades been the hope of the Cape Breton people that a bridge will be built across the strait.

## Sydney

Sydney is the second city of Nova Scotia with a population of 32,162 in 1956. It is the centre of an industrial and mining region which contains nearly one-fifth of the people of the province. Within a few miles of the city, there are five towns ranging in population from 3,000 to 25,000 as well as dozens of thickly settled rural areas.

The growth of Sydney has taken place recently. Before 1900 it was a rather quiet little seaport with about 2,500 people, in 1901 it had 10,000 and had become one of the important steel towns of the country.

In the early days, Sydney Harbour was known as Spanish River and was frequented by fishermen from Europe. In May, 1784, the first English home was established and in 1785 Sydney became the capital of the newly created province of Cape Breton. Three shiploads of colonists arrived during the first year. At first the colony had considerable hardship, but within a few years the coal mines nearby were brought into production. The Highland Scots, who have set their seal upon Sydney and Cape Breton, began to arrive in 1802 and before long outnumbered all other colonists. In spite of recent immigration into this industrial area, the Scots are still the dominant group.

Sydney has a large safe harbour, open most of the year. Its docks are well equipped with mechanical devices for loading and unloading. In volume of traffic it rivals Halifax and Saint John. Normally, the bulk of its outward trade is made up of coal for Saint Lawrence River ports while the incoming freight consists of iron ore and limestone for the steel works.

The Sydney steel plant is one of four large centres of blast furnace activity in Canada. Operated by the Dominion Steel and Coal Corporation, it is located on a 460 acre site on the eastern shore of the harbour to the north of the city. Here, there are assembled great batteries of coke ovens, huge blast furnaces for smelting the ore, great "open hearth" steel-making furnaces, a blooming mill, a billet mill, a bar mill, and rod, wire, and nail mills. The company has its own power plant and repair shops. More than fifty miles of railway tracks are needed to connect the various departments. Iron ore and limestone are brought from Newfoundland. At the close of navigation approximately 1,000,000 tons of these commodities are stockpiled for the winter season. The necessary coking coal is obtained from nearby Cape Breton mines.

In 1957 the capacity for ingot steel production was increased to about 1,000,000 tons per annum. Aside from this the plant has an annual capacity for 650,000 tons of pigiron, 750,000 tons of blooms and billets, 200,000 tons of rails and tie plates, 67,000 tons of bars, 135,000 tons of wire rods and 55,000 tons of wire and nails.

The geographical relationships of the Sydney steel industry are similar to those of other great centres. The ore is brought to the coal for it requires from three to five tons of fuel to produce a ton of steel.

"Steel is Sydney" for while there are numerous other plants, by far the majority of the 6,000 engaged in manufacturing are employed in "the works" and by the activity of this one plant Sydney is able to rank with the much larger cities of St. John and Halifax.

The Sydney mining and industrial area contains, beside the city of Sydney, the towns of Glace Bay (25,000), New Waterford (10,400), Sydney Mines (8,700), North Sydney (8,200) and Dominion (3,000). North Sydney is an important seaport and fishing station. Other places that are really unincorporated small towns are Florence, Reserve, Dominion No. 6 and Port Morien. Louisbourg is connected by rail with the Sydney area and serves as a winter port when Sydney harbour is blocked by ice. Nearby are the ruins of the old French fortifications.

## III. The South Shore of Nova Scotia

A long and intricately indented coast line stretches from the Strait of Canso to St. Mary's Bay, providing a natural, if attenuated, regional focus. The climate is extremely moist with a rainfall of over 50 inches per year and a great prevalence of fog. The population is, in general, aggregated into small fishing towns and villages and a few larger seaports. Agriculture of an extensive nature is impossible in the rocky hinterland and only small patches are cultivated as part-time occupation. This shore has considerable industrial activity based upon raw material from the sea or from the forest hinterland and, in the larger seaports, imported from overseas.

There is one large urban development, the Halifax Harbour area which is the most important industrial and commercial cen-

Plate 26. Lunenburg Harbour, home port of many sailing vessels.

tre of the Maritime provinces. Yarmouth, at the western end of the province, is also an important gateway while Lunenburg, Liverpool, Lockeport and Shelburne are fishing and shipbuilding centres which have regional importance.

## Halifax

Halifax, capital city and chief seaport of Nova Scotia, had a population of 93,301 at the census of 1956. It was founded in 1749 by Lord Cornwallis, who considered Chebucto Bay to be the best harbour on the Atlantic coast. Here he established a military and naval station to offset the power of the great French fortress at Louisbourg on the Island of Cape Breton. Until 1905 it was the summer station of the British North American squadron and until 1906 the Citadel was occupied by a British garrison. Since then it has been a Canadian

naval base and was of great importance during both the first and second World War. On December 6, 1917, the north end of the city was devastated by an explosion which took the lives of 1,600 people, injured about four times as many and left thousands homeless. The blast occurred when the *Mont Blanc,* a French vessel carrying 3,000 tons of T.N.T. collided with the Norweigan freighter *Imo* which carried a cargo for Belgian relief.

*The Harbour.* Halifax Harbour is a drowned valley extending inland for about 14 miles from the Atlantic Ocean. Its mouth is divided by a large island into two channels, the Eastern Passage which is too shallow for large vessels and the Western Passage which is the entrance to the harbour. Actually, there are two harbours connected by a constricted channel known as "The Narrows". The outer harbour is about a mile in width and six miles in length and is lined with docks and piers capable of accommodating the largest ships. The inner harbour, known as Bedford Basin is about four miles long and 2½ miles

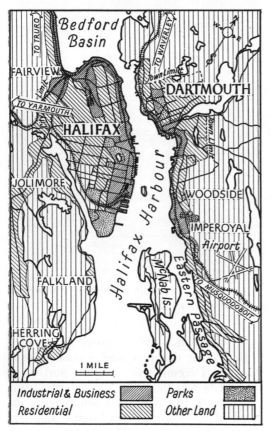

Figure 78. *The Halifax Harbour Area.* The city of Halifax is located on a small peninsula between the harbour and the Northwest Arm. With its protected anchorage in Bedford Basin, Halifax has one of the most commodious harbours in the world.

wide. In this commodious haven many huge wartime convoys were assembled.

Halifax Harbour has 33,000 feet of berthing space, and although normally not as busy as Montreal or Vancouver, it was used by more than 16,000,000 tons of shipping (4,300 vessels) in 1940. In 1951, 2,000 vessels with a net registered tonnage of 5,000,000 tons entered the harbour.

*The City Site.* The city of Halifax is built upon a small peninsula, about 4½ miles in length and less than 2 miles in width, lying between the harbour and the Northwest Arm, and about midway between the ocean and the head of the harbour. Upon the rock floor of the peninsula are several drumlins, oval hills of glacial drift one of which is surmounted by the fortifications of the Citadel. Fort Needham, in the north end of the city, is also built upon a drumlin while several others are found on islands in the harbour.

*The Urban Landscape.* Halifax is a wooden city, save for its downtown area— over 90% of its dwellings are of frame construction. Nearly half of the people live in single houses and there are few large apartment buildings. Normally it is not overcrowded for 70% of its dwellings have from 4 to 7 rooms. Most of the older residential streets are lined with trees and there are many parks and open spaces. From the top of Citadel Hill, more than 200' above the Harbour, most of the city can be seen. Halifax contains no skyscrapers, even the modern buildings are of modest height. To the east, between the hill and the harbour is the half square mile of downtown Halifax. Directly below the hill is the old town clock, erected in 1810 by the Duke of Kent and still faithfully keeping time. Across Brunswick Street lies the city market, three streets farther down is the city hall and old St. Paul's Anglican Church erected in 1750. Farther down are the Province House where the Legislature of the Province meets, the Provincial Building which houses the government departments, the Post Office and the Federal Buildings. Opposite the Custom House is the dock used by the ferry to Dartmouth across the harbour. About half a mile to the north are the old Ocean Terminals. Half a mile to the south are the huge new Ocean Terminals, the Union Station, the Nova Scotian Hotel, the cold storage plant and the 4,000,-000 bushel terminal elevator.

The extreme southern end of the peninsula is occupied by the wooded Point Pleasant park, some 200 acres in extent containing an interesting old Martello Tower and several other forts.

Along the Northwest Arm is a series of wooded lots and the clubhouses of many aquatic sporting associations. Near the Northwest Arm, also, lies the Campus of Dalhousie University, Kings University and the Nova Scotia Archives. Somewhat nearer the hill are the Victoria General Hospital, All Saints Cathedral, the Lord Nelson Hotel and the Public Gardens.

Immediately to the west of the Hill is a large open space known as the Common, while a mile or so to the northwest are the Exhibition Grounds.

The western side of the city contains many fine residential streets.

In the far north are Fort Needham hill and the Hydrostone district which occupies the area devastated in 1917. In the north also, are many hundreds of small houses built since the end of World War II.

Land transportation facilities all enter the city from the north, there are no bridges across either the harbour or the Northwest Arm. The city is almost surrounded by railways. The old terminals and the dockyards are served by a line which skirts the edge of the harbour while the new Ocean terminals are reached by a new line which follows the Northwest Arm and crosses the southern part of the peninsula in a deep open cut.

Across the harbour to the east lies the town of *Dartmouth* (22,000) which in many ways can be regarded as a suburban part of the Greater City of Halifax. Southward along the eastern shore of the harbour are Woodside with its sugar refinery and the oil refinery at Imperoyal.

Beyond these urban developments lie great stretches of woods and rocks; the immediate hinterland of Halifax is not by nature suited to agriculture and much of it has so little soil that it is not even well forested.

*Population.* The population of Halifax, according to the census of 1956, was 93,301, while that of the greater city or metropolitan area, including Dartmouth, Woodside, Imperoyal, Eastern Passage, and adjoining settlements, was over 164,000. Halifax thus stands eleventh in the ranks of the greater cities of Canada. Halifax, however, has grown rather slowly in comparison with some other metropolitan cities. Its population is now about five times as great as it was at Confederation, while Greater Montreal is more than ten times as large, and Metropolitan Toronto, more than twenty times as large as it was then.

Halifax had two periods of rapid population growth during the two world wars. It has continued to grow, although somewhat more slowly in the post-war period.

Halifax has not attracted large numbers of foreign immigrants. More than 80% of the population is Nova Scotia born. Of the migrants the largest groups are those from Newfoundland, New Brunswick, and the British Isles.

More than 80% claim British origin while about 8% are of French origin and 7% are Netherlands and German. Among others is a small group of African origin.

The dominant religious denominations in Halifax are: Anglicans 29%, Roman Catholics 40%, United Church of Canada 18%, Baptists 7% and Presbyterians 3%.

*Economic Functions.* Although important, the manufacturing industries of Halifax are not dominant; even under war conditions, only about 20% of the wage earners were so employed. The services pertaining to government require a great many workers and the number engaged in transportation is much higher than in most Canadian cities. It is also an important trade centre.

Culturally, also, it is the centre of the province, being the seat of Dalhousie University, the Nova Scotia Technical College and other institutions of learning.

The Halifax Harbour area, including the city of Halifax, the town of Dartmouth and adjoining eastern shore, constitutes an important manufacturing region. Oil and sugar refineries, shipbuilding plants and dockyards are among the important industries. Together they produced goods to the value of $95,000,000 in 1954, rivalling Saint John as the most important manufacturing area in the Maritime Provinces.

Halifax is a busy port. In 1951 almost 4 million tons of freight passed over the docks. The chief items of import were

tained steamship service to the U.S.A. There is a small agricultural district nearby, but most of the people of the area are fishermen. Many of the shore villages are inhabited by Acadians.

## IV. The Interior of Nova Scotia

A great part of peninsular Nova Scotia is a rough rocky, forested and very sparsely populated area. Its resources are lumber,

National Film Board.

Plate 27. Halifax, Nova Scotia, a year-round port of call for ocean liners.

petroleum, coal, gasoline, fish and motor vehicles. The exports include gasoline, lumber, flour, grain, petroleum products, motor vehicles and parts, and fish.

Halifax is the leading commercial centre in the Maritime Provinces. It handles about one-third of the total retail trade and two-thirds of the wholesale for the province of Nova Scotia.

Yarmouth (8,100) is a manufacturing town and a seaport from which is main-

pulpwood and a little mining. In some areas, particularly on the drumlins of Queens and Lunenburg counties, there is land suited to agriculture and small farms have been developed. There are no urban centres and practically all trade goes to the shore settlements. There are two large game sanctuaries, Liscomb in the east and Tobeatic in the west. The future of this area should lie in a scientific development of wood production.

## V. Northern Nova Scotia

Northern Nova Scotia consists chiefly of a series of lowlands along Northumberland Strait and bordering the Bay of Fundy and its headwaters. In the main underlain by softer rocks, it has a better development of soil than other parts of the province. There are, however, included areas of upland in which the soils are shallow and rocky. It has a favourable climate with about 40 inches of rain per year and fairly warm summers (July mean, 66°F.)

It has considerable diversity of resources, including forests, agricultural land, fisheries and mines. Here is found the greatest development of agriculture in the province including the fruit growing of the Annapolis Valley and the dairying of the Colchester and Pictou areas. Dairying is also being developed near Amherst and Antigonish.

Population is well distributed and there are a number of mining and industrial towns, transportation nodes and supply centres of fair size.

While considered as a geographic region, Northern Nova Scotia falls rather naturally into a number of smaller units, some of which are physiographic and others more dependent upon the pattern of settlement. Among the better known of these are the Annapolis Valley, the Windsor area, the Cobequid Bay, the Amherst Basin, the North Shore, The Pictou Basin, the Stewiacke Valley and the Antigonish Basin. Even within these areas there is an intricate detail of valley settlement pattern and a good deal of uncleared woodland.

### Truro

Truro, "the Hub of Nova Scotia", is the most centrally located town in the province. The census of 1956 records a population of 12,250 but Salmon River and Bible Hill, just outside the town limits, swell the urban population to about 17,000. During World War II the town was temporarily overcrowded with wartime migrants.

The Cobequid area was colonized by the French and a thriving settlement existed

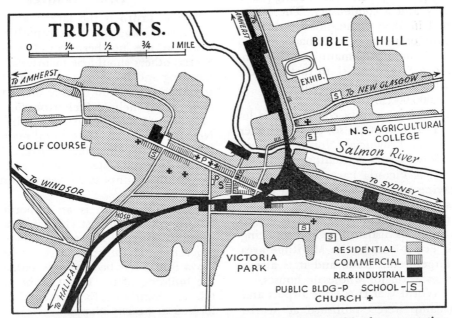

Figure 79. *Truro—the Hub of Nova Scotia.* Truro is the centre of land transportation routes in the peninsula. The converging routes have had a great influence in developing the pattern of the town.

at the time of the expulsion in 1755. Four years later the area was granted to the "New England Planters" whose descendents still make up a large part of the population.

Built on a flat gravel terrace near the head of the tide, Truro has a strategic location as a "bridge" and "cross roads" town. This has supported its development through the age of the stagecoach, the railway and now in the age of the automobile. Truro is too far inland ever to have been much of a port but small ships used to come as far as the "Board Landing Bridge", about two miles to the west.

Truro is a neat well-kept town with tree shaded streets. It has two more or less distinct business centres separated by a zone of public buildings and large residences, some of which are of considerable age. The eastern end of the town is dominated by the railway yards and shops, Truro being an important junction and division point. Industrial plants are scattered in various parts of the town. They include knitting mills, a shirt factory, small machine shops, grist mills, planing mills, a creosoting plant, a creamery and a condensery. The latter, established in 1885 is the oldest industrial dairy plant of its type in Canada. Truro ranks fourth among the manufacturing centres of Nova Scotia and sixth in the Maritimes with a total production value of about $10,000,000 in 1954.

The Colchester county courthouse is located in Truro, as are, also, the Colchester Hospital, the Provincial Normal College and the Nova Scotia Agricultural College. Of interest is Victoria Park, 1,000 acres of scenic ravine and natural woodland to the southeast of the town.

The most important function of Truro appears to be its distributing and servicing facilities. Few places in the Maritime area have a larger retail trade and it is also a favoured location for wholesale houses.

During World War II, a large airport and military camp were established at nearby Debert, stimulating considerable growth of the town itself.

Figure 80. *The Settlements of the Pictou Coal Field*. Stellarton and Westville are the chief mining centres, Trenton is the site of the steelworks, New Glasgow is the commercial and manufacturing centre and Pictou is the port. The valleys have a pattern of agricultural settlement, while most of the upland remains forested.

## Other Centres

While Truro is the largest and, during the forties, was the most rapidly growing town in the northern counties of Nova Scotia, others should be mentioned. An interesting and important cluster of towns is found in the Pictou mining and industrial area. They include Stellarton (5,500) and Westville (4,300) which are mining towns, New Glasgow (10,000) general manufacturing a n d commercial centre, Trenton (3,200) with its steel works, and Pictou (4,600), the county town, seaport and shipbuilding centre.

Springhill (7,400) is an important coal mining town. Amherst (10,300) is a county town, commercial and general manufacturing centre. Its function as the gateway to Nova Scotia has been greatly enhanced by the building of the Fort Cumberland Hotel. A Dominion Experimental Farm is located at nearby Nappan.

The towns of the Annapolis valley are smaller. Kentville is the headquarters of the apple industry and also the site of an Experimental Station. Wolfville is the seat of Acadia University. Annapolis Royal, noted chiefly as a historical site, is the location of Fort Anne National Park and the area of first European settlement in Canada. Digby is connected with Saint John, N.B. by Canadian Pacific Steamship service.

Windsor, centre of its district along the Avon river, is the site of important gypsum quarries while Hantsport, some miles down the estuary, is a shipping point for gypsum and the site of a pulp mill.

## VI. Eastern New Brunswick

Eastern New Brunswick is part of the great lowland underlain by Carboniferous rocks. Its climate is characterized by a moderate rainfall (36 inches) and by a fairly warm summer. The area is largely covered by coniferous and mixed forests and settlement is confined to the larger river valleys and the gulf shore area. The population is of mixed origins with a preponderance of French speaking people, especially toward the north. Agriculture is not highly developed and is often a part-time occupation. Manufacturing is chiefly concerned with forest products. Peat bogs near Shippegan in the northeast are being commercially developed. Important lead and zinc mines are found south-west of Bathurst.

There are few towns, but a considerable number of villages. *Chatham* (6,300) and *Newcastle* (4,700) on the Miramichi River owe their development to the sawing and shipping of lumber since the early days of settlement. *Bathurst* (5,300) at the mouth of the Nipisiguit River is the site of a large pulp mill and a college.

## VII. Southern New Brunswick

The southern part of New Brunswick is, physiographically, a rather complex association of valleys and uplands. Its climate is characterized by a moderate rainfall and moderately warm summers, except for the cool, foggy and rainy strip of coast along the Bay of Fundy.

In contrast with the north, the inhabitants of this area are chiefly of British origin. Close settlements are found in the larger valleys while the uplands remain as unsettled forest land. Here are located the three cities of the province. Fredericton, the capital, Saint John, the chief port and industrial centre, and Moncton, the chief railway centre, highway node and a rapidly growing distribution point.

While the area devoted to agriculture is not extensive, there is a well developed dairy industry supplying the cities.

## Fredericton

Fredericton, the capital of New Brunswick, is located on the St. John River about 85 miles from its mouth, and approximately at the head of navigation. Its population

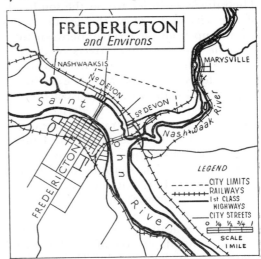

Figure 81. *Fredericton, the Capital of New Brunswick.* Founded on a terrace on the south bank of the St. John River, the city has recently been enlarged by the annexation of a large area on the north bank. The river is spanned by both railway and highway bridges.

in 1941 was 10,062, nearly all of British origin. By 1956 its population had grown to about 18,000, in large measure through the annexation of the urban areas on the left bank of the St. John River.

Fredericton was settled by Loyalists in the autumn of 1783, upon the site of the former French village of Ste. Anne. On account of its central location it was chosen as the capital of the new province of New Brunswick, created in 1784. The Governor established his residence there in 1786. The town grew slowly and was incorporated as a city in 1848 with a population of about 4,000.

The site of the original settlement and most of the built-up area of the city is located on a low terrace at a bend in the St. John River. There are several wharves along the water front formerly used by river boats. A highway bridge, half a mile in length, connects the suburbs on the north bank.

A small down-town section, about a block away from the river, contains most of the public and commercial buildings. The railway facilities are on the south side of the city just below the gentle slopes leading up from the terrace. Between these areas lie the residential streets of the city so closely lined with shade trees as to appear a forest from the air. The dwellings are practically all of frame construction.

The chief function of Fredericton is as the capital and administrative centre of the province. Here is to be found the University of New Brunswick, pleasantly located on the slopes which overlook the city from the southwest. It was founded as the College of New Brunswick in 1800. Instruction at first was of secondary school level but in 1820 studies leading to the B.A. degree were introduced. By Act of the Provincial Legislature it became the University of New Brunswick in 1859. It has an important School of Forestry which has taken the lead in forest research in Eastern Canada. On the southern outskirts of the city is the Dominion Experimental Farm where scientists are engaged in solving the agricultural problems of the province.

The vicinity of Fredericton is one of the important manufacturing areas of the province. Here are located a number of lumber mills and woodworking plants. The textile industry is also important.

## Saint John

Although not the capital of the Province of New Brunswick, Saint John is its largest and oldest city. Its population according to the census of 1956 was 52,491. Saint John also claims the honour of being the oldest incorporated city in Canada, having been granted a Royal Charter in 1785. During the succeeding century it rivalled Halifax as a seaport and for a time was the more populous city. It is the eastern terminus of the Canadian Pacific Railway.

*The Harbour.* St. John Harbour has been notable ever since it was discovered and mapped by Des Monts and Champlain in 1604. It is the sheltered estuary of the St. John River which enters the Bay of Fundy at this point. At the head of the harbour is the famous reversing fall. Here the river narrows to a width of 350 feet between rocky walls nearly 100 feet high. When the tide is out the river pours out in a turbulent flood, falling about 15 feet. When the tide comes in the water in the harbour rises higher than the river above the gorge and the rapids are reversed. The mean range of the tide in St. John Harbour is about 28 feet. The minimum depth of the channel is maintained at 30 feet. Piers line both sides of the harbour; the new ocean terminals are located on the west side. Harbour facilities include more than 15,000 feet of berthing space, grain elevators of 3,000,000 bushels capacity, coal docks and oil tanks. The large St. John drydock is situated in East St. John on the east side of Courtenay Bay which, protected by a long breakwater, forms a second harbour. River steamships use a wharf located above the falls.

*The City Site.* The fabricated city occupies a series of peninsulas abutting on the harbour. The earliest English settlement was at Portland Point in 1762. Upon the arrival of the Loyalists in 1784, two towns were laid out. Parrtown, named after the

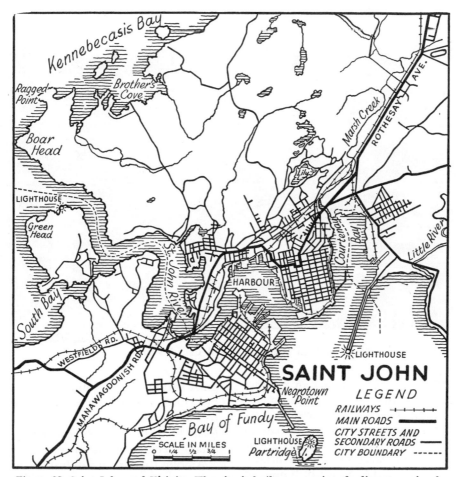

Figure 82. *Saint John and Vicinity*. The city is built on a series of adjacent peninsulas about the harbour at the mouth of the river. The long mole and the great dry dock make Courtenay Bay a second harbour.

Governor was located on the peninsula between the harbour and Courtenay Bay, while Carleton was laid out on the west side of the Harbour. Beaconsfield and Fairville are built-up areas lying west of the city limits. The incorporated city includes several square miles of forest stretching north to Kennebecasis Bay.

*The Urban Landscape.* The functional areas of the city are somewhat crowded within the single square mile of the central peninsula. King's Square, Queen's Square and the "Old Burying Ground" form rather welcome open spaces. King Street, leading from King's Square to the Market Slip is wider than most streets of the city and is the centre of the downtown shopping district. Many of the buildings in this part of the city are of brick construction.

The residences of the city are almost entirely of wood and for the most part rather crowded. Less than one-eighth of the homes are in individual buildings and more than four-fifths are in apartments or flats. However, St. John also possesses a number of pleasant residential suburbs within reasonable distance from the downtown area.

*The Population.* The population of Saint

*Photographic Surveys (Quebec) Ltd.*

Plate 28. Saint John Harbour, one of Canada's great ocean ports.

John in 1951 was 50,779, being an increase of about 25% in numbers since the time of Confederation. Growth has been rather slow in comparison with other Canadian cities. According to the 1941 census about 2/5 of the people were of English origin, about 1/4 Irish and 1/6 Scottish. Those of French origin, dominant in many parts of the Province, number about 4,000 or 8%. In 1941, the metropolitan district of Saint John which includes Beaconsfield, Fairville and East St. John contained about 66,000 of whom less than 1,900 were foreign born, while fully 83% were natives of New Brunswick. The migrant population numbered about 10,000, mostly from other parts of Canada. Saint John had a preponderance of young people in the age groups from 15 to 29 years of age. In 1956, Greater Saint John was estimated to have a population of 85,000.

*Economic Functions.* Besides being an important transportation centre, the terminus of the Canadian Pacific Railway and a great seaport, Saint John also stands in the first rank among the manufacturing centres of the Maritime Provinces. It is also a focus for the wholesale and retail trade of a large section of the province.

Among the leading industries of the city and vicinity are sugar refining, the processing of spices and other imported goods, railway rolling stock, marine construction and repair, and pulp and paper manufacture. The city is also the centre of the printing and publishing business of the province. The total value of the manufactured goods produced in 1954 was over $85,000,000.

As a port, Saint John has long been a rival of Halifax. In 1951, a little over 2,300,000 tons of shipping used the harbour and over 2,300,000 tons of freight were handled. Coal, sugar, gasoline and fuel oil were the chief imports while the largest items of export were grain, flour, lumber, logs, newsprint and potatoes.

## Moncton

Moncton, with a population of 36,000 in 1956, is the second city of New Brunswick. To this may be added several thousands of people living in the suburbs. In 1956, Moncton and its suburbs were estimated to contain about 50,000 people.

Located at the head of navigation on the Petitcodiac River, it was first settled by the French and, after their expulsion, by German and British settlers. At the last census 62.4% of the people claimed British origin and 32.3%, French.

For many years the settlement was known simply as "The Bend" because of its location at the bend in the river. For about 40 years, from 1830 to 1870, it was an important shipbuilding centre with sometimes as many as eight or ten vessels under construction at the same time. The last full rigged ship was built in 1874. "The Bend" became the town of Moncton in 1875 and in 1890 was incorporated as a city.

The focus of the city, however, is not its river-port but its railways. In 1860 it became a way station on the line from Saint John to Shediac and, with the completion of the Intercolonial in 1876, an important junction. It is the headquarters of the Atlantic Region of the Canadian National Railways, including the General Offices and the main repair shops. Just outside the city is an airport with 6,000 foot runways used by Trans Canada Airways and, as an alternative, by Transatlantic Airliners also.

Moncton today functions as a transportation node and as a distribution centre. By comparing the values of sales *per capita,* its retail trade is found to be nearly twice as brisk as that of Saint John. Its wholesale business is also considerable. About 23% of Moncton's gainfully employed are engaged in transportation, 22% in trade and 15% in maufacturing. Amongst the manufactures to be found are textiles, biscuits, meat packing, oil refining, wire fences, woodwork and metal products, totalling over $32,000,000 in 1950. The surrounding

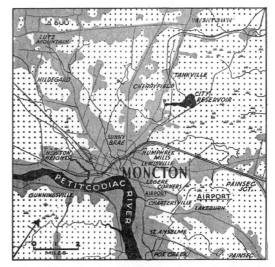

Figure 83. *Moncton, N. B.* Founded at the "Bend" and head of navigation on the Petitcodiac River. Moncton is now a centre of rail, road and air transport. It is also important in trade and manufactures. Note, however, the large areas of unsettled forest land (dotted).

area is an important agricultural and lumbering region.

*Sackville* (2,850), in the southeast, is the seat of Mount Allison University, while in the southwest are found the seaside resort of *St. Andrews,* and *St. Stephen,* which, with its American counterpart of Calais, Maine, forms an important international gateway. Grand Manan, Deer and Campobello Islands are large scenic islands in Passamaquoddy Bay, now becoming celebrated as summer resorts.

## VIII. The Saint John Valley

The region, in actuality only the mid-portion of the valley, comprises a rather narrow strip along the western border of the province.

It is a fairly well settled area with an extensive type of agriculture with a dependence upon field crops rather than livestock. Along with the adjacent Aroostook area of Maine, it is noted for its production of potatoes, and potato storage houses are common objects in the landscape.

It is a cultural frontier, the inhabitants

*Courtesy Exp. Farms Service.*

Plate 29. Potato Storehouse in the St. John Valley, New Brunswick.

of the southern part being of British origin while those of the north are French. For the most part the people are rural dwellers but there are a number of small towns; Woodstock and Grand Falls being the most important. The latter is noted for the hydroelectric development on the St. John River and for the wide boulevard on its main street. At Hartland, a covered wooden bridge 1,280 feet in length spans the St. John River. A potato starch factory is located at Hartland.

## IX. Central and Northern New Brunswick

Several factors combine to set this region apart from the rest. While it has sea coast and valley areas a large part of it is rather elevated and it has a cool climate. It is largely an unsettled and forested region, the source of much of the lumber and pulpwood produced in the province. It has several large rivers which have proved of great value in transporting logs from the interior, and as a source of power.

The population is preponderantly of French origin and speech, and is rapidly increasing. In consequence a number of pioneer areas are being opened up.

*Edmundston,* the county seat of Madawaska county, is the largest and most rapidly growing urban centre in the region. Fourth in size among the incorporated cities of the province, it had a population of 12,000 in 1956. It is located on the St. John River at the mouth of the Madawaska, opposite the town of Madawaska, Maine. It is an important gateway, railway junction and node, leading to both the U.S.A. and the province of Quebec. It is the headquarters of the largest pulp and paper manufacturer in the Maritime Provinces, as well as smaller concerns. An important retail centre, it is the outfitting point for the loggers, pulpwood cutters and sportsmen of the forests of northwestern New Brunswick.

*Campbellton,* at the head of navigation on the Restigouche River, has a population of 8,400 and is a railway divisional point and an important lumbering centre. There is a pulp mill at nearby Atholville. *Dalhousie* (5,500), sixteen miles west of Campbellton, has a large pulp and paper mill.

## Selected References

Harrington, Lyn. *The Cabot Trail.* Canadian Geographical Journal XXXVI, pp. 204-21. 1948.

Harvey, D. C. *Charlottetown.* Canadian Geographic Journal IV, pp. 201-19. 1932.

Harvey, D. C. *Halifax, 1749-1949.* Canadian Geographical XXXVIII, pp. 6-37. 1949.

Peacock, Fletcher. *The Province of New Brunswick—Geographical Aspects.* Canadian Geographical Society. Ottawa. 1949.

Phillips, Fred H. *Fredericton—Centennial City.* Canadian Geographical Journal XXXVI, pp. 80-93. 1948.

Shaw, Lloyd W. *Province of Prince Edward Island. Geographical Aspects.* Canadian Geographical Society. Ottawa. 1949.

Simpson, R. A. *Province of Nova Scotia. Geographical Aspects.* Canadian Geographical Society. Ottawa. 1949.

Taylor, G. *Town Patterns in the Gulf of St. Lawrence.* Canadian Geographic Journal XXX, pp. 254-75. 1945.

Webster, J. C. *Historical Guide to New Brunswick.* Fredericton. 1944.

# CHAPTER 6

# The Province of Quebec
# Physical Background

Q UEBEC is the largest province in Canada, and is surpassed only by Ontario in population and economic development. Its shores were discovered more than four centuries ago and have been settled for nearly 350 years. The St. Lawrence is still the main gateway to a large section of North America.

## Position and Extent

Quebec extends from the international boundary at the 45th parallel of north latitude, to Cape Chidley on Hudson Strait at about 62° N., a distance of almost 1,200 miles. It thus spans several climatic and vegetation zones, from the deciduous forest to the Arctic tundra. Its greatest east-west distance is over 1,600 miles, from the 57th meridian, at the Strait of Belle Isle, to the Ontario boundary at 79°33′ west longitude. Quebec thus has two time zones. The North Shore of the Gulf of St. Lawrence and the Gaspé Peninsula fall in the Atlantic Standard Time Zone, four hours later than Greenwich Mean time, while the rest of the province has Eastern Standard Time which is one hour later.

The area of the province is 594,860 square miles, 15.5% of the area of Canada. It is a land of great diversity, 71,000 square miles being occupied by fresh water lakes and 160,000 square miles by treeless tundra, waste land and unproductive forest. An area of approximately 70,000 square miles is occupied by agricultural settlement and somewhat less than 300,000 square miles by productive forest, half of which is still untouched.

## Physiography

Quebec has the advantage of a lengthy shoreline. The uninviting coast from Cape Chidley to the southern part of James Bay is 2,550 miles long. The north shore of the Gulf of St. Lawrence and the estuary have a shoreline of 1,160 miles from Blanc Sablon to Quebec while it is nearly the same distance along the south shore and around the Gaspé Peninsula to the New Brunswick border at the head of Baie de Chaleur. The seaway is prolonged inland by the navigable waters of the St. Lawrence River and its tributaries. The largest cities of Quebec are located on the waterway and settlement has extended from its shores.

The province of Quebec falls naturally into three distinct but very unequal physiographic regions: (a) the Canadian Shield, sometimes called the Laurentian Plateau; (b) the St. Lawrence Lowland; (c) the Appalachian Highlands. (See Figure 84)

## The Canadian Shield or Laurentian Upland

By far the greater part of Quebec, more than 500,000 square miles, is underlain by the hard old Precambrian rocks of the *Canadian Shield*. Because its nature was

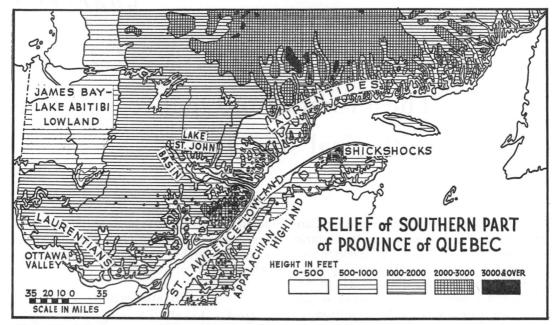

Figure 84. *Relief of Southern Quebec.* This generalized contour map emphasizes the important geographic divisions of the province, viz. the Appalachian Highland, the St. Lawrence Lowland, and the Canadian Shield with its various subregions.

first known and studied in the rugged plateau-like highlands north of the St. Lawrence River, the name *Laurentian* is often used for the whole region. The rocks are, largely, granites, diorites, quartzites, gneisses, schists, and slates. Except on rounded hill tops and in stream gorges, however, the surface material is mostly of glacial origin, or the sand, gravel and clay deposits of the post-glacial period. The skyline as seen from the air is "monotonously even". The main trend of relief is a plateau-like surface arising from the sea-level, on the shore of James and Hudson Bays, to 1,000 feet in Abitibi, 1,500 feet in the Laurentian mountains, and above 2,000 feet along the Labrador boundary. Scattered monadnocks rise a few hundred feet above the upland in the interior, but the most conspicuous summits are found toward the eastern edge of the Shield in the Laurentide National Park north of Quebec City (3,900 feet), and Mont-Tremblant Park west of Montreal (3,150 feet).

Numerous cycles of erosion have reduced the Laurentian Upland to its present level. The history of peneplanation dates back to Precambrian Times. On the western margin of the Shield, fragments of old peneplains are buried beneath the Paleozoic sediments. Then a marine invasion occurred over most of the Laurentian Upland, and several hundred feet of Paleozoic sediments were accumulated. As the land was uplifted at the close of the Paleozoic period, a new series of erosion cycles, lasting for some 500 million years, removed the overburden of sedimentary rocks. But before the last glaciation, the region was uplifted again, and the rivers were rejuvenated. The active streams deepened their valleys, and with their tributaries have excavated large basin-like areas. Those cycles of erosion that took place before Quaternary glaciation shaped the basic features of the present physiography of the land. The three main peneplains of Quebec, referred to later, were formed before the occurrence of ice sheets.

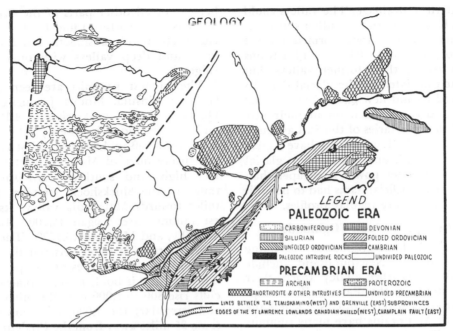

Figure 85. *The Geology of Quebec*. Comparison of this map with **Figure 84 brings out** the correlation of rock type and physiographic relief.

## The Ice Age

Even a casual observer cannot doubt that the Laurentian area, like the other regions of Quebec, was covered by gigantic glaciers in the Pleistocene period. The evidence of such action is given by features of glacial erosion such as U-shaped valleys, grooved and striated rocks, rounded hilltops, called *roches moutonnées;* by glacial deposits including terminal, recessional and ground moraines, eskers and drumlins, and other morainic deposits. Above all, proofs are shown by innumerable lakes of glacial origin, sediments in ice-front lakes, sand and gravel deposited by streams which issued from melting ice, and lastly by a pattern of rivers newly organized after the retreat of the glaciers.

The Labrador ice-sheet that covered Quebec is estimated to have been more than 7,000 feet thick. It spread slowly from the center outward, until warmer weather melted away the ice from the south to the north. The enormous weight of the ice-

cap had lowered the surface of the plateau, and as soon as the burden was removed, the surface began to rise to its former level. The process being slower than the retreat of the ice, the sea invaded the land. The Champlain sea occupied the St. Lawrence Lowlands. Hudson and James Bays expanded inland also at a slightly later time.

Two depressions were filled by fresh-water in front of the northward retreating glacier: the lake St. John basin, which still contains a large body of water, and another much larger one in Western Quebec known as Lake Barlow-Ojibway, of which Lake Abitibi is but a tiny and shallow remnant. Proofs of such a marine invasion and lake formation are of two kinds: elevated beach lines and shore features, and deep deposits of clay. Much more arable land is available in those basins than on top of plateaus where the glacial moraine is too rough for the plow.

Another result of the glaciation from which men have taken opportunity is the new pattern of drainage. The valleys could not regain their normal gradients at once. Lakes and swamps were formed on the height of the land. Rivers and streams tried to regain their former valleys, but were often deviated by the glacial deposits and forced to find new paths. Local glacial erosion also caused changes in their profiles. All the tributaries of the St. Lawrence, flowing across the Laurentians, have a great number of rapids and falls, due to glacial action. Thus water power is cheaper than it would be if artificial dams had to be built on rivers with more regular profiles.

## The Appalachian Highlands

The Appalachian Highlands, extending from Alabama to Newfoundland, include South-eastern Quebec. They reach their widest extent in the Eastern Townships and their greatest relief in Gaspé where the Shickshock Mountains have many summits above 3,500 feet.

The rocks here are different from those of the Laurentian Upland. They are mostly sediments of the Paleozoic Era, ranging from Cambrian to Carboniferous. The Cambrian rocks are mostly altered sediments: quartzites, argillites, schists and slates; the other formations contain limestones, sandstones and conglomerates as well as schists and slates. The strata have been folded, broken and crushed by mountain building. In the process igneous rocks were intruded. Bodies of serpentinized peridotite date from the earliest period; basalts, granites, diabases and syenites appeared later. The intrusive rocks are harder than the sediments and stand out now as the highest summits.

The Appalachians became ridges of high mountains during the latter part of the Paleozoic Era. Two chief periods of mountain-building are known: the Taconic revolution at the close of the Ordovician; and the Acadian during the Devonian; other disturbances occurred later. Then came cycles of erosion lasting for more than 200 million years, until glaciation happened

here as in all other parts of the Province. So, it is no surprise to find in the Appalachian Highlands a smooth relief of plateaus and deep valleys with only a few ridges.

The highest summits are seen in the Gaspé peninsula. Mount Jacques-Cartier, Quebec's highest peak, rises to 4,160 feet and is surrounded by twenty others ranging from 3,500 to 4,000 feet. Westward the serpentine mass of Mount Albert is 3,775 feet high, and southwestward the bold range of the Shickshocks stretches for 55 miles towards Matapedia valley. Its highest summits are: Logan (3,700′) Bayfield (3,470′), and Mattawa (3,370′). There is a great contrast in relief between the northern and southern shores of the peninsula. The first one is bold; in some places shore cliffs rise 800 to 1,000 feet; the other is low and irregular; the 1,000 foot contour lies some 25 miles away from the Chaleur shoreline.

Between the Matapedia and Chaudiere Valleys, very few summits rise above the old peneplain of 1,200 feet. Valley floors afford easy passages from the St. Lawrence estuary to New Brunswick. In the Eastern Townships the relief becomes bolder. From west to east, three parallel ranges are to be found: the Sutton range, extending from the Green mountains of Vermont into Canada, the Stoke range, from west side of lake Memphremagog to lake St. François and the Megantic range, close to the New Hampshire and Maine border. Amongst the highest summits are: Sutton (3,200′), Orford (2,860′), Chapman (1,800′), Gosford (3,875′) and Megantic (3,620′). Between the ridges, the deeply dissected plateaus seldom exceed 1,200 feet in altitude.

The Pleistocene glaciation is nearly as evident here as in the Laurentian plateau. Ice erosion has deepened the long lakes such as Memphremagog in the south; Temiscouata and Matapedia in the north. A mantle of glacial drift covers the underlying rocks. The rivers were ponded back of the glacial ridges forming high level lakes. The moraines have yielded better soils for agriculture than in the Laurentians, especially when buried by more recent clay and sand deposits.

## The St. Lawrence Lowlands

The smallest physiographic region of Quebec is a triangular lowland bounded by the edge of the Canadian Shield to the northwest, the great Champlain fault,

rises in the neighbourhood of Quebec City to about 300 feet. This uniformity is broken by the Monteregian Hills extending in a line from Montreal to the Appalachian Highlands: Mount Royal (769'), St. Bruno (712'), Beloeil (1,437') Rougemont (1,250'), Yamaska (1,470') and Johnson (875'). They are extrusions of igneous rocks that forced their way up during the Devonian period, when orogenic movements were active.

*Provincial Publicity Bureau, Quebec.*

Plate 30. The Central Laurentians, along the dual highway north of St. Jerome.

bordering the Appalachian Highlands to the east, and the Adirondack Mountains in New York State, to the south. The underlying rocks are sandstone, shale and limestone of the Ordovician, Silurian and Devonian periods. The strata are gently dipping, or lie in low, broad, dome-like folds, traversed by faults, some of which are of considerable throw; but compared with the highly folded measures of the Appalachians, they seemed relatively undisturbed. The present surface is low and flat, especially around Montreal (100 feet), but it

There need be little wonder that the relief is so low. The unfolded sediments were easily removed by the numerous cycles of erosion, the base-level being furnished by the antecedent St. Lawrence River. The hard igneous rocks of the Monteregian Hills stand as monadnocks. But here also glaciation left its marks. The course of the St. Lawrence was altered. Upstream from Montreal, the river forms a series of impounded waters: Lakes St. Louis and St. Francis, and many rapids: Lachine, Cedar, etc. Downstream, the glacier excavated a deep trough on the site of lake St. Peter, now being filled by river deposits. In front of Quebec City, the St. Lawrence had to find a new course and its cliffs are still very steep. After the melting of the ice the whole area was invaded by the Champlain Sea, whose deep clay deposits form valuable agricultural soils.

### The Major Landforms

As in the Maritime Provinces, it has been shown that there are three main levels of peneplanation in Quebec. They are fully discussed in Prof. R. Blanchard's regional studies. The lowest, called the *Quebec Platform* lies in the St. Lawrence Lowlands. It was fashioned by the pre-glacial network of rivers. It is well developed around Montreal, being some 70 miles in width between the Laurentian plateau and the Appalachians. It is very low, ranging from 100' to less than 300' above sea level. Towards Quebec City, the platform is narrower and seems to be pinched between the edge of the Canadian Shield and the Appalachians. The Upper City is built on a fragment of that platform about 300 feet high. It is thought to be a Pliocene peneplain, achieved toward the end of the Tertiary Era. This erosion level is also found along the Ottawa River as far as Hull, along the South shore of the Estuary, as far as Matane, and along the Baie de Chaleur. The best farmlands were first settled on this peneplain, and its low relief is favourable to transportation.

The second level of erosion is the *Appalachian Platform*. Its altitude varies from about 700 to 1,300 feet. It is evident in the fairly uniform level in Gaspé peninsula except in the central part, on the South Shore of the Estuary, above the escarpment facing the shoreline, and is widespread in the Eastern Townships except for the summits of ranges. The same platform exists on a much larger scale in the Laurentian Upland. The peneplain was carved during the Miocene and Oligocene periods. Much of it is still covered with forest, but some parts are settled, as in the Eastern Townships, in Central Laurentians, in Western Quebec and elsewhere.

The third level of erosion, called the *Shickshock Platform* by Blanchard, rises above 2,000 feet. Only a few fragments of that oldest landform remain. They are located in Central Gaspé, in a few summits in the Eastern Townships, in the Laurentide National Park, around Mont-Tremblant, and within the Canadian Shield, north of the Saguenay. Since it dates back to the Eocene and perhaps even to the Upper Cretaceous Period, it is found in most places to be a dissected and broken country, as in the Shickshocks and in the Laurentide Park. But the skyline is nevertheless fairly level. These wooded hills and plateaus have, for the most part, been set aside as forest preserves.

### Drainage

The whole area of Quebec is drained, either directly or indirectly into the Atlantic Ocean. There are two main watersheds: (a) The St. Lawrence River and Gulf, and (b) Hudson Bay. The former is the most important on account of its location in the settled part of the Province.

### St. Lawrence Watershed

The area of the St. Lawrence watershed in Quebec is over 250,000 sq. miles. The main artery is the St. Lawrence, a mighty river of which all Canadians are proud. It may be divided into four reaches.

### a) The Upper St. Lawrence

Above the Island of Montreal, is a stretch about 60 miles long broken by two rapids: Lachine, near Montreal, and Cedar between St. Timothee and Valleyfield. Above the rapids the water is impounded into Lake St. Louis and Lake St. Francis, 69 and 153 feet above sea level respectively. The Lachine and Cedar canals are used for navigation, while the new and deeper Beauharnois canal is now used for water power development only.

The St. Lawrence has the largest volume of any river in Canada. Its average rate of discharge at Lachine in cubic feet per second is 248,000 for the whole year. The highest water is in May (312,000 c.f.s.) and the lowest in October (213,000 c.f.s.).

## b) The Lower part of the River

From Montreal to Quebec, a distance of 160 miles, the river has a very low gradient, from less than 25 feet in the harbour of Montreal to mean sea level at the exit of Lake St. Peter. The tide dies out at Three Rivers. The mean width of the river is over a mile; it widens to 9 miles at Lake St. Peter, but here the water is very shallow (11 feet), being constantly filled by river deposits. There is a real delta in front of Sorel. Below Three Rivers, the river narrows to three-quarters of a mile at the Quebec Bridge and between Quebec and Levis. A ship channel has been dredged to a depth of thirty-five feet, permitting ships of 20,000 tons to enter the harbours of Three Rivers, Sorel and Montreal.

## c) The Estuary

On all official maps the St. Lawrence River extends as far as Gaspé but geographers prefer to apply the term *Estuary* to the wide stretch below Quebec. It is about 245 miles long and 30 miles in width at its mouth. As in the Bay of Fundy, tidal action is increased in this long funnel spring tides having a range of 18 feet at Quebec. Above Father Point, near Rimouski, all large ships employ a St. Lawrence River Pilot.

## d) The Gulf

The gulf of St. Lawrence has an area of 80,000 square miles, its waters washing the shores of Newfoundland and the Maritime Provinces as well as Quebec. Along the North Shore, Quebec territory extends to Blanc Sablon on the Strait of Belle Isle. Anticosti Island and the Magdalen Islands belong to Quebec. The former is a forest preserve but the latter is an archi-

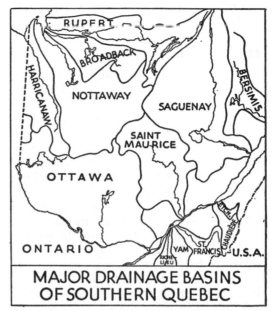

Figure 86. *Major Drainage Basins of Southern Quebec.* The Ottawa, St. Maurice and Saguenay are the largest tributaries of the St. Lawrence; the Harricanaw, Nottaway, Broadback and Rupert flow into James Bay.

pelago densely populated by fishermen. Baie de Chaleur is a body of navigable water between Quebec and New Brunswick forming the southern shore of the Gaspé peninsula.

## The Tributaries of the St. Lawrence

The more numerous and the largest tributaries are those of the left or north bank of the St. Lawrence, draining a wide area of the Laurentian Plateau. No less than 17 rivers exceed 100 miles in length, the longest being the Ottawa River (685 miles), a large section of which forms the boundary between Ontario and Quebec. One trait is common to all; the drainage is hesitant at the source but the flow of waer becomes swifter and swifter as their courses cross the edge of the Plateau in the Laurentian hills. These are all rejuvenated rivers, developing new valley profiles amongst glacial deposits, and supplying abundant water power.

A few of these rivers will be described in detail.

## The Ottawa River

Its source is to be found nearly 1,200 feet above the sea level, back of Lake Barrière dam located at Longitude 76° 45' W. and Latitude 47° 30' N. The river flows southwestward to Lake Timiskaming (588 feet) and then southeastward to lake Two-Mountains (70 feet) where it empties into the St. Lawrence. At Grenville, half-way between Ottawa, and Montreal, the Ottawa becomes the second most powerful river of Quebec; the mean annual flow is 67,330 c.f.s., the highest water being 145,150 c.f.s. in May, the lowest, 42,640 c.f.s. in September. Besides many unused tributaries like duMoine River, the Ottawa has three tributaries along which settlement and industry are flourishing: the Gatineau, whose head is impounded back of Mercier dam on Lake Baskatong (600 feet above sea level), has a flow at Paugan Falls (half-way between Maniwaki and Hull) of 12,200 c.f.s. annually (varying from 19,100 in May to 10,000 in September); the Lièvre River, beginning away north of Mont-Laurier, has about half as much water as the Gatineau; the North River, draining the Central Laurentians northwest of Montreal. The Ottawa River empties into the St. Lawrence around Montreal and Jesus Islands by three channels: to the south by the way of Lake St. Louis and the main channel of the St. Lawrence, to the northwest by the Prairie or Back River, which divides Montreal and Jesus Islands, and by the Mille-Isle River, separating Jesus Island from the mainland. They are two mighty streams; the first one having a mean annual flow of 37,400 c.f.s. (69,800 in May and 25,100 in February), the second, a mean annual flow of 7,000 c.f.s.

## The St. Maurice River

The next important tributary on the same bank is the St. Maurice River. In its 300 mile course from the summit of the Laurentian Upland, the river drops from an elevation of 1,325 feet at its source in the Gouin Reservoir to sea level at Three Rivers. At Grand'Mère, 20 miles upstream, the rate of discharge varies from 72,000 c.f.s. in May to 13,400 c.f.s. in February, the annual mean being 25,000 c.f.s. Its main tributaries, the Manuan and Mattawin, are also regulated by dams at their head waters.

## The Saguenay River

The most important tributary, next to the Ottawa River, is the Saguenay. It is a short river, 100 miles long, from Lake St. John (322 feet above sea level) to the Estuary. Lake St. John is fed by many streams, the most powerful of which are (clockwise on the map) Ashuapmuchuan River, Mistassini River, Mistassibi River and Peribonka River. Reservoirs are being established on the latter. The Kenogami and Shipsaw rivers are also tributary to the Saguenay. Measured at its very source, at Isle Maligne, the Saguenay has a mean annual rate of discharge of 52,600 c.f.s. (117,200 in May and 22,100 in February and March). That whole amount of water falls to the sea level in the first 30 miles of its course. That explains why industry based on water power is so important there. Another asset of the Saguenay River is the fjord-like stretch between Chicoutimi, Haha Bay and Tadoussac. The splendour of that part culminates in front of Trinity and Eternity capes, where steep cliffs on the southern side of the fjord reach over 1,000 feet above the water.

The North Shore of the Estuary and the Gulf has also a great many tributaries that are not used except for logging purposes: Bersimis River, 249 miles long. Outarde River at Baie Comeau, 240 miles long, flowing 33,860 c.f.s. in May and 4,000 in February, Manikuagan River, 310 miles long, Ste. Marguerite River at Clark City, 130 miles long, Moisie River, 210 miles long, Romaine River, 270 miles long, and Natashkuan River, 220 miles long.

The Photographic Survey Corporation Ltd.

Plate 31. Eaton Canyon, in the Koksoak River System, where power will be obtained to operate the new iron mines.

Tributaries of the right or south bank of the St. Lawrence are shorter and less powerful. They are located nevertheless in much more settled regions and a few ought to be mentioned. The Richelieu River, drains Lake Champlain (95 feet above sea level), into the St. Lawrence at Sorel. It is 70 miles long. Besides being used for navigation, it has the greatest volume among the tributaries of the South bank: 25,810 c.f.s. in May, 5,331 c.f.s. in September, and a mean annual flow of 11,870 c.f.s.

The two main rivers of the Eastern Townships are the St. François and Chaudière Rivers. The first one (165 miles long) has its source in the lake of the same name (951 feet above sea level) and flows southwest to Sherbrooke and thence northwest to Drummondville and Lake St. Peter. At Drummondville the rate of discharge is 6,950 c.f.s. annually (22,880 c.f.s. in April, 2,980 c.f.s. in August). The Chaudière River, 120 miles long, heads in Lake Megantic (1,294 feet above sea level), close to the United States border, and flows through Beauce County, where its spring floods are to be feared. At Ste. Marie, for instance, low water in February has only a flow of 1,065 c.f.s. while high water has a flow of 13,380 c.f.s. in April; and these are averages for a 25 year period. The bad spring flood of 1934, showed a catastrophic range from 587 c.f.s. in February to 22,700 c.f.s. in April.

## Hudson Bay Watershed

The area of Quebec, draining into James Bay, Hudson Bay and Hudson Strait, is even larger than the St. Lawrence watershed. It covers approximately 350,000 square miles. There are ten rivers on that watershed that exceed 200 miles in length and the largest lakes of the Province are at the headwaters of those rivers. The Fort George River and Koksoak River are more than 500 miles long; Lake Mistassini, 1,243 feet in elevation has an area of 840 square miles. Their economic use is very limited, except as hydroplane bases in summertime. Some are free of ice only from the end of June to the end of September. In Western Quebec, at the head waters of the Harricanaw and Nottaway Rivers, settlement is progressing in the mining district and the Clay Belt.

*Observations*: The drainage pattern of Quebec is still in a stage of youth, following the interruptions of the glacial period. There are thousands of lakes, ponds and swamps; waterfalls and rapids are common along most of the stream courses. The flow of these rivers is naturally very irregular; winter freezing, spring break-up and summer drought cause the rate of discharge to vary enormously. Navigation is possible only on the St. Lawrence and on a few short stretches of its tributaries; but water power is abundant, logging may be organized with proper devices, and the canoe offered a good means of transportation until the advent of the hydroplane.

## Climate

Quebec has a great variety of climatic conditions due to its geographical position, large area and complex physiographic relations.

## Climatic Controls

The main factors regulating the distribution of climatic influences are not to be sought in latitude or proximity to the ocean only. The position of the great masses of cold and warm air over the North American continent have a direct influence on the Quebec weather. For instance, the succession of cold waves in winter, and that of warm and humid ones in summer are logical results of air mass movements. The St. Lawrence valley happens to be one of the regular paths followed by cyclonic storms between the Great Lakes and the Atlantic Ocean. Those are disturbances that account for the irregularity of our climate, for the rapid changes in the weather and for the many departures from "normal conditions". In fact, as far as temperature is concerned, Quebec has a rather continental climate, in spite of its nearness to the sea board. The climate is very severe in wintertime, even in the south, and very warm and humid in summertime.

## Temperature

Amongst the various elements of the climate, let us first consider temperature. The mean annual temperature ranges between 42° around Montreal to 36° in the northmost inhabited parts except on the North Shore of the Gulf. Of more significance are the isotherms for the extreme months of January and July. See figures 87,88. In January the coldest inhabited

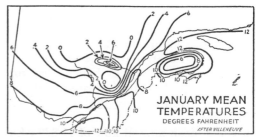

Figure 87. *January Mean Temperature.* Quebec has a cold winter, with midwinter means 0°F. and 12°F. Note the cold areas in the highlands of Laurentide Park and Gaspé Peninsula.

regions are located in the Laurentian Upland. The average temperature there stands between 8° in the Ottawa Valley and 4° in the region of Northwestern Quebec and in the Lake St. John area. In the south, January mean temperatures range between 12° in Montreal and 10° at Quebec and in the Eastern Townships. The

Figure 88. *July Mean Temperatures.* Midsummer temperatures in Southern Quebec have a range of about the same magnitude as those of midwinter, varying from 56°F. to 70°F.

marine influence also raises the average temperature to 10° on the Gaspé shores and to 12° in Anticosti and Magdalen Islands. Some features worthy of observation on the January map are the following: the 8° isotherm skirting the outside edge of the Laurentians from the Ottawa Valley to Tadoussac, the contrast of lower temperature on bolder reliefs (Laurentide Park and Shickshocks) with the higher temperature in the low Lake St. John district. These temperatures are easy to explain. The inland parts of the province are more likely to be covered by polar continental air than the southeast, where low pressure storms

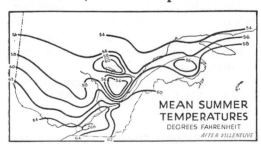

Figure 89. *Mean Summer Temperatures.* This map shows average conditions for the three summer months and is a good indication of the warmth of Quebec summers.

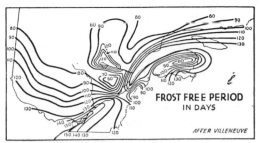

Figure 90. *Average Length of the Frost-free Period.* The average frost-free period in Southern Quebec ranges from 60 to 150 days. Note how long it is near the St. Lawrence River and Lake St. John, and how short it is in the highlands.

bring milder temperatures in wintertime.

In July, none of the inhabited parts of Quebec fall below 60°. Montreal averages 70° and the whole St. Lawrence Lowland nearly as much. Most of the other settled parts average between 64° and 66°. The coolest parts are on the shores of Gaspé (62°), except Chaleur Bay (64°), and the North Shore of the Gulf (60°). See map.

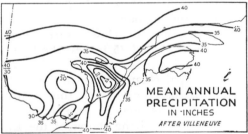

Figure 91. *Mean Annual Precipitation.* Southern Quebec has a good supply of moisture, receiving an equivalent of 30″ to 50″ of rain per year. A large part of this comes in the form of winter snowfall.

In summer Southern Quebec is invaded by warm air currents from the southwest. Temperatures over 90° are frequent; and if the air mass has a high relative humidity, as is often the case, the weather is not pleasant for city dwellers. They find cooler places along the shores down the St. Lawrence where breezes of more northern latitudes dissipate the heat, and where a cold marine current keeps the water at a lower temperature than that of the air.

The number of frost-free days is very

important for agriculture. Around Mont-treal the average is 150 days per season; it is 130 at Quebec and along the south shore as far as Matane. Here the influence of the wide estuary is important. The average length of the frost-free season is well over 100 days in all sections where agriculture is practised. This correlates rather closely with the isotherm of 60°F. average temperature for the four months of June, July, August and September. It extends from Abitibi in Western Quebec to the Isle of Orleans and along the south shore to Lake Temiscouata. It also forms a closed circle around the Lake St. John district.

## Precipitation

The distribution of rainfall, so impor-tant for vegetation and animal life, is fairly uniform in Southern Quebec where the mean annual precipitation ranges be-tween 35 and 40 inches. It decreases to 30 inches westward and to 20 and even 15 inches in Northern Quebec. In the Lauren-tide Park, the summits receive as much as 55 inches, but are closely surrounded by isohyets of 50 and 45 inches; the latter one expands far south of the massif, and joins the Appalachian heights in the East-ern Townships. Away from this centre precipitation decreases in two opposite directions: eastward the shores of the Es-tuary and the Gulf are below 35 inches from Rivière du Loup and Tadoussac to Gaspé; westward, the upper Ottawa Val-ley is even below 30 inches. (Fig. 91). On one hand cold waters seldom produce rain while on the other the decrease towards the interior is to be explained by the more continental type of weather. The heavier precipitation between is produced not only by higher altitudes north of Quebec City, but by the fact that in summer the warm air masses from the south collide here with the colder masses of the north.

Quebec has the heaviest snowfall in Eastern Canada. At 19 stations out of 49 where the snowfall is recorded and pub-

lished,[1] the depth of the snow is over 100 inches. Montreal and Quebec have 112 and 123 respectively. Few stations have less than 80 inches. The many ways in which the snow cover is beneficial to the land are well-known. Snow is not only wel-comed by sportsmen but by foresters and farmers. It protects the roots of the plants and affords easier ways of transport even for truck driving in the bush. Water from the melting snow also adds moisture to the soil in springtime.

A further idea of climatic conditions is obtained when we consider the number of precipitation days and the hours of sunshine. Montreal and Quebec are only 160 miles apart and they both have about 40 inches of precipitation. But, for a pe-riod of ten years, Montreal averaged 164 days per year with measurable precipita-tion while Quebec had 174 days. Montreal had 1803 hours of sunshine while Quebec had 1745 hours per year. Continental climates are characterized by short periods of precipitation, even though it may be relatively abundant. On the other hand, Maritime climates have fine persistent rain even though the total amount is less. In this respect then, Montreal has a more continental climate than Quebec.

## Winds and Weather

In the St. Lawrence Valley prevailing winds are from the northwest in Winter and from the southwest in Summer. They are usually accompanied by fine weather. In the Gulf and the Estuary northeast winds bring bad weather in Summer. Win-ter winds from the south and southeast are likely to raise the temperature, but they often bring snow storms followed by thawing. In any case, Southern Quebec enjoys the kind of weather to which it is entitled by latitude.

[1] G. Oscar Villeneuve. *Climatic conditions of the Province of Quebec and their relationship to the forests.* Bull. no. 6, Meteorological Bureau, Forest Protection Service, Dept. of Lands and Forests, Province of Quebec, 1946.

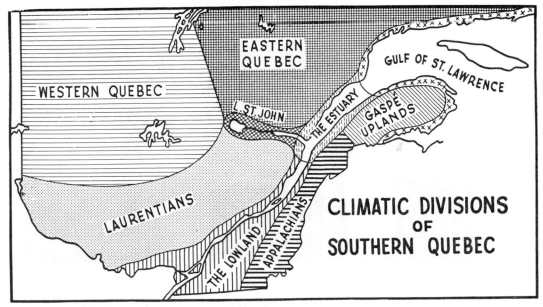

Figure 92. *Climatic Subdivisions of Southern Quebec.* (After Kling)

## Climatic Subdivisions

Based upon consistent differences in the average climatic statistics, nine climatic subdivisions may be recognized in Southern Quebec.[1] As represented in Figure 92, they are: the Appalachians, the Gaspé Uplands, the St. Lawrence Lowlands, the Estuary of the St. Lawrence, the Gulf of St. Lawrence, the Laurentians, the Lake St. John Area, Western Quebec and Eastern Quebec. The large cold area of Northern Quebec may be regarded as a tenth climatic subdivision.

Climatic diagrams constructed from the statistics of six selected stations are shown in Figure 93. Particularly noticeable is the variation in precipitation regimes. Precipitation is adequately distributed over the year at all southern stations but in the north there is a tendency for the early spring to have less and the late summer months to have more moisture than the average.

## Vegetation

Climatic conditions are best reflected by the natural vegetation of a country. Except for the tundra region in Arctic Que-

bec, the whole of the territory is covered by a large portion of the great Canadian forest: mostly composed of conifers, although the small southern part had a forest of hardwood, before it was partly cleared for settlement. We follow Halliday's forest classification[2], although Villeneuve has suggested minor changes in his recent publication[3].

## 1. Tundra

The treeless tundra formation covers a large area in the Ungava peninsula, north of a line running from Richmond Gulf on the eastern shore of Hudson Bay to Cape Hopes Advance on Ungava Bay, and along the shoreline to the Labrador border. Mosses and lichens prevail over a vast swampy area, where only a thin

---

[1] Sidney Kling. *Climates of Southern Quebec.* Unpublished thesis. University of Toronto 1948.

[2] W. E. D. Halliday. *A Forest Classification for Canada.* Forest Service Bull. 89, Dept. of Mines and Resources, Ottawa. 1937.

[3] Oscar Villeneuve. *Opus citum,* p. 34 and following.

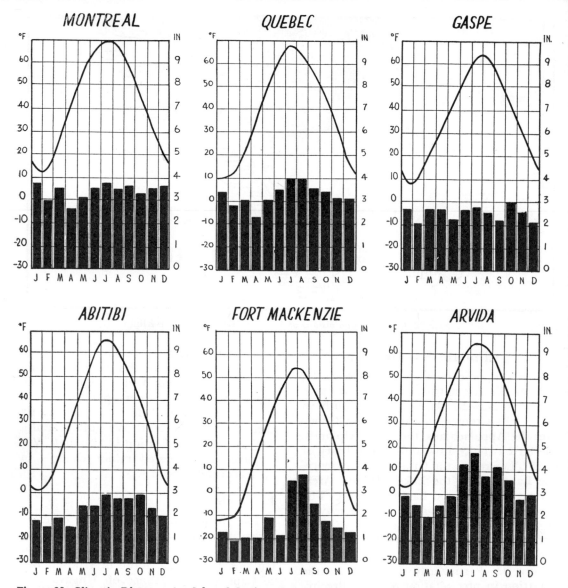

Figure 93. *Climatic Diagrams for Selected Stations.* The stations were selected as representative of the conditions of their respective climatic subdivisions.

layer of soil is not permanently frozen. In the more sheltered places some woody plants can grow, including dwarfed willows and shrubby birches. Bleak as it may appear, that region of 50,000 sq. miles is not a completely barren land. Over 200 species of flowering plants have been identified there.[3] Eskimo groups along the

shores live almost entirely on the products of the sea. It might be possible to improve their way of life by the introduction of reindeer here as elsewhere in Northern Canada.

[3] N. Polunin. *Botany of the Canadian Eastern Arctic.* Part 1, Bull. 92, National Museum of Canada. Dept. of Mines and Resources, Ottawa, 1940.

Figure 94. *Vegetation Regions of Quebec.*

## 2. Coniferous Forest

The great coniferous forest, known also as the Boreal forest or Taiga, extends over the most of Quebec. Its northern limit is the southern edge of the Tundra while its southern boundary runs from the northern end of Lake Timiskaming to Baskatong Reservoir and to St. Zenon in Berthier county, thence northward beyond La Tuque to include the forests of the lower part of the St. Maurice valley, thence southeast again, skirting the Laurentide Park to the shore of the St. Lawrence Estuary, north of Beaupré. Outlying patches of this forest are found on Anticosti Island, in Central Gaspé and in the highlands between the Matapedia and Temiscouata valleys. The forests of the Lake St. John Basin, however, belong in the mixed class.

Black spruce is found throughout the region. Other conifers including balsam fir, white spruce, tamarack and jack pine are of wide occurrence and characterize some sections. A few deciduous trees are present, including aspen, paper birch and, sometimes, balsam poplar. White and red pines may be found along the southern border.

*The Ungava Forest.* From Lake Mistassini northward lies an area of poor forest which Halliday terms the "Northeastern Transition Section". It is an open woodland composed of stunted black spruce and balsam fir with scattered birch. and jack pine interspersed with treeless moors. The surface vegetation is composed largely of white lichens. Trees of commercial size occur in sheltered valleys on the eastern side of James Bay and in the Koksoak valley far to the north.

The southern portion of the coniferous forest constitutes a large reserve of merchantable timber, the various sections of which have characteristic associations.

*The Clay Belt Forest.* The poor drainage of the Clay Belt favours an association with black spruce as the dominant species, mixed with tamarack and some northern white cedar. With better drainage the podzol soils carry a mixed stand of white spruce, balsam fir, white birch, aspen and balsam poplar.

*The North Shore Forest.* Here black spruce and balsam fir are of equal importance, jack pine and white spruce are the secondary species, associated with white birch and aspen on lake shores and bottoms of valleys. The latter species are likely to take a predominant place after forest fires. The same trees are found on Anticosti Island.

*The Laurentian Forest.* It extends from Lake Timiskaming to the Upper St. Maurice River and the Laurentide Park. It may be looked upon as a transition region, where climatic conditions, differences of soils and exposure of the slopes influence the vegetation. Here species are more numerous and growth is more luxuriant. Black spruce and balsam fir are dominant species, but other associates differ: white birch is dominant on high, southward facing slopes, Jack pine on the sandy terraces of the St. Maurice, white pine on sandy plain and red pine on gravel ridges. In the Laurentide park, the cool and moist climate, podzol soils and higher altitude are responsible for the typical association of black spruce and balsam fir.

*Gaspé and the South Shore Highlands.* Surrounded by the mixed forest in lower altitudes, there are patches of the great Boreal forest on the highlands of Central Gaspé and on the South Shore of the Estuary. The heavy precipitation of Gaspé favours pure stands of black spruce and balsam fir, mixed with white spruce, aspen and white birch on slopes and valley floors. Farther south, black and white spruce become predominant, associated with balsam fir and white birch.

## 3. Mixed Forest

Higher temperatures and a longer period of vegetation are responsible for the transition from the coniferous forest of the north to the mixed coniferous and deciduous stands of this intermediate belt which extends from Lake Timiskaming to the estuary of the St. Lawrence. Because of local differences, four different sections may be described.

(a) The *Timiskaming* section is the western portion of the belt. It has clay soils and relatively higher summer temperatures. The predominant tree species are black spruce and balsam fir, aspen and white birch.

(b) The *Laurentian* section, besides the four species just mentioned, carries white pine, hemlock, maple, red and jack pine. Its "pineries" formed the source of much of the timber which came down the Ottawa River.

(c) The *Lake St. John and Saguenay* section forms an enclave in the coniferous forest where warmer summers and more favorable soils have permitted the growth of maple, white birch and aspen among the conifers.

(d) The *St. Lawrence Estuary* section, due to its proximity to the sea as well as its marine clay soils, also has a favorable environment. Here additional broad leaved species such as black ash, balsam poplar and white elm are found with the conifers. Here, also, is found the northern range of the white cedar.

## 4. Hardwood Forest Region

In the warmest regions of Quebec, the St. Lawrence and Ottawa Valleys and the Eastern Townships, hardwoods are predominant. Before it was cut for the purpose of settlement, the virgin forest was the finest in Quebec and included a great variety of species: white and yellow birch, sugar and red maple, aspen, associated with white pine (the best timber tree of Eastern Canada), balsam fir, hemlock and white spruce. Species of a warmer climate are to be noted also, such as red oak, beech, white ash, butternut, cottonwood and balsam poplar. Rare species in the upper St. Lawrence are basswood and rock elm.

## Fauna

Climatic conditions have less influence on wild life than on vegetation, but a real picture of the vegetation cover would be incomplete without a short reference to "hosts of the forests". Game, fur bearing animals, water fowl live in more or less close association with one another in the wildest parts of our forest. Their fear is the presence of man, looked upon as a common foe. Quebec has four main wild life zones.[1]

## 1. The Arctic Life Zone[2]

Its extent is the same as that of the tundra. Typical land mammals are: the Barren Ground caribou, on which the natives depended largely for food and clothing, but that is decreasing greatly, and could perhaps be replaced by domes-

---

[1] *R. M. Anderson.* Faunas of Canada. Canada Year book 1937, p. 29.

[2] *J. Lewis Robinson.* An outline of the Canadian Eastern Arctic. Dept. of Mines and Resources, Ottawa, 1944.

ticated reindeer in Ungava peninsula; polar bear, whose meat is used as dog food, and fur for bedding and robes; and Arctic fox, chief fur bearing animal of the native hunters. The fox is a scavenger along the coast and its chief prey is lemming and other small rodents. Sea mammals are walrus, hunted mostly for its ivory tusks (a practice that is discouraged), two kinds of seals: the ringed seal and bearded seal, which affords the staple diet of the Eskimo (skins are used for clothing and boat building, blubber for heating and cooking lamps), white whales and narwhal in certain coastal areas. The most common food fish is the Arctic char; and among the various species of birds, the snowy owl and ptarmigan are to be mentioned.

## 2. The Hudsonian Life Zone

It extends from the timber limit to the south of James Bay, Lake Mistassini and Pointe des Monts on the North Shore. There are few animals limited to this zone; but it is visited and becomes the habitat of more southern species, seeking refuge away from the settlements. The mammals of the Arctic meet with those of the woodland. The caribou is a typical example of a migrating species. Brown bears are seen in the interior, while the polar bear does not leave the arctic shores. Ptarmigan overlaps the range of spruce grouse. Fur bearing animals are plentiful in places. Indians from the North Shore and from Mistassini posts wander in winter time over the whole area; their annual catch includes, in order of importance: beaver, mink, muskrat, marten, foxes (specially red), lynx, ermine, otter and seals.

## 3. The Canadian Life Zone

It extends over most of Southern Quebec both sides of the St. Lawrence Lowlands. Here is the typical habitat of the many fur-bearing animals mentioned above and others such as fisher, skunk, squirrel,

porcupine, hares and rabbits. The moose is the largest mammal (pride of the sportsman); smaller deer, black bear and wolves are also to be seen occasionally. The number of bird species is greater than northward: sparrows, warbles, thrushes, jays and woodpeckers, but the hunters look specially for the spruce and sharp-tail grouse. Migrating water fowl, ducks and geese, have two of their main flyways in North America over Quebec; the Atlantic flyway and that of the Mississippi.

## 4. The Transition or Alleghanian Life Zone

Quebec has a very small extension of this zone, which is more widespread in Southeastern Ontario. The Lowlands being wholly settled, few species of wild life are to be found here: gray and red squirrels, cottontail rabbit, wood-chuck, striped skunk, racoon and wild cat. The birds are all those familiar to settled areas: sparrows, bluebirds, woodthrush, vireos, etc.

## Soils

It has already been shown in a previous section that several soil zones cross the province of Quebec. Further detail is possible only in the southern part of the province where soil surveys have been carried on for a number of years, although no general map on a provincial scale has yet been published. While not perfect, there is a strong correlation between land form region and soil region. The St. Lawrence Lowland is characterized by deciduous forest and a type of soil development which normally produces Grey-Brown Podzolic soils. The Appalachian Highlands and the Canadian Shield, on the other hand, normally have Podzols and Brown Podzolic soils.

## I. The Soils of the St. Lawrence Lowland

### a. Southwestern Section

The section upriver from Lake St. Peter to the borders of Ontario and New York

State is the best known part of the province. It happens to be the widest and lowest part of the plain. The soil materials are of two different kinds. The most recent and, for the most part, occupying the lowest levels, are the sediments of the Champlain Sea and of the various post-glacial lakes and streams. The older materials are of glacial origin including till and glacio-fluvial outwash.

1. *Sedimentary alluvium.* These sediments vary in texture including sand, silt and clay and various classes of loam. The heavy textured clay and loam soils are usually neutral to slightly acid in reaction

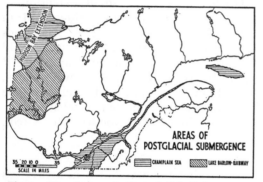

AREAS OF
POSTGLACIAL SUBMERGENCE

35 20 10 0        35
SCALE IN MILES        CHAMPLAIN SEA        LAKE BARLOW-OJIBWAY

Figure 95. *Areas of Post-glacial Submergence.* At the close of the ice-age Quebec was invaded by the sea, and large areas of water-sorted sands, silts and clays were deposited in the lowlands. A large glacial lake, also, for a time, occupied much of Western Quebec. These areas now form the important agricultural lands of the province.

with some free carbonates in the subsoil. Known as the Champlain soils, they have a fair balance of mineral fertility with none of the elements present in outstanding amounts. Organic matter and nitrogen content vary considerably. The Champlain association has large areas of imperfectly drained soils on the surface of which organic matter has accumulated. When drained these soils produce excellent farm crops.

The sands and sandy loam deposits of the old beaches and deltas have tended to develop into Podzols which are distinctly acid in reaction and lower in fertility.

The degree of podzolization varies considerably. The leached horizon of the profile tends to be quite thin along the left bank of the St. Lawrence but is thicker on the flanks of the Monteregian Hills and farther eastward. Though poor in natural fertility and of less value for general farm crops than the Champlain clays, the lighter soils have been found useful for special crops. An outstanding example is the cultivation of flue-cured cigarette tobacco on the sand-plains of Joliette.

The gravelly soils of the "Champlain Terraces" on the flanks of the Monteregian Hills have been utilized as orchard sites. The advantage lies not only in the well-drained soils but also in the good air drainage of the slopes.

2. *Glacial materials.* The largest areas of glacial materials are the ground moraine areas which were unmodified by the Champlain Sea. They may be either high or low in lime depending upon the rocks from which they are derived. They have reasonable fertility but are sometimes stony.

### b. The Northeastern Section

This section extends from Lake Saint Peter to Quebec. Below Sorel, Lake St. Peter has flat shores covered by deep clay and loam extending from the water's edge inland to the terrace escarpments. These flats are fairly wide on both sides of the lake, extending to Pierreville on the south and St. Cuthbert on the north. They are narrower to the northeast in Nicolet and Three Rivers. This plain contains the typical hay land of the province, especially the area between Berthier and Maskinongé. It is, for the most part, imperfectly drained and normal soil profiles are rare.

On the south, the loams become more and more sandy as one proceeds inland in Yamaska, Nicolet and Drummond counties. Large tracts of peat and muck are found in eastern Nicolet and Lotbinière. Closer to the Appalachian Piedmont, however, a good strip of clay and loam is found from Victoriaville to Lyster in Megantic county.

North of the St. Lawrence, the St. Maurice River accumulated a large Pleistocene sand delta extending from Three Rivers to Shawinigan Falls at the foot of the Laurentians. Eastward in Champlain and Portneuf counties, there is a narrow belt of clay along the shore, and of loam on top of the terrace.

East of Quebec a narrow extension of the St. Lawrence lowland is found in the Beaupré coast. Because of tilting, the level of the peneplain here is between two and three hundred feet above sea level. At sea level, there are wide clay flats utilized as hay meadows. On the terraces there are belts of clay and loam. The surface soils are deep, friable and porous and show little podzolization. The subsoil at a depth of four feet or so is neutral or slightly acid and is in part derived from limestone formations. Further inland at the foot of the Laurentians there are deep sands on which highly podzolized soils have developed.

On the Island of Orleans, sandy clays are found above the river flats, as a narrow strip from the end of the Orleans Bridge to Ste. Famille. At higher elevations is found the most extensive soil formations of the island, Sillery gravelly loam. It is derived from the underlying Sillery shale. The surface soil is about four to six inches in depth, low in organic matter, acid and shows traces of podzolization. In the centre of the island is a swampy depression covered with peat.

The older orchards of Orleans and Beaupré have been planted on well-drained loams; grain and hay crops thrive better on the heavier loams and clays while the gravelly soils appear admirably suited for potato and strawberry culture.

## II. The Soils of the Appalachian Highlands

This region extends from the Vermont border to the extremity of the Gaspé Peninsula. The southern part has been pretty well surveyed but no information is available for the north.

The soils of the Eastern Townships are Podzols and Brown Podzolic soils. On the upper peneplain remnants, the parent material is usually glacial till while in the valleys there are terraces and glacial outwash plains as well as some old lake sediments.

Most of the soils derived from till are loams; they are fairly fertile and well cultivated except where the slopes are too steep. The Greensboro loam derived from limestone and slate, is a widespread soil type in Standstead and Compton counties. Berkshire loam, another till soil derived largely from Precambrian schists is used for pasture in Richmond and Sherbrooke counties.

Some of the glacial outwash soils are coarse and infertile, others such as the St. Francis loamy sand and Calton fine sandy loam are useful for truck crop farming.

Stony soils are very common in the Eastern Townships. In Bellechasse county, a lowland 10 to 15 miles in width lies between the shore and the "mountain". Recent alluvium is found along the rivers while older alluvium, including Champlain clay and Sillery loam, makes up most of the cultivated land.

There are extensive settled areas in the uplands of Rimouski, Matapedia, Bonaventure and Gaspé. The river valleys have podzolic soils developed on glacial outwash materials while on the till covered slopes there are rather cold, sandy, acid soils, often strewn with boulders. The subsoil is impervious and because of the poor drainage, muck and peat have developed. Marl deposits in the lakes of Bonaventure, called "vase des lacs", have been used on the land. Heavier, deeper loams are found along the shore of Baie de Chaleur upon which the old settlements grew up. Similar soils are found in north Gaspé but as smaller and much more isolated patches in a much more rugged terrain.

## III. The Laurentian Plateau

The whole of the Canadian Shield in Quebec is *terra incognita,* as far as soil types are concerned. By comparison with Ontario we may infer that the same broad divisions will apply, at least along the western border of Quebec.

South of James Bay lies the Podzol zone, but the soils are mainly wet zonal and intrazonal bog soils. The "clay belt" region of settlement in Abitibi county has *Peat-glei* and *podzol-glei* (groundwater podzol) soils while with better drainage, zonal Podzols develop. In the Timiskaming area the zonal soils are Brown Podzolic but weak Podzols develop on the dry sand plains. Close to Lake Timiskaming, however, in Quebec as in Ontario, there are wet intrazonal soils. Further south and east in the Laurentian Hills, the soils are mostly Brown Podzolic with some weak Podzols. The limitations of the soils were a major factor in delaying the settlement of the Laurentian Plateau. It has, however, been settled on its southwestern edge and in two interior basins: Western Quebec and the Lake St. John-Saguenay region.

### a) Laurentian Hills

The hills rise more or less abruptly above the St. Lawrence Lowlands and the north shore of the Estuary, from Pontiac county to the mouth of the Saguenay River. On the hills the soils have developed from glacial till and in the valley and lake bottoms from glacial outwash. The loams are less fertile than those of the Appalachians, because the parent material is composed mostly of intrusive rocks. The glacial moraine is acid and sandy. In places the farmers used to add clay as a fertilizer, as at St. Raymond and St. Basile in Portneuf county, for instance. On the heights of Joliette, Berthier and Maskinongé counties, there are fewer boulders than is the case in Beauce and

Frontenac counties. The outwash plains, found along the tributaries of the St. Lawrence, permitted settlement to take a good hold. They are less hilly than the surroundings and in many places afford sizable patches of fertile soils. They are "gates" to the interior. The best of these gates and the most convenient for transportation is located on the southwestern border of the Province, along the Ottawa River. In fact, the river itself flows in the Lowlands from Calumet Island to the Lake of Two Mountains. The southern parts of the bordering counties of Argenteuil, Papineau, Gatineau and Pontiac rise rapidly above the valley on Precambrian rocks. Pockets of good soils are found along that narrow corridor, two of which will serve as illustration. West of Hull, from Aylmer to Shawville in Pontiac county a deep loam, developed from a mixture of clay deposits and river sands, offers an ideal site for dairy farms; north of Papineauville and Montebello, back of the first ridges of the Shield, the same type of soil makes Ripon township a prosperous region, although to the eastward Petite Nation Seigniory is much more sandy.

Along the Gatineau and Lièvre Rivers tributaries of the Ottawa River, sandy alluvium is dominant while loams and clay are seldom met. But around Mont-Laurier in Labelle county, on the summit of the Laurentian peneplain (800 to 900 feet) another pocket of clay loam has been deposited along the upper course of Lièvre River, giving to that region soils that are comparable in fertility to those of Timiskaming, in Western Quebec. Settlement in Terrebonne County is mostly located along North River, where the loams are more sandy.

Eastward, between the St. Maurice and Saguenay Rivers the Laurentian Hills are very sparsely settled. The soil along the St. Maurice River looks poor, except in the surroundings of the cities of Shawinigan Falls and Grand'Mère; those along the Batiscan River are better, but large holdings of timber limits have prevented colonization in that direction. In Portneuf, Quebec and Montmorency counties, the rugged relief adds difficulties to the expansion of farm land. The heights of Charlevoix have been settled on a larger scale, because the valleys of the Goufre and Malbaie Rivers are filled with fertile alluvium; but the rolling peneplains above them have poorer farmlands because the sandy soils are acid, rocky, and likely to suffer from excessive erosion. On the North Shore, below Tadoussac, a narrow strip of fair soils is in the process of being settled as far as Baie Comeau.

## b) The Interior Basins

### 1. *Western Quebec*

This is a vast area near the Ontario Border from the Upper Ottawa River in Timiskaming county to Abitibi county in the North. Over ten million acres of farm land are found here, of which about one million are now occupied. Glacial clays were deposited in the great fresh water Lake Ojibway and Barlow, formed by the retreating glacier. The region forms the Quebec part of the *Clay Belt*. The best clay and clay loams are found near lakes Abitibi and Macamic in the west, along the Harricanaw River in the center in Dalquier township near Amos, and along the Bell River, where new settlements are progressing north of Senneterre. More sandy loams and patches of sand are located mostly in two sectors: one in Launay and Trecesson townships west of Amos, the other in Landrienne and Barraute east of Amos. The former soils are suited to grain and fodder crops for dairying, the latter are best suited for potatoes.

### 2. *Lake St. John - Saguenay*

The depression of Lake St. John and its outlet the Saguenay River forms an oasis for settlement carved into the hard Precambrian rocks. The site of the lake was invaded by the Champlain sea, and was consequently covered by its deposits. But powerful converging rivers have carried their load of sand over the clay after the emergence of the land.

About half of the occupied land is estimated to consist of clay loams. The best lands are distributed in a crescent south of the lake in Chambord, Roberval, St. Prime, St. Félicien and Albanel. Even there, sandy patches are noticeable. In the northeast, from Dolbeau to Alma, sandy loams are the dominant soil types. Muck and peat are also found. Along the Saguenay River the best farm land is around Chicoutimi on both shores, but the upper terraces are mostly sandy, while clay and clay loams form narrow strips below. About 1½ million acres are occupied in the whole region.

## The Physical Stage

The Province of Quebec is a vast area, more than twice the size of France, in which physical diversity sharply limits the possibilities of human occupance. More than nine-tenths of the surface is underlain by the Canadian Shield, rugged, rocky and with little depth of soil. The Appalachian Region, also, contains much rugged land. Only the St. Lawrence Lowland, an area of about 15,000 square miles, has the depth of soil and the gentleness of relief to encourage intensive agricultural settlement. Even here, there are wide plains of coarse, infertile sand. Fortunately, the lowland is also the area having the most favourable climate for human activity, while the St. Lawrence serves as a corridor into the heart of the country.

Quebec contains a wealth of natural resources. Fish, furs and, later, timber were in demand on European markets, encouraging colonial trade. A wealth of minerals in the Canadian Shield and the abundant water power of Quebec's great rivers awaited exploitation in the modern industrial age. With only a limited area of potentially arable land the people of Quebec have other ways of making a living. Thus the physical factors set the stage for the activities of man.

# Selected References

Anderson, R. M. *Faunas of Canada.* Canada Year Book. 1937.

Blanchard, R. *L'Est du Canada Français.* Beauchemin. Montreal. 1935.

Blanchard, R. *Le Centre du Canada Français.* Beauchemin. Montreal. 1947.

Blanchard, R. *L'Ouest du Canada Français.* Beauchemin. Montreal. 1951.

Brouillette, B. and Dagenais, P. *La Province de Québec (physique).* A wall map in ten colours, approx. scale: 16 miles to one inch. Beauchemin. Montreal. 1953.

Cann, D. B. and P. Lajoie. *Soil Survey of Stanstead, Richmond, Sherbrooke and Compton Counties in the Province of Quebec.* Experimental Farms Service. Canada Department of Agriculture. Ottawa. 1942.

Cann, D. B., P. Lajoie and P. C. Stobbe. *Soil Survey of Shefford, Brome and Missisquoi Counties in the Province of Quebec.* Experimental Farms Service. Canada Department of Agriculture. Ottawa. 1947.

Dresser, John A. and T. C. Denis. *Geology of Quebec.* Province of Quebec Department of Mines. Geological Report 20, 1944.

Fontaine, Charles A. *Les sols du Québec.* L'Actualité Economique. XVIIe année Vol. II- No. 5, pp. 401-42. mars, 1942.

Halliday, W. E. D. *A Forest Classification for Canada.* Forest Service Bulletin 89. Canada Department of Mines and Resources. Ottawa. 1940.

Hare, F. Kenneth. *Climate and Zonal Divisions of the Boreal Forest Formation in Eastern Canada.* Geographical Review, XL: 615-35. 1950.

Hills, G. A. *Pedology—the Dirt Science and Agricultural Settlement in Ontario.* Canadian Geographic Journal. Vol. 29: 106-127. 1944.

Polunin, N. *Botany of the Canadian Eastern Arctic.* National Museum of Canada Museum Bulletin 92, part 1. Canada Department of Mines and Resources. Ottawa. 1940.

Robinson, J. Lewis. *An Outline of the Canadian Eastern Arctic.* Canada Department of Mines and Resources. Ottawa. 1944.

Rousseau, L. Z. *La Classification des Terres.* Actualité Economique. Avril. 1938.

Thériault, J. E., Lucien Choinière et August Mailloux. *Les Sols du Comté de Bellechasse.* Ministère de l'Agriculture de la Province de Québec. 1942.

Villeneuve, G. Oscar. *Climatic Conditions of the Province of Quebec and their relationship to the Forests.* Bulletin No. 6. Meteorological Bureau, Forest Protection Service. Department of Lands and Forests. Quebec. 1946.

# CHAPTER 7

# Human Geography of Quebec
# The Spread of Settlement

## 1. The French Period

THE French explorers of the 16th century, amongst whom Jacques Cartier is the best known for his written account, established no permanent settlements. The real founder of New France was Samuel de Champlain, sent out by De Monts in 1608, who laid the foundation of the first permanent establishment at Quebec, "where the water narrows". Besides the extensive explorations that led him from the Atlantic coast (Acadia to New York) inland to Lake Huron, Champlain's main objective was to bring settlers from France and to induce them to cultivate the land. It was not an easy task. Nine years passed before he could bring out the first "colon canadien", Louis Hébert. He granted him a piece of land, near his "Abitation" (a fortified house), built on the present site of Quebec upper city. The crop of the ensuing year (1618) was admired by Champlain, who wrote that those "labourages" (tillage) yielded wheat and vegetable as nice as those of France. Other fields were opened at the foot of Cape Diamond, and another settler, Abraham Martin, gave his first name to the battle field (The Plains of Abraham) where the armies of Montcalm and Wolfe met in 1759.

The fur trade was more attractive than pioneer farming and moreover the Rouen Company (successor to De Mont's) did not fulfill its obligations to send colonists to Quebec. "They (the company officials) fear" wrote Champlain, "that, if the country were colonized, they would get furs only through the settlers and would finally be driven out of New France". At the founder's suggestion, Richelieu set up a new venture in 1627 known as "la Compagnie des Cent Associés". In that year seven ships and 200 emigrants were sent out but, war having broken out, the fleet was captured by the English before it reached Quebec. Quebec, itself, was taken by Kirke and was restored to French hands four years later.

Champlain returned with a few more colonists in 1632 and resumed the task with those that remained. When he died at Quebec on Christmas Day 1635, there were 85 adults living in the colony, 23 settlers, 20 fur trappers, 14 company clerks, 11 interpreters, 10 priests and 7 traders. It was a poor result for a quarter century of effort. However, foundations had been laid for Quebec and Beauport had permanent residents and Three Rivers, founded by La Violette in 1634, was an outpost upstream. Near Quebec the Jesuit Fathers and the Ursuline and Hospitaller nuns had received large grants of land. Robert Giffard's seigniory extended from Beauport, founded in 1634, to the Montmorency River. The Seigniory of Beaupré, granted to Cheffaut de la Regnardière, extended from Giffard's property to Baie St. Paul. Six other nobles also received large grants southwest of Quebec. Montreal Island, a few years later, was given to a pious company organized in France by de la Dauversière. The real founder of Montreal, however, was de Maisonneuve who in 1642 established a small group of settlers in defiance of the Iroquois warriors.

The first period of colonization closes with the return of the colony to the Royal power in 1663. By that time, 1,500 immigrants had arrived and 400 families were established on the land. Intendant Talon took the first known census and found 3,215 inhabitants in 1666. The immediate vicinity of Quebec, including the Beaupré coast and the Island of Orleans, held two-thirds of the population. The two other posts were isolated; Three Rivers at the mouth of the St. Maurice River and Montreal where the Lachine rapid stopped navigation upstream. The importance of that first period of settlement cannot be over-estimated. Those 3,000 people were the very nucleus of a new nation. They had adapted themselves to the environment and already had many children. Numerous later immigrants

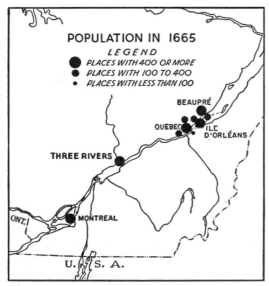

Figure 96. *Population of Quebec in 1665.* At the first census there were only 3,000 people in the colony, clustered close to the river at Quebec, Beaupré, Three Rivers and Montreal.

followed their example, lived and intermarried with them without much altering the fundamental type of the early colonist of New France.

Plate 32. Bilingual route signs in the province of Quebec remind the traveller of the historical background and diversity of population groups.

The mother country, France, knew that her colony could not thrive or even survive, if an impulse was not given to a larger settlement. A man of Champlain's character was needed. Talon was invested, as intendant, with extensive power of police, justice and finance. The second and most important period had begun. The increase of population, under his rule (1665-1673) was the largest during the whole French regime, and it gave the country a sound basis of existence. During the next 20 years over 2,500 immigrants came to New France. The census of 1683 (9,695) shows that the population had tripled since 1666. The surroundings of Quebec still held the greater part of the population, but the settlement was growing all along both sides of the St. Lawrence and along the Richelieu River. Pioneer agriculture and commerce were progressing and the administration of the colony was reorganized. The area under cultivation had grown from 11,448 arpents in 1667 to 26,669 in 1692; the cattle, from 3,107 head to 7,456; not including 400 horses and 4,000 sheep and swine for the latter census. The 1692 grain crop was estimated at 120,000 minots (bushels), 90,000 of which were wheat. There were some 43 mills (saw and grist mills), a shipyard at Quebec, and iron ore deposits were worked at Forges St. Maurice, near Three Rivers. Before his departure, Talon could write to the king that several kinds of woollen cloth were manufactured and tanneries supplied one-third of the leather required in the colony: "I have Canadian fabrics to dress myself from head to foot".

During the last 20 years of the 17th century, the number of immigrants dropped to 1,092, and to half that number (659) for the next 20 years. In spite of that the population numbered 25,000 inhabitants in 1721. The natural increase among the French Canadians was already high. The 10,000 mark was nearly reached in 1734. That census shows 163,111 acres of land under cultivation, 17,657 in pasture, a wheat crop of 738,000 bushels, and 33,119 cattle, 29,000 sheep, 5,000 horses. Tobacco, hemp and flax were also produced. Ships, built at the Quebec dockyards, were sold to the West Indies and carried loads of Canadian lumber there and to France.

More immigrants came to Canada after 1720, about 1,000 strong up to 1740, and a larger group afterwards, some 3,500, being mostly demobilized soldiers. The total of arrivals during the whole French period is estimated at 10,000; but the number of departures is also high, 3,000 to 4,000. Nevertheless, a population of 55,000 is registered for 1754, and of 70,000 six years later, when Canada passed under the British rule. The population was distributed in over 100 inhabited localities (figure 97). The area of

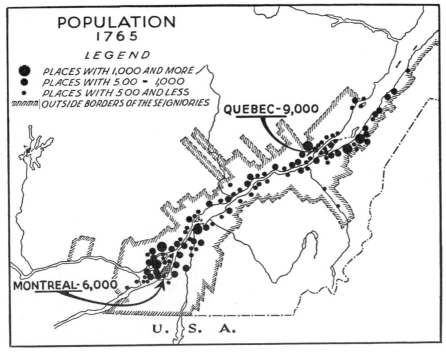

Figure 97. *Population of Quebec in 1765.* At the close of the French regime there were nearly 70,000 people in New France; Quebec and Montreal were fair-sized cities; the banks of the St. Lawrence were closely settled, and colonization was beginning along the Chaudiere and the Richelieu.

occupied farm land was 1,000,000 acres; there were 50,000 cattle, 13,500 horses, 28,000 sheep and 28,500 swine.

The policy of concentrating all settlements within a limited territory (Colbert's policy) was not carried out after Talon's departure. The exodus of *coureurs de bois* never slackened, despite penalties imposed upon these deserters. Moreover, far away settlements were founded along a line of military posts, stretching from the St. Lawrence to the Mississippi Valley: Fort Chartrain (Detroit), the Wabash, and Louisiana (New Orleans). France with 12,000,-000 people was at that time the most populous country of Europe; the British Isles with only 6,000,000 had raised the population of her colonies south of Canada to over one million inhabitants by 1750, while the intermittent French efforts and the adverse natural conditions had resulted in a handful of small communities distributed on the fringe of a huge, wild country.

## 2. The English Period

British rule imposed new conditions upon the expansion of settlement. The conquered people, the French, had already developed a strong society well adapted to their geographical habitat. The British who had overthrown the French rule merely to reduce the threat to their own colonies farther south were little interested in placing settlers in such a harsh environment. During the first ten years after the conquest, there were only a few hundred immigrants of British origin, including New England traders, demobilized soldiers and other adventurers. Most of them located in Quebec and Montreal where they hoped to reap fortunes in exploitive trade. Many of them remained but a short time and were replaced by a more responsible merchant class.

Their presence in the colony brought on a conflict between two ways of life which still seethes in the province of Quebec. On the one hand are the static rural habitants who live close to the soil and regard themselves as part of the land in which they live; on the other hand are the commercial urban dwellers who regard Mother Earth simply as a source of good things. In the beginning, of course, there was the further cleavage of language and religion, but in present day Quebec cities French Catholics far outnumber the English Protestants, and indeed outnumber their brethren on the farms.

Land tenure changed also with the new regime. Only eight new seigniories were granted from 1760 to 1824. A new land tenure was inaugurated in 1763, the holding in free and common socage. The land was distributed free to the new settlers; but they had to pay for surveying the townships and for their permits and letters-patent of the title. Township areas varied from 61,600 to 67,200 acres.

The first influx of immigrants to Canadian soil after the conquest was that of the Loyalists. Some 25,000 emigrated from the former British colonies after the American revolution, but few of them settled in Quebec. In 1784, a group of less than 2,000 was distributed as follows:

| | | |
|---|---|---|
| Montreal and surroundings | | 617 |
| Lachine " " | | 207 |
| St. Johns " " | | 379 |
| Chambly | | 136 |
| Sorel | | 95 |
| Baie de Chaleur | | 450 |

Another group of immigrants that came to reinforce the French about the time of the conquest was the Acadians, expelled from the Maritimes in 1755. "A few thousands" settled in the St. Lawrence Lowlands and along Chaleur Bay.

During the first quarter of a century of British rule, the population of Quebec more than doubled, from 69,810 in 1765 to 161,311 in 1790. The origin of the population was unrecorded for that census, but its geographical distribution by parishes shows only a small increase in their number (106 to 136) and a very limited territorial expansion, the most noteworthy being the southeastern part of the plain of

Montreal along the Chateauguay, Richelieu and Yamaska Rivers.

The expansion towards the southern part of the Eastern Townships was made possible by the Constitutional Act of 1791. The settlers were chiefly Loyalists, Vermonters and New Yorkers, many of whom had come as squatters before. Twenty years later (1814) some 27,000 settlers were established there, being mostly English speaking. That section of the country was the scene of land grabbing, not by the settlers who were not granted more than 1,200 acres each, much less in most cases, but by speculators, who were often government officials. In one instance, 1,425,000 acres were granted to sixty persons. A list of the first grantees, published in 1814, contains about 200 entries totalling over 3,000,000 acres of the best land.

The question might be raised why the French did not, like the British, settle in the townships. The answer is quite simple. Up to the end of the 18th century they had enough land within the seigniories, where they clustered near the old spires of their parishes. They were better off for transportation here along the river, and moreover they looked upon the townships as a stronghold of the English Protestants. The period of 1760-1800 was a crucial one for the very existence of the French group. "People could look back at forty years under an alien flag without excessive reason for complaint. They had their own laws, their system of landholding, their church. They were talking over their situation and discovering something of the first importance, that is to say, themselves. The discovery came as a great light. They had borne the storm wind of conquest and had survived."[1]

Survival for them was not enough. They were *enfants du sol* (children of the soil), but they wanted more of it at the beginning of the new century. Their leaders called attention to the fact that the old parishes were over populated; some had already emigrated south of the border, fore

[1] Lower, A. R. M. *Colony to Nation*, p. 153.

runners of many more to go. Biological expansion was taking place. The migration out of the Lowlands started at the very moment when, after the Napoleonic wars, Great Britain was sending out a second wave of British emigrants (1820-1850). Most of them, however, went to Upper Canada (Ontario).

By 1831 the total population of Lower Canada had reached 553,134. The ethnic elements are unknown for that census, but the Catholics numbered 422,807. Deducting some 20,000 Irish, we find that the French Canadians had grown from 161,000 in 1790 to about 400,000. Expansion had already begun outside the St. Lawrence Lowland which now held 78% of the total.

The most populous region, away from the shores of the St. Lawrence, was the Eastern Townships, equal in numbers to the old Three Rivers region. This was a stronghold of British settlers, especially in the five counties of Missisquoi, Stanstead, Sherbrooke, Shefford and Megantic, where 95% of the 38,650 inhabitants were Protestants. But the French penetration of the Townships was already slowly beginning. They were 12,000 strong in Beauce and 2,000 out of 3,500 in Drummond (Bois Francs region). Down the south shore of the estuary they had doubled their numbers in 40 years and were also migrating to the opposite shore and to the region along Chaleur Bay. In the latter region they had only a small majority. The Ottawa Valley had received a few settlers also, more than two-thirds of whom were British.

During the next thirty years, the population of Lower Canada was doubled, the census of 1861 recording a total of 1,111,546. The greatest increase was in the newer regions for the Lowlands now held only 64% of the inhabitants. The Eastern Townships had, by that time, almost twice the population of the Three Rivers region and even more than the region around the ancient capital at Quebec. While in the seven original counties, 83% of the population were of British stock, they were being grad ually and peacefully encircled by the French. To the northeast, Beauce, Dorchester and Arthabaska had large French majorities; so also had Wolfe and Megantic, two new counties in the heart of the region and, surprisingly enough, the old county of Shefford.

Another growing region was the South Shore of the Estuary (entirely French) which had doubled. Gaspé had tripled, and nearly half of its population was English. During the same period, the Laurentian Plateau was the principal area for settlement. In 30 years more than 100,000 settlers made an assault on its forests in search of living space. Half of them followed the old trail of the Ottawa Valley in the southwest; two-thirds of these were English speaking. Argenteuil, Ottawa and Pontiac counties were set up, Ottawa being the most densely populated. The Central and Eastern Laurentians had about 25,000 each: a sparsely distributed population, with small concentrations at both ends in Terrebonne and Charlevoix.

Lake St. John was the only interior region reached by both lumbermen and

Plate 33. Open air baking ovens are found in many parts of Quebec, a rather unique feature of the cultural pattern.

permanent settlers. It received 10,000 people. Down the Gulf, the long North Shore had a population of fishermen in summertime, some of whom decided to stay the year long in small and scattered groups.

The 1860 census results show that the French as a whole were leading by 77% over the other ethnical origins. By their cradles full of children they were keeping pace with the flood of immigrants, the most numerous of whom were still to come at the beginning of the next century.

During the last 40 years of the 19th century, the Quebec population increased by half a million people (1901: 1,649,000). Of that increase 200,000 took place in the Montreal region; but the percentage in the Lowlands (57%) was the smallest for any census. The expansion towards the Appalachians was still conspicuous, whilst the Laurentian Plateau, had doubled its population. That was the result of improved communications during the era of railway building. The Eastern Townships became two-thirds French and the English began to leave the region. They had a majority in 2 counties only: Brome and Stanstead, but they were still fairly numerous in other southern counties, including Compton, Sherbrooke, Shefford, Megantic, and Missisquoi.

The push towards the Laurentians was more spectacular: the western part more than doubled its population, while that of the central part had almost tripled. Along the Ottawa valley, the French had gained a majority in the two most populous counties of Wright (formerly Ottawa) and Labelle. But the English were leading at both ends of the region in Argenteuil and Pontiac. The enormous gain in the Central Laurentians was due to the colonization spirit of enthusiastic leaders such as Curé Labelle. Two counties stood out: Terrebonne, north of Montreal, and Champlain county between the St. Maurice and Batiscan Rivers. Another area which tripled its population was Lake St. John, where settlement took place in the fertile lands along the railway line which was built a few years before 1900.

Thus before the advent of modern industry, the French had increased their majority to 80% of the population. That result was partly due to the fertility of the people, but also to the fact that the former British settlers moved out to Ontario and the West. On the other hand, the French group itself lost a great many to the cotton factories of New England and elsewhere south of the border.

The 20th century is witnessing a great increase of population in Quebec as elsewhere in Canada. The whole population has doubled in 40 years, reaching 3-1/3 millions in 1941 and over 4,000,000 in 1952. It is not difficult to see why. Canada is no more a purely agricultural country. Tremendous industrial development has occurred in the central provinces of Ontario and Quebec. But the limits of settlement are still expanding; the Lowlands hold only 60% of the population, although most of the large cities are found here. The Appalachians (21%) and the Laurentians (19%) are now nearly equal in population. The Eastern Townships where the French are six times as numerous as the English, are still the leading region. Brome is the only county where the latter have a small majority. The South Shore of the Estuary has also doubled its population because of an inland expansion onto the plateau. Gaspé is settled all around the peninsula, but predominantly in the south. Industry is mainly responsible for the increase in the Central Laurentians, especially the St. Maurice valley, with the thriving cities of Shawinigan, Grand-Mère and LaTuque. The same is true for the Saguenay. A new region of settlement has also appeared in Western Quebec. Here there has been a pincer movement. The earlier prong was set in Timiskaming with the construction of the Angliers C.P.R. line while a few years later (1914) the National Transcontinental (C.N.R.) opened the Abitibi clay belt. Between the prongs the mining centres of Noranda and Rouyn grew up during the '20's, and Val d'Or in the '30's. More railways were built, and a highway network links these towns and villages to Montreal via the Central Laurentians (Mont-Laurier). Within the region both mining and agricultural populations are still expanding rapidly.

## Natural Increase

The natural increase of a population is a good yard stick of its vitality. The 240% expansion of the Quebec population since the Confederation is mostly due to its natural increase. This has varied considerably even in the last twenty years. It was 17.3 per 1,000 in 1926, dropped to 12.8 in 1937, but increased rapidly during the war and post-war years to 21.5 in 1950. The average for Canada was 17.9 in 1950. The Quebec birth rate (29.9 in 1950) is among the highest of the white race. The death rate, which was the highest in Canada (14.3 in 1926), had decreased to 8.4 in 1950, slightly below the average for the whole country (8.9 in 1950).

## Immigration During the 20th Century

How much of the Quebec increase of population is due to the immigrants? It is a difficult question to answer. According to the official statistics, Quebec should have received some 800,000 immigrants (about 14% of the Canadian total) between 1901 and 1951. It is likely that half of these newcomers have moved away. The British part of our population has not gained much from that influx, unless many of the older residents (290,108 in 1901) left the Province, because their actual number in 1951 (492,000) is in line with their rate of natural increase. Immigration has brought to Quebec people of other origins than British and French. Their number has increased from 36,500 in 1901 to 237,000 in 1951, 79% of them living in Montreal. They belong mainly to the following groups: Hebrew (31%), Italian

*Courtesy Canadian National Railways.*
Plate 34. St. Jean de Port Joli, a typical rural village along the St. Lawrence.

(14%), Polish (7%). Indians and Eskimos in 1951 numbered less than one per cent of the population.

### Rural and Urban Distribution

At the beginning of the 20th century the population of Quebec was 60% rural. In 1951 the urban population was over 67%. The distribution of rural and urban population by regions is very interesting. The Lowland was always the most urbanized region: more than half in 1901, 80% in 1951, the same percentage as the whole of England and Wales. The other regions in 1901 had over 80% of rural population. In 1951, only the Appalachians still held two-thirds of the population on the land, while the Laurentian industrial centres had attracted 44% of the people of that region. Let us explain what rural and urban population means to the geographer.

### The Rural Habitat

The rural habitat in Quebec is a dispersed one due to the main ways of living: farming, lumbering, fishing and hunting. The dispersion of the houses is explained by the fact that each family of farmers lives on the piece of land tilled by its members. Each lot is divided on the cadaster as a long strip one mile deep and 600-700 feet wide on the front road. The property is fenced all around and the fields are subdivided in-

side according to their use. Fences along the roads and between each field are required to keep the cattle away from cultivated fields. The farmer's residence is a wooden house, one or two stories high, built very close to the road and surrounded by other separate buildings such as a large barn, a stable, a few sheds. The buildings are scattered to prevent disaster by fire.

The dispersed pattern shows a trend towards agglomeration along "double ranges". That means two parallel ranges served by a single road, both sides of which have rows of houses. The pattern and the narrowness of the land strips bring the houses closer together and tend to break the isolation of the inhabitants. The centre of each community is a village, where the functions of the inhabitants are h a l f w a y between the rural and urban life. The villages have grown around a social or economic nucleus, such as the church and the schools, the railway station, a few small industrial plants, or a wharf. The inhabitants living on small lots, are mostly laborers, traders, retired farmers, and so on. They may be looked upon as part of the rural population. But if the village is incorporated as a separate municipality, its population is computed as urban in the census. There were some 336,000 people living in such villages in 1951; so 8% should be added to the rural population.

## The Urban Habitat

The cities and towns have drawn more than half of the Quebec population during the last 50 years. The industrial development is mostly responsible for the agglomeration since factory workers must live near the plants where they are employed. The older commercial function has also grown tremendously during the twentieth century with the development of harbours, tend to draw more and more rural inhabitants toward modern cities.

The cities and towns of over 10,000 inhabitants now contain about half of the population of Quebec. The greater cities of Montreal and Quebec contain more than 60% of the urban population, while Montreal itself contains more than one-quarter of the total population of the province. Apart from these there were in

*Photographic Survey Corporation Limited.*

Plate 35. The spreading metropolis. A new subdivision at Cartierville, P. Q.

railways, highways and airways. The handling and storing of goods and merchandise employs many city dwellers, so also do the associated functions of selling in the wholesale and retail trades, banking, insurance and other financial business. Large cities show their chief functions by their geographic divisions or zones; in Montreal, for instance, there is a business section centred on St. James street, a wholesale area near the Harbour, a retail district along St. Catherine Street, as well as various types of residential areas. Other than commercial functions serve to attract people to cities, such as professional duties, teaching, religion and administration. All these factors

1951, twenty-two other cities and towns of more than 10,000. Most of these are in the older regions, but there are also newer ones such as Rouyn-Noranda, Arvida, Jonquiere and Chicoutimi.

## Population Density

It is geographical nonsense to state that the population density of Quebec is 7.74 to the square mile. To begin with, out of all the vast area of the province, less than 30,000 square miles are effectively occupied, so that on the basis of the 1951 census figures, the average density of the occupied land is 135 per square mile. The five largest cities, including their suburbs, with a

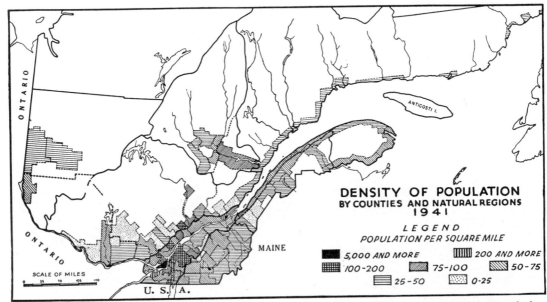

**Figure 98.** *Density of Population in Quebec in 1941.* By far the largest part of Quebec's population is found in the south-central section contained in the St. Lawrence Lowland and the Eastern Townships. Important concentrations are located, also, in the Saguenay, Ottawa, and Western Quebec areas.

total area of 135 square miles, held a population of 1,845,000 having an average density of 13,700 per square mile. The remaining open country and smaller urban places, then, have an average density of 65 per square mile. If we subtract the populations of all urban places of over 10,000 inhabitants, we bring our average density down to about 60 per square mile for the year 1951.

Even this average density is meaningless, however, for nowhere in Quebec except in the St. Lawrence Lowland is the land fully occupied. One-third of the land in the Eastern Townships is unoccupied, two-thirds of the South Shore plateau and 85% of Gaspe are also empty. The accompanying map is based upon the densities of the areas occupied by municipal units, although in many cases these contain a good deal of unoccupied land.

### Ways of Living

Type of occupation is a good indication of what the human geographer calls "the way of living." In Quebec in 1951 slightly more than half of the population of 14

years and over were gainfully occupied. This force of one and one-half millions were distributed amongst the major groups of occupations as shown in the following table.

**Table 4    Labour force by Industry in Quebec, 1951**

| | |
|---|---|
| Manufacturing, Power and Construction | 38.6% |
| Transportation, Trade and Finance | 21.6% |
| Service | 19.8% |
| Agriculture | 13.2% |
| Mining, Forestry and Fishing | 4.8% |
| Not stated | 2.0% |
| | 100.0% |

There is great difference in the returns from different types of activity. Lacking figures on average incomes, we may gain some insight into the problem from a consideration of the values of production of various industries.

**Table 5    Net values of Production in Quebec**

|                | 1939 | | 1945 | | 1951 | |
|                | $000 | Per Cent | $000 | Per Cent | $000 | Per Cent |
|----------------|------|----------|------|----------|------|----------|
| Agriculture    | 105.286 | 13.6 | 209,834 | 12.6 | 375,110 | 11.4 |
| Forestry       | 31,843 | 4.1 | 81,824 | 4.9 | 149,767 | 4.6 |
| Fisheries      | 1,690 | 0.2 | 4,988 | 0.3 | 3,376 | 0.1 |
| Trapping       | 1,081 | 0.1 | 3,364 | 0.2 | 2,350 | 0.1 |
| Mining         | 48,561 | 6.3 | 59,238 | 3.6 | 164,881 | 5.0 |
| Electric Power | 56,121 | 7.3 | 80,350 | 4.8 | 129,474 | 3.9 |
| Manufactures   | 470,385 | 60.7 | 1,149,391 | 69.2 | 2,083,934 | 63.4 |
| Construction   | 60,007 | 7.7 | 72,800 | 4.4 | 376,148 | 11.5 |
| Totals         | 774,974 | 100.0 | 1,661,789 | 100.0 | 3,285,040 | 100.0 |

Dominion Bureau of Statistics

Agriculture employs about one-seventh of the labour force to produce an average share of 10% of the total net value, logging and mining employ less than five per cent of the labour force but produce one-tenth of the total while manufacturing and construction with less than 40% of the labour force account for over two-thirds of the productivity. Obviously, there are differences in the use of capital and in other costs as well but it is plain that the agricultural worker must accept a lower wage than the worker in industry.

There are interesting facts to be learned about the distribution of the workers. In the first place, nearly two-thirds of them are located in the St. Lawrence Lowland, the balance being divided about equally between the Appalachians and the Laurentian plateau. In the second place, it must be noted that the Lowland has three-fourths of the industrial workers, but only one-third of the farm workers. The latter are more numerous in the Appalachians where 40% are located, leaving 26% to be found in the Laurentians. The workers engaged in the exploitive industries (logging, mining, fishing, etc.) are rather few in the Lowland (11.4%), one-third being in the Appalachians and more than half in the Laurentian region. All other workers are, by an overwhelming majority, to be found in the Lowland.

### Human Geography Summary

The colony founded in this country 350 years ago by the French has shown remarkable growth. Left alone after the British conquest of Canada, the French have withstood the tide of immigration and make up more than 80% of the present population. The ecumene or living space has been expanded from both shores of the St. Lawrence into the interior. Detached areas in the Saguenay-Lake St. John region and in the Clay Belt have also been occupied.

Before the twentieth century, Quebec had a predominantly rural population. This century has seen a tremendous population shift. Only one-quarter of the workers are engaged in agriculture and the exploitive industries, the rest are found in occupations which are mainly located in the big cities.

Rural population densities remain low, perhaps even lower than in the last century. Mechanization has released many farm workers for industrial jobs or for the colonization of the frontiers. Thus the population of Quebec faces many changes in social behaviour which will have their effect upon the future patterns of human geography.

## Selected References

Caron, Ivanhoe. *Colonization in the Province of Quebec under French Domination* (1608-1760). Province of Quebec Statistical Year Book, pp. 2-101. 1915.

Caron, Ivanhoe. *Colonization in the Province of Quebec under English Domination.* Province of Quebec Statistical Year Book, pp. 18-37, 1916.

*Census of Canada.* Dominion Bureau of Statistics. Ottawa.

Gérin, Léon. *Le type économique et social des canadiens.* Montreal. 1937.

Hughes, E. C. *French Canada in Transition.* University of Chicago Press. Chicago. 1943.

Lanctot, Gustave. *The Founding of French Canada.* Chap. III in *Canada,* edited by Geo. W. Brown. University of Toronto Press. 1950.

Langlois, Georges. *Histoire de la population canadienne-française.* Editions Albert Levesque. Montreal. 1934.

Lower, A.R.M. *Colony to Nation.* Longmans, Green and Company. Toronto. 1946.

Miner, Horace. *St. Denis—a French-Canadian Parish.* University of Chicago Press. Chicago, 1939.

*Notre Milieu.* (Edited by Esdras Minville) Troisième Partie. *Le Milieu Humain.* École des Hautes Études Commerciales. Montreal. 1942.

*Province of Quebec Statistical Year Book.* Published by the Minister of Trade and Commerce. (Annual).

*Survey of Production,* Dominion Bureau of Statistics, Ottawa.

Wade, Mason. *The French-Canadian Outlook.* The Viking Press. New York. 1946.

# CHAPTER 8

# Economic Geography of Quebec

QUEBEC is the second most populous province in Canada and is also second in the economic field, accounting for about 26% of the net production per annum. On the average, more than two-thirds of this wealth is produced by the manufacturing industries, but agriculture, forestry, mining and the generation of electric power are highly important, not only for the value of their primary products but as a basis for the development of manufacturing.

## Agriculture

Although now outranked by manufac-

turing as an employer of labour, agriculture was, and still is, a fundamental way of living. Without the development of a colonial agriculture, permanent settlement of New France would have been impossible. In the closed family economy of the past, subsistence farming was the rule and there was little for sale. Modern agriculture, however, feeds large cities, supplies raw material for great industries and provides bulky freight to be transported over widespread railroad and highway systems. Moreover, the rural population functions as a source of labour and as a market for manufactured goods.

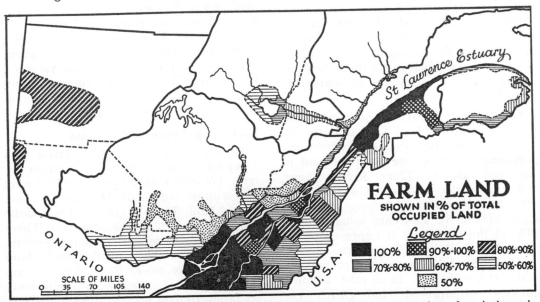

Figure 99. *Distribution of Occupied Farm Land in Quebec.* Note the concentration of agriculture in the lowland.

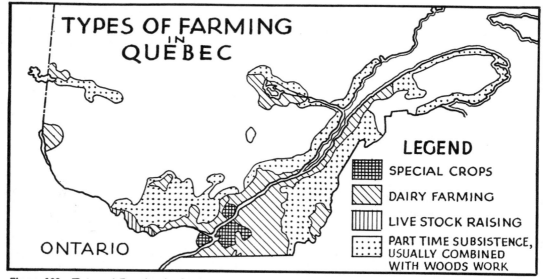

Figure 100. *Types of Farming in Quebec.* Dairying and special crops are concentrated in the Montreal region. The hilly, partly forested Appalachian and Laurentian borderlands have a great deal of part-time and subsistence agriculture.

## Agricultural area and wealth

Since Confederation the area of farmland in Quebec has increased from 11,000,-000 to 17,000,000 acres, of which 9,000,000 are under cultivation. Field crops occupy over 6,000,000 acres and pasture lands over 2,500,000 acres, the balance being devoted to gardens, orchards, etc. Woodlots occupy two-thirds of the unimproved land while most of the remainder is in natural pasture. Nearly 1,000,000 acres are in marsh or waste land.

The highest density of both occupied land and improved land is found in the St. Lawrence Lowland. Around Montreal approximately 75% of the occupied land is improved, around Three Rivers about 68% and in the vicinity of Quebec about 58%. In the narrow zone along the south shore of the St. Lawrence estuary, over 60% of the farm land is improved while in both the Eastern Townships and in the Lake St. John region the proportion is almost exactly 50%. In all other regions, however, unimproved land greatly exceeds the improved area.

Farm values have not changed much since 1911 when total farm capital was estimated at $788,000,000. In the post-war inflation periods of 1921 and 1945, total farm wealth was over one billion dollars. The figure now stands at $1,166,700,000 made up as follows: Land and buildings, $718,500,000; Implements and machinery, $121,900,000; Live stock, $326,300,000. The average Quebec farm is worth about $8,700 but, of course, regional variation is very great. The average farm near Montreal is worth over $12,000 while one in Gaspé averages less than $2,000.

## Farm Population and Income

In 1951 there were 134,336 farms with a population of 767,000 or 5.7 persons per farm. For each person there were 21.9 acres of occupied land and 11.5 acres of improved land. There is great regional variation in land use. In the Montreal, Three Rivers and Eastern Townships regions, there is considerable specialization in dairy and other live stock. Near Montreal are many specialized vegetable, fruit and poultry farms. In most other regions subsistence farms are the most numerous group. In 1951, total cash income amounted to $433,-

000,000 while net farm income was estimated at $337,000,000, which is somewhat more than $2,000, per farm. Naturally the income of a specialized dairy farmer is much higher, while that of a subsistence farmer is much lower, than this average figure.

### Agricultural Products

The gross value of agricultural production in Quebec was half a billion dollars in 1951, about 16% of the Canadian total. The production of animals and animal products provides over 79% of the returns.

Field crops to be fed to animals are the most important, averaging 6,500,000 acres in area in recent years. About two-thirds of this is devoted to hay, with an average yield of nearly 4,000,000 tons, valued at $80,000,000. About 2,000,000 acres are sown to spring grains each year; usually about three-fourths of this is oats, the rest is mixed grain, barley and buckwheat valued at $75,000,000. Alfalfa, fodder corn and root crops cover about 260,000 acres, producing forage valued at about $15,000,000 annually.

For human food about 150,000 acres of potatoes, 75,000 acres of green and dry vegetables and 25,000 acres of spring wheat are grown, besides fruits and other edible products. These items are valued at about $40,000,000.

The chief industrial crops include 10,000 acres of tobacco grown, mainly, in Joliette, 5,000 acres of fibre flax in Vaudreuil and Soulanges and 10,000 acres of sugar beets in the Richelieu Valley adding 5 millions more to the value of production.

### Dairying

Cattle were introduced in 1629 and for 250 years milk and milk products were made and consumed on farms. The first cheese factory was established in Missisquoi county in 1865 and the first butter factory near Huntingdon in 1873. In 1900 cheese was the more important product since it was then a better staple for export. After World War I butter became predominant due to the increasing urban demand and improved handling facilities. The fluid milk trade also increased rapidly and now takes about 30% of all milk produced; 48% is made into butter, the output of which is about 100,000,000 pounds, 4% goes into the making of 20,000,000 pounds of cheese and 8% into the manufacture of concentrated products and ice cream. The farm value of dairy production doubled during World War II, reaching a total of $150,000,000 in 1951.

### Live Stock Production

In 1951 the value of the cattle, sheep and lambs, hogs, poultry and eggs sold off Quebec farms amounted to over $220,000,000,

*Courtesy Canadian National Railways.*

Plate 36. An agricultural landscape along the St. Lawrence.

consisting of 350,000 cattle and calves, 1,000,000 hogs, 120,000 sheep and lambs, and $43,000,000 worth of eggs and poultry meat. The outstanding areas for cattle production are the Eastern Townships and the Ottawa Valley; hogs are widespread, but particularly important south of the St. Lawrence in Quebec and Three Rivers' regions and in the Lake St. John district; sheep are raised in the counties of Beauce, Temiscouata and Lake St. John; poultry is most common near Montreal.

Fur farming is carried on mainly in the Eastern Laurentians and Lake St. John-Saguenay region, foxes and mink being the most important. Pelts and breeding stock to the value of about $1,000,000 are sold annually.

**Other Farm Products**

Gardens and orchards provide substantial revenues. Vegetable gardens for household use are found on most farms while there are also specialized market gardens which, near the larger cities, usually have considerable space under glass. In 35 years the area of market garden has expanded fourfold, now extending over 52,000 acres. The chief crops are tomatoes, sweet corn, green peas, cabbage and cauliflower which are either sold fresh on the city markets or sent to canning plants. The output of the market gardens is worth about $9,000,000 per year while the value of canned goods has grown to about $20,000,000 since World War II.

Apples, strawberries, raspberries and blueberries are grown in Quebec. The apple orchards, located chiefly on the lower slopes of the Monteregian Hills, produce about 3,000,000 bushels annually, about one-third of the supply needed by the local markets. The Island of Orleans and the Beaupré Coast near Quebec specialize in the production of small fruits but the production of 7,000,000 to 8,000,000 quarts per annum is insufficient for the local market. During World War II the gathering of blueberries for the American market be-

came important in the Lake St. John region.

Quebec produces about 90% of the maple products of Canada, over 2,000,000 pounds of sugar and 2 to 3 million gallons of syrup. Although the sugar maple (*Acer saccharum*) is widespread, the greatest production comes from the northern part of the Eastern Townships and the edge of the central Laurentians in Joliette and Montcalm counties.

Forest products form an important source of farm revenue, amounting to $75,000,000 in 1951. Fire wood accounts for half of this and the remainder is made up of pulpwood, sawlogs, fence posts and miscellaneous wood products.

**The Quebec Farmer and His Aims**

The Quebec farmer is often regarded as the genuine counterpart of the European peasant in a North American environment. Of medium height, strong and sturdy he is usually surrounded by numerous children. He knows his job well and is versatile, becoming, if the occasion demands, a carpenter, a blacksmith, a mechanic or even an electrician. Reliable and steady in his work, hospitable and friendly, he is also conservative and stubborn. Though he works hard most of the time he enjoys himself during the numerous festivities.

Although formerly ignorant and a slave of routine, the habitant has been awakened in the 20th century. The new generation is better educated and most of the younger farmers have had some training in agricultural schools. Agricultural societies and co-operative marketing associations have made great progress. Co-operative people's banks, founded in 1906, are largely used by farmers. A provincial farm credit system, established in 1936, has been of great benefit.

Agriculture in Quebec is in a state of rapid transition. Mechanization and specialization are taking place. There is a keen lookout kept for new cash crops such as tobacco, sugar beets and flax and the use of commercial fertilizers is being extended.

Behind the farmer stands the provincial department of agriculture which has more than doubled its expenditure in recent years. The department looks after the farm credit bureau, the rural electrification office, the dairy industry commission and the Quebec sugar refinery. Among the technical services provided are extension, agricultural education, horticulture, field husbandry, animal husbandry, health of animals, rural economy, rural engineering and home economics. Expert guidance in all these fields is provided to help the Quebec farmer to solve his problems in order to place his agriculture on a level with that of the rest of the continent.

## Forestry

Forestry and its related industries rank next to agriculture in the Quebec economy, employing 120,000 workers and providing a livelihood for 500,000 people. As raw material for pulp and paper mills, sawmills and other wood-using industries, in recent years the annual timber cut has exceeded a value of $250,000,000, while the gross value of wood products has been more than $650,000,000 per annum.

### Forest Area and Resources

With more than 345,000 square miles, Quebec contains the largest area of forest in Canada. Productive forests are estimated to contain 200,000 square miles, of which only 126,000 square miles of forest are presently accessible. Forests cover 61% of the territory of Quebec with 50% in a productive state but only 21% at present accessible. The area of economic forest, is, then, six times as large as the farm land which occupies only 3.6% of the area of the province.

The accessible forests of Quebec are estimated to contain 46,000 million cubic feet of softwood and 18,000 million feet of hardwood. Stated in another way there are 41,000 million f.b.m. of softwood saw timber and 453 million cords of smaller material, 14,000 million f.b.m. of hardwood saw timber and 176 million cords of smaller material. Quebec possesses one-third of the total volume of accessible timber in Canada. British Columbia has more than twice as much saw timber, but much less small material, while Ontario, the closest rival, has about the same amount of saw timber but somewhat less of the smaller timber.

Most important are the regions located in the Canadian Shield, containing 85% of the productive area and the same percentage of the softwood resources. The two outstanding regions are the Lake St. John-Saguenay and the North Shore, comprising

National Film Board.

Plate 37. Logging in Quebec. Logs are hauled by sled trains to the frozen rivers where they are piled to await spring break-up.

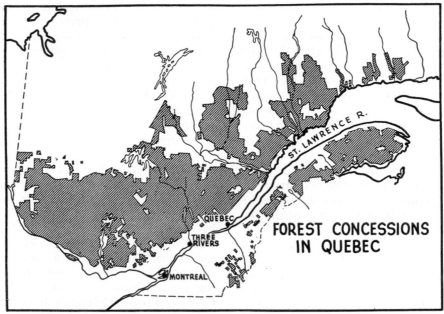

Figure 101. *Forest Concessions in Quebec.* The shaded areas on this map represent the extent of crown land leased by the Quebec government to lumber and pulpwood operators.

one-third of the area and one-half of the total volume of softwood. The Central and Western Laurentians and Western Quebec are also important while Gaspé and the Lower St. Lawrence still hold considerable reserves. The lowland is devoid of good timber while the forests of the Eastern Townships and the South Shore have been largely depleted.

Almost four-fifths of the accessible forest area is held as Crownland, of which three-fourths is made up of "Timber Limits" leased and operated by pulp and paper and lumber companies. The government requires these companies to prepare and adhere to scientific programs of forest exploitation. There are numerous small township reserves and domanial forests which are mostly exploited by farmers and settlers as a source of firewood and building material. Special cutting regulations are enforced and the sale of the wood is forbidden. Other special cutting permits are granted for the exploitation of vacant forest lands. These are granted after enquiry

and are mostly concerned with the salvage of burned timber.

Privately held forest lands are divided among farmer's woodlots, small holdings by lumbering companies and a few large company holdings. Here many of the government cutting regulations do not apply and private forests tend to be rapidly depleted.

The accompanying table No. 6 shows the areas of forest under different types of tenure in Quebec.

### Table 6   Tenure of the Accessible and Productive Forested Lands of Quebec

| *Crownlands:* | *Area in sq. miles* |
|---|---:|
| Timber limits (Pulp & Paper) | 71,614 |
| Timber limits (Lumber) | 8,408 |
| Township reserves | 2,828 |
| Domanial forests | 2,374 |
| Indian and military reserves | 296 |
| Special reserves | 752 |
| Colonization lots available | 3,000 |
| Vacant forest lands | 10,894 |
| | 101,166 |

*Privately-owned forests:*

| | |
|---|---:|
| Large company holdings | 8,517 |
| Small holdings by farmers | 9,709 |
| Other small holdings | 6,891 |
| *Total privately-owned forests* | 25,117 |
| *Total area of accessible and productive lands* | 126,283 |

## Forest Production

Quebec is the greatest producer of wood in Canada, producing almost as great a volume as British Columbia and Ontario together. In recent years the average cut has been about 1,000,000,000 cubic feet with an average annual value of more than $250,000,000. The volume of pulpwood is normally about twice as large as that of saw logs. Approximately two-thirds of the wood comes from the Laurentian Plateau and one-third from the Appalachian Highlands. Pulpwood cut on Crown lands accounts for about 80% of the production in the Central Laurentians and the Lake St. John regions. Lumber comes largely from Western Quebec, Western Laurentians, the Eastern Townships and the plateau south of the estuary. The distribution of pulp and paper mills and sawmills is in close agreement. More than 44,000 men are engaged in logging operations alone in Quebec each year.

## The Pulp and Paper Industry

While classed as a manufacturing industry, the making of pulp and paper is very closely connected with the cutting of wood being, frequently, part of the same enterprise. Amongst the 40 leading industries of Quebec, the pulp and paper industry stands

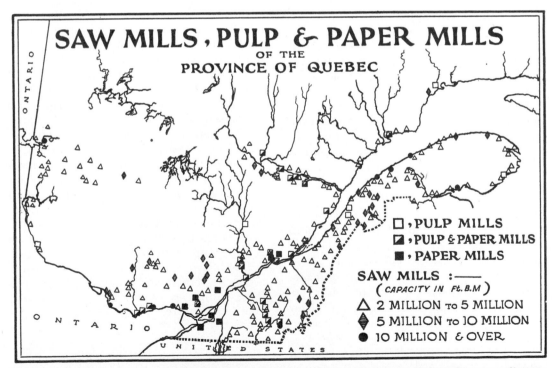

Figure 102. *Distribution of Sawmills and Pulp and Paper Mills in Quebec.* Small sawmills are well scattered over the southern part of the province and in Western Quebec. Pulp and paper mills are found chiefly along the larger rivers which furnish power and transportation for logs.

first. In 1951 there were 55 establishments with 24,500 employees and a gross value of production of $524,000,000.

Pulp and paper mills are large plants but they are rather decentralized, often being found in small centres near the source of wood supplies. The leading region is the St. Maurice Valley which gets its wood from the central Laurentians. Three Rivers, with four plants, is the pulp and paper capital. There are mills also at Shawinigan, Grand'Mère and La Tuque. The second region is Lake St. John-Saguenay, with plants at Kénogami, Jonquière, Port Alfred, Riverbend and Dolbeau. In the Ottawa valley there are plants at Gatineau, Hull, Buckingham, Masson and Kipawa. The Eastern Laurentian region supplies plants at Quebec city, Donnacona, Ste. Anne de Beaupré and Murray Bay; while far down the North Shore there are plants at Baie Comeau and Clarke City. The old section in the Eastern Townships has mills at East Angus, Bromptonville and Windsor Mills. There is one plant at Chandler in the Gaspé Peninsula. There are several plants in the Montreal region at St. Jerome, Lachute, Mont Rolland, Joliette and Beauharnois.

Pulp making is the first stage in the manufacture of pulp and paper. Most of the wood cut in the province is made into pulp in the local mills, but a small amount is sold to mills in Ontario and United States. In 13 years (1939-51 inclusive) the production of pulp rose from 2,100,000 tons valued at $49,000,000 to 4,300,000 tons worth $300,000,000. About four-fifths of the pulp is further processed into paper in Quebec mills which produce 3,500,000 tons, about half of all the paper made in Canada. Eighty-two per cent of the total is newsprint which is in great demand in New York, Chicago and other large American cities. The United States takes about 93% of the Canadian output and Great Britain most of the rest. Newsprint is the largest single item in the list of Canadian exports.

## The Lumber Industry

The lumber industry is much older than the pulp and paper industry and, while for over 50 years, Quebec has taken second place to British Columbia, Quebec mills turn out about 18% of the Canadian total. About 2,300 small mills, employing 20,000 men produced over 1,250,000,000 f.b.m. besides a quantity of other wood products in 1951. The total value of sawmill products was about $83,000,000, slightly less than one-third of the value of the pulp production. Nearly one-half of the lumber is exported while the rest goes into construction or into the secondary wood-using industries which are expanding in Quebec.

## Forest Conservation

Forestry is highly important in Quebec and it is necessary to maintain the forests in a state of equilibrium between depletion and increment. The provincial government is trying to enforce scientific methods of cutting on all Crown lands, but over exploitation may still take place on private holdings. Forest fires, insects and diseases constitute the greatest dangers. Over 6,000 square miles of timber land has been burned in the last twenty years. Large tracts of forest have been destroyed by the larch sawfly and spruce bud worm. Quebec maintains a vast protective service, research station, ranger school and forest tree nurseries. Research and education in forest problems is also carried on at McGill and Laval universities. Research is also needed in the social aspects of forest exploitation. For a large part of Quebec, the forest is more important than agriculture in providing a living for the inhabitants. In such areas a permanent cooperation between these industries should be set up to safeguard the future.

# Mining

The discovery of gold and copper in Western Quebec during the 1920's raised

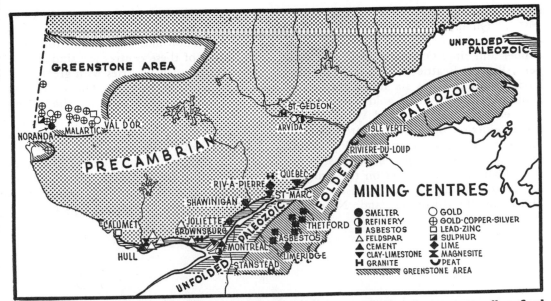

**Figure 103.** *Mining Centres and Mineral Industries in Quebec.* Metallic minerals are pretty well confined to Western Quebec, the non-metallic minerals are obtained chiefly in the southern part of the province. The iron area of the Lake Plateau and the Allard Lake titanium area are shown in Figure 39.

Quebec to second place in mineral production. Now outranked only by Ontario, the value of Quebec's mineral production in 1952 was over $260,000,000, ten times as great as in 1926, before the opening of the new mining camps. Mining provides work for more than 25,000 men. Metals account for nearly half of the total value, industrial minerals for about one-third, the remainder being made up of building materials. The important metals in order of value are: copper, gold, zinc, silver, lead, selenium, and molybdenum. The important non-metallics are: asbestos, dolomite, sulfur, titanium dioxite, quartz and peat moss. The structural materials include cement, clay products, sand and gravel, stone and lime.

### Mining Districts

Two natural regions stand out in mineral production: Western Quebec with 50% and the Eastern Townships with 28.5%. The rest is divided amongst the St. Lawrence Lowlands, the Ottawa Valley, the South Shore, Gaspé and Saguenay.

*Western Quebec* produces nearly all the gold and copper of the province and 75% of the zinc and silver as well as substantial quantities of pyrites, molybdenite, selenium, arsenic and lead. Mineral occurrences are most abundant in the area where the belts of Keewatin volcanics and Timiskaming sedimentaries have been intruded by belts of Algoman granite rocks. These rocks had already given Ontario a number of famous mines when claim staking started in Quebec in 1923. So rich were the finds that the Noranda smelter was opened in 1927. Two branch railways were built, linking with the C.N.R. at Taschereau and westward to the O.N.R. at Swastika, Ontario. Ten years later another branch line was built eastward from Noranda through Malartic and Val d'Or to Senneterre on the C.N.R. Three modern towns have grown from mining camps scattered in the bush: the twin-cities of Noranda-Rouyn (25,000), Malartic (6,000) and Val d'Or (9,000). There are thirty producing mines, the most important being clustered in three notable areas. Around Noranda-Rouyn there are ten, including Horne, producing about 46% of Quebec's gold and about 63% of the copper; Waite-Amulet, producing gold, copper and zinc; Quemont (gold and copper), Rouyn, Beattie and others. The Malartic group contains six mines producing about 22% of the total gold output. The most easterly group, around Val d'Or, began production in 1936. Here are five gold mines including Lamaque and Sigma and one gold, copper and zinc mine, East Sullivan. There are two mines on the margins of the gold fields; Belleterre, east of Ville Marie in Timiskaming, and Normetal,

portant centres of production are Asbestos, Thetford Mines, Black Lake, Coleraine, Robertson and East Broughton. The landscapes of these centres are similar, featuring huge open quarries with great pyramids of debris beside them. On windy days great clouds of gray dust fill the atmosphere.

The production of asbestos began in 1878, reached 100,000 tons in 1910, 200,000 tons in 1923, and nearly one million tons in 1952. In order to obtain this amount of raw asbestos about 12,000,000 tons of rock has to be moved, making an ugly mark on

D. F. Putnam.

Plate 38. Asbestos workings at Thetford Mines, P. Q.

(copper and gold) north of La Reine on the Transcontinental railway.

The *Eastern Townships* region is outstanding for the production of asbestos, producing over 80% of the world supply. The only other important sources are in the U.S.S.R. and South Africa. Asbestos is found in the serpentine belt of igneous rocks intruded during Lower Devonian time. The best asbestos comes from the chrysotile variety of serpentine, localized at the crests of the major anticlines. Asbestos is found in veins within the serpentine. The veins are numerous, varying from half an inch to more than three inches in width and up to 50 or 100 feet in length. The im-

the landscape. Most of the raw material is exported to the U.S.A. with some going to Great Britain and other countries. About 10% is made into consumers' goods in Canada, including roofing, insulating and fire proofing materials.

Other minerals produced in the Eastern Townships include industrial lime, granite and marble, building stone, soapstone, chromite and copper.

In the *St. Lawrence Lowland* the production of building materials is important. Montreal produces about 33% of the cement made in Canada; limestone is quarried on Montreal and Jesus Islands, and at Joliette, Three Rivers and St. Marc; La-

Prairie is noted for clay products, and iron oxide is found near Three Rivers.

The last region to be mentioned is the *Ottawa Valley*. Zinc, lead, silver and a small percentage of gold are obtained from a mine on Calumet Island. The industrial mineral include magnesitic dolomite and brucite at Wakefield and Grenville; quartz, industrial sand, feldspar and mica at Buckingham, besides a small production of phosphate and kaolin in the same district.

Peat deposits are worked in many places but especially near Rivière du Loup. A fine grained black granite is obtained from St. Gedeon east of Lake St. John.

### Iron

Iron mining and smelting were established by Intendant Talon near Three Rivers and remained important up to the end of the nineteenth century. Quebec has recently become an important producer of iron ore from the vast deposits in Northern Quebec. The occurrence of iron on the Lakes Plateau was reported by A. P. Low in 1885 but little attention was paid to it until the 1940's. More than 500,000,-000 tons of high grade ore has been located. In order to exploit it, a railway from the north shore has been built and nearby supplies of power developed. The output is expected to reach 10,000,000 tons per year.

A large deposit of ilmenite, an iron-titanium ore has been discovered at Allard Lake, 25 miles north of Havre St. Pierre. A railway was built to a dock at this port. A smelting industry has been set up at Sorel to handle 1,500 tons of ore per day.

### Mineral Industries

Quebec has a very important aluminum industry which places Canada next to the U.S.A. as a producer of this useful light metal. This is because of the abundance of waterpower. In 1904 an aluminum reduction plant was built at Shawinigan Falls on the St. Maurice River and in 1926 an-

other was built at Arvida on the Saguenay. During World War II, the latter became the greatest aluminum producing centre in the world. The ores used are bauxite from British and Dutch Guiana and cryolite from Greenland.

Copper ores are smelted at Noranda, in the heart of the mining region, while a refining plant is located at Montreal East. The non-ferrous smelting and refining industries of Quebec give work to more than 8,000 workers, and have a gross value of production of $300,000,000.

## Fisheries and Fur Trade

### The Fishing Industry

The Quebec fisheries come far behind those of the Maritime Provinces, Newfoundland and British Columbia and rank beside those of Ontario and the Prairie Provinces. During the post-war years Quebec has had about 4% of the total Canadian production. About 10,000 people or 13% of the total for Canada, found employment in the industry. However unimportant now, fishing, along with the fur trade, was important in colonial days and was mainly responsible for the settlement of the Gaspé peninsula, Magdalen Islands and the eastern part of the North Shore.

Although Quebec has both sea and in-

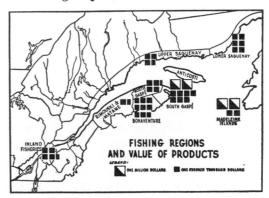

Figure 104. *Fishing Regions of Quebec and Value of Fisheries* (1946). Gaspé Peninsula and Magdalen Islands are the most important fishing areas.

land fisheries the former are much more important. The Estuary and Gulf of St. Lawrence and Chaleur Bay have 1,700 miles of coastline, while easily accessible offshore banks (Miscou, Natashquan, Parent) have an area of 7,000 square miles.

The Gaspé peninsula which includes

volume. Formerly the fish trade had been in the hands of a few big dealers, who were interested chiefly in Gaspé-cured dried cod. The provincial government has assisted the fishermen to change over to the fresh fish market. Thirty-nine fishermen's cooperatives have been organized

### Table 7    Quebec Fisheries*

| Fishing Districts | Chief Species | % of Provincial total |
|---|---|---|
| 1. South Gaspé | (Cod, Herring) | 34.3 |
| 2. Magdalen Islands | (Lobster, Mackerel, Cod, Herring) | 28.0 |
| 3. Bonaventure | (Cod, Salmon, Smelts, Herring) | 11.1 |
| 4. Lower Saguenay | (Cod, Seal, Salmon, Herring) | 7.6 |
| 5. North Gaspé | (Cod, Herring) | 5.8 |
| 6. Upper Saguenay | (Cod, Salmon, Halibut) | 4.8 |
| 7. Matane and Rimouski | (Cod, Herring, Smelts) | 2.4 |
| 8. Inland Fisheries | (Catfish, Eels, Sturgeon) | 5.9 |
| | Total value of fish caught | $7,900,000 |

*Data for 1945—Quebec Department of Fisheries

three regions, North and South Gaspé and Bonaventure, produces more than half the total. There are active fishermen in every coastal village. Rivière-aux-Renards, Gaspé, Grande Rivière and Port Daniel are important centres. The peninsula markets four-fifths of Quebec's cod and 50% of the salmon catch. The Magdalen Islands are next in importance. Here fishing ports are provided with modern equipment for handling, freezing, curing and canning fish. Fresh lobsters are flown by plane to markets in the U.S.A. On the North Shore, from Seven Islands to the Strait of Belle Isle, every settlement is devoted to fishing and hunting. Most of the halibut, over 40% of the salmon and 12% of the cod come from this district. Seal hunting is an important activity.

The inland fisheries are relatively unimportant. Before the war the chief catch consisted of eels for the European market.

Fishing in Quebec has undergone profound changes. Before World War II the average annual value of fish caught was about $2,000,000. In 1946 it was $8,000,000 and in 1950, $5,500,000 with an increasing

under the guidance of the Superior School of Fisheries at Ste. Anne de la Pocatière where fishermen may also get advanced technical training. Since 1932, some fifty cold storages with a capacity of 15,000,000 lbs. have been built; the three largest, at Rivière-aux-Renards, Grand Rivière, and Gaspé each have a capacity of 1,000,000 lbs. The government also has 100 cooling houses where fish are chilled before being sent to the filleting plants, 36 culling sheds and one artificial drying plant at Rimouski. Special instructors are also provided to teach new methods to the fishermen. Scientific research is promoted by both provincial and federal departments of fisheries; a station for marine biology is found at Grand Rivière and work is also carried on in the Biological Department of the University of Montreal.

### Furs

The fur trade has been carried on since the discovery of Quebec. So vast are the unoccupied lands that trappers still make a fairly good living. Fur trading posts are scattered over most of the province outside

Figure 105. *Fur Trading Posts in Quebec.*

the small closely settled southern part. There are about 2,900 trappers (16% of the Canadian total) two-thirds of whom are Indian and Eskimo. Fur production reached a peak in 1946 with a total value of $7,500,000, about 17% of the Canadian production. About one-third of this, however, came from fur farms. Beaver was the most important species in the past and although once threatened with extinction is now becoming plentiful in the preserves along the James Bay shore. White fox is the main fur in New Quebec (Ungava), while red foxes are found farther south. Many new type fox pelts are marketed from fur farms. Mink is trapped in the wild as well as raised in captivity. Other furs, mainly wild, are muskrat, ermine, marten, lynx and otter.

## Power

Water power has been a key factor in the industrial development of Ontario and Quebec, both of which are without coal resources. Quebec leads the Dominion in both available power and turbine installa-

tion. Of 50,000,000 H.P. available at ordinary six-month flow, Quebec has 20,000,-000 H.P. Of the total Canadian power installation of 13,900,000 H.P. in 1952, Quebec had 52%, 7,300,000 H.P. For 1956, 8,130,000 H.P. is planned.

The geography of Quebec is favourable for water power. The elevated Canadian Shield with its glaciated surface and interrupted drainage provides good storage for the abundant precipitation (35 to 40 inches per year). This storage capacity has been increased by the building of large dams. The Quebec Streams Commission, created in 1910, now operates 28 reservoirs and a few others are operated by private companies. The faulted edge of the Shield gives a steep gradient to all rivers which cross it, thus providing many advantageous power sites.

## Regional Distribution of Power Resources

The Canadian Shield has more than 80% of the available power and three-quarters of the power plant capacity. The three most important regions are the Saguenay, Central Laurentians and Western Laurentians.

The Saguenay, although the latest to be developed, provides the most power. Lake St. John is a mighty natural reservoir which was dammed in 1923 to raise the water level and to regulate its outflow. During the 1920's, two large power houses, Ile-Maligne, 540,000 H.P. and Chûte-à-Caron (now known as Shipshaw No. 1) 280,000 H.P., were built. Lake Kenogami also serves as a reservoir for smaller power plants at Kenogami and Chicoutimi. The largest project, however, was carried out during World War II, when Shipshaw No. 2 (1,200,000 H.P.) was built. It is the largest central electric station in Canada. Further storage was created by huge dams far upstream on the Peribonka and its tributary the Manouan, where 500,000 H.P. was added in 1953. Most of the power is used locally in the aluminum and pulp and paper

*Photographic Surveys (Quebec) Limited.*

Plate 39. The Shipshaw hydro-electric developments on the Saguenay River provide abundant power for the industries of the region. Shipshaw No. 1 is in the background, No. 2 in the foreground.

industries but the region is linked to Quebec by a high voltage transmission line so that excess power may be used anywhere along the provincial network.

The Shawinigan Water and Power Company was founded in 1898. It operates the following stations: La Gabelle, 172,000 H.P., Shawinigan, two plants, 416,000 H.P., Grand'Mère, 200,000 H.P. La Tuque, 225,000 H.P., La Tranche, 325,000 H.P. and Rapide Blanc, 200,000 H.P., on the St. Maurice River. The headwaters are impounded by the Gouin Storage Dam, and there are two others on the Manouan and Mattawin Rivers.[1] The Shawinigan Water and Power Company serves not only the local pulp and paper, chemical and electro-metallurgical industries, but distributes power to the whole of the St. Lawrence Lowland including Montreal and Quebec, the northern part of the Eastern Townships as

far as Thetford Mines, and both shores of the upper part of the Estuary.

In the Western Laurentians the chief developments are on the Upper Ottawa and two tributaries, the Gatineau and the Lièvre. The Gatineau River is regulated by two big storage dams, Mercier and Cabonga. On it the Gatineau Power Company has three plants with a capacity of 528,000 H.P.; it also has three others of 130,000 H.P. capacity in the region. Maclaren-Quebec Power Company, with three stations on the Lièvre River, has a capacity of 300,000 H.P., while the Ottawa Valley Power Company at Les Chats develops 112,000 H.P. More than half of the power in this region is sold to Ontario.

On the St. Lawrence above Montreal, only about one-third of the available power has yet been developed. Here are located Beauharnois, which will have 1,300,000 H.P. when the second unit is opened,[2] and Les Cèdres with a capacity of 206,400 H.P.

---

[1]Canada, 1951. See map facing p. 182.
[2]The last step of the development will add 600,000 H.P.

Both of these plants are under the management of Hydro-Quebec which supplies power to Montreal, to Ontario and to the U.S.A.

The St. Francis river system in the Eastern Townships has a number of small power houses, with a total of about 100,000 H.P., supplying industries in Sherbrooke,

Although greatly expanded during World War II, Quebec power plants are faced with further increase in the demand for power. New industries, urban expansion and rural electrification have absorbed the increases since the end of the war and further new plants are in building.

Although making possible vast employ-

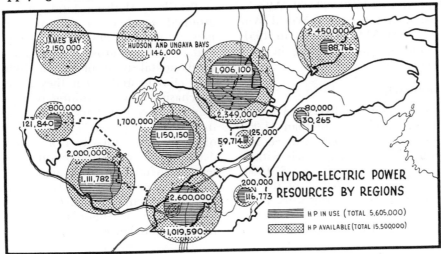

Figure 106. *Hydro-electric Power Resources of the Quebec Regions.* Northern regions still have large unexploited resources.

Drummondville and other towns of the region. The Lower St. Lawrence is also being developed: Baie Comeau (paper) is supplied by a 77,300 H.P. plant on Outardes R., new mining camps in Gaspé, by submarine power cables from a 100,000 H.P. plant on Manicuagan R., and Seven Islands (iron ore), by a smaller plant on Ste. Marguerite R.

### The Output and Use of Electricity

The total output of electrical energy in 1951 amountd to over 30,000,000,000 kilowatt hours valued at $120,000,000. About 88% of this energy is at very low rates, thus producing about 60% of the total revenue. The retail sales, although relatively small, bring in 40% of the revenue. Domestic service with but 6% of the energy brings in 20% of the revenue. The average rate per kilowat hour is 1.99 cents, compared with 1.22 in Ontario.

ment in industry the production of power itself employs relatively few workers. Many people are needed for construction, but once a plant is in operation they move to other jobs. A total force of about 7,800, about one-third of whom are officials and clerks, operate the industry.

### Manufacturing

Quebec is the second greatest manufacturing province in Canada, producing about 30% of the gross output, Ontario ranking first with 50%. The importance of these industries is reliably indicated by the growth of employment. At the turn of the century, manufacturing already employed 100,000 workers. The number rose to 200,-000 in 1928 and, after a drop during the depression was again above 200,000 in 1939. The peak of industrial employment was reached in 1943 with over 437,000 workers on the payrolls. After the post war readjustment the total in 1951 stood at 453,000. The increase in value of production is much more spectacular due to the changes in the purchasing power of the dollar. In 1900 the total value of manufactured goods was $158,000,000, in 1920, 1928 and 1939 it was just over $1,000,000,000, but by 1944 it had climbed to $2,930,000,000. After a slight recession at the end of World War II it rose to over $4,900,000,000 in 1951. The net value of manufacturing in 1951 was $2,084,000,000.

## Leading Industries

Quebec is a region of diversified manufacturing industry with more than 11,900 plants in operation in 1951. Sixteen important groups of industries, each with a gross annual production of over $70,000,000 produced over half (54%) of the total and employed 45% of the workers in that year.

Pulp and paper form the leading group

with 10% of the gross output and about 6% of the workers. There are 54 plants, among them being some of the largest in the country. If to them we add the sawmilling industry, we find that 12% of the output and nearly 10% of the labour force are concerned with the processing of raw materials from the Quebec forest.

Textiles, clothing and shoes, when grouped together, far outrank forest products, providing 20% of the employment and 14% of the gross output. Clothing is a fundamental need of people living in a cold climate and when they have a high purchasing power clothing is in good demand. Meats and dairy products are foods in demand by people with a high standard of living, while tobacco is a luxury also in demand. The other important groups, non-ferrous metal, electrical apparatus, petroleum products and railway rolling stock are fundamental supports to a machine culture. From a labour standpoint this is a fairly well-balanced array of heavy and

## Table 8　Leading Industries of Quebec 1951

| | No. of Establishments | No. of Employees | Salaries and Wages $000,000 | Average Annual Wage $ | Cost of Materials $000,000 | Net Value of Products $000,000 | Gross Value of Products $000,000 | % of Canadian Total |
|---|---|---|---|---|---|---|---|---|
| 1. Pulp and Paper | 55 | 24,449 | 89.0 | 3,640 | 213.6 | 273.0 | 524.2 | 42.0 |
| 2. Non-ferrous Metals | 8 | 8,633 | 28.4 | 3,300 | 195.8 | 85.8 | 307.0 | 35.7 |
| 3. Petroleum Products | 7 | 2,435 | 8.5 | 3,520 | 181.9 | 55.6 | 247.6 | 41.3 |
| 4. Slaughtering and Meat Packing | 37 | 4,017 | 11.4 | 2,840 | 167.5 | 23.5 | 191.9 | 21.5 |
| 5. Cotton Yarn and Cloth | 21 | 18,161 | 37.4 | 2,060 | 117.2 | 62.3 | 182.1 | 66.5 |
| 6. Men's Factory Clothing | 347 | 17,838 | 33.3 | 1,870 | 75.2 | 60.0 | 135.7 | 56.6 |
| 7. Women's Factory Clothing | 554 | 18,800 | 35.9 | 1,910 | 69.9 | 64.1 | 134.3 | 67.7 |
| 8. Railway Rolling Stock | 10 | 15,572 | 41.6 | 2,670 | 73.1 | 50.0 | 125.4 | 41.5 |
| 9. Butter and Cheese | 750 | 5,647 | 11.1 | 1,970 | 90.2 | 19.3 | 111.5 | 29.8 |
| 10. Tobacco, Cigars, Cigarettes | 33 | 7,290 | 19.4 | 2,660 | 59.2 | 49.0 | 108.5 | 60.5 |
| 11. Electrical Apparatus | 32 | 11,905 | 34.4 | 2,900 | 44.7 | 62.4 | 108.0 | 48.7 |
| 12. Synthetic Textiles and Silk | 33 | 13,016 | 31.6 | 2,440 | 44.3 | 59.2 | 105.9 | 63.5 |
| 13. Sawmills | 1,931 | 10,763 | 16.1 | 1,510 | 54.8 | 33.7 | 89.4 | 15.1 |
| 14. Misc. Food Preparations | 84 | 2,463 | 5.5 | 2,240 | 54.8 | 20.3 | 75.6 | 29.0 |
| 15. Bread and Bakery Prod. | 962 | 9,425 | 18.1 | 1,920 | 35.8 | 32.5 | 70.4 | 29.0 |
| 16. Footwear, Leather | 182 | 12,188 | 20.8 | 1,710 | 39.4 | 30.2 | 69.9 | 58.3 |
| Sixteen Leading Industries | 5,046 | 182,602 | 442.5 | 2,420 | 1,517.4 | 980.9 | 2,587.4 | 15.8 |
| Total, all Industries | 11,861 | 417,182 | 1,005.6 | 2,400 | 2,696.6 | 2,083.9 | 4,916.2 | 30.0 |
| Leading Industries as per cent of all Quebec Industries | 42.5 | 43.7 | 44.2 | 101.0 | 56.2 | 47.1 | 52.6 | |

Data from D.B.S. 1953.

light industry providing work for both male and female members of families.

## Geographical Distribution of Manufacturing Industries

Greater Montreal is the foremost manufacturing district in Quebec and, indeed, in all Canada, outranking Greater Toronto by a narrow margin. With over 4,500 plants and 220,000 workers, 56.5% of the labour force of the province, it accounts for 55%

hind those mentioned above. The Montreal area is important for the production of aircraft, petroleum products, clay products and cement.

The importance of the transportation routes centring on Montreal is to be seen in the assembling of iron, coal, wood pulp, cotton and many other materials brought from outside the area. The diversity of industry provides work for both male and female labour. Iron workers, for instance, are mostly males, while more than two-

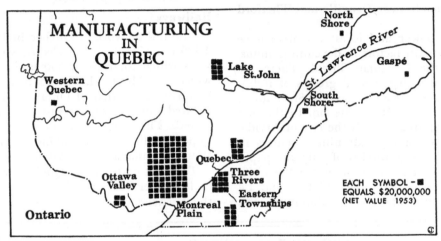

Figure 107. *Regional Distribution of Manufacturing in Quebec.* The manufacturing industries contribute nearly two-thirds of the total annual commodity production of the province. Note the dominant position of the Montreal Plain which includes the metropolitan area of Greater Montreal.

of the total output. The city itself had about 4,100 factories producing a great diversity of goods, worth $1,700,000,000 in 1950. Most important were the textiles (24%) with factory clothing alone making up 18% of the total. Vegetable products ranked second (21%) with tobacco, brewing and miscellaneous food products as the largest items. Almost equally great was the value of iron products with railway rolling stock (8%) as the largest single industry. The fourth class in importance was animal products with meats, leather goods, and furs as the leaders. Wood and paper products, chemicals and electrical apparatus are very substantial industries although be-

thirds of the textile and tobacco workers are females.

Two other industrial regions are located in the St. Lawrence Lowlands: the Quebec metropolitan area and the Three Rivers region. The products of Quebec are less varied than those of Montreal, but they include leather shoes, wood and paper products, textiles, tobacco, meats and other food products. Wartime activity included shipbuilding which was located across the river at Lauzon. In the Three Rivers region newsprint and textiles are the most important products.

Taken together, the industrial districts of the St. Lawrence Lowlands employ 80%

of the labour force of the province and turn out 75% of the total production.

The Eastern Townships has been an important manufacturing area since the beginning of the twentieth century. It contains about a dozen thriving centres. Sherbrooke, the largest, produces textiles and machinery. Magog, Granby, Farnham, Cowansville and St. Georges de Beauce are textile towns. Pulp and paper mills are located at Windsor Mills, Bromptonville, East Angus and Megantic. Victoriaville manufactures furniture while asbestos products are made near Danville and Thetford Mines.

Water power and forest resources have been the main factors in developing industries in the Canadian Shield. There are now three widely spaced groups of industrial centres: the Saguenay, the St. Maurice Valley and the Ottawa region. In the first mentioned area there is the city of Arvida, one of the foremost aluminum centres in the world, and a number of pulp and paper towns. On the St. Maurice are the cities of Shawinigan Falls, Grand'Mère and La Tuque. Pulp and paper, aluminum and

chemicals are important here. Two other small cities of the Central Laurentians should be mentioned: Lachute and St Jerome (paper, textiles, chemicals). Along the Ottawa, Hull, Gatineau, Buckingham, and Masson are devoted almost exclusively to pulp and paper.

## Transportation

Transportation facilities are important factors in the economic development of the province. These facilities also influence the distribution of population.

### Railways

The rail network of Quebec in 1951 was 4,780 miles, exclusive of electric street railways which total about 350 miles most of which is in Montreal. This total is less than half as great as that of Ontario yet the inhabited portions of the province are well served. The Quebec railways perform an important function in linking Ontario and Western Canada to the Atlantic seaports.

The first railroad in Quebec was built in 1837 over the portage from Laprairie to the Richelieu River, a distance of fifteen

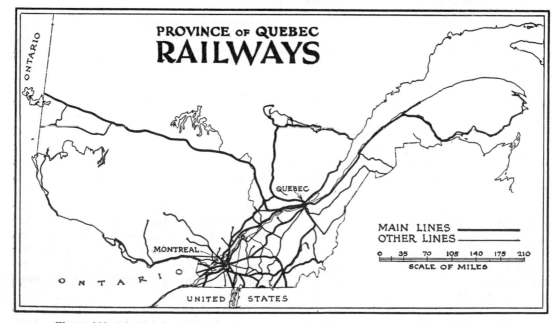

Figure 108. *The Quebec Railway Net.* Note how the railway net is focused upon Montreal.

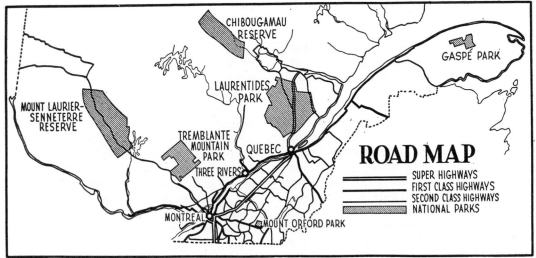

Figure 109. *The Highway Net of Quebec.* Highways are most completely developed in the St. Lawrence Lowland and in the valleys of the Eastern Townships. Main highways have been extended into other regions.

miles. In 1857 the Grand Trunk Railway was completed between Toronto and Montreal, later being extended to Sherbrooke and to Portland, Maine, the nearest harbour on the Atlantic coast. The Intercolonial was built along the south shore of the St. Lawrence via Lévis, Rivière du Loup and the Matapedia Valley to link Montreal to Halifax. All of these lines are now integral parts of the C.N.R. system. The C.P.R. line from Montreal to Quebec was completed in 1880 and in 1885 Montreal became the eastern terminus of the first transcontinental line in Canada. In 1890 the C.P.R. obtained an Atlantic winter terminal by building a line across the Eastern Townships and the State of Maine to St. John, New Brunswick. Toward the close of the nineteenth century the Quebec Central (now C.P.R.) was built from Lévis to Sherbrooke and the U.S. border, and the Canadian Northern (C.N.R.) ran a line along the southern edge of the Laurentians through Joliette, Shawinigan and Quebec finally reaching Chicoutimi and Lake St. John. In 1915 the National Transcontinental (now C.N.R.) was built from Quebec westward through La Tuque to Western Quebec and Northern Ontario; it was also

extended eastward over the Quebec Bridge to Edmundston and Moncton, New Brunswick. American lines serving Montreal are the Central Vermont, the Delaware and Hudson, and the New York Central.

The province of Quebec has about one-fifth of the total Canadian railway business. In 1951 about 29,500,000 tons of freight were loaded at Quebec railway stations and 33,500,000 tons were unloaded. Of the tonnage loaded, about one-third was of mineral origin including coal landed at Quebec ports; about two-fifths consisted of manufactured goods including pulp and paper, petroleum products and cement, one-fifth was provided by forest industry and about 4% consisted of agricultural products.

## Highways

There were roads in Quebec long before the advent of railways. Even during the French regime some of the settlements were linked by road, the most important being the King's Highway from Quebec to Montreal. Montreal was connected with Toronto by road in 1817 and ten years later the Royal Mail could be sent overland from Halifax to Montreal via the old

Kempt Road which linked the South Shore to the Maritimes. The Craig Road, however rough it may have been, played an important part in the opening of the Eastern Townships from Quebec. During the railroad building period roads were regarded mainly as feeders, radiating from the railroad stations.

The provincial government instituted its "good roads" policy in 1907. At that time Quebec had about 40,000 miles of roads. In 1951, excluding city streets there were 42,000 miles of public roads, of which 27,000 miles, or two-thirds, are improved. About 5,200 miles have a cement or asphalt surface and the rest, a gravel surface. Nearly all parts of the province are linked by automobile roads except the North shore of the St. Lawrence beyond Baie Comeau. Western Quebec was connected with Montreal via the Mont Laurier-Senneterre highway in 1939. The Department of Roads together with the various municipalities try to maintain winter motor traffic on about 18,000 miles of road.

It is difficult to estimate the volume of highway traffic; 500,000 motor vehicles were registered in 1951. Of these 332,000 were private cars, 20,000 were taxis, 3,000 were buses, 130,000 were trucks and 16,000 were motorcycles. In 1950 rural and inter-urban bus lines carried 31,000,000 passengers while city buses carried nearly 75,000,000. Together they accounted for 30% of the bus passengers in Canada. Freight carriers handled approximately 5,800,000 tons or 30% of the total highway freight of Canada.

### Waterways

The most important waterway in Quebec is the St. Lawrence River which is open for navigation for seven and one-half months each year. It has a 35 foot channel as far as Montreal capable of accommodating vessels up to 22,000 tons. The largest ocean vessels may dock at Quebec.

Two of the St. Lawrence canals, Lachine and Soulanges, are in Quebec. To-

gether they have a length of over 23 miles. They are navigable by vessels of less than 270 feet in length and 14 foot draught. The Ottawa River canals have a depth of 9 feet while the Chambly canal on the Richelieu has a depth of only 6½ feet.

Water traffic is heavy from April to December. The ports of the St. Lawrence have steamship connections with all parts of the world. In 1951 over 2,600 ships in foreign service used Quebec waters, a total of over 6,000,000 tons. In addition 10,000 smaller vessels with a total of 8,000,000 registered tons operated in coastal and inland service. The total, over 14,000,000 tons, accounted for about one-sixth of Canada's shipping traffic.

Quebec has four of the eight ports administered by the National Harbours Board. They are: Montreal, Quebec, Three Rivers and Chicoutimi. There are many other smaller ports. Montreal is normally the most important port in the country despite its winter closed season. It has ten miles of dock space and very large storage facilities including grain elevators of over 15,000,000 bushels capacity and oil tank storage of 50,000,000 gallons. In 1951, 4,400 vessels of 7,700,000 tons registry used this port. They unloaded 6,800,000 tons of cargo and took away over 8,200,000 tons. The dominant inbound commodities are coal, crude oil, fuel oil, gasoline, raw sugar, gypsum and grain. Grain for overseas is the dominant outbound commodity. Petroleum products are next in order, being distributed by coastal and inland traffic from the big oil refineries of Montreal East. Three Rivers currently handles more cargo than Quebec, although its docking and storage facilities are much smaller. In 1951, the port was used by 2,800 vessels, of 2,245,000 tons. More than 2,600,000 tons of cargo were unloaded, the chief items being pulpwood, coal and grain. The 550,000 tons of outbound cargo were composed largely of grain, newsprint and lumber. Quebec was used by 4,600 vessels of 4,700,000 tons registry. The inbound freight was composed chiefly of pulpwood, coal, petroleum and cement with a total of over 1,900,000 tons. The 860,000 tons loaded were composed of timber and miscellaneous freight. Since the end of World War II little grain has been shipped from Quebec. Quebec passenger traffic averages 90,000 per year, about one-half that of Montreal.

Sorel, which is not a national port, is situated at the mouth of the Richelieu river. It has a large elevator, 4,000,000 bushels capacity, and may ship more than 20,-000,000 bushels of grain in a year. Port Alfred at Ha Ha Bay on the Saguenay river is the entry point for the aluminum ores used at Arvida and for sulphur used in the pulp and paper mills of the region. Bagotville, also on Ha Ha Bay, is the chief passenger port with daily summer service by Canada Steamship Lines. Chicoutimi, a national harbour, is the main port of entry for coal. It also has considerable passenger traffic.

Baie Comeau, on the north shore of the Estuary and isolated from all rail services, ships the whole output of its newsprint mill, 150,000 tons, by water. Rimouski and Matane, on the south shore of the Estuary and served by railways, serve as terminal ports for freight and passenger service to the North Shore.

## Airways

Air transportation became important soon after the close of World War I. Pontoon planes were used for forest fire patrol, air photography and the transportation of prospectors and others having duties in the wilds. Lac à la Tortue, twenty miles north of Three Rivers, was the first air base in 1919. Five years later there was air service to Noranda in Western Quebec. A number of flying clubs were organized in 1927 and 1928. Public airports were built at St. Hubert near Montreal and at Rimouski. Three other fields near Montreal were built by aircraft firms. By 1930 Montreal was linked by daily service to New York, Toronto, Detroit, Ottawa, Quebec, Rimouski and St. John, N.B. The transcontinental

service of Trans-Canada Air Lines was inaugurated in 1938.

World War II brought a great expansion in air activity. Many airports were built for the use of the R.C.A.F. Dorval, on the island of Montreal, is an important airport used by Trans-Canada Air Lines with connections to all parts of Canada, the U.S.A., the West Indies, Britain, France and Germany. Other airports are: Loretteville, near Quebec; Bagotville on the Saguenay; Mont Joli, on the South Shore; Baie Comeau and Seven Islands on the North Shore, and at Noranda. There are fields at Rimouski and Matane and at various places on the North Shore, some of which are accessible only in the winter time. A year round airport at Knob Lake has been built to serve the iron field of New Quebec. Hydroplane bases are also available in many places.

## Transportation Problems

While land, water and air transportation facilities have been greatly improved, there are still many problems. Foremost among them is the question of the St. Lawrence Seaway. When realized, it will be of tremendous significance to Quebec. Some people fear that Montreal may lose part of its trade but if they look closely at the matter they will see an equal chance of improvement. Somewhere a trans-shipment point must exist between the slow inland water transportation and that of the more rapid service of the ocean liners. Montreal is already equipped to perform this function. The nature of its trade may be changed, but there is little doubt that it will grow. The waterway will be expensive to build, but this is partly offset by the prospect of additional water power which will become available close to the industrial centres of Quebec.

There are also railway problems in Quebec. The railways are expensive to operate and trains are slow. Services to Western Quebec and the Saguenay are inadequate. Val d'Or may be reached from Montreal more quickly by bus than by rail, the same is true of the journey from Quebec to Chi-

:outimi. The development of the iron ore deposits of New Quebec has made necessary the building of 360 miles of railway north from Seven Islands.

Undoubtedly the new mining field will need highway service, and the road that now stops at Baie Comeau is being lengthened by one hundred and twenty-five miles up to Seven Islands. Other new mining fields need highways also. New highways are not the only problem, however, traffic between the cities of Old Quebec grows denser year by year and the old routes need constant rehabilitation. The elimination of toll bridges is another problem which the Quebec government has dealt with steadily. Highway bridges also have been built to supersede outmoded ferries.

### Electrical Communications

Telegraph lines for the most part parallel railway lines. Throughout Quebec there are 900 telegraph stations, second in rank to Ontario, although three western provinces have more miles of line.

Telephone service is constantly increasing: in 1950 there were 700,000 phones in service, about 16 per hundred population. More than half of these instruments are in the city of Montreal. Over 80% of the business is in the hands of the Bell Telephone Company of Canada. There are 13 other systems, none of which has more than 10,000 subscribers.

Quebec has approximately as many private receiving radio sets as telephones, ranking second and not far behind Ontario. A special French network of thirteen stations administered by the Canadian Broadcasting Corporation serves French language listeners. C.B.C. broadcasting stations using the English language operate in Montreal, Quebec and Sherbrooke. Approximately 28% of C.B.C. program time in Canada was released over the French network.

## Economic Development

Quebec is dominantly an industrial province; two-thirds of its new wealth is annually derived from manufacturing, custom and repair. It is not yet completely industrialized but the process is well advanced. More and more labour is being expended on domestic raw materials before they go to market while many industries produce consumers' goods also from imported raw materials.

Economic geography is an explanation of the patterns of economic activity. Early Quebec was dependent upon primary production. Patterns of commerce and centres of population grew up in response to the fur trade, the timber trade and a subsistence agriculture. The present largely reflects the influences of the past but new elements are continually being added, such as the mines, power plants and highways of recent decades. In spite of all peripheral developments, however, the St. Lawrence Lowland remains the chief economic focus of the province.

## Selected References

Canada Year Book.

Province of Quebec Statistical Year Book.

Industry in Action in "la Province de Québec". Prov. Publicity Bureau, Quebec, P.Q. 1951.

Notre Milieu. Deuxième Partie. Le Milieu Économique. pp. 133-312. École des Hautes Etudes Commerciales. Montreal. 1942.

L'Agriculture. (Edited by E. Minville) École des Hautes Études Commerciales. Montreal. 1943.

La Forêt. (Edited by E. Minville) École des Hautes Études Commerciales. Montreal.

Pêche et Chasse. (Edited by E. Minville) École des Hautes Études Commerciales. Montreal. 1946.

# CHAPTER 9

# The Regions and Cities of Quebec

THE geographic pattern of Quebec is dominated by its division into three great physiographic regions: the Laurentian Uplands, the St. Lawrence Lowlands and the Appalachian Highlands. Within the larger framework, the position of rivers, lakes and ridges, the choice of original settlement sites, the economic development of areas and routes, and last, but not necessarily the least influence, is the location of administrative boundaries.

It has already been pointed out that the census of 1951 reported that 66% of the people dwelt in incorporated places and over half of them in cities with more than 10,000 population. There are 25 such cities and towns, some of which provide a useful regional nucleus in most regions. Where there are no towns of that size, as in outlaying regions, other features are more characteristic than the urban habitat. The functions of the main cities are studied here as a suitable approach to the regional geography of Quebec.

## I. The Montreal Region

Surrounding the city of Montreal, the flat lands of the extreme southwestern part of Quebec constitute the Montreal Plain or Montreal Region. Extending from the borders of Ontario and New York to Lake St. Peter and from the edge of the Laurentians to the first slopes of the Appalachians, it has an area of slightly over 4,700 square

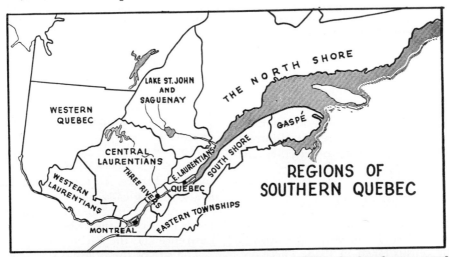

**Figure 110** *Geographic Regions of Southern Quebec.* Within the broader structural framework, human relations mark out ten geographical regions for detailed study. The undeveloped Northland constitutes still another region.

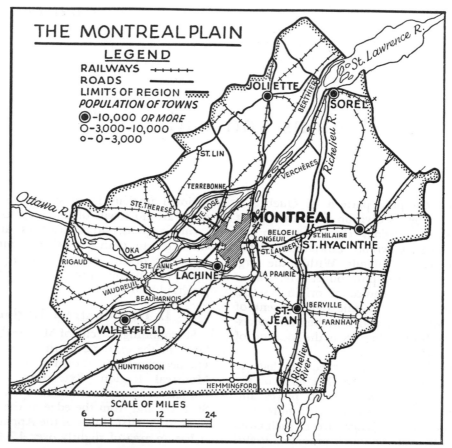

Figure 111. *The Montreal Plain.* The broad southern portion of the St. Lawrence Lowland, its flatness broken only by the Monteregian Hills, this is the most densely populated region in Canada.

miles. This territory is fully occupied, being carved into an intricate pattern of urban and rural municipalities inhabited by more than 1,850,000 people. Only 14% of the population is rural. The city of Montreal itself contains 1,100,000, Greater Montreal 1,600,000, and there are six other cities and towns on the plain.

## Montreal

Montreal is a modern complex metropolis of more than 1,600,000 people according to the census taken in 1956. The more important municipalities and their populations are given in Table 9.

### Geographical Setting

Montreal is located at 73°30′ west longitude and 45°30′ north latitude, approximately the same latitude as Portland, Oregon; Lyons, France; Milan, Italy, and Odessa, U.S.S.R.

Montreal arose at the head of navigation on the St. Lawrence where further progress inland is blocked by the Lachine Rapids. It is also strategically located with respect to the natural routes radiating north, west and south by way of the Ottawa, the upper St. Lawrence and the Richelieu.

The site of the original settlement was a terrace on the left bank of the St. Lawrence, at the foot of the Lachine rapids. Behind

## Table 9    Major Municipalities of Greater Montreal*

| | | | |
|---|---|---|---|
| Montreal (city) | 1,109,520 | St. Lambert (city) | 12,224 |
| Verdun (city) | 78,262 | Pointe aux Trembles (town) | 11,981 |
| St. Laurent (city) | 38,291 | Laval des Rapides (town) | 11,248 |
| Lachine (city) | 34,494 | Mackayville (town) | 9,958 |
| Jacques Cartier (city) | 33,132 | Pont Viau (town) | 8,218 |
| Outremont (city) | 29,990 | L'Abord a Plouffe (town) | 8,099 |
| Montreal North (town) | 25,407 | St. Jean de Dieu (mun.) | 6,855 |
| Westmount (city) | 24,800 | Rivière des Prairies (town) | 6,806 |
| St. Michel (city) | 24,706 | Côte St. Luc (town) | 5,914 |
| La Salle (town) | 18,973 | Le Moyne (town) | 5,662 |
| Mount Royal (town) | 16,990 | Beaconsfield (town) | 5,496 |
| Pointe Claire (town) | 15,208 | Montreal South (town) | 5,319 |
| Longueuil (city) | 14,332 | St. Pierre (town) | 5,276 |
| Dorval (city) | 14,055 | Montreal East (town) | 4,607 |

*Census of Canada, 1956.

it rose Mount Royal, 769 feet in height, dominating the whole countryside. The city has grown up the slopes of the mountain, around it on all sides, clear to the Back River (Rivière-des-Prairies) on the other side of the island. The site has an interesting geological history. The underlying rocks were laid down in the Ordovician period. In the quarry on Fleurimont Street may be seen a 75-foot face revealing the three main formations of the island: Chazy limestone at the bottom, Black River limestone above it and Trenton limestone on top. The strata are still almost horizontal but have been faulted. At the end of Devonian time eruptive rocks broke through to form the volcanic neck which constitutes Mount Royal. Being made of harder rocks it withstood erosion better than the surrounding sedimentary s t r a t a and n o w stands as a monadnock above the plain. All around it the surface land forms are Pleistocene terraces, sloping from the sides of "the mountain" to the water level.

The upper terraces are more than 200 feet above sea level. The largest of these (200-225 feet) extends to the north of Mount Royal, through Outremont from the corner of Park and Mount Royal Avenues to the Jean Talon station of the C.P.R. and Côte Visitation. A narrower terrace at the same level is found in the Notre Dame de Grâce section of the city. The fine residential district of Westmount is built on terraces between 200 and 500 feet in elevation. Fairly level streets follow each terrace, but the cross streets between them climb at difficult angles.

The middle terrace, between 125 and 200 feet in elevation, is the most extensive underlying a large part of the city. Sherbrooke Street runs along its lower limit from Bleury Street to Pie IX Boulevard and Upper Lachine Road follows it southwestward. Cross streets, such as Bleury, St. Lawrence and St. Denis, mount it by the "Sherbrooke Street hill", an old shoreline of the Champlain Sea.

The lower terrace, 50 to 75 feet in elevation, is found in the downtown district. Ontario, St. Catherine and Dorchester Streets are built upon it. Near the river a ridge was isolated by the valley of the small creek which ran along Craig street before it was buried under the modern pavements. The old townsite, located on this ridge in order to be safe from spring floods is now the business section about St. James and Notre Dame streets.

The city developed from a riverside nucleus overlooking the main part of the harbour. In colonial days it was surrounded by a stockade. From this early site it has grown in three main directions: down the river to Montreal East, up the river and along the Lachine Canal to Lake St. Louis

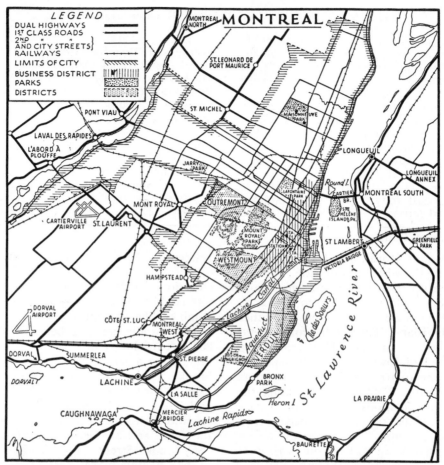

Figure 112. *Greater Montreal.* The twenty-eight municipalities of Greater Montreal contain ten per cent of Canada's population. Montreal is Canada's foremost seaport and manufacturing centre.

and across the island to Cartierville, Ahuntsic and Montreal North on the Back River. Before the days of rapid transit the city was small and overcrowded. The wealthy who could afford to come to work in private coaches established their residences in Westmount and Outremont on the slopes of the mountain. These remain as independent cities but now completely surrounded by the working class districts of Greater Montreal. Since the building of bridges across the St. Lawrence, suburbs have developed on the south bank, among them being Longueuil, St. Lambert, Montreal South and Greenfield Park.

## Population

In 1951 the population of Greater Montreal was 1,395,400. Of these 900,825, or 64.6% were of French origin and 307,236 or 22% were of British origin. Jews, Italian, Poles and many other groups make the other 13%. Roman Catholics with 75% comprised the largest religious group; there are 16.7% Protestants and 5.8% Jews.

The gainfully occupied numbered 445,-000 in Montreal proper, 43.6% of the total population. Their chief occupations were classified as follows: professionals, business owners or managers 16.4%, factory workers 24.6%, office clerks 16%, employees in services 10.6%, in transportation 8.5%, in commerce and finance 8%, in construction 6.5%, as labourers 9%.

## Economic Functions of the City

As indicated by the census figures, manufacturing is the most important function. This is true for the greater city, also, which in 1950 had 4,580 plants employing 220,000 workers. Size and diversity are the main characteristics of Montreal industry. Among the most important are factory clothing, electrical apparatus, railway rolling stock, tobacco, meats, boots and shoes, breweries, fur goods, food products and paints.

The harbour front and the banks of the Lachine Canal are favoured sites for heavy industries where large amounts of material are imported by ship. The railway belt around the city and its suburbs has also attracted many industries. Lighter industries such as the clothing trades are scattered in hundreds of small factories throughout the city, thus being close to the homes of their employees. Even so, the problem of transportation to and from work has become acute. Street cars and buses are overcrowded and long lines of motor vehicles jam the intersections. Following the lead of Toronto, the Montreal City Planning Commission is considering the construction of an underground system of rapid transit.

The importance of Montreal as a market place is shown by the development of its harbour and by the concentration of other means of transport. This function is older than the manufacturing industry and was one of the chief causes for the development of the city. The harbour setting and equipment are those of a great world port. Lying one thousand miles inland from the Strait of Belle Isle, it is tideless, but closed by freezing from December to April.

There are two groups of harbour installations. The upper harbour extends from Victoria Bridge at the exit of Lachine Canal to Jacques Cartier Bridge. It is protected from the swift river current by a mole parallel to the bank and is the most active part of the harbour. There are eight basins 30-35 feet deep flanked by shore wharves and piers projecting from them at right angles. Railroad tracks, land bases and floating cranes, warehouses, cold storages, three grain elevators with a capacity of 10,000,000 bushels and a network of grain conveyors make for fast work in loading and unloading ships. The other group of piers is found downstream at the foot of Pie IX boulevard where Montreal's largest grain elevator is located. Adjoining it is Vicker's drydock for ship repair while much

*Provincial Publicity Bureau, Quebec.*

Plate 40. The Jaques Cartier Bridge forms an important highway connection between Montreal and the south bank of the river. From it one may get an excellent view of the port facilities.

farther down are the piers of the oil companies beside their great oil refineries.

Wholesalers and manufacturers have stores and warehouses in the harbour area. The nearby streets swarm with motor trucks and heavy horse drawn vehicles. Many types of vessels are to be seen in the harbour: great liners, freighters, the shorter canal and Great Lakes' boats, palatial river cruise boats, schooners, tugs, barges and various small craft. Navigation is seasonal and very active. The harbour scene, especially if viewed from the central arch of the Jacques Cartier bridge, 100 feet above the water, is colourful in the extreme.

Montreal is the largest railway centre in Canada. The two main terminals, the Central Station of the C.N.R. and Windsor Station of the C.P.R. are both located in the downtown area between St. Catherine Street West and Notre Dame Street West. The Turcot freight yard of the C.N.R. is at Pointe St. Charles near the entrance to Victoria Bridge; those of the C.P.R. are spaced along its belt line at Westmount, Viger and Jean Talon. A peculiar feature of the rail net of the city is the four-mile tunnel under Mount Royal by which traffic from the northern part of the city is brought directly to the Central Station. The main bus terminal is also located near the stations on Dorchester Street West. Montreal Airport is at Dorval, ten miles to the west, but the passengers collect and depart from the traffic centre of Montreal near the corner of St. Catherine and Peel.

The commercial function of Montreal is national and even world wide. The focused transportation systems bring floods of goods and crowds of travellers. But within the city itself, retail trade must provide for more than a million citizens and hundreds of thousands of transients. There are large stores in specialized shopping districts like those of St. Catherine Street, East and West, where every shop attendant seems to be perfectly bilingual, and there are multitudes of more modest shops in smaller commercial districts throughout the city. There are, moreover, the banks, trust companies, insurance companies and other financial institutions of the downtown business district where, within the last three decades, the first skyscrapers of the city have been erected. Finance is not merely the servant of the local commerce, it is the mainspring of Canadian business.

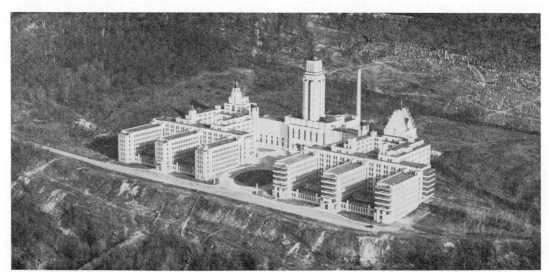

*Photographic Surveys (Quebec) Limited.*

Plate 41. The new buildings of the University of Montreal occupy a commanding site on the western slope of Mount Royal.

Other major urban functions of Montreal are administrative and intellectual. The City Hall and two court houses may symbolize the civil and judicial functions while the religious functions are represented by St. James Cathedral on Dominion Square, Christ Church and the multitude of parish churches of which Notre Dame, on Place d'Armes, is the oldest. The educational role of Montreal is marked by a large number of institutions: primary, secondary and special schools. There are two universities: Université de Montréal giving instruction in French and McGill University using the English language. Together they enrol about 15,000 students. McGill, founded in 1821, is located on Sherbrooke Street directly north of the downtown area where its campus and buildings add dignity to the urban landscape. Université de Montréal was founded in 1876 as a branch of Laval University. As an independent university it now has a large campus with new buildings on Mount Royal Boulevard. With its libraries and museums, its literary circles and learned societies, newspapers and periodicals, theaters and recreation centres, the city has all the earmarks of a great metropolis. The recreational function is emphasized by the city parks, the golf courses and, above all, Mount Royal Park from which the whole urban landscape may be seen.

## St. Hyacinthe

Founded at the end of the French regime, St. Hyacinthe is located on the Yamaska River, thirty-six miles east of Montreal. It remained a small village until the railway age, since which it has developed into a busy industrial city with a population of more than 20,000 in 1956. It is served by the main C.N.R. lines to Halifax, N.S., and Portland, Maine, and by branch lines to Farnham, Drummondville, and Sorel. Paved highways link the city to both Montreal and Quebec. Industry developed early, there were four plants in 1870. In 1950, there were 100 factories with

5,400 employees. Textiles are most important, employing four-fifths of the labour force. The three largest plants manufacture woollen and cotton underwear, cotton tire fabrics and silk hosiery. Other textile plants produce factory clothing, shirts and silk shirts. There are numerous plants producing boots and shoes, agricultural implements, castings, builders supplies and canned vegetables. Here also are built the famous Casavant organs known over the whole continent. St. Hyacinthe is a commercial centre of regional importance because of its rail facilities and the newly built highways. There is also a classical college. Raoul Blanchard cites St. Hyacinthe as the typical *ville canadienne*. The older town is built on the lower terrace (60 feet) of the left bank of the Yamaska River, the buildings are crowded and the streets are narrow; the newer areas are on the upper terrace (100 feet) and have wider, tree-lined streets.

## Valleyfield

Valleyfield (22,000) is located on the south bank of the St. Lawrence, thirty-seven miles west of Montreal. It is partly built on De Salaberry Island and partly on the right bank at the entrance to the old and now abandoned Beauharnois Canal. The city developed from a construction camp of workers who built the canal in 1850 and stayed there to work in the small industrial plants attracted by local water power. Montreal Cotton Mills established themselves in 1874 and continue to employ about three-fourths of the total labour force. There are about forty other small plants, but Valleyfield is a typical one-industry town which might be rather hard hit in a depression.

## Beauharnois

Beauharnois (6,800 inhabitants) is located a few miles east of Valleyfield at the outlet of the new Beauharnois Canal. Before the war it had only a small industrial force, but plenty of water power. Large electro-metallurgical plants, producing ferro-alloys and aluminum, grew up in wartime and gave work to more than 1,500 employees. Older plants continue to produce paper and furniture.

### St. Johns

Located 24 miles southeast of Montreal, about half-way to the American border at Rouse's Point, St. Johns lies on the left bank of the Richelieu River at the head of the Chambly canal. It thus has the benefit of water transportation northward to Sorel and southward to New York. The main C.P.R. and C.N.R. lines connect it with Montreal as do, also, the bus services to New York and Boston. The population was 25,000 according to the census of 1956. Across the river lies Iberville (6,300) which may be considered a residential suburb. In 1950, 66 plants employed 5,000 workers and produced over $40,000,000 worth of goods. The largest plant, founded in 1904, produces Singer Sewing Machines. There are also eight textile plants as well as those producing electrical equipment, paper products and canned vegetables.

### Farnham

Situated 15 miles east of St. Johns, at the foot of the first Appalachian ridge, Farnham is a small town (5,800) which grew up when the first railway was built through the area in 1858. Until 1910 a C.P.R. shop employed about 500 hands. Later textile industries were established, giving work to about 1,000 people. A Dominion Experimental Station is located nearby.

### Sorel

Sorel occupies a strategic position on the right bank of the St. Lawrence at the mouth of the Richelieu River, 45 miles northeast of Montreal. Including nearby St. Joseph, the population of greater Sorel is about 20,000. It has a natural harbour where shipbuilding and repairs have been carried on for a long time. During World War II, it

became one of the largest centres of war industry in the province, producing ships and guns. Since the war a large artificial silk plant has been established. A new smelter to handle the titanium ores from the north shore was set up and began operation in 1951.

### Joliette

Situated on the left bank of the Assomption River, about 35 miles north of Montreal, the city of Joliette contained a population of 17,000 in 1956. It is served by both major railways. Founded as a mill town in 1823 it was first known as "l'Industrie" but was given the name of its founder after his death in 1850. At that time it had a population of 2,500, but in 100 years it has grown to 16,000. It is less of an industrial centre than the other cities of the plain having only about 2,200, one-half of its working force, engaged in manufacturing. It is the trading centre and regional capital of a prosperous agricultural area, specializing in tobacco culture. Tobacco processing plants employ about 600. Textiles give work to about 800, while steel, lime, and paper products, with other minor industries employ the rest. However, it is its function as a regional centre of trade, transportation and education which gives to Joliette the appearance of an active and complete little town.

### Ste. Thérèse

An important C.P.R. junction, 18 miles northwest of Montreal, Ste. Thérèse developed rapidly as an industrial town during World War II. About 1,500 of its 8,000 inhabitants are employed in manufacturing. Wood using industries, plywood and furniture, and textiles are the most important.

### II. The Three Rivers Region

Situated about half-way between Montreal and Quebec, the centre of the St. Lawrence Lowland is occupied by the Three Rivers Region. It extends from the

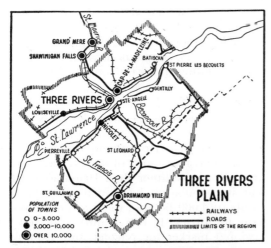

Figure 113. *The Three Rivers Plain.* The lowest and most poorly drained part of the St. Lawrence lowlands, its population is small, apart from its industrial cities.

foot of the Laurentians on the northwest, to the base of the Appalachians on the southeast. The southwestern boundary may be placed along the eastern borders of Berthier and Richelieu counties while the northeastern one is placed along the northeastern county lines of Nicolet and Maskinonge. Drained by the lower courses of large rivers on both banks of the St. Lawrence, the flat lowland, nevertheless, contains areas of bog and swamp. The area is approximately 2,280 square miles, 90% of which is occupied. The population numbers about 210,000, half rural, half urban. The flat lands by the lake are devoted to hay growing while the rest of the area is becoming an important dairy region. There are two fairly large cities devoted to commerce and industry: historic Three Rivers at the mouth of the St. Maurice, and Drummondville on the St. Francis, near the borders of the Eastern Townships. Nicolet and Louiseville are the only other towns.

## Three Rivers

Astride the mouth of the St. Maurice River, Three Rivers with a population of 50,000 and Cap de la Madeleine with 23,000 together constitute the fourth rank-

ing urban centre of the province. Located in the western angle between the St. Maurice and the St. Lawrence, the city of Three Rivers extends inland to the foot of a series of sandy terraces locally known as "les côteaux". Cap de la Madeleine occupies a terrace on the east bank of the St. Maurice, linked by railway and highway bridges. Founded in 1634 as a trading post, it has grown into an important city in the 20th century as a result of the development of the St. Maurice Valley. It has good communications. It is on the main highway and railway lines from Montreal to Quebec with branches leading into the St. Maurice Valley. It has a deep ocean harbour with a 2,000,000 bushel elevator and, in recent years, it handles more freight than Quebec. A ferry makes connection with St. Angèle de Laval on the south shore

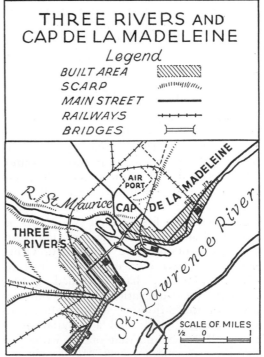

Figure 114. *The Cities of Three Rivers and Cap de la Madeleine.* Situated at the mouth of the St. Maurice River, Three Rivers is the most important pulp and paper manufacturing centre in Quebec. Cap de la Madeleine is a growing residential city.

of the St. Lawrence. The local airport lies behind Cap de la Madeleine. The twin cities have over 10,000 workers engaged in manufacturing, producing goods worth $150,000,000 in 1954. Four large pulp and paper mills make this the "paper capital" of the province. They employ about 3,200 workers but are outranked by textiles and leather goods which employ over 3,500. About 2,500 are employed in producing metal goods, mostly of iron. Trade and other urban functions, however, provide employment for more people than the manufacturing industries. The city is a regional capital and gateway to the hinterland of "la Mauricie". Rue des Forges is the main street, its name commemorating the former iron smelting activity. It leads from the waterfront across the busiest section of the city to the Exhibition field on the upper terrace. The older residential districts contain fine shaded streets and there are many newly built sub-divisions. Cap de la Madeleine has also greatly expanded its built-up area. Its old Rosary shrine is a famous pilgrim objective.

## Drummondville

Situated about 30 miles up the St. Francis River, Drummondville is 62 miles from Montreal to which it is closely linked by direct railway and highway routes. Founded in 1815, it had in the passage of a century as a county seat become a village of 2,800 people. In 1915 Southern Canada Power built the first of their two plants on the St. Francis and in the next ten years six textile plants were established. Other new plants have been established more recently. The city has expanded greatly through the annexation of the built-up areas of the adjoining municipalities. In 1956 the city itself had a population of about 27,000, while that of the whole urban area was about 35,000. About 9,000 are employed in manufacturing, of whom more than 85% are engaged in textiles. Other smaller plants produce rubber goods, pencils, paper boxes and electrical goods. The total value of manufactured goods made in Drummondville in 1950 was over $70,-000,000. To a greater degree, perhaps, than Three Rivers, Drummondville represents the expanding industrial might of Quebec.

## Other Towns

*Nicolet* overlooking the delta of Nicolet River where it enters Lake St. Peter has been, more than Drummondville, the capital of the region south of the St. Lawrence. In 1921 it was larger than Drummondville but its population has remained stagnant at about 4,000 because there are no important industries. It is a county seat and a regional market for Nicolet and Yamaska counties, a prosperous dairy farming region.

*Louiseville,* eighteen miles southwest of Three Rivers, with a population of about 4,400 has been the commercial centre of a flat hay growing region. Recently two textile factories have been established employing about 1,500 workers.

The Three Rivers region is a striking example of the way in which the deep isolation of rural Quebec is being shattered by the mushroom growth of industrial towns. The future may see other village nuclei suddenly expand in similar fashion.

## III.   The Quebec Region

The northeastern part of the St. Lawrence Lowland is a narrowing region compressed between the Laurentians and the Appalachian Highlands. Except where trenched by the St. Lawrence and its tributaries, the general elevation of the surface is from 200 to 300 feet above sea level. Downstream the region includes the Beaupré coast, the Island of Orleans and the flats of Bellechasse on the south bank of the river. Here in an area of about 2,000 square miles, 75% of which is occupied, some 400,000 people live and work. Here in the centre of the region is Quebec City, the ancient capital which, with its satellites, contains nearly three-fourths of the population.

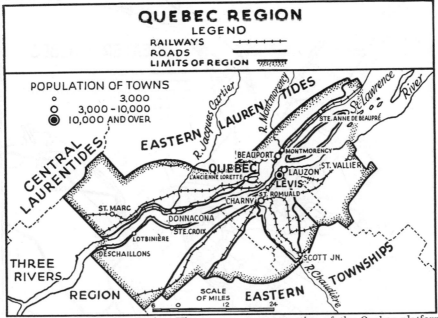

Figure 115. *The Quebec Region.* The narrow, eastern portion of the Quebec platform, deeply trenched by the St. Lawrence River became the earliest theatre of settlement in New France.

## Greater Quebec

At the census of 1956, Quebec and its suburbs had a population of 310,000.

**Table 10   The Population of Quebec**

| | |
|---|---:|
| Quebec (city) | 170,703 |
| St. Foy (city) | 14,615 |
| Lévis (city) | 13,644 |
| Sillery (city) | 13,154 |
| Lauzon (city) | 10,255 |
| Giffard (city) | 9,964 |
| Charlesbourg (town) | 8,202 |
| Quebec West (town) | 7,945 |
| Beauport (town) | 6,735 |
| Montmorency (town) | 6,077 |
| St. Romuald d'Etchemin | 5,278 |
| Loretteville (town) | 4,957 |
| St. Michel Archange | 4,530 |
| Courville (town) | 3,772 |
| Charny (village) | 3,639 |
| Notre Dame de Lorette | 3,464 |
| Other areas | 23,025 |
| Greater Quebec | 309,959 |

## The Geographic Setting of Quebec

The City of Quebec enjoys one of the finest urban sites on the continent. Its name in the Algonquin language means "where the river narrows". This occurs between Cape Diamond and the heights of Lévis across the river. Below this constriction the wide estuary of the St. Lawrence opens out. In few places is there to be found such an abrupt transition from a river to its estuary. The strategic position of Quebec at this entrance to the continent has earned it the title of "the Gibraltar of North America".

The city site falls naturally into two divisions. The upper town is perched upon a detached fragment of the widespread Quebec Platform which underlies the whole St. Lawrence lowland. The Citadel and the old walled city is surrounded by steep cliffs which are climbed by steep tortuous streets and flights of stairs. On this upper level are found the Parliament buildings and government offices, Laval University and the main hotels, largest of which is the

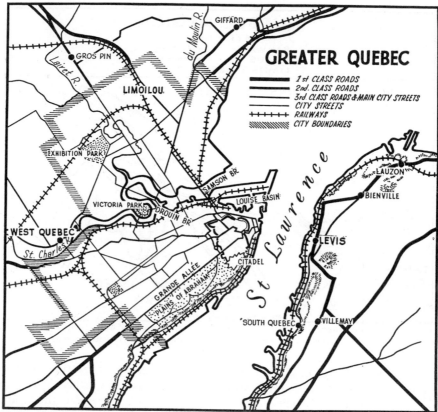

Figure 116. *Greater Quebec*. Quebec, "where the river narrows", was the chief gateway to Canada, and is still to be counted among its "greater cities".

immense Chateau Frontenac. Fine buildings stretch westward along the Grande Allée to Battlefield Park, the Plains of Abraham, on which the armies of Wolfe and Montcalm decided the fate of Canada.

The old Lower Town is exceedingly crowded in its narrow space between the cliff and the river, but it has found space for expansion north and west into the Valley of the St. Charles River. This wide depression is an abandoned course of the St. Lawrence and a great misfit for the meandering St. Charles. The mouth of the river is adjoined by extensive railway yards. Upstream on both sides are the industrial sites and the residential districts of the factory workers. This used to be the site of the shipyards during the first half of the nineteenth century when Quebec was one

of the greatest lumber and shipping centres in the world.

Lévis and Lauzon lie on the right bank directly across from Quebec. The latter point is the location of the modern shipyards and drydocks. A ferry links these suburbs to the city more effectively than the Quebec Bridge which lies ten miles up the river. Quebec is a railway terminal, second only to Montreal, while Lévis is an important divisional point on the main C.N.R. line from Montreal to Halifax. The other suburbs are clustered about the city on the north bank of the river.

### The Urban Functions

Quebec has become an important industrial centre, nevertheless it remains much less dominated by that function than Montreal, or any other town in Quebec.

The chief occupations of the 65,600 gainfully employed in the city proper have been classified in 1951 as follows: professionals, business owners or managers 20%, factory workers 15%, office clerks 16%, employees in services 14%, in commerce and finance 10%, in transportation 8.5% and in construction 7%.

The major role of Quebec is that of capi-

The intellectual role of Quebec has also high priority. The Jesuits conducted a centre of higher learning in Old Quebec before Harvard was founded. Laval University carries on the tradition with 8,000 students registered in 1956. Its old buildings are located in the shadow of the basilica, but new and larger buildings are being built as a "Cité Universitaire" along De

*Courtesy Canadian National Railways.*

Plate 42. St. John's Gate—old Quebec was a walled city.

tal. The very aspect of the Upper Town reflects that function in many ways. In the past Quebec was the capital of Canada, and is now the capital of the second greatest province. It houses thousands of civil servants of the provincial, federal, and municipal administrations. The Parliament buildings along Grande Allée contain both lower and upper chambers and the huge annexes house all departments of government. Quebec is also a judicial centre and a military headquarters, symbolized by the Court House and the Citadel.

Quebec is the oldest Roman Catholic metropolis north of Mexico, with one hundred dioceses. Some 2,000 priests and nuns live in the city, who, besides their religious tasks, are devoted to teaching and hospital work.

l'Entente Boulevard, outside of the upper town. The intellectual role is carried by a good many other citizens engaged in professional duties.

The tourist traffic may be added to the functions of the capital city. The tourists, who are mostly summer visitors, look for the typical French touch of Quebec, "the only walled city in North America". The battlefields of 1759, the old churches, the narrow streets "sous le cap", a few museums, and the picturesque surroundings combine to attract hundreds of thousands who are taken care of by the large hotels, many tourist homes and restaurants. Tourists bring as much money to Quebec as its largest industries.

The function of the capital is also stressed by the fact that 40% of the active

Plate 43. Chateau Frontenac and some of the old houses, as seen from the ramparts of the citadel.

population is engaged in services and office work.

The industrial function is represented by the 30% of the workers engaged in manufacturing and construction. After the deepening of the St. Lawrence in 1870, Montreal replaced Quebec as the main river port, thus making available a great reserve of labour which was glad to engage in manufacturing. The development of electrical power at the turn of the century also helped. There was ample space for industrial sites along the St. Charles river. The parishes of St. Roch and St. Saveur are crowded with the houses of the workmen. Within the city limits the most important establishments are shoe factories, tobacco, clothing, slaughtering and meat packing plants. North of the St. Charles, Limoilou is the site of the big Anglo-Canadian pulp and paper mill; Lauzon has a large drydock and shipyards. In 1954 the gross value of the manufactures of Greater Quebec amounted to $250,000,000 (net $115,000,-000).

The commercial function of Quebec employs about one-fifth of the workers. The old harbour, at the foot of the cliff below the citadel, is still used by many types of water craft, especially the coasting lines and the Lévis ferry which maintains a year-round service. A larger port was built, after 1890, at the mouth of the St. Charles where 20 berths for large ships were provided in locked basins. When this was considered inadequate, a new harbour was begun in 1931, at Wolfe's Cove on the St. Lawrence. This port can accommodate the largest ocean ships such as the Canadian Pacific Empresses. It is linked by a tunnel with the network of railways behind the city in the valley of the St. Charles. There is a 4,000,-000 bushel grain elevator at the St. Charles. Quebec is thus well equipped as a port of call for all ocean and inland shipping.

Quebec is the terminal of all railway lines on the north bank of the St. Lawrence. Most important is the Canadian Pacific line from Montreal. Canadian National lines also radiate in many directions linking Quebec to Murray Bay, Lake St. John and

Chicoutimi, Western Quebec, Montreal via Shawinigan Falls and Edmundston, N.B. via the Quebec Bridge. Across the same bridge the Quebec Central trains run to Beauce and Sherbrooke. Lévis has Canadian National service to Montreal, the cities of the South Shore and the Maritime Provinces.

An improved network of good roads gives to Quebec even greater accessibility than its railways. Chicoutimi, for instance, may be reached in four hours by road instead of nine hours by rail. Montreal is less than four hours by the improved Number 2 highway.

The commercial hinterland of Quebec embraces all the natural regions down the estuary and the gulf, part of the Eastern Townships, half of the St. Lawrence Lowlands, Lake St. John and the Saguenay and a goodly share of Western Quebec. In the latter region, however, the influences of Montreal and Toronto also compete.

The urban functions of greater Quebec are well balanced. It is one of the nicest cities in Canada and geographically the most interesting.

## Other Towns in the Quebec Region

In contrast with the Montreal region, there are no large independent cities within the orbit of Quebec. Most of the inhabitants of the surburban towns earn their living in the conurbation of Quebec-Lévis-Lauzon. There are, however, three towns worth mentioning. *Donnacona* (4,100) twenty-five miles to the southwest, at the mouth of the Jacques Cartier River, is the site of a pulp and paper mill, employing about 500 workers. Pulpwood is floated down the river or brought in by barge from Sault au Mouton on the North Shore. In summer paper is shipped to Newark in canal boats by way of the Richelieu-Lake Champlain waterway. *Montmorency* (6,-000), eight miles northeast of Quebec, located at the famous falls of the same name, is not only a favourite tourist spot with its fine park and hotels, but also the site of a large cotton factory, operated by the water power of the falls and giving work to about 1,500 employees. *Ste. Anne de Beaupré* (2,200) is fourteen miles northeast of Montmorency. Here at the end of the 17th century the renowned shrine of Ste. Anne was established. It has become the most popular Roman Catholic shrine in the world attracting twice as many pilgrims as Lourdes in France. It is visited by more than half a million people every year.

## The Island of Orleans

The Island of Orleans is also a detached portion of the Quebec peneplain now somewhat elevated through the general upward tilt of the lowland toward the north east. Its flattish summit is about 400 feet above sea level and it is bounded by gentle slopes and intermittent escarpments fringed by Pleistocene river terraces. It has an area of 94 square miles.

It was settled in 1641-48 by colonists from northern France. By 1667 it already had a

*Provincial Publicity Bureau, Quebec.*

Plate 44. A rural landscape on the Island of Orleans.

population of 529. By 1851 there were about 4,400, somewhat more than the present total. The island has only one incorporated village, *Beaulieu* (Ste. Pétronille) (400), at the southern end, but its rural areas preserve interesting aspects of the old rural life. Its isolation and some of its charm have disappeared since it was joined to the mainland by a bridge over the north channel in 1932. It is a region of specialized agriculture producing tree fruits, small fruits, potatoes and vegetables for the Quebec market. Formerly these products reached the city by boat, but river life has decayed since the coming of the highway.

### Geographic Personality

The Quebec region is unique, its geographic qualities cannot be matched anywhere else. Picturesque in its natural landscape, its human geography is just as interesting. Scene of the early colonization efforts in Canada, it still preserves many buildings and land use patterns from that historic time. This is the cradle of French Canadian culture.

## IV. The Eastern Townships

The region known as the Eastern Townships (Les Cantons de l'Est) is an irregularly shaped area lying between the St. Lawrence Lowlands and the American border and extending Northeastward as far as the line between the counties of Dorchester and Bellechasse. It is somewhat elevated and hilly, being a part of the worn down, folded Appalachian

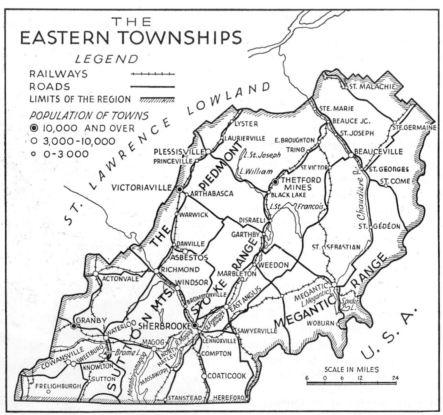

Figure 117. *The Eastern Townships.* A picturesque region of ridges, plateaus and valleys, the Eastern Townships have prosperous mixed farming communities and thriving industrial cities.

mountain system, drained by the deeply en-trenched streams of the St. Francis, Chau-dière and Etchemin river systems. Of a to-tal area of 9,120 square miles, about 7,000 (77%) is occupied. The total population is about 450,000 of whom at least half are living in the numerous towns.

The region lies outside the boundaries of the old seigneuries granted by the French and was laid out in townships after Canada changed hands. It was termed the "Eastern" townships in contrast with those lying to the west of Montreal in what is now On-tario.

The first settlers in the southern part of the area were English speaking and for a long time they were the dominant element. The northern area, including the plateau of Beauce, was settled by French who came up the Chaudière from Quebec. Now, how-ever, practically every county has a major-ity of French speaking people.

It is an area of mixed farming, the care of livestock having been stressed by the original English speaking settlers, many of whom were United Empire Loyalists. Dairying is important. The northern por-tion has the largest sheep industry in east-ern Canada. It is also the headquarters of the maple sugar industry.

The multitude of small power sites stimu-lated an early development of sawmills, grist mills and local manufacturing plants. This has given way to the much more ex-tensive industrial activity of the present day. From this as well as because of the hilly landscapes, the Eastern Townships have been called "the New England of Can-ada". The hills, lakes, streams and thriving towns have scenic values which draw visi-tors in spite of the attractions of the great expanse of the Laurentians farther north.

## Sherbrooke

Founded in 1794, Sherbrooke was at first known as "Great Forks" from its location at the confluence of the St. Francis River and its left bank tributary the Magog. Sher-brooke is 96 miles east of Montreal, 140

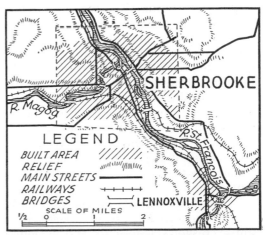

Figure 118. *Sherbrooke and its Environs.* Found-ed because of the possibilities of water power. Sherbrooke is located at the junction of the Magog and St. Francis Rivers.

miles south of Quebec and 30 miles north of the American border. Strategically situ-ated, it soon became the nucleus of roads and railways and the site of important in-dustries, earning the title, "Queen of the Eastern Townships". Railways radiate in six directions: the C.P.R. to Montreal and St. John, N.B.; the C.N.R. to Portland, Maine, and to Montreal, and the Quebec Central to Quebec and to Boston. Provin-cial Highways 1, 5 and 22 provide road service. The population exceeds 60,000.

The urban functions resemble those of a New England town. Industry is domi-nant, more than half of the active popu-lation being employed in manufacturing and the building trade. About twenty plants have more than 100 workers each. The largest are the textile factories produc-ing hosiery, rayon and cotton fabrics and woollens. Metal products are also impor-tant including mining machinery, locomo-tive parts, scales and jewellery. In 1954 there were over 130 plants, employing 8,500 people and producing goods to the value of $80,000,000. The other half of the working force is found in services, transpor-tation and commerce.

Sherbrooke, picturesquely surrounded by Appalachian hills, is built on the lower slopes and on the river terraces on both banks of the St. Francis River. The largest part, containing four of the five wards, is located on the left bank. Through this area the Magog river flows in a narrow gorge below the 100-foot fall, providing an excellent power site. There are two main streets: King Street, sloping from a bridge above the fall on the Magog to another one across the St. Francis below; and Wellington Street, at right angles to the former, serving as an axis to the business district in the centre ward.

Three miles south of Sherbrooke, yet almost contiguous, *Lennoxville* (3,000) is the site of Bishop's University and a Dominion Experimental Station.

The variety of functions gives to Sherbrooke the aspect of a regional capital. It is also becoming a tourist headquarters. Fine lakes and forest-covered hills are close at hand, attracting many summer visitors; while, in recent years, skiing resorts have developed. The shores of Lake Massawippi, Lake Memphremagog and Lake Brome and Mount Orford Provincial Park are the most popular resort areas.

## Other Towns Near Sherbrooke

*Granby*, half way between Sherbrooke and Montreal. is the second town of the region with a population of 27,000 (census of 1956). Only a village during the nineteenth century, it has become a thriving industrial town. In 1954 it had 90 factories with 7,000 workers producing $57,000,000 of goods. Tobacco, textiles and rubber goods are the largest industries.

*Magog* (12,500), sixteen miles southwest of Sherbrooke, served by the C.P.R. and by Provincial Highway, has one large industry, a cotton factory employing over 2,000 people. Situated at the outlet of Lake Memphremagog it is a summer resort area.

*Waterloo* (4,000), half way between Magog and Granby, is a railway junction and local commercial centre which has a number of factories producing plywood, plastics and kitchenware. Here also is found

the only large scale mushroom growing establishment in Quebec.

*Cowansville* and *Sweetsburg* are twin towns about 50 miles west of Montreal on the C.P.R. The latter is a judicial centre and residential village with a typical New England outlook; the former is an industrial town producing textiles and furniture.

*Coaticook* (6,500) is a clean looking small town on the floor of a glacial valley, 20 miles southeast of Sherbrooke. It is a regional market for dairy products and live stock and has textile factories.

Small towns along the St. Francis include: *East Angus* (3,700) 20 miles upstream from Sherbrooke, and *Bromptonville* (2,000) 26 miles downstream. Both are paper mill sites. *Windsor Mills* (4,700), 10 miles further downstream, was once a sawmill town, but now has a paper mill as its only large industry. *Richmond* (3,500), a few miles further down, is an important C.N.R. junction having also textile and shoe factories. *Actonvale* (3,400), 20 miles east of Richmond was once a copper mining centre but now has rubber and textile plants.

## The Mining Centres

The asbestos mines of the Serpentine belt support several towns and villages including: *Asbestos, Danville, Thetford Mines, Black Lake, East Broughton* and *Robertsonville*. Asbestos is a fibrous hydrated magnesium silicate ($H_4Mg_3Si_2O_8$) formed by recrystallization of serpentinized peridotite, an ultra basic rock which was intruded into the folded Paleozoic rocks of the region. The asbestos fibres of the silky crysotile variety are found in veins, several inches in width and many feet in length. The asbestos laden rock is quarried from huge open pits. The longest fibres are selected by hand and the rest of the rock is crushed and the fibre sorted mechanically. The resultant waste is dumped in huge pyramids beside the pits. Asbestos finds many uses; long fibres, over half an inch, may be spun and woven into fire-proof textiles, shorter ones, down to one-twentieth of an inch are made into fire-proof paper, insulating materials and shingles. Nearly one million tons, worth $90,000,000, were mined in 1952.

*Asbestos,* situated about six miles northeast of Richmond on the C.N.R. is at the southwestern extremity of the belt. It had a population of 9,000 in 1956. The quarries here have been exploited since 1880 and have produced half of Canada's output of asbestos. Two thousand men are employed. The nearby suburb of Danville has a population of about 2,000.

*Thetford Mines,* halfway between Sherbrooke and Quebec on the Quebec Central Railway, is a typical mining town of 20,000 inhabitants. It is surrounded by deep pits and mountainous dumps of waste rock; the mills are located along the tortuous and sloping main streets of the town. Over 3,000 people work in the mines and mills.

*Black Lake* (3,700) four miles southwest of Thetford Mines and *East Broughton* (1,700), fifteen miles northeast, also have large asbestos quarries.

## The Piedmont

The piedmont is an interesting contact zone between the Eastern Townships and the St. Lawrence Lowlands. Here the rivers leave the plateau and take their courses over the plain at a much lower gradient. The break in slope makes a convenient

power site and mill villages were early established. Some of these have grown to fair sized towns in recent years. It is difficult to know which region should claim some of them. Farnham, Granby, Actonvale and Drummondville have already been discussed. Farther northeast there is another line of towns on the railway and highway that skirts the region. We assign them to the plateau because they are separated by a wide zone of swampy forests from the main zone of lowland settlement along the St. Lawrence.

*Victoriaville* (16,000) is a rapidly growing market and industrial centre on the Nicolet River, about half way between Thetford Mines and Three Rivers. In 1950, it had 56 factories employing 2,600 workers and producing goods worth $16,000,000. The leading products are textiles, woodwork and furniture. *Arthabaska* (2,400) two miles to the south, is a pleasant residential town and judicial seat of the surrounding county.

*Plessisville* (5,800), ten miles northeast, is the trade centre of the district locally known as "Bois francs" (hardwoods). Varied industries have developed here: working in metals, leather, textiles and furniture. Here also are the headquarters of the Quebec maple sugar producers and the Quebec flax producers. Nearby *Princeville* (3,000) has woodworking plants and an important meat packing industry.

D. F. Putnam.

Plate 45. The Chaudière Valley provides a corridor deep into the Appalachian Plateau.

## The Chaudière Valley

The Chaudière Valley has been an important corridor since early times. It still has this function, being traversed by the Quebec Central Railway and the Jackman-Lévis highway. At the very source of the river is *Megantic* (6,800), located at the northern end and outlet of Lake Megantic, and not far from the border of Maine. The railways (C.P.R. and Q.C.R.), a wood-pulp mill and several sawmills employ about 1,000 men. Further down the river in Beauce county are: *St. Georges* (7,000), site of a woollen factory, and *Beauceville* (2,700), *St. Joseph* (2,400) and *Ste. Marie* (3,000). These are all picturesque valley towns, functioning as market centres for the surrounding agricultural districts.

## V. The South Shore of the Estuary

This region lies south of the St. Lawrence river, extending between the Eastern Townships and the Gaspé Peninsula. It has a population of 275,000, only 22% of which is urban. The region has two distinct physical zones: a flattish piedmont along the shore about 1,200 square miles in area, which is mostly occupied; and a vast inland plateau of 10,000 square miles, of which only one-third is occupied, the settlements lying along the main roads, rivers and lakes. The old parishes along the shore have been settled for two hundred years or more while those of the plateau, offshoots of the former, have for the most part arisen within the past century. It is a rural area now well tied together by road and rail services. Only a few places deserve the name of towns, yet some of them have been expanding in recent years.

*Montmagny* (6,500) is located 33 miles northeast of Lévis, at the confluence of the two branches of Rivière du Sud. Its main functions have long been commercial and administrative, but it has large wood-working industries, a silk factory and a stove foundry as well as many smaller plants. Its products for 1950 were worth $12,000,000. *L'Islet* (2,500), chief town of L'Islet County is the site of another stove foundry. *St. Jean Port Joli* (2,600) has many wooden handcraft workers. *Ste. Anne de la Pocatiére* (3,000) is an important educational centre with a classical college and the agriculture and fishery schools of Laval University. *Rivière du Loup* (10,500), 120 miles northeast of Lévis, is the only city on the south shore of the estuary. An important C.N.R. junction, it developed and has remained an active centre of traffic. The railways employ about 900 workers. A ferry service makes connection with St. Simeon on the north shore of the St. Lawrence. The Trans-Canada highway turns inland here to reach Edmunston and the Maritime Provinces.

*Trois Pistoles* (3,500), 30 miles east of Rivière du Loup is a busy sawmill town.

*Rimouski* (15,000) has more than doubled its population since 1941. It is a railway division point 70 miles down the coast from Rivière du Loup. It has the only deep water pier along the shore and is the main point of departure for the north shore. It has also an important airport. It is an important commercial centre and the site of large sawmills. *Mont Joli* (5,000) has the largest airport in Eastern Quebec. It is the starting point of the highway around the Gaspé Peninsula and the point at which the main line of the C.N.R. leaves the shore to pass through the Matapedia Valley into New Brunswick. *Priceville* (3,000) nearby, has large sawmills. *Metis Beach*, 15 miles east of Mt. Joli, is one of the finest summer resorts in Quebec. *Matane* (8,000) twenty miles further on is the gateway to the Gaspé Peninsula. It is the end of steel, a navigation centre and has several sawmills.

The Matapedia Valley contains the large villages of Saybec (2,200), Amqui (2,600), and Causapscal (2,600); Cabano (2,600) and Notre Dame du Lac (1,400) are sawmill towns on Lake Temiscouata; Rivière Bleue and St. Pamphile are villages near the Maine border.

The South Shore is composed of two contrasting areas from the standpoint of hu-

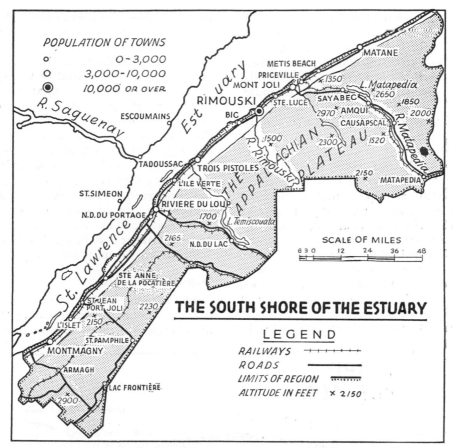

Figure 119. *The South Shore of the Estuary.* Here are two definite natural regions: a narrow, closely populated littoral lowland; and an extensive sparsely populated plateau.

man as well as physical geography. The former is largely agricultural despite the large sawmills which get their wood from the plateau. The latter, on the other hand, is an area of scattered forest settlements. There has been some settlement of cut over lands, but agriculture is mainly of a part-time subsistence type and the mainstay is still exploitive forestry. Town and village alike are built of wood, the extreme fire hazard being exemplified by the disastrous fires which swept both Cabano and Rimouski in 1950.

## VI. The Gaspé Peninsula

Surrounded on three sides by the sea, the Gaspé Peninsula, "la Gaspésie", has an area of over 7,500 square miles. Its interior is rugged, containing the highest hills of the Appalachians, the Shickshock Range with summits over 4,000 feet. The original settlers, who were fishermen, clustered along the shore. The occupied area today is still an encircling belt comprising less than one-seventh of the total area. The total population is a b o u t 100,000, including the people of the Magdalen Islands, an archipelago over 100 miles away in the Gulf which is attached to Gaspé County for purposes of administration. Less than 5% of the population is classified as urban. Actually there are no towns, and only a few large villages. Most of the population lives along the shore of Chaleur Bay which is lower, more indented and more hospitable than that of the St. Lawrence Estuary. Settlement is practically continuous from Matapedia to Percé and Gaspé, the highway being somewhat like a string on which the villages are strung as beads. *Chandler* (3,300) is a pulp mill town; *Grande Rivière*, (2,000) is a fishing port and the site of a marine biological laboratory; *Percé* (1,500) has a large summer population; its cuestaform hills and "pierced" rock appeal to both geographers and tourists. *Gaspé* (2,000) with a deep natural harbour, at the end of the rails, is the regional capital. Murdochville (1,700) is an important copper mining centre in the interior.

On the North Shore, *Rivière au Renard* (2,000) has a modern sea products factory; *Ste. Anne des Monts* (3,000) and *Cap Chat* (2,000) both have large sawmills. Copper ore will soon be exploited near Mont Louis.

Visitors like Gaspé; there are awe-inspiring vistas along the north coast and isolated little villages tucked into sheltered coves. They like to see primitive ways of doing things: the fish flake, the ox-cart and the outdoor oven. The coastal belt is equipped for tourists with its fine road, cabins and hotels, but the interior with its great forest has not yet come into its own. Gaspé Provincial Park which includes some of the highest of the Shickshocks, when properly outfitted, will be accessible from the south along the Cascapedia Valley and from the north via Ste. Anne des Monts. Another proposed route follows the York Valley from Gaspé. The highest summit, Mt. Jacques Cartier may be reached from Mont Louis by a road built for war purposes.

**Magdalen Islands.**

The Magdalen Islands are a small group in the Gulf of St. Lawrence about 150 miles from Gaspé and about 60 miles from Prince

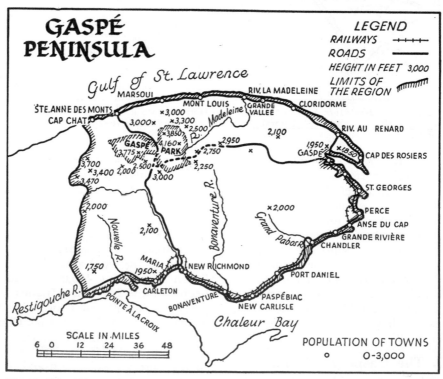

Figure 120. *The Gaspé Peninsula.* Scenic Gaspé has a rugged forested interior, bordered by a string of picturesque fishing villages.

Edward Island. The total land area is less than 50 square miles. The population numbers about 10,000, practically all of whom get their living from fishing. The population, entirely rural, has a density of 200 per square mile. The islands have boat connections with Gaspé and with Souris and Charlottetown in Prince Edward Island.

## VII. The Laurentians

Long known as the Laurentian Hills, the southern marches of the Canadian Shield in Quebec constitute a dissected and glaciated plateau of considerable relief. The southern border is a bold fault line scarp along which the harder Pre-cambrian rocks stand about one thousand feet higher than the less resistant Ordovician sedimentaries of the St. Lawrence Lowlands. A similar type of relief is found all along the edge of the Plateau from the Ottawa River to beyond the Saguenay a distance of 450 miles. River patterns and human settlements make it advisable to treat the Laurentians as three sub-regions.

### a. The Western Laurentians

The western portion is the Ottawa Valley Region, "Le Nord de l'Outouais", including the counties of Pontiac, Gatineau, Hull and Papineau. It is a large area since these counties extend inland to the highest part of the plateau covering more than 13,700 square miles. The occupied area, however, is small; the organized municipalities take in 3,660 square miles but the settled area is not more than 2,000. Beside the Ottawa itself, the Gatineau and Lièvre provide corridors of settlement into the interior. The total population is about 150,000, one-half of which is urban.

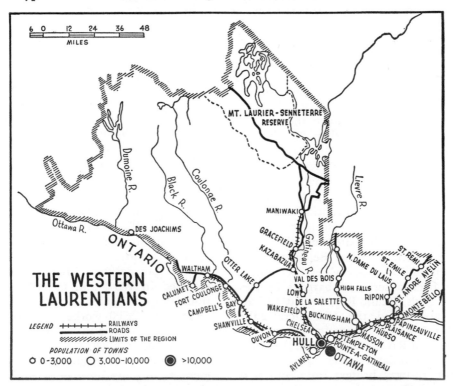

Figure 121. *The Western Laurentians.* This district includes the Ottawa Valley and the highlands which are accessible from it.

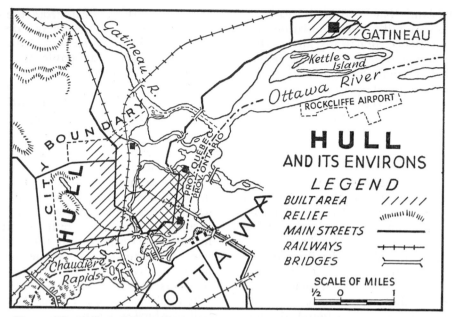

Figure 122. *Hull and its Environs*. Hull and its smaller satellites may all be considered as part of the Greater Ottawa metropolitan district.

## Hull and Its Environs

Facing Ottawa from the north bank of the river, Hull is the fifth city of Quebec, with a population (1956) of over 50,000. Within a radius of five miles, up the river to include Aylmer and down the river to include Gatineau, more than 20,000 additional urban dwellers may be counted. Further, it must be remembered that this Greater Hull is itself only part of an urban metropolis of more than 345,000 people. This remarkable concentration of population is due, in the first place, to the physiography of the site and the forest resources of the interior. Below the vast expansion of Lake Deschênes the Ottawa tumbles over a series of barriers in Deschênes Rapids, Remic Rapids, Little Chaudière Rapids and the Chaudière Falls. Though preventing navigation between the lower Ottawa River and the lake, they have provided abundant water power. Four road and railway bridges link Hull with the Federal Capital. Entering the Ottawa just below Hull from the north, the Gatineau transports logs from the interior and also provides more power than this section of the Ottawa itself. The river terraces, about 50 feet above the water, offer ample room for urban expansion, industrial sites and transportation facilities. Founded in 1800 by Philemon Wright, an early "timber king", Hull and Ottawa were the chief centre of the square timber trade and the succeeding lumber trade during the 19th century and became an important site of the pulp and paper industry in the 20th century. Hull is much more of an industrial city than Ottawa; 22% of its 17,000 workers are employed in manufacturing. Two large paper mills, E. B. Eddy Company founded in 1851, and Canadian International Paper, located at Gatineau, employ more than 2,500 workers. Textile plants, largely specializing in woodmen's clothing, employ about 1,000; while, amongst other industries a meat packing plant and a cement factory are most important. In 1954 the manufactures of Greater Hull were worth $100,000,000 ($45,000,000 net).

Services employ 15% of the working population. The proximity of Ottawa is thus felt. Street cars and busses carry hundreds of daily commuters across the river, most of whom are civil servants. Hull is thus a dormitory suburb of the Federal Capital. Transportation is important, both transcontinental railways serve the twin-cities and three branch lines radiate from Hull. Highways along both sides of the Ottawa and from the Gatineau Valley add to the traffic. The economic life of the whole region is focused upon Hull and Ottawa.

## Valley Settlements

The Ottawa valley west of Aylmer is almost completely rural, containing a few villages of which *Fort Coulonge* (1,400) is the largest. Its chief activity is lumbering. *Shawville* serves as a market centre for the agricultural district in Pontiac county.

The Gatineau valley is a scenic tourist resort area containing Gatineau National Park. A railway and highway thread the valley, passing through Wakefield and Gracefield to *Maniwaki*. Situated 65 miles from Hull, this is a railway terminus and commercial centre of 3,800 people. The highway branches in two directions, east to Mont Laurier and northwest to Senneterre through the great provincial park.

The valley of the Lièvre River is parallel to the Gatineau and a few miles to the east. This river is also used for log driving and the production of power. It is followed by a highway which makes connection with the one previously mentioned. In the lower part of the valley are the towns of *Buckingham* (6,000) and *Masson* (2,000) containing a pulp mill and paper mill respectively. The mining of quartz and feldspar is also carried on in the neighbourhood.

Another string of villages lies to the east along the Ottawa Valley served by the Canadian Pacific Railway and Quebec Highway Number 8. *Thurso* (2,000) is a centre of hardwood utilization, making flooring and sewing machine cabinets. A logging railway extends inland for 30 miles,

giving service also to a fairly good agricultural district. *Papineauville* (1,300), 36 miles east of Hull, is a small market centre for a dairy district and the point of departure for highway to the Central Laurentians. *Montebello* (1,500), four miles farther east, plays the same roles. Beside this village stands the Seigniory Club, one of the most exclusive resorts in Eastern Canada. The main hotel is built on the bank of the river while a score of villas and bungalows are spread over the whole Petite Nation Seigniory, a fishing and hunting paradise.

## b. The Central Laurentians

The Central Laurentians extend from Argenteuil and Labelle counties in the southwest, to Portneuf and Quebec counties in the northeast. The region has a frontage of 150 miles along the edge of the plateau and an area of 24,000 square miles. Settlement, however, clusters along the southern border and in the main valleys. One-fifth of the region is in municipal units but only one-tenth is really occupied. The total population is about 220,000, divided about equally into rural and urban groups.

There are two groups of towns worth mentioning, one in the southwest, the "Laurentians" of the Montrealers, and one in the northeast, called "Mauricie" by the citizens of Three Rivers.

## Laurentians

*Lachute* (6,900) as its name implies, grew up at the last fall on the North River. Its industries include a paper mill, a felt and wool mill and, more recently, a veneer plant. *Brownsburg* (3,500), three miles away has a large explosive and chemical products plant. The hilly exterior of Argenteuil county is a fine playground, but Lachute is more of an industrial than a resort town.

Highway 11 is the main route from Montreal to the Laurentian resorts; leaving the lowlands it follows the valley of the North

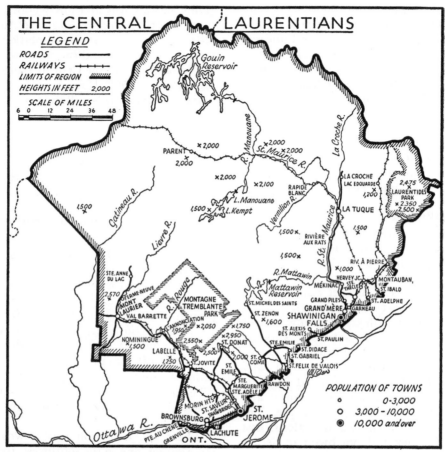

Figure 123. *The Central Laurentians.* A vast vacation land of rivers, lakes and mountains is easily accessible from Montreal and Three Rivers.

River. The gateway to this vacation land is *St. Jerome* (21,000) a busy market and industrial centre. Here are found two paper mills, a large rubber goods factory, a woolen mill and many smaller plants. In 1950, 54 plants employed 4,000 workers and produced goods worth $24,000,000. Northward along the highway are numerous resort villages such as *Shawbridge, Ste. Adele* with nearby *Mont Rolland,* the site of a pulp-mill, together containing about 2,500 people, and *Val Morin.* The first town is *Ste. Agathe des Monts* (5,200), 30 miles from St. Jerome, a peaceful and picturesque place, headquarters for a large resort region. *St. Jovite* (1,500), 20 miles further

on, is a resort area near Mont Tremblant Provincial Park, a rugged wilderness area of 1,200 square miles. Trembling Mountain which gives its name to the Park, has an elevation of 3,750 feet. *Mont Laurier* (5,500) is about 100 miles from St. Jerome. It is the terminus of the C.P.R. branch line and the starting point of highway 58 to Western Quebec. It is a lumbering and local commercial centre. Lying in the upper Lièvre Valley, Mont Laurier might perhaps have been included in the western section of the Laurentians, except that its road and railway connections link it more directly with Montreal rather than Hull.

## Mauricie

Mauricie, the St. Maurice Valley, is very different. There is very little agriculture along the river, but the forest resources and the abundant water power have, during the present century, made it a region of large scale industrial development.

*Shawinigan Falls* (40,000) is the largest city. Located at the falls of the same name on the St. Maurice River, 20 miles from Three Rivers and 100 miles northeast of Montreal, it was but a small village in 1901, when a pulp and paper mill and an aluminum smelter were established. These pioneer industries have both expanded to employ about 800 workers each. Other large plants added since include a carbide factory, two chemical plants, one for explosives and a cotton textile plant. In 1954, 50 plants employed over 5,500 workers and produced $118,000,000 worth of goods, outranking Hull and Sherbrooke, both of which are considerably more populous cities. A very high proportion of the active population is engaged in manufacturing making it particularly susceptible to the effects of booms and depressions. It is a typical city in which outside capital has been applied to the utilization of both the natural resources of the land and the labour of the French Canadian population.

*Grand'Mère* (14,000), three miles up the river looks much like Shawinigan Falls. A large pulp and paper mill was established here at the end of the 19th century and still provides employment for numerous workers. Woolens, shirts, knitting and shoe manufacturing now employ more people than the pulp and paper industry. Altogether there were 26 factories with 2,400 employees and a gross production of $30,000,000 in 1954.

Ten miles northeast of Grand'Mère, a former village, *St. Tite* has grown into a small town of 3,500. It has been and still is an outfitting centre for woodsmen as well as a local farmers' market.

*La Tuque* (10,000), 60 miles north of Grand'Mère, was put on the map in 1908 when a pulp mill was established on the local waterfall. Power plants at La Tuque and at Rapide Blanc, 20 miles up the river, have a total capacity of 422, 500 H.P. La Tuque is on the Northern Transcontinental line of the C.N.R. and is the terminus of the St. Maurice Valley highway. It is the centre of forest exploitation on a large scale and is also a sportsmen's headquarters for hunting and fishing.

### c. The Eastern Laurentians

Extending from Portneuf county to Charlevoix county where they abut onto the St. Lawrence, the Eastern Laurentian Plateau occupies 7,200 square miles, an

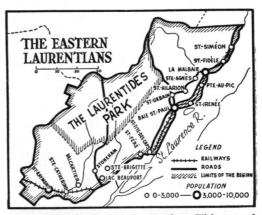

Figure 124. *The Eastern Laurentians.* This rugged sector of the border of the Canadian Shield is most easily accessible from Quebec.

area about as large as the Gaspé Peninsula. The settled portion is a narrow southern fringe of about 800 square miles although 1,600 square miles are included within the borders of the municipalities. The total population is about 47,000 of which only 30% is urban. Included in this region is the largest forest, fish and game preserve in the province, the Laurentides Provincial Park. With an area of 3,670 square miles it has a rugged surface, much of which is more than 3000 feet above sea level, and is well supplied with lakes and streams. There are two hotels and about 20 fishing camps. The park is traversed by highway 54, from Quebec to Chicoutimi and Lake St. John.

*St. Raymond* (3,100) is located 30 miles northwest of Quebec, where the C.N.R. crosses the Ste. Anne River. Here a small paper mill was founded in 1900. Chute Panet supplies the power and the pulpwood comes partly from Desbiens in the Lake St. John district.

*Baie St. Paul* (4,000), at the mouth of the Gouffre River in Charlevoix County, is amongst the older settlements in the country. Lumber was shipped from Baie St. Paul during the French period and the trade is still carried on. There is also some agriculture on the adjoining alluvial plain. It is a junction point in the provincial highway system; Route 15 continues along the north shore while Route 56 turns inland leading directly to Bagotville.

*Murray Bay* (La Malbaie) (2,500) is located in a similar cove at the mouth of Malbaie River about 90 miles northeast from Quebec. It is the end of steel on the C.N.R. branch line from Quebec and a port of call for coastal navigation. Richelieu Manor is a noted resort at nearby Pointe au Pic. A pulp and paper mill and other wood using industries give work to a few hundred people. The tourist trade is very active in the summer time.

## VIII. Western Quebec

The "far west" of the province of Quebec includes "the Clay Belt" and the adjoining mining districts. It comprises an area of 85,000 square miles, of which less than 2,000 may be considered settled territory. The population, at the census of 1951 was 141,500 having gained 30% in ten years. This is a pioneer region where the government of Quebec is promoting the development of organized rural communities and at the same time new mining towns are being built. About one-half of the population may be classed as urban.

The largest urban centre of Western Quebec comprises the twin towns of Rouyn and Noranda.

*Rouyn* (17,000), located on Lake Oisiko, 421 miles by highway northwest of Montreal, is the commercial centre of the mining region. It was founded about 1923, at the beginning of the exploitation of the gold and copper ores of the district. *Noranda* (10,000), built along the railroad just to the north is a "company town" set up to

*National Film Board.*

Plate 46. The mines and smelter at Noranda in Western Quebec.

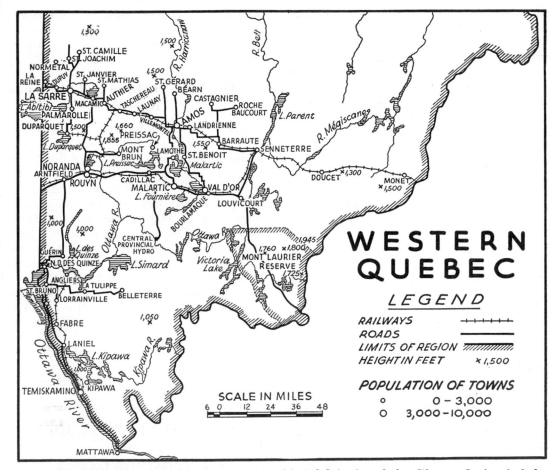

Figure 125. *Western Quebec.* A rather large region with indefinite boundaries, Western Quebec includes the agricultural settlements of the "Great Clay Belt", the mining settlements from Rouyn to Val d'or, and the older settlements of the Témiscamingue District.

house workers of Noranda mines. Nearby are the mineshaft headings, the tall stacks and huge buildings of the smelter which remind the observer of the essential function of this area. Over 2,500 men are employed.

*Val d'Or* (10,000), about 60 miles east of Rouyn, was founded in 1937, when the C.N.R. branch was built from Senneterre to Noranda. It is the urban centre for a number of mines including Sigma, Siscoe, Lamaque, Sullivan and Perron. There is no attempt at farming in the neighbourhood of these mines and only a little lumbering and pulpwood cutting. *Bourla-*

*maque* (3,000), close to the mine of the same name, is about one mile from Val d'Or. A direct highway links Val d'Or to Amos.

*Malartic* (7,000), in the township of the same name, is situated 17 miles west of Val d'Or. There are four mines nearby and lumbering also is carried on fairly extensively.

*Amos* (5,200), on the Harricanaw River, is the real capital of the Western Quebec. It is 435 miles west of Quebec City by the C.N.R. and was founded when the road was built in 1912. It is 400 miles northeast of Montreal by road. The town has passed through three stages of evolution: 1912-26 was the pioneer period in which forest cutting and land clearing took place; 1926-38 witnessed the period of the gold rush, while 1938 to the present has been a period of adjustment to new conditions. Amos has lost trade to newly-developed mining centres and must seek compensation by an increase in the agricultural activity of its upland. There are few industries, but there is an active retail trade and a fairly important administrative function.

*La Sarre* (3,200), 50 miles west of Amos and *Senneterre* (2,200), 40 miles east, are local trading centres.

South of the mining district is an older area of settlement near Lake Timiskaming. *Ville Marie* (1,500), is the nucleus of a dairy farming and lumbering region. Gold has been discovered at nearby Belleterre.

*Timiskaming* (3,000), 50 miles further south, on the left bank of the Ottawa, is a company town developed near a large pulp and paper mill. It has direct highway connection with North Bay.

Western Quebec gives promise of be-coming a diversified area, but at present its outstanding effort is the production of an average of $100,000,000 per annum of metallic minerals.

## IX. The Lake St. John and Saguenay Region

The Lake St. John and Saguenay Region is located north of the Central and Eastern Laurentians and west of the North Shore. In the midst of 41,000 square miles of rugged, forested plateau country, lies a tiny occupied area of 1,500 square miles containing 235,000 people. It is a down-faulted area surrounding Lake St. John (375 square miles) and opening to the St. Lawrence by the fjord-like Saguenay. Land settlement began here in 1849, soon to be followed by forest exploitation, first for lumber and later for pulpwood. The availability of water power and the accessibility of the area have led to the development of one of the largest aluminum industries in the world. Today more than half of the people are urban dwellers.

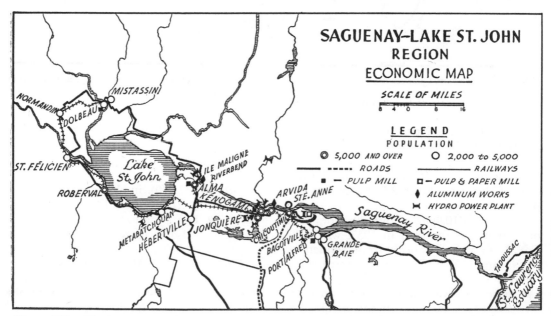

Figure 126. *The Saguenay—Lake St. John Region.* The development of the enormous water-power resources of this region has created an industrial empire in the wilderness.

## Chicoutimi

Located on the right bank of the Saguenay River at the confluence of two tributaries, Chicoutimi and Du Moulin Rivers, it has the farthest upstream deep water harbour. With a population estimated at 25,000 it is not the most populous urban centre, but it is the most important by reason of its diversified functions.

The city is built on low semi-circular terraces around "the basin" and is surrounded by hills three to four hundred feet high. Viewed from the rocky cliffs along the road to Arvida, Chicoutimi looks as picturesque as one of the cities in the narrow gorge of the Rhine Valley.

It has grown because it is the focus of favourable transportation facilities, its harbour, its railway and highway connections. The C.N.R. line to Quebec was opened in 1893. A more direct highway now puts it only 125 miles from Quebec. The Bagotville airport is just ten miles away.

Chicoutimi was first a lumbering centre and the gateway of an expanding pioneer agricultural settlement; it is now a commercial, manufacturing and administrative centre. Many labourers live here and find employment at Arvida or elsewhere. Racine Street, along the waterfront, is the focus of business activity. To the observer who lingers here, the character of the city is quickly revealed. Large retail stores are seen on both sides, and there are a crowded bus terminal, a railway station and freight yards, the City Hall, the county court house and many hotels and restaurants. The cathedral sits on the bluff overlooking the river and is surrounded by educational institutions. Chicoutimi is the capital of the whole region.

## Jonquière-Kénogami

The adjoining towns of Jonquière (26,-000), and Kénogami (11,000), 8 miles west of Chicoutimi, constitute the largest urban agglomeration in the region. They are located mainly on the right bank and below the last fall of the Au Sable River which flows from Lake Kénogami into the Saguenay. A large pulpmill is located at Jonquière and a pulp and paper mill at Kénogami. There are a few small manufacturing plants and a retail trade almost as important as that of Chicoutimi. Many people who live here work in Arvida.

## Arvida

Arvida, situated about half-way between Chicoutimi and Kénomagi, is a planned town founded by the Aluminum Company of Canada in 1927. The site which was originally farmland extends over a large flat terrace about 450 feet above sea level, giving ample room for expansion. A model town was built which during World War II grew to have a population of about 11,000. The plant extends for a mile along the railway near the townsite. Modern principles of town planning have been applied here. Nothing ugly is to be seen; the view from the Saguenay Inn, the best hotel in the region, is unique. The panorama of the mighty river and the two great Shipshaw power houses is impressive and explains why Arvida was called into being. The geographic factors behind this enterprise are abundant water power, ease of transportation and a facile labour force supplied by the rural population of this region and the rest of the province. Its future is linked with the prosperity of the aluminum industry.

### Other Centres

*Alma, Riverbend* and *Ile Maligne* are three towns in a group at the source of the Saguenay. They have a population of about 9,000. Leaving Lake St. John, the river flows in two branches around Alma Island. St. Joseph d'Alma and Riverbend face one another across Petite Décharge, the southern branch, while Ile Maligne lies beside a waterfall on the northern branch, or Grande Décharge. The latter was developed as a model town when an aluminum reduction plant was opened during World

War II. It is Arvida in miniature. River-bend is the site of a big pulp and paper mill while Alma is a residential town of factory workers, lumberjacks and retired farmers. Its main function is more commercial than industrial.

*Bagotville-Port Alfred* (13,000), is another twin-town located at the west end of Ha-Ha Bay, one of the best natural harbours in Eastern Canada. Mars River, a small stream separates Port Alfred on the south from Bagotville to the north. Port Alfred has a large pulp and paper mill and extensive docks at which bauxite ore is transhipped for Arvida and from which aluminum metal is exported. Bagotville is more residential and its wharf in summer time is the terminal of a daily steamship service to Quebec and Montreal. The surroundings are scenic, both sides of the fjord are high, steep and well forested. Inland,

farms are found on the terraces which rise gradually to 400 and 500 feet above the water. A modern airport was built during World War II on the upper terrace about five miles west of the town.

*Roberval* (7,000), 60 miles west of Chicoutimi is the regional centre of the farming district around Lake St. John. Having few industries, it is the main commercial and administrative town of the county. It has a landing strip and a hydroplane base and serves as the point of departure for the new mining fields of Chibougamau and Lake Mistassini.

*Dolbeau* (5,000), is an industrial town located at the confluence of the Mistassini and Mistassibi rivers. The large tracts of forests upstream have attracted the lumberman and, more recently, a pulp and paper mill has been established. It is also

*Aluminum Company of Canada Limited.*
Plate 47. Arvida, the aluminum centre of the Saguenay region.

an outfitting centre for hunting and fish-ing.

## An Industrial Empire in the Wilderness

In the past fifty years the development of the Saguenay Basin has mirrored in a somewhat exaggerated fashion that of the province of Quebec itself. At the turn of the century it was a pioneer settlement of agriculturists and lumbermen, isolated in the wilderness. Of a total of 36,000 people about 16% were classed as urban and there was little manufacturing. Since then there has been a vast change. The present popu-lation, estimated at 200,000, is more than 60% urban. Rural population has dou-bled, but the towns have grown tenfold. There are differences, of course, the west-ern or Lake St. John area still has a ma-jority of rural dwellers; it has no large cities and only a scattering of small manu-facturing towns and commercial villages. The banks of the Saguenay in Chicoutimi county, on the other hand, furnish the sites for some of the most rapidly expand-ing cities in the province. Here the urban outnumber the rural dwellers, three to one. Here, of course, is the origin of the great industrial output. In recent years the whole region, though having only 3½% of the population of Quebec has been produc-ing 5-7% of total manufactures, (1943 — $196,000,000; 1954 — $330,000,000). The major items have been the bulk of the aluminum plus a fair share of the pulp and paper. Behind this stands the development of a tremendous power resource of over 2,000,000 H.P., one-fifth of the total in-stallations of the province.

## X. The North Shore

The North Shore extends over 655 miles from Tadoussac to Blanc-Sablon at the Strait of Belle Isle and inland to the height of land which forms the boundary of the Coast of Labrador. The region has an area of 88,000 square miles and has less than 35,000 inhabitants. The effectively oc-cupied area is very small, consisting of scattered locations along the shore. It may be considered as several arbitrarily stated sub-regions.

The southeastern part, from Tadoussac to Ste. Anne de Portneuf, is a region of pioneer farming and forest exploitation. The population numbers about 9,000. The central section extends from Forestville to Clark City and contains a population of 16,000. Forestry is the only occupation. Small settlements of forest workers are found in coves along the shore, each with its wharf and log sluice. The bark is re-moved at local rossing mills and the pulp-wood is loaded for shipment on river steamers. Thousands of lumberjacks from other parts of Quebec move into the for-ests each winter to cut pulpwood. Shipping is done during the summer.

*Baie Comeau* (4,000), was built by the Quebec North Shore Paper Company in 1937. Located a few miles northeast of Outardes River, its modern pulp and paper mill gives work to 600 men, while more than 3,000 obtain work in the bush. The town is well equipped and is a pleasant place in which to live. It is the terminus of provincial highway 15, but in summer most of the traffic is carried by boat. From its airfield there is daily service to Que-bec and Montreal.

*Clarke City* (700), is at the northeastern end of the forest district near the mouth of the Ste. Marguerite River. It is the location of one of the oldest pulpmills in Quebec, a small plant established in 1908.

The eastern part of the North Shore extends from Seven Islands to Blanc Sab-lon; it has about 10,000 inhabitants whose main occupations are fishing and hunting.

*Seven Islands* (6,000), is the largest cen-tre. A new airfield makes it the point of departure for the iron fields of New Que-bec and Labrador. Eventually it will be an important port and railway terminal.

*Havre St. Pierre* (2,000), is a trading centre, and the shipping port for the ti-tanium ores of Allard Lake about 22 miles inland. *Blanc Sablon* (500) is also a trading centre and the seat of the Roman Catholic Bishop of the Labrador Coast.

The Island of Anticosti lies in the northern part of the Gulf of St. Lawrence and may be considered along with the North Shore. It is a forested private domain of over 3,000 square miles and a total population of less than 500.

## XI. New Quebec

Officially known as New Quebec, the former territory of Ungava became part of the province in 1912. As defined by the Privy Council Award of 1927, the area of this empty land is 227,176 square miles. The census of 1951 enumerated about 4,200 inhabitants, mostly Indians and Eskimos who wander widely in search of game and fish. In the summertime they gather at a few trading posts on Hudson Bay and Ungava Bay, such as Port Harrison, Cape Smith, Wolstenholme, Cape Hopes Advance, Fort Chimo and Port Burwell. Inland also there are a few posts including Mistassini and Fort McKenzie.

The age-long isolation of the interior has now been broken by the development of the iron discovery on the Lakes Plateau. Air services are maintained to Knob Lake. A railway 360 miles long will convey the ore to tidewater at Seven Islands, over which it is planned to ship 10,000,000 tons of ore per year. At the northern terminus of the railway stands the new mining town of Schefferville.

## Significance of Quebec Regions

Although it must be admitted that equal geographical significance cannot be claimed for all the regions outlined in this chapter, they do serve as a convenient framework for the human geography of the province. Moreover, since Quebec was one of the first settled areas on the continent, there has been sufficient time for human activity to become adjusted to space and resource relationships. This is true, particularly in the St. Lawrence Lowlands and the Appalachian Plateau. The country system of the province, being somewhat archaic, has little real geographic significance. It has been suggested that local government could be much better served by the creation of new administrative units. If and when this is achieved, the new map will probably bear a close relationship to the one which has been used as the plan of this chapter. Beyond the borders of the Canadian Shield, however, regions and regional boundaries, especially, must be regarded as tentative. They consist of small settled areas to which are attached large unoccupied areas. It is not impossible that other regional centres may arise in the future.

## Selected References

Blanchard, R. *L'Est du Canada Français*. 2 Vol. Beauchemin. Montreal. 1935.

Blanchard, R. *Le Centre du Canada Français*. Beauchemin. Montreal. 1947.

Blanchard, R. *L'Ouest du Canada Français*. Beauchemin. Montreal. 1953.

Blanchard, R. *La Mauricie*. Editions du Bien Public. Trois Rivières. 1950.

Brouillette, B. *Le Canada par l'image*. Beauchemin. Montreal. 1946.

*Geographical Distribution of Manufacturing Industries*. Dom. Bur. of Statistics. Ottawa. Annual.

Minville, E. (ed.) *Montréal Economique*. Ecole des Hautes Etudes Commerciales. Montreal. 1944.

Minville, E. (ed.) *Notre Milieu*. Ecole des Hautes Etudes Commerciales. Montreal. 1942.

*Planning for Montreal*. Jour. Roy. Arch. Inst. of Canada. 22 No. 5. Toronto. 1945.

Tanghe, Raymond. *Montréal*. Albert Levesque. Montreal. 1936.

*Travellers' Guides for Canada. Vol. 1. Quebec*. University Editions. Collins. Toronto. 1950.

*Urbanisation de Montréal*. Plan directeur. Service d'urbanisme. Montreal. 1944.

# CHAPTER 10

# Southern Ontario
# Physical Background and Settlement

## The Province of Ontario and Its Major Divisions

ONTARIO, although somewhat centrally located, is by no means completely an inland province. It possesses a salt water shoreline of about 680 miles on Hudson Bay and James Bay, and a fresh water shoreline on the Great Lakes about 2,362 miles in length. The southernmost point, in Lake Erie, lies in north latitude 40° 41', while the northernmost point is in north latitude 56°50' at a distance of over 1,000 miles. The east and west extent, from approximately 74° west longitude to approximately 95° west longitude, is also about 1,000 miles. Within its boundaries lies an area of 412,582 square miles or 10.7% of the Dominion. Included in this are the surfaces of numerous fresh water lakes amounting to more than 49,000 square miles. Ontario is larger than any other province save Quebec, and is as large as the combined areas of Texas and California, the two largest states in the United States of America.

Being in large measure controlled by natural boundary lines, Ontario is a very irregularly shaped body of land, almost separated into two very unequal portions along the line of the Mattawa River, Lake Nipis-

sing and French River. South of this line is "Old Ontario" or Southern Ontario, the region which was first settled and which is distinguished on the map by an irregular division into counties and townships which were surveyed on base lines laid out more or less parallel to the shores of the St. Lawrence River and the Great Lakes. It is by far the smaller region, containing about 50,000 square miles, approximately the same as the Maritime Provinces or New York State. To the north of this narrow neck lies Northern or New Ontario, even yet only partially surveyed, laid out in townships which are oriented with the meridians in accordance with the instructions issued to the surveyors in 1857. Because of the differences between these two areas in both natural and man-made characteristics, it will be more convenient to deal with them separately.

## Land Forms of Southern Ontario

Geologically, Ontario belongs to two major regions: the rough Canadian Shield with its ancient igneous and metamorphic rocks of Precambrian age, and the gentler lowlands of the Great Lakes and St. Lawrence, underlain by Paleozoic sedimentary rocks. The areal relationships of these formations are shown in Fig. 127 which has been compiled from the publications of the

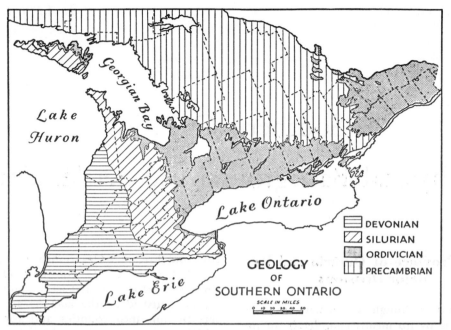

Figure 127. *Bedrock Geology of Southern Ontario.* In Southern Ontario the crystalline rock area of the Canadian Shield is prolonged to the southeast in the Frontenac Axis which crosses the St. Lawrence at the Thousand Islands. Eastern Ontario and the peninsula of southwestern Ontario are underlain by successive Paleozoic formations.

Canadian Geological Survey and the Ontario Department of Mines.

Concerning the long and imperfectly known history of the Precambrian period, little need be said here. It was several times as long as all subsequent time and it ended about 500,000,000 years ago. Rocks were deposited, mountain ranges were elevated and reduced to sea level several times before the beginning of the Paleozoic era. Then, for more than 200,000,000 years, Southern Ontario was submerged beneath the sea and the various systems known as Cambrian, Ordovician, Silurian and Devonian were laid down. In general, they are composed of three types of rock, sandstones, limestones and shales. Since then, for the most part, Ontario has been land and its geological history has been one of continuous erosion for nearly 300,000,000 years. Only yesterday, we might say, this process was interrupted by the Glacial Period during which a comparatively thin mantle of unconsolidated material was spread upon the bed rock.

## Evolution of the Bedrock Topography

When the seas of the Paleozoic era withdrew, they left a widespread coastal plain, similar in some respects to the one now found along the southeastern shores of the United States. Horizontal at first, the strata gradually became deformed by earth movements. Domes were pushed up in the regions of the Adirondacks, Algonquin Park and Wisconsin. From these, the less resistant sedimentary rocks were gradually removed although preserved in the basins between them. Besides the warping or tilting of the beds, huge cracks or faults also developed in some places. This is particularly true of Eastern Ontario where a large part of the Ottawa Valley is interpreted as a block of the earth's crust which has dropped down, thus preserving the younger rocks from the full force of erosion.

The drainage from Southern Ontario, for long ages, must have escaped toward the Mississippi Valley. Even today the divide between the Mississippi and the St. Lawrence lies but a few miles south of Lake Erie. The Great Lakes and the St. Lawrence itself, from Lake Ontario to Montreal, are accidents of post-glacial time. The master stream of Eastern Ontario was the Ottawa which must have drained a large portion of the upper lakes region by way of the Mattawa gap, a very old and well-marked valley. At present, the Ottawa drains practically all of Eastern Ontario; its valley is deep and the water divide is within sight of the St. Lawrence which receives hardly any tributaries at all.

The most striking feature of the landscape in Southern Ontario is the Niagara cuesta. It is due to the presence of a resistant layer of rock, the Lockport dolomite of Silurian age, which outcrops all the way around the Michigan Basin. Because of the ease with which the underlying shales are eroded, the edge of this formation becomes a magnificent escarpment, the crest of which stands from two hundred to one thousand feet above the plains at its base.

It is probable that, in the period immediately preceding the ice age, Ontario was somewhat more elevated than it is at present. The bottoms of all the Great Lakes, except Erie, are below sea-level. Even with generous allowance for over-deepening by ice, they could not have been cut without a change in base level.

Pre-glacial Ontario must have been dominated by two contrasting land forms: limestone plateaux, along the edges of which swift flowing streams had already begun the work of dissection; and a softer, more mature, more gently sloping topography with wider valleys and narrower interfluves, developed upon the shales.

## The Mantle of Glacial Drift

Earth history during the last million years has recorded a series of remarkable climatic changes. On the whole, it has been considerably cooler than during most of the long ages of the past. The ice age is with us yet, for both Greenland and Antarctica are still covered with ice. During four separate periods most of Canada was buried under ice which melted upon the arrival of warmer and probably drier periods. Most of the land forms of today, however, are the work of the last ice sheet, which has been called the 'Wisconsin' because it was first identified in that state.

The most characteristic and widespread glacial deposit is the *ground moraine* laid down under the ice. It is composed of an unsorted mixture of clay, sand and stones, known as *till*, usually spread out as a slightly undulating blanket, but sometimes heaped up into curious oval hills called *drumlins*. A typical drumlin is about a mile long, a third of a mile wide and fifty to one hundred feet high. They occur in groups with their long axes parallel to the line of movement of the ice which formed them. There are about 7,000 of these hills well distributed throughout Southern Ontario.

Where the ice made temporary halts or readvances, the till is pushed into long rough ridges and sometimes covered with sand and gravel. These areas of rough topography are called *moraines* and are a strong feature of the central and western parts of Southern Ontario. *Spillways*, or large valleys, which carried the drainage from the melting ice are also common. At present they carry streams which are obviously much too small for them. Other features left by the ice sheet are long narrow ridges of sand and gravel known as *eskers*, and irregularly shaped gravel hills called *kames*.

## Deposits in Standing Water

As the ice front melted back, the great depressions became flooded. Dammed up by the glacier itself, the water in the Great Lakes Basin rose higher than it does today, covering much of the lowland of Ontario. Great areas along the shores of the present lakes are therefore floored by sands, silts and clays which settled to the bottoms, creating flat plains in place of the undulating surfaces of the glacial drift features. Along their former margins are found many shore forms such as wave-cut cliffs, beaches, bars and deltas, abandoned when the ice dam melted from the St. Lawrence. For a time Eastern Ontario was below sea level and there are deep salt water deposits there. Many marine shells are found in the beach gravels and even skeletons of whales have been unearthed near Smith's Falls.

There were many old lakes in Ontario, all of which have been named by geologists, but reference will be made only to the most important. The lacustrine deposits in the Lake Erie and southern part of the Lake Huron Basins are referred to Lake Warren which had its outlet across the state of Michigan. Those in the Upper Lakes Basins are mostly the work of Lake Algonquin which during a long lifetime made use of three outlets at Chicago, Sarnia and Kirkfield, Ontario. It was finally drained when the Mattawa Valley was uncovered at North Bay. The huge forerunner of Lake Ontario has been named Lake Iroquois. Its outlet was at Rome, N.Y. The marine invasion of the lowland of Eastern Ontario and Quebec is known as the Champlain Sea.

## Regional Landforms

The landforms of Southern Ontario may be classified in the following categories, the distribution of which is shown on the accompanying map, Fig. 128.

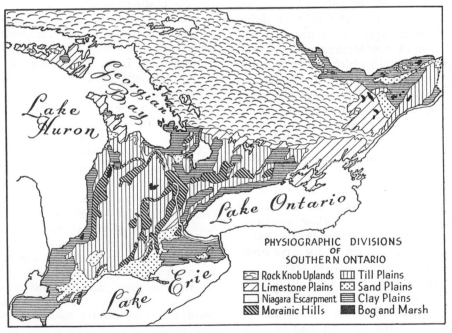

Figure 128. *Physiographic Divisions of Southern Ontario.* Although occurring in a rather complex mosaic of small areas, the landforms of Southern Ontario may be classified into the few general types shown here.

*Courtesy Ontario Dept. of Lands & Forests.*
Plate 48. The Niagara Escarpment at Grimsby, Ontario.

## Rock Knob Uplands of the Canadian Shield

Even in what is termed Southern Ontario, nearly one-third of the area is underlain by the Canadian Shield. Much of it is more than 1,500 feet above sea level. Rock knobs or hills, often with very little in the way of soil covering are characteristic. Even though there may be small intervening areas of flat land there is little encouragement for agriculture in the Highlands of Haliburton and Algonquin Park. They will always remain as forest and recreational areas.

## The Niagara Escarpment

This most striking feature of Southern Ontario extends from Niagara Falls to the northern tip of the Bruce Peninsula, a distance of more than 250 miles. The vertical cliffs along the brow are composed of dolomite limestone while the slopes below are carved from red shale. The highest and most picturesque part is the Blue Mountain near Collingwood, reaching an elevation of 1,775 feet A.T., almost 1,100 feet above the waters of Georgian Bay. Northward along the Bruce Peninsula it forms a precipitous cliff almost at the water's edge, gradually becoming lower until it disappears at Tobermory. Beyond this are a few remnants such as the famous Flower Pot Islands which have escaped destruction. South from the Blue Mountain to the Caledon Mountain, the face of the escarpment is covered with moraines, but from there to Hamilton its cliff-like character is reasserted although becoming gradually lower. In the Niagara Peninsula its crest is about 600 feet A.T. or about 350 feet above the waters of Lake Ontario.

The scenic effects are much enhanced by deep V-shaped valleys which have been cut by rivers leaving the plateau. Two of them, now drowned, form the harbours of Wiarton and Owen Sound. The most striking is the Beaver Valley, a great gash 1,000 feet in depth extending inland many miles from the shores of Georgian Bay. Others are the Bighead, the Pretty, the Pine, the Nottawasaga, the Credit and the Dundas Valleys, all of which have scenic attraction. Most noted of all the features of the escarpment are the Niagara Falls. The river draining Lake Erie into Lake Ontario tumbles over the escarpment in a vertical drop of 168 feet. The force of the water has undercut the cliff causing the continuous retreat of the falls and the formation of the Niagara Gorge. The distance from the Falls to Queenston at the foot of the Escarpment is about 7 miles.

## Rock Plains

On both flanks of the Frontenac Axis which, in the vicinity of the Thousand Islands, joins the Canadian Shield to the Adirondack Mountains of New York State, there are extensive areas of smooth plains underlain by fairly hard limestones with a very shallow soil covering. In places the plains are separated by low limestone escarpments which reach their best development along the Bay of Quinté. The western portion is sometimes referred to as the Napanee Plain while Smith's Falls is the approximate geographic centre of the eastern plain. Together they occupy about

*Courtesy L. J. Chapman.*

Plate 49. Glacial striae in limestone, Bruce Peninsula, Ontario.

2,500 square miles. Rock plains also occupy most of the Bruce Peninsula.

## Morainic Hills

The chief areas of this type are found in the vicinity of the Horseshoe Moraines which encircle the uplands of Southern Ontario, and along the Oak Ridges moraine which forms the watershed in South Central Ontario. These are areas of considerable relief and great complexity of land forms. In addition to ridges of boulder clay and mounds of gravel there are many steep sided valleys of the old spillways.

## Till Plains

Probably one-third of Southern Ontario (exclusive of the Canadian Shield) is occupied by ground moraine, consisting of rock fragments of all sizes from finest clay to huge boulders. Some of this boulder clay, or till, was left in the form of hills but the largest part of it was spread out as fairly flat or undulating plains. Portions of the till plain were later flooded and modified by a shallow covering of clay, silt or sand. In places, too, they are cut by the deep valleys of the old spillways. The most extensive area of till plain is found in the upland region of Southwestern Ontario, but Central and Eastern Ontario also have their share.

Geographically, the presence of these

Courtesy L. J. Chapman.

Plate 50. Glacial landforms in Southern Ontario.
Upper left—An abandoned glacial meltwater spillway near Hillsburg.
Lower left—An esker on a till plain near Jessopville.
Upper right—A typical drumlin in South-central Ontario.
Lower right—A typical morainic landscape near Erin.

vast undulating till plains is most important. On them are found good durable loam soils which have permitted the development of general farming and livestock production.

## Drumlins

The drumlins are special features of the ground moraine and are composed of the same kinds of boulder clay as the till plains. They occur in groups which may contain anywhere from ten to many hundreds, with their crests all trending in the same direction. A group of drumlins looks very much like a school of huge whales basking on the surface and they are often locally termed "whalebacks". This effect is heightened when, as in Rice Lake, they are surrounded by water. The Eastern Ontario groups contain about 500;

the Central Ontario groups, of which the concentration about Peterboro is the most striking, contain more than 4,000; the Guelph field contains about 300; while the Arran, Bighead, Teeswater and other groups in the northwestern part of the peninsula contain about 2,000 drumlins.

## Clay Plains

Clay plains result from the deposition of finely divided rock material in fairly deep water, either in lakes or seas. The chief areas of lacustrine clay is the region between Lake Erie and Lake Huron in southwestern Ontario, in the Niagara Peninsula, in the Georgian Bay-Lake Simcoe region and to a lesser extent along the north shore of Lake Ontario. Clay plains in the counties of Frontenac, Leeds, Dundas, Russell and Renfrew in Eastern Ontario are of marine origin. The richest soils in Ontario are undoubtedly those of the clay plains. Included with the clay plains in Fig. 128 are fairly large areas of silt.

## Sand Plains

Sand plains are also of marine or lacustrine origin. In Southwestern Ontario there are extensive deltas of the Thames river forming the Kent and Caradoc sand plains. The Norfolk sand plains were laid down as a delta of the Grand River system while Camp Borden sands formed a delta of the Nottawasaga. In Eastern Ontario, the Petawawa and the Plantagenet sand plains were deltas of the ancient Ottawa River built into the Champlain Sea. The sands of these plains vary greatly in texture. Some of them are coarse and drouthy and are apt to blow badly, while others of finer texture make good soils for agricultural use.

## Rivers

For one hundred miles stretching from the Thousand Islands to Lake St. Francis, Ontario possesses a half share in one of the great rivers of the world. The portions of the system connecting the Great Lakes, the Niagara, Detroit and St. Clair are also half in Ontario. Both as a source of power and as a highway of commerce they are important.

The Ottawa forms the boundary between Quebec and Southern Ontario for its whole distance. It is a large river, its mean volume being about one-third that of the St. Lawrence. It is navigable only to a limited extent, but has been greatly used for the transportation of logs. It is a great source of water power.

The major tributaries of the Ottawa from the Ontario side between the Mattawa and the St. Lawrence are the Petawawa, Bonnechere, Madawaska, Mississippi,

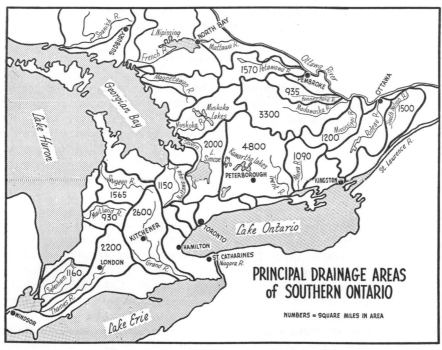

Figure 129. *Principal Drainage Basins of Southern Ontario.* There are many small drainage basins in Southern Ontario, with only a few of the larger ones having areas of 2,000 to 5,000 square miles.

Rideau and the South Nation. All except the last take rise in the forested area of the Shield. The Madawaska (130 miles long) is the largest, draining an area of more than 3,000 square miles of rugged uplands. It supports important p o w e r plants. The South Nation River (90 miles) is much smaller and it flows entirely in the flat plains of Eastern Ontario. Largely because of its lack of gradient it is notorious for its annual floods. The Rideau, because of the canal built in 1826-34, was f o r m e r l y an important transportation route.

The Trent (150 miles long) is the largest river along the north shore of Lake Ontario. It drains an area of 4,800 square miles, part of which lies in the uplands of the Shield. It also was canalized at a cost of several millions of dollars, but is now used only by pleasure craft.

In southwestern Ontario the only large tributary to Lake Erie is the Grand River (165 miles in length) which, rising not far from the highest part of the Niagara cuesta, drains an area of 2,600 square miles. Its flow is notoriously irregular, spring floods carrying 500 times the volume of the low water stage. Remedial measures are being undertaken, the first unit being the Shand Dam which was finished in 1942 at a cost of $2,000,000. The lower course of the Grand was at one time considered navigable as far as Brantford, a distance of about 30 miles.

The Thames River (length 163 miles) enters Lake St. Clair after draining 2,200 square miles of agricultural land. It is navigable for 20 miles to Chatham. A large dam has been built at Fanshawe, on the North Branch, in order to control the spring floods which formerly inundated London and the lower Thames valley.

Two important streams flowing into Lake Huron are the Maitland and the Saugeen. They maintain a much greater minimum flow than either the Grand or the Thames, although draining less territory. The Saugeen was at one time used

for navigation as far as Walkerton, a distance of about 30 miles.

Flowing into Georgian Bay are: the Nottawasaga, rising on the Niagara cuesta and crossing several flat basins which are subject to flood; the Severn which drains Lake Simcoe (284 sq. miles) the largest lake in Southern Ontario; the Muskoka, draining the scenic Muskoka Lakes; the Magnetawan; and the French River, which drains Lake Nipissing (330 sq. miles), forming the boundary of the region under discussion.

## Climate, Vegetation and Soils
### Climate

Lying between 42° and 46° north latitude, Southern Ontario is directly in the path of the westerly winds and is particu-

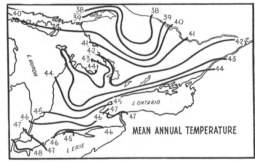

Figure 130. *Mean Annual Temperature.* The variation of more than 10°F. in this small area and the irregular pattern reflects the topographic pattern of large lakes and uplands.

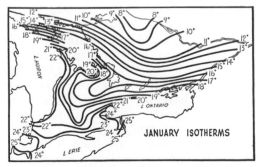

Figure 131. *Isotherms of January Mean Temperature.* The midwinter range is more than 18°F. Note the influence of the Great Lakes in Southwestern Ontario.

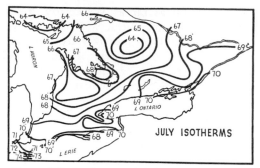

Figure 132. *Isotherms of July Mean Temperature.* The highland of Algonquin Park is the coolest part of Southern Ontario in July.

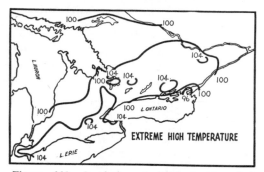

Figure 133. *Isopleths of Highest Recorded Temperature.* A large part of Southern Ontario has experienced temperatures of over 100°F. at some time or other.

larly stormy in winter, although somewhat less so in summer. The differences in relief, although not great, are significant. On its margins are extensive lowlands, the waters of the Great Lakes adjoin it to the south and west, while the northeastern boundary is traced by the Ottawa Valley. There are two important upland regions, the northern part of Southwestern Ontario rising to almost 1,800 feet, and the Algonquin Park region at about 1,600 feet above sea level. It will be seen that these differences have a definite influence on both temperature and precipitation.

Mean annual temperatures (Fig. 130) though often quoted, are limited in their usefulness, but they aid in general comparisons. They range from 48° F. in the extreme southwest to 38° F. in Algonquin Park. It is much better to know something

about the range of temperature conditions. In general, January (Fig. 131) is the coldest month and July (Fig. 132) is the warmest. Winter isotherms are seen to follow closely the outline of the shores of the Great Lakes, and the "cold loops" of the two upland areas are well in evidence, while there is also a steep north-south gradient of about 1° F. for every 20-25 miles. In spring the "cold loops" are even more pronounced, while a cooling effect is also noticeable along the northern shores of Lake Erie and Lake Huron. The St. Lawrence lowland warms up more rapidly than Southwestern Ontario, consequently we find that, in summer, the Ottawa valley is just about as warm as it is along Lake Erie. Pelee Island is the warmest, with a July average of 74° F. In the fall

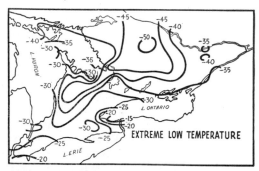

Figure 134. *Isopleths of Lowest Recorded Temperature.* The Niagara Peninsula appears to have the best protection against extreme low temperatures.

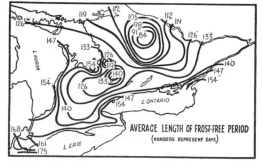

Figure 135. *The Average Length of the Frost-free Season.* The Algonquin Park Upland is the area most subject to frosts in the growing season. Note the protection afforded the shores of the Great Lakes.

the inland regions cool more rapidly than the lake shores, even relatively small lakes such as Simcoe and Nipissing having a definite effect. The Georgian Bay region, the Niagara Peninsula and the western end of Lake Erie are noted for prolonged mild autumn conditions.

Considerable interest is always attached to the occurrence of "record high" or "record low" temperatures. Figure 133 is an isopleth chart of the highest temperatures ever recorded; incidentally, most of them occurred in July, 1936. Figure 134 is a similar chart of extreme low temperatures, most of which were recorded in February, 1934. The latter show a much more reasonable distribution; the cold loops are again in evidence as well as the protecting influence of the lakes. It is important that the Niagara Fruit Belt has never experienced temperatures below −16° F. The presence of the lakes has still more effect upon the length of the frost-free season, (Figure 135.) This is because they produce a diminished difference between day and

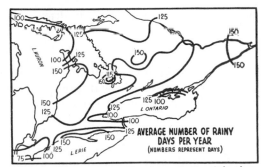

Figure 138. *Average Number of Precipitation Days per Annum.* Any day on which there is a measurable precipitation of 0.01 inch is counted as a precipitation day.

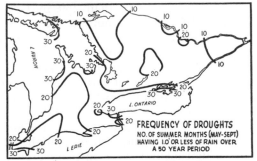

Figure 139. *Frequency of Droughts.* A summer month with less than one inch of measurable precipitation is counted as a drought. The map shows the number of droughts occurring in a fifty-year period.

night temperatures; the average or the *mean daily range,* as it is called, is only 14° F. along Lake Erie and 24° F. in Algonquin Park. In consequence, the frost-free period varies from 170 days at Leamington to less than 100 days in Algonquin Park.

The mean annual precipitation, (Figure 136) varies from 26 to 40 inches, and, in the main, may be considered adequate. It is fairly uniformly distributed throughout the year with no pronounced wet or dry season. The isohyets show that there is somewhat less rainfall over the lakes than on the inland areas sloping upward from their shores. Pelee Island, the Niagara Peninsula and Prince Edward county all show this tendency. The heaviest precipitation occurs on the west slopes of the uplands facing Lake Huron and Georgian

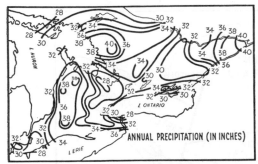

Figure 136. *Mean Annual Precipitation.*

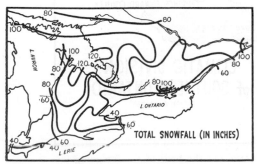

Figure 137. *Mean Annual Snowfall.*

Bay, while "rain shadows" or drier areas are found to leeward. The extreme eastern part of Ontario is also an area of heavy precipitation.

The distribution of snowfall, (Fig. 137), is similar to that of total precipitation. A belt of heavy snowfall extends through southwestern Ontario, from London to Owen Sound, and crosses Georgian Bay into Muskoka and Parry Sound. Both Owen Sound and Parry Sound average more than 10 feet of snow per winter.

The number of precipitation (rain or snow) days varies from less than 75 on Pelee Island to more than 150 in Grey, Bruce and Glengarry counties, (Fig. 138). In a general way this map also agrees with that of total precipitation.

Frequency of drought is no less important than frequency of rainy days. There is no agreement upon what constitutes a drought but it is generally felt that any month during the growing season which receives less than one inch of rainfall will have a detrimental effect on plant growth.

Figure 139 shows the frequency of dry months during the growing season over a period of fifty years.

On the basis of these factors, and others as well, it is possible to divide Southern Ontario into a number of minor climatic regions which are shown in Figure 140. Placing the primary emphasis on temperature, three major divisions are easily made. First, a line may be drawn from Grand Bend to Hamilton. Second, on the basis of annual and winter temperatures, a line may be drawn from Georgian Bay to Kingston, but in summer it must be bent sharply northward to the Ottawa River. Eastern Ontario is thus delimited as a separate climatic region by reason of its great seasonal range of temperature, coupled with greater precipitation. High summer temperature, lower rainfall and drouthiness characterize Prince Edward County. The two upland areas can be delimited on the basis of lower temperature and higher rainfall. In the central section the north and south slopes can be separated on the

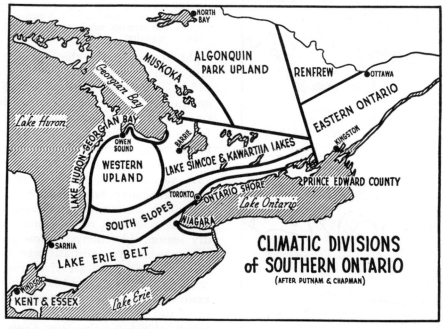

Figure 140. *Climatic Divisions of Southern Ontario.* On the basis of the foregoing factors, Southern Ontario may be divided into a number of climatic areas of varying size, as shown on this map.

Figure 141. *Forests of Southern Ontario.* (After Halliday). The natural vegetation of Southern Ontario is forest. The Algonquin-Laurentides area contained great stands of white pine as well as hardwoods. The other areas were characterized by associations of deciduous species.

basis of temperature, particularly in winter, while the narrow strip along the shore of Lake Ontario may be distinguished by greater freedom from frost. The Niagara Fruit Belt enjoys a warmer summer, a greater freedom from spring and fall frosts and a lack of extremely low winter temperatures. In the extreme southwest, Kent and Essex counties, with distinctly higher summer temperatures and lower rainfall, may be considered as a region, while within it, a narrow shore area has such a long frost-free season that it merits separation.

## Vegetation

The original vegetative cover of Southern Ontario was a dense forest which has practically all been removed or greatly modified by the operations of the farm-clearing pioneers or by lumbermen. Large uncleared areas are still present on the Shield but, in most of the townships to

_____
1 *A Forest Classification for Canada. op. cit.*

the south of it, the wooded area has been reduced to about 10% of the total. It is therefore somewhat difficult to visualize the "forest primeval". In Figure 141 the boundaries of the four forest regions are shown according to W. F. D. Halliday.[1] They correspond rather well to those of the major climatic divisions. It is to be expected, however, that land form and soil differences will give rise to rather varied distribution of tree types within regions.

The Niagara section is part of the great deciduous forest region of eastern North America and is the only part of Canada in which Carolinian vegetation is found. Chestnut, tulip-tree, magnolia, paw-paw and sassafras are some of the southern types which occur. The chief species in the forests of the well drained till plains are sugar maple, beech, basswood, walnut, butternut, black cherry, red, white and bur oaks. On the clay plains, elms, ash, hickories, blue beech, silver maples, swamp, white and pin oaks are found. The drier sand plains originally had stands of white pine with black and scarlet oaks as an understory. Red cedar (juniper) and sumach occupy droughty sites. This section is probably the most well endowed forest region in all of Canada.

The Huron-Ontario section takes in the main body of peninsular Ontario. Here again the trees are prevailing broad-leaved hardwoods. The well drained uplands have sugar maple and beech with some hemlock and white pine on the drumlins. Elms, ashes, blue beech, silver maple and yellow birch are common on imperfectly drained clay plains. The sand plains of the Algonquin Lake bottom originally supported fine stands of white and red pine as did also the sandy moraines. White and red oak were common also. White cedar is the common tree of swampy areas, but toward the north, and in more elevated places, tamarack, spruce and balsam fir occur.

The Upper St. Lawrence section occupies the lowland of Eastern Ontario. Here, as in the previous section, the till lands support a maple-beech forest with fair admixture of white cedar. The extensive shallow lands have maples also, but a great deal more white cedar and red cedar (juniper). The sand plains originally supported magnificent stands of white and red pine, and some second growth is found amongst poplar, soft maple and white birch. The clay plains such as those of the Nation and Carp valleys still support woodlots with elm, ash and soft maples. There are, also, extensive sphagnum bogs which may have a marginal forest of tamarack, black spruce, black alder and black ash. Other poorly drained areas carry dense thickets of white cedar.

The Algonquin-Laurentides section, which in Southern Ontario includes all of the Shield area, is the region in which the white pine reached its best development, and was the origin of much of the

timber exported during the famous period of rafting. There is, of course, much second growth pine but, in general, the forest now has a very mixed stand including sugar maple, yellow birch, hemlock, white pine, white spruce, balsam fir and many other species. The more poorly drained valleys have red maple, black ash, black spruce and tamarack.

In contrast with the other sections where forests have been reduced to small farm lots, most of this area remains uncleared in spite of the isolated forest settlements which have persisted since the lumbering days. The forest is the chief resource, but it has suffered from many years of neglect which followed its early exploitation.

## The Soils

The mature soils of Southern Ontario are typical of those developed under a mixed forest vegetation in a humid temperate climate. They are all 'podzolic' in nature, although only a few of them are true *Podzols* with the typical ashy grey upper horizon described for the forested soils of Northern Russia. In general there may be said to be two major soil zones: (a) the Brown Podzolic Soil Zone which is almost coincident with the area of the Shield, and (b) the zone of the Grey

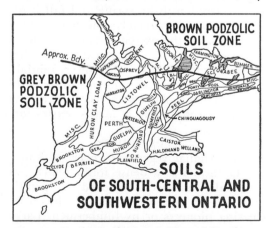

Figure 142. *Generalized Soil Map of Southern Ontario.* (Based on data from the Ontario Soil Surveys). The names, in most cases, indicate the dominant soil series in the indicated areas.

Brown Podzolic Soils which comprises the remainder. It should be noted, however, that it is not rock formation alone which determines this boundary for we find it expressed, also, in both the climatic and vegetational maps. No systematic soil surveys have, as yet, been conducted in the northern area, but in the Grey Brown Podzolic Soil Zone most of the counties have been investigated, although only a few county reports have been published. Maps and manuscript data have been made available for the remainder through the courtesy of the workers at the Ontario Agricultural College. Since no general account of Ontario Soils is available, the following discussion will make use of the land form classes already discussed as basis for soil geography. In each of these, where possible, some account will be given of the dominant normal *zonal* soils and the associated *intrazonal* soils.

### Soils of the Rock-Knob Uplands

On the well drained sand plains laid down by Lake Algonquin, and on the sand and gravel terraces of the rivers running into it, there are well developed podzols which were formed under the extensive red and white pine forests. Here a shallow surface mat of pine needles ($A_0$) covers a dark grey topsoil ($A_1$), an inch or two deep. Under this is the $A_2$ horizon of ashy-grey leached sand, which may be from one to six inches in depth. The B horizon is often divisible into $B_1$, a yellowish-brown loamy sand, in places slightly compacted, and $B_2$, pale yellowish-brown sand which may extend to a depth of two feet or more, before the grey unweathered sand and gravel is encountered.

The Brown Podzolic Soils were formed under mixed forests of sugar maple and pine on well drained till, low in lime and often rather shallow. They are like the Podzols except that the $A_2$ horizon is very shallow or missing altogether, and the whole profile is shallow.

Between the rocky ridges and stony till

uplands there are many poorly drained areas where Bog and Half-bog soils have developed under black spruce, tamarack, black ash, willow and other moisture-loving vegetation.

The *Escarpments* are too steep to develop normal soil profiles.

The *Rock Plains* are too shallow. They are too wet in spring and fall and too dry in midsummer. There is usually little difference in the horizons below the surface leaf mat.

### The Soils of the Morainic Hills

Because the parent material is, in most cases, rather sandy, drainage is excessive and the soil profile is rather featureless. Such a condition obtains under the pines, oaks, sumachs and poison ivy of the Oak Ridges Moraine. In the Waterloo Hills a typical Grey Brown Soil is found on more loamy material.

### The Soils of the Till Plains and Drumlins

These loam and clay loam soils are the best examples of the development of the Grey Brown Podzolic Soils. On the gently rolling, well drained areas normal profiles have developed under hardwood forest. Under an inch or two of partly decomposed forest litter ($A_0$) there is a dark brown surface soil from 3 to 5 inches deep underlain by a yellowish-grey or buff $A_2$, which may be from 2 to 6 inches deep. Below this is a medium brown to coffee brown B horizon which may be from 6 inches to 2 feet in depth. On many of the drumlins which are rather steep and composed of rather limy till, the profiles are very shallow and free lime is found in the surface soils. On the other hand, in the flat areas between the drumlins and in the open till plains there are many areas where drainage is underdeveloped and immature, *Half-bog* soils are found. These are also fairly high in lime.

The soils formed on till are all good for general agriculture including both

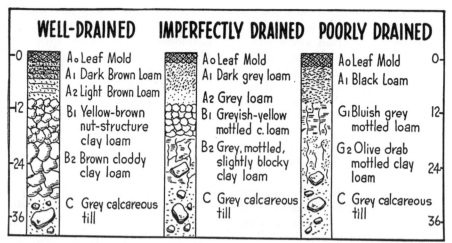

Figure 143. *Profiles of a Representative Soil Catena in Southern Ontario.* On the same parent material and within the same climatic environment, soil profiles vary according to conditions of slope and drainage.

field crops and pasture. There is, however, considerable waste land in steep slopes, stony areas and interdrumlin swamps. These rolling lands also have considerable soil erosion when unwisely handled.

### Soils of the Lake Plains

While there are sand, silt and clay plains with sufficiently good drainage for the formation of a mature soil, it is more usual to find a condition of impeded drainage with the formation of a Half-bog soil under elm and ash forest. As a rule they have deep black surface soils, high in organic matter, and when artificial drainage is provided, they become very fertile soils. The flat clay lands of Kent and Essex counties are probably the most fertile in the province, producing large crops of wheat, corn, sugar beets and other specialties.

The deep sands of the old deltas, in Norfolk county and elsewhere have become high producing tobacco lands, while orchards, vineyards, truck gardens and canning crops are found in abundance on the easily worked soils of the old lake plains. Areas of bog, such as those near Leamington, Thetford, Rondeau and Bradford, have been drained and now produce large crops of onions, celery, carrots and other market vegetables. Southern Ontario has a great variety of soils, which in combination with its favourable climate, has made possible the development of a very diversified agriculture.

## Population and Settlement

The population of Ontario was reported to be 5,404,933 in the census of 1956. Southern Ontario, although containing only 14% of the land surface, had more than 90% of the people. Indeed, the concentration is even more localized for the area underlain by the Canadian Shield contains a rather sparse permanent population. The average density in the closely settled part of Ontario, where three and one-quarter millions live in about 30,000 square miles, is therefore over 100 per square mile. This is not crowded in comparison with Britain and some European countries where there are from 500 to 700 people per square mile, but in Canada it is equalled only by the St. Lawrence Lowlands in the Province of Quebec.

Even within the smaller area, there is no uniformity of population distribution. York County, containing the huge metropolitan district of Toronto, has over 1,000 people per square mile, while a strictly rural county such as Dufferin has only 25. Of the fifteen "Greater Cities" or Metropolitan districts, listed in the census, five are in Ontario. In 1941 the population living in urban centres numbered 62% of the total and it had increased to more than 75% at the census of 1956. In Figure 144 the population distribution is shown by the dot and circle method. In addition to the five "Greater Cities", all over 150,000, there are thirty other places with a population of 10,000 or over. Most of these have attracted a rather dense rural population in their suburban districts. In general, there are three regions of dense population: the central district around the western end of Lake Ontario, including Toronto, Hamilton, the Niagara Peninsula and the Grand River Valley; the extreme southwest around Windsor; and the extreme east with Ottawa as its nucleus. Northward, toward the Shield, populous towns are few indeed. Land form,

climate and soil, all combine to keep the population in the south.

The location of population nuclei is always an interesting study. Toronto was founded because it had the best harbour on Lake Ontario. It has continued to grow because the transportation system of the province was centred upon it. Kingston and Owen Sound are also harbour cities. Hamilton has a lake head position but never was much of a trans-shipping point. It grew because all land transportation routes were forced to centre upon it, making it an ideal manufacturing centre. Ottawa, before it became the capital, was a river town. Most inland towns have grown up along rivers, at former water power sites, especially if they happened to be convenient to main transportation routes. Occasionally the growth of a city can be ascribed entirely to business initiative. There is, for instance, no geographical reason why Oshawa should now be a city of over 50,000 while the older settlement

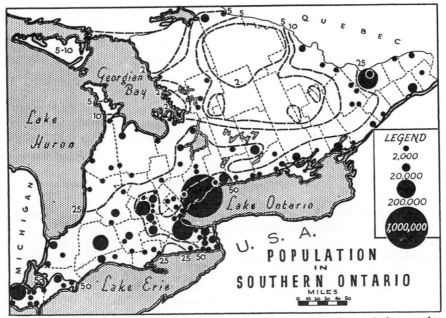

Figure 144. *Population Distribution in Southern Ontario.* Rural population reaches its greatest density in the southern part of the province in the belt which also contains most of the large cities. On the Canadian Shield it falls to less than two per square mile. Isopleths indicate density of rural population.

of Whitby, with a better harbour, still remains a town of 9,000.

The people of Ontario are predominantly of British origin. In 1951, 35% claimed English ancestry, 16% Irish, and 15% Scottish. Of the non-British groups, those of French origin are most numerous with 10%, while German and Dutch together total about 8%. These groups include most of the Ontario pioneer stock although, of course, they have received many reinforcements by more recent migration. Later immigration was also responsible for numerous other groups including Italian, Jewish, Polish and Ukrainian. The newer Canadians are more numerous in the cities than in rural districts. The aboriginal population is about 37,000 which is less than 1% of the total.

## Settlement Patterns

The earliest inhabitants of Southern Ontario were American Indians. They were hunters, of course, but also farmers with more or less fixed villages surrounded by their patches of beans, corn and pumpkins. Their settlements were very thinly scattered over the province, utilizing what are now considered to be rather inferior lands. These drier, warmer, sandy soils were suitable for primitive agriculture, however. They were more easily cleared and worked than heavier soils, and they also offered drier and more healthful village sites.

European settlement during the French regime was negligible. Fort Cataraqui (Kingston) was founded in 1673, Fort Niagara in 1678, Fort Rouille (Toronto) in 1749, while the Detroit River settlement dates from 1701.

The conquest of Canada (1759-60) did not immediately initiate settlement by British peoples. Garrisons were placed at Niagara, Kingston and elsewhere, but for twenty years no effort was made to bring in new population. In 1779, farming was begun along the Niagara River and, in 1881-1884, a number of new townships were surveyed in the Niagara Peninsula and along the St. Lawrence and the Bay of Quinte. Here the United Empire Loyalists found new homes and about 10,000 had reached Upper Canada by the end of 1784. In that year Kingston became a town of 50 houses.

In 1791, the separate province of Upper Canada was established with its capital at Niagara, but, in 1793, Governor Simcoe selected a new site for the capital on the north shore of Toronto Bay and founded the town of York. The new province contained 25,000 people, about four-fifths of whom were Loyalists. The Loyalist influx, however, was about over, and, in fact, many of the original settlers returned to their old homes. Many other American settlers came in as well as fresh immigrants from Britain and the population continued to grow. Hamilton (1798), Port Dover (1793), Ingersoll (1793), Woodstock (1798), Whitby (1794), and Bowmanville (1794) are among the settlements founded before 1800. With the Loyalists came about 5,000 Indians of the Six Nations Confederation who were granted lands along the Grand River.

In 1803 the members of a Scottish regiment were given lands in Glengarry. Other military settlements in the east were at Perth (1815) and Richmond (1819).

During the early years of the century, settlement was influenced by exploitation of the timber resources along the Ottawa following the founding of Hull (P.Q.) by Philamon Wright in 1800; although settlement at Ottawa was not begun until 1827, when Col. John By commenced the construction of the Rideau Canal. Merrickville and Smith's Falls, although actually founded some time previously, began to grow at this time.

Around 1800, also, German people from Pennsylvania bought land from the Indians along the Grand River and began settlement of Waterloo county. Later they were joined by Germans direct from Europe under whose influence Berlin (now

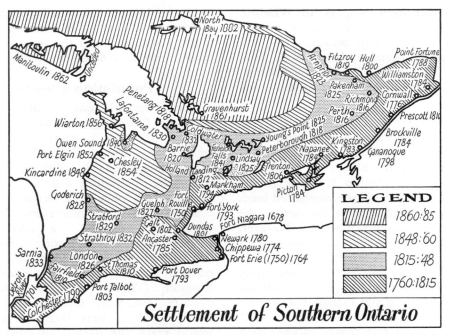

Figure 145. *Early Settlements in Southern Ontario.* Southern Ontario was settled in waves under the stimulus of various historical factors. The zones on the map show the approximate extent of the areas settled in each historical period.

Kitchener) was established in 1826. From this nucleus they have spread into the adjoining areas of what are now Perth, Wellington, Bruce and Grey counties.

During the first half of the 19th century there was a great influx of immigrants from the British Isles who swelled the population of the towns already established, and filled in the unoccupied spaces of the old townships and overflowed into the hinterland. The Scottish settlers of Glengarry have been mentioned; other predominantly Scottish places were Galt and the adjoining township of Dumfries, Zorra in Oxford county and McNab on the Ottawa River. Elsewhere the Scots are pretty well mingled. The Irish came in two great waves, following the potato famines of 1816 and 1846; they outnumbered the Scots in many Ontario counties. There are some strong Irish settlements such as that in Peterborough County, colonized by the Hon. Peter Robinson in the years after 1825. Adjoining

parts of Victoria and Hastings counties are also largely Irish. Carleton, Dundas, Renfrew, Frontenac, Grey, Huron, Lanark, Leeds, Peel, Perth and North Wellington all have districts in which the original settlers were predominantly Irish. Settlers from England were most numerous, however, and their descendants, together with those of the original Loyalists constitute the bulk of the population.

### The Talbot Settlement

Col. Thos. Talbot was one of the most colourful of the colonizers of Southwestern Ontario. In 1803 he obtained an officer's grant of 5,000 acres in the townships of Dunwich and Aldborough on the shore of Lake Erie. He set up his headquarters at Port Talbot and for 35 years he administered the settlement of the London district. For every 50 acres upon which he settled a pioneer family, he received 150 acres for himself. He settled some 40,000 people on the land and laid out and built the

Talbot road from Niagara to Windsor. His headquarters did not become a town, however, most probably because of the lack of a harbour. London, founded in 1826, and St. Thomas, named for the Colonel, have both become important inland cities.

### The Huron Tract

The most ambitious colonization project was that of the Canada Company which is associated with the names of John Galt and Dr. (Tiger) Dunlop. It was originally intended to buy up all the ungranted land, but the government wisely objected to the creation of a monopoly. They did, however, handle over 2,000,000 acres, about half of which was in the famous Huron Tract. Guelph with its interesting radial street pattern was founded in 1827, the Huron Road to Stratford and Goderich was built in 1828. Goderich was laid out in 1827 and Stratford in 1829. Later another road was built from Goderich to London. By

1842, the Huron Tract had a population of 7,000 people, about 25% of whom were native Canadians, and the rest from other lands, Irish and Scots predominating.

### Population Trends

During the half century, the population of Upper Canada grew very fast. Instead of the 25,000 people present in the newly created province of 1791, the census of 1851 disclosed 952,000. Of these, 42% were non-native, including 9% English, 19% Irish and 8% of Scottish origin.

Many of the newcomers settled in the towns. York attained to a population of about 10,000 and was incorporated as the city of Toronto in 1834; in 1851 it had reached 30,000. Hamilton (14,000) and Kingston (12,000) were incorporated as cities in 1846, while Ottawa (7,800), and London (7,000) were large towns which would reach the dignity of cities within half a decade. Altogether there were 26

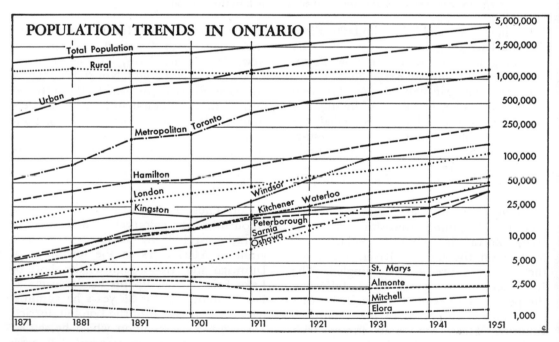

Figure. 70. *Population Trends in Ontario.* Rural population has been static while the urban population of the province has increased seven-fold. Some of the busiest industrial cities were very small towns at the time of Confederation.

incorporated places (cities, towns and villages) in the province, but the bulk (86%) of the population was rural and predominantly engaged in agriculture. The frontier regions and, in particular, the Ottawa Valley remained the home of the timber trade. In addition all the little crossroads hamlets, of which there were more then than now, had their various craftsmen such as blacksmiths, carpenters and shoemakers. Many of these were also part-time farmers.

The years from 1851 to 1881 were eventful. Immigration continued to pour in. From 1854 to 1866, Canada was prosperous because of reciprocity with the United States. In 1867 Confederation took place and Ontario became the leading province in the Dominion of Canada. During this period the densely settled southern part of the province was tied together by railways. The first railway was the short portage line from Queenston to Chippawa, around Niagara Falls, which was built in 1839. Various other short lines followed, but the most important date was 1856, when the Grand Trunk Railway began its services between Montreal and Toronto. Railways, henceforth, became the most important geographical factor in the distribution of population. Many new towns were created and many others infused with new growth by the coming of the "iron horse"; many others, founded in the pioneer days, died because the railway passed them by.

The population of Ontario reached 1,900,000 in 1881, an increase of 100% in thirty years. During this period many counties reached a peak which has not since been surpassed. Among these are Wellington, Victoria, Prince Edward, Perth, Northumberland, Huron, Haldimand, Durham and Bruce. Others reached a temporary peak, which they were not able to pass until 40 or 50 years later, while still others reached their peaks in the next decade. By 1881 the maximum density of

rural population had been reached; since then, with few exceptions, all increases have been in the towns while rural densities have decreased.

During the next twenty years while Manitoba and the Northwest Territories were beginning to develop, Ontario gained little in population. In many counties the countryside began to thin out rapidly. On the other hand, cities like Toronto, London, Ottawa and Berlin (now called Kitchener), doubled their numbers. These tendencies have continued to the present day. Rural hamlets and even villages have disappeared while certain cities have grown enormously. A great many Ontario born people have left Canada and are to be found in the great cities of the U.S.A.

The period of 1941-51 saw great changes in populations during both the war and post-war periods. In 1956 the total population of the province was found to be 5,404,-933 with most of the increase being in Southern Ontario where the growing "metropolitan districts" are located. Including Toronto (1,358,028), Hamilton (327,831), Ottawa (345,460), Windsor (185,865) and London (154,453), these urban nuclei contain over 40% of the total population of Ontario.

The pattern of population distribution in Southern Ontario seems to be completely set. Even though the population may, as it seems now, double itself during the ensuing half century, the great majority of them will be found in the "city belt", and all to many of them trying to live and work in the Greater Toronto metropolitan area. Within the "city belt" new cities may arise after the fashion already indicated by the development of Ajax between Toronto and Oshawa. Some smaller cities outside the "city belt" will undoubtedly develop, perhaps as expansions of such places as Barrie and Orillia in Central

Ontario or Pembroke in the Ottawa Valley. Perhaps some new site along the Ottawa River might be selected for development. There will always be a great contrast be-tween the crowded areas and the compar-atively sparsely inhabited region of the Canadian Shield, yet it is probable that even there fair sized towns may develop.

## Selected References

Census of Canada.

Chapman, L. J. and D. F. Putnam. *The Moraines of Southern Ontario*. Trans. Roy. Soc. Canada 37, Sec. 4, pp. 33-41, 1943

Chapman, L. J. and D. F. Putnam. *The Recession of the Wisconsin Glacier in Southern Ontario*. Trans. Roy. Soc. Canada 43, Sec. 4, pp. 23-52. 1949.

Chapman, L. J. and D. F. Putnam. *The Physiography of Southern Ontario*. University of Toronto Press. 1951.

Coleman, A. P. *The Pleistocene of the Toronto Region*. Annual Report Ontario Dept. of Mines 41, Pt. 7. 1932.

Coleman, A. P. *Lake Iroquois*. Annual Report Ontario Dept. of Mines 45, Pt. 7. 1936.

Guillet, E. C. *Early Life in Upper Canada*. Toronto. 1933.

Hills, G. A. *Pedology, "The Dirt Science", and Agricultural Settlement in Ontario*. Canadian Geographical Journal XXIX, pp. 106-127, 1944.

Ontario Soil Surveys. Reports for Carleton, Durham, Essex, Grenville and Prince Edward Counties.

Paterson, Gilbert. *Land Settlement in Upper Canada*. Toronto, 1921.

Putnam, D. F. and L. J. Chapman. *The Climate of Southern Ontario*. Scientific Agriculture 18, pp. 401-446. 1938.

Putnam, D. F. and L. J. Chapman. *The Drumlins of Southern Ontario*. Trans. Roy. Soc. Canada 37, Sec. 4, pp. 75-88. 1943.

Schott, Carl. *Landnahme und Kolonisation in Canada am Beispiel Südontarios*. Kiel University. 1936.

Shepard, F. P. *Origin of the Great Lakes Basin*. Journal of Geology 45. pp. 76-88, 1937.

Taylor, F. B. *The Moraine Systems of Southwestern Ontario*. Canadian Institute Transactions 10, pp. 1-23. 1913.

Wilson, A. W. G. *Physical Geology of Central Ontario*. Canadian Institute Transactions 7, pp. 165-183. 1901.

# CHAPTER 11

# Industries and Economic Development
# of Southern Ontario

ONTARIO annually accounts for about 40% of the national income of the Dominion of Canada, being the most productive province. Four major industries produce the bulk of this wealth: they are manufacturing (67%), construction (13%), agriculture (13%) and mining (4%). By far the greater proportion of the agriculture and manufacturing can be credited to the more settled regions of southern Ontario while the mining and forest industries are located in the northern part of the province. Other sources of wealth such as fisheries, the development of hydro-electric power and the tourist trade are shared by both major sections of the province.

Table 11    Net Values of Production in Ontario

| Industry | 1939 | | 1945 | | 1951 | |
|---|---|---|---|---|---|---|
| | $000 | Per Cent | $000 | Per Cent | $000 | Per Cent |
| Agriculture | 190,306 | 15.1 | 381,052 | 15.6 | 670,579 | 12.6 |
| Forestry | 21,086 | 1.7 | 42,592 | 1.7 | 88,588 | 1.7 |
| Fisheries | 2,515 | 0.2 | 6,484 | 0.3 | 7,035 | 0.1 |
| Trapping | 1,550 | 0.1 | 5,088 | 0.2 | 5,213 | 0.1 |
| Mining | 136,966 | 10.8 | 108,845 | 4.4 | 178,554 | 3.3 |
| Electric Power | 52,100 | 4.1 | 72,394 | 3.0 | 127,319 | 2.4 |
| Manufactures | 791,429 | 62.6 | 1,720,938 | 70.5 | 3,569,400 | 67.1 |
| Construction | 68,536 | 5.4 | 104,201 | 4.3 | 673,352 | 12.7 |
| Totals | 1,264,488 | 100.0 | 2,441,594 | 100.0 | 5,320,040 | 100.0 |

Data from D. B. S.

Table 12    Occupations of the Gainfully Employed in Ontario 1951*

| Industrial Groups | Numbers | % |
|---|---|---|
| Agriculture | 201,482 | 10.6 |
| Forestry, Fishing, Trapping, etc. | 25,289 | 1.3 |
| Mining, Quarrying, Oil wells, etc. | 30,653 | 1.6 |
| Construction | 127,494 | 6.7 |
| Manufacturing | 615,358 | 32.8 |
| Transportation, Communication, etc. | 158,125 | 8.3 |
| Trade, Finance, Insurance, etc. | 328,995 | 17.5 |
| Service | 379,129 | 20.2 |
| Not stated | 18,416 | 1.0 |
| Total | 1,884,941 | 100.0 |

* 14 years of age and over, Census of Canada

Primary production employs 13.5% of the active force, secondary industries employ 39.5%, while distribution and service make work for 46.0%.

## Agriculture

Agriculture is not the greatest, but it is the longest established and most fundamental economic activity in southern Ontario. As we have already noted, the climate, land forms and soils of the area are all favourable to agricultural exploitation. Only a few areas such as the steep slopes of the Niagara Escarpment, the rough moraines and the shallow soils of the limestone plains and the Canadian Shield are definitely unfavourable. On the other hand some areas are doubly blessed; lying close to the large lakes, they are free of frost hazard and they also have deep loamy soils which are easy to work. A further great advantage enjoyed by the farmers of southern Ontario is the presence, close at hand, of the markets of large centres of population such as Toronto, Hamilton, Ottawa, Windsor and many lesser cities. Their demands for milk and other dairy products, meats, eggs, fruits and vegetables have, in large measure, led to the diversification of agricultural production and to specializations in areas particularly favourable to the various commodities. Thus there are sections devoted to early vegetables in Essex county, tobacco in Norfolk county, peaches and grapes in the Niagara Peninsula, apples and canning crops along the north shore of Lake Ontario and corn and sugar beets in Kent county, to name the most outstanding.

We tend to regard all this as commonplace and to forget the adjustments that have taken place since pioneer days. The early settler had little knowledge of these potentialities. He was confronted by a hundred acres of forest from which to make a farm. The trees were his enemies; even when felled, he could not profitably dispose of the timber but must pile it up to burn. Perhaps, from the ashes, he salvaged the potash which he sold as his first cash crop. The early farm was a general farm, it grew a variety of things not found on even the most unspecialized farms of today. Apart from a very few imported articles, it produced everything which was used by the pioneer family. Wool and flax were grown, spun and woven and made into clothing on the farm. Hides were made into leather and finally into shoes and harness. Home-made tallow candles served for light. Furniture and implements were home-made. Wheat was grown and ground at the nearest water-driven grist mill for home consumption.

During the first half of the nineteenth century wheat became an export commodity. To supply this demand the clay plains of southern Ontario were rapidly deforested. At every little port along the Great Lakes vessels loaded grain for the United States. From Buffalo and Rochester it found its way to New York by the Erie Barge Canal. Grain entered the United States freely under the Reciprocity agreements but when they were ended in 1866, Ontario fell back on the overseas market by way of Montreal and Quebec. Within twenty years the western prairies began to open up, producing a hard wheat, crowding Ontario wheat off the market.

The clay lands were turned to grass and a cattle industry replaced grain in Ontario. In 1880, wheat was grown on about 1,750,-000 acres; in 1951, less than 400,000 acres were sown. In 1880, there were about 1,-500,000 cattle in Ontario; in 1951, and indeed for the past forty years, there were about 2,500,000. Hog populations increased from about 800,000 to about 1,800,000, and poultry from 5,000,000 to 24,000,000. Sheep, however, declined from over 1,000,000 to less than 400,000. At first the cattle were all of the beef producing breeds such as the Shorthorn and Hereford but, as the demand for dairy products increased, the dairy breeds took their places in many areas. Holstein-Fresians are most popular, but there are many Jerseys, Ayrshires and some Guernseys as well.

There are other notable adjustments. At

one time Ontario had more than 300,000 acres of orchard, mainly apples. Nearly every farm had an orchard of an acre or more. The census of 1951 records only 100,000 acres of orchard and vineyard. One still sees the remnants of thousands of these old farm orchards, but most of the fruit now comes from certain small, well-defined areas where fruit growing is made a specialty. Grapes, peaches and other tender fruits are confined to the Niagara Peninsula and the extreme south-west. Apples are grown along the shores of Lake Ontario, Lake Erie and Georgian Bay. The growing of flue-cured cigarette tobacco be-

on the limestone plains and the moraines, one sees many stone houses. Barns vary also. In western Ontario, the bank barn is common with a basement stable for the animals. Barns are wide in the beef cattle districts; narrow, with lots of windows in the dairy districts. In eastern Ontario bank barns are a rarity. There, also, particularly in the districts of shallow soil, many small log barns are still in use. Sometimes a dozen or more of these structures will be found on one hundred-acre farm. Odd combinations are sometimes seen; an old squared-log house will stand beside a bright new steel barn, or a modern brick house

D. F. Putnam.

Plate 51. A farmstead in South-central Ontario.

came localized on the sandy soils of Norfolk county in the years 1925-40. Since then it has been spreading to similar sandy soils in other counties where the frost-free season is less reliable. Corn for grain production has long been confined to the counties of Kent and Essex, but with the development of earlier maturing hybrid strains it is spreading to other areas also.

There are geographical differences in types of farm buildings. The original log shanties were probably much of the same type, so also were the squared-log houses which followed them. Today's farm houses are built of a variety of materials. In eastern Ontario and in the extreme southwest, wooden buildings are the rule. In most of southwestern Ontario, the houses are of brick but in central Ontario, particularly

will be flanked by a group of old log barns.

Buildings are changed rapidly when new specialties are adopted. Old general farm barns are converted into three-or-four-storey poultry houses and new special types are built. Special barns are built for the curing of hops in eastern Ontario. The layout of a tobacco farm in Norfolk county is specific. The old barn remains for storage purposes, while a long, glass starting-house, a water tower and a half-dozen or more curing barns or kilns are added. The latter are usually spaced at some distance because of the risk of fire. The long barn used in the air-curing of burley tobacco is a distinctive landscape feature also.

The greatest geographical contrast is to be seen on crossing the border of the Canadian Shield. Cleared land at once becomes

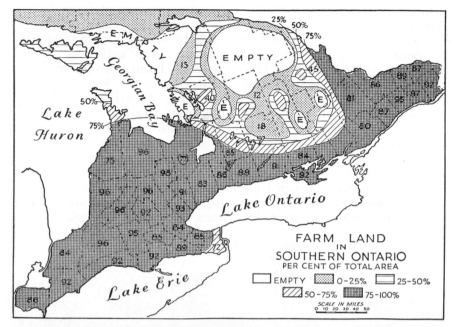

Figure 147. *Occupied Farm Land in Southern Ontario.* Almost all of Southern Ontario, outside of the Canadian Shield, is occupied, either as farms, residential or industrial land. Many counties have more than 90% of their areas in farms. Along the border of the Shield there is a fringe area in which some agriculture was attempted along colonization roads, while intervening areas have no farms.

the exception rather than the rule. Fields are small, houses and barns are poorer in appearance and invariably of unpainted wood. There is more variation, pockets of the better soils support small settlements with a measure of prosperity, while between lie rough woodlands broken here and there by scattered, struggling, subsistence and, probably, part-time farms. Some of the aforementioned contrasts can be seen in the accompanying maps.

### Occupied Land

As can be seen from figure 147, there is very little land unoccupied by farms in Ontario, south of the Canadian Shield. Some of the cities are large enough to be surrounded by suburban areas in which a great proportion of the lands has passed out of agricultural use. Portions of the Bruce Peninsula are unoccupied because of the shallowness of the soils. On the Cana-

dian Shield the pattern of occupied land is very patchy. Only a few areas are really satisfactory from the standpoint of soil and topography and their development has been greatly influenced by road and rail facilities. At the peak of colonization a great deal of unsuitable land was occupied but has since been abandoned.

### Improved Land

Many counties, especially those which have much flat land, have more than 80% of their farm area improved. (Figure 148) Among these are Kent, Essex, Perth, Lincoln and Dundas. Others with more rolling surfaces have slightly less but, in nearly all of Ontario south of the Shield, more than two-thirds of the farm land is capable of cultivation. The most glaring exceptions are to be found upon the limestone plains with their shallow and stony soils. Here there are large areas of unimproved pasture.

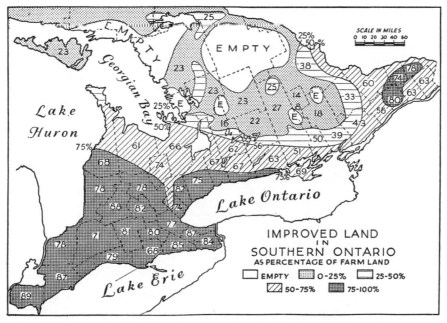

Figure 148. *Improved Land in Southern Ontario.* The farms of southwestern Ontario have very little uncleared land, whereas those of the Canadian Shield have large areas of woodland.

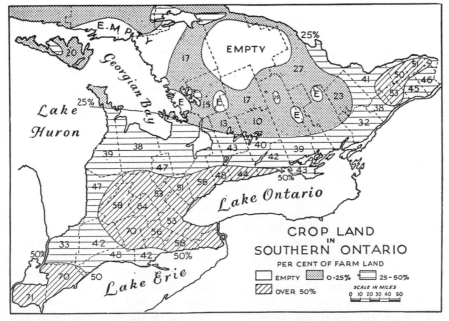

Figure 149. *Crop Land in Southern Ontario.* The crop land pattern differs from that of improved land because of the large areas of pasture land in the general live stock and dairy areas.

## Crop Land

In many of the counties of Ontario, south of the Shield, about half of the farm area is occupied by crops. (Figure 149) In Kent and Essex which have developed crop specialties, the percentage rises to 70% or more. In Bruce, Grey and Huron counties much of the cleared land is in permanent pasture, hence the percentage of land in crop falls below 40% in most townships. On the shallow soils of eastern Ontario the area of crop is lessened, also, and the area of pasture increased.

in Oxford county where fluid milk for city consumption is most important. In both of these centres there are over 12 cows per hundred acre farm on the average. Here also, practically all the cows are of the dairy breeds with Holstein-Fresians predominating. On the other hand, in the general farming areas the cows are often of the beef breeds or dual purpose types. In these areas the number of milking cows per hundred-acre farm is about four. In the districts on the Canadian Shield the density drops to an average of two.

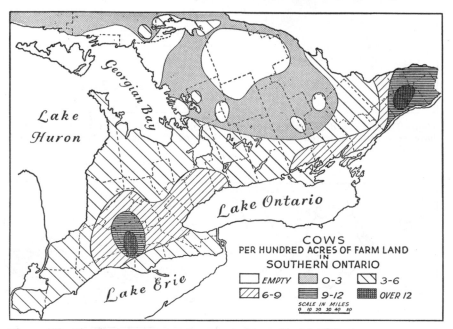

Figure 150. *Distribution of Dairy Cows in Southern Ontario.* There are two striking concentrations of dairy cows; Oxford county in Southwestern Ontario and Dundas county in Eastern Ontario.

## Milch Cows

Southern Ontario is regarded by economic geographers as part of the dairy region of eastern North America. Figure 150 indicates a great difference in the intensity of specialization in dairying. There are two dairy regions, one in eastern Ontario centering in Dundas and Stormont counties where cheese has been the chief product, and one in southwestern Ontario centering

## Agricultural Regions

Boundaries of regions tend to be overlapping zones and this is certainly true of agricultural regions in Ontario. However it is possible to give some guidance to the student of Ontario agriculture in formulating a general picture of conditions. The placing of the boundaries in figure 151 is based upon both statistical and field evidence.

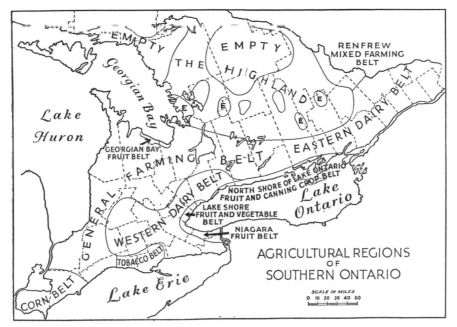

Figure 151. *Agricultural Regions of Southern Ontario.* With the help of the factors shown in the previous maps, Southern Ontario may be divided into several agricultural regions. The lake shores have a number of small regions characterized by the production of special crops.

**A.** *The Corn Belt.* Consisting of the counties of Kent and Essex, this is a region of very mixed farming with many special crop enterprises, especially in Essex county. Husking corn is, and has long been, an important crop. Sugar beets, tobacco, canning crops and fruits and vegetables for shipment to distant city markets are the largest revenue producers.

**B.** *The Tobacco Belt.* The sandy soils of Norfolk county and some adjacent areas produce the bulk of the Canadian flue-cured tobacco crop. Fruits and canning crops are also important.

**C.** *The Niagara Fruit Belt.* Situated mainly between the Niagara escarpment and Lake Ontario, but including also some areas above the escarpment, this region produces most of the peaches and grapes of the Dominion. Other fruits, vegetables and canning crops are grown.

**D.** *The Lakeshore Fruit and Vegetable Belt.* Bordering Lake Ontario, between Hamilton and Toronto, is a narrow plain of sandy soils which are utilized to grow apples, strawberries, tomatoes, sweet corn and other special crops which find a ready sale on the Toronto market. Peaches and grapes are not grown to any great extent.

**E.** *The North Shore of Lake Ontario Fruit and Canning Crops Belt.* Extending from Toronto to Kingston and including the peninsula of Prince Edward county, lies a narrow belt which enjoys a somewhat modified climate because of its proximity to Lake Ontario. It also has areas of loamy soils developed upon old lake bed deposits. Although not as intensively specialized as some other regions yet, it produces quantities of apples and canning crops such as sweet corn, tomatoes and peas.

**F.** *The Western Dairy Belt.* Extending from Oshawa to London is a belt in which dairying is definitely the dominant form of agriculture. This belt also contains most of the urban population of the province

Courtesy L. J. Chapman.
Plate 52. A pea viner in operation. The shelled peas are transported in trucks to the cannery in a nearby town.

thus providing a ready market for fluid milk. Industrial dairy plants are also found in the area.

G. *The Eastern Dairy Region.* Extending from Hastings county to the Quebec border is another region in which dairying is dominant. The cities of Ottawa and Montreal furnish markets for fluid milk, but the chief market for many years has been the local cheese factory and most of the Canadian Cheddar cheese comes from this region. Because a large part of the region has shallow soils, grain crops are not grown extensively and summer dairying is the rule. In areas of deeper soils, as in Dundas county, where reliable year round production of milk is possible, condenseries have been established. A small area near Ottawa is devoted to market gardens while along the St. Lawrence are a number of apple orchards. Hops are grown on the sand plains of Prescott county.

H. *The General Farming Belt.* Extending

Courtesy Exp. Farms Service.
Plate 53. A corn harvester at work in Southern Ontario.

from Lake Erie and the southern end of Lake Huron to the Trent Valley is an extensive belt in which a general crop and livestock farming is practised. Throughout this area over 70% of the farm income is received from livestock and livestock products sold off the farms. Cattle and hogs are the leading items. In such a broad belt, of course, there are many small centres of specialization. Among these may be mentioned the Thedford Marsh near the southern end of Lake Huron, the Holland Marsh near Lake Simcoe, both of which produce truck crops exclusively, and the Beaver Valley near Georgian Bay which is famous for its apples. Near towns and cities there are some specialized dairy farms.

D. F. Putnam.
Plate 54. A covered milkstand, a common roadside feature in the cheese producing districts.

I. *The Renfrew Mixed Farming Belt.* This is a small region in the Ottawa valley which has not become so specialized to dairying as the rest of eastern Ontario. Cattle, sheep and swine are leading income producers, but seed grain, clover seed and peas are important.

J. *The "Highland".* This is an area of sparse agricultural settlement with a few "pockets" of moderately well developed farms some of which are indicated on the map. For the most part the agriculture is of a subsistence and part-time type. The sale of milk and cattle are the most important sources of cash income apart from outside work.

## Summary

Ninety-five per cent of the agricultural wealth of the province is found in the southern section which is the most intensively developed area in Canada. Here an annual cash income of more than $700,-000,000 is obtained from an occupied area of 20,000,000 acres, usually greater than that obtained in Saskatchewan from 60,-000,000 acres. While not competing in field crops, particularly wheat, the values of animals, milk, eggs, fruits, vegetables and tobacco are much greater. This specialization has meant subdivision and increase in numbers of farms and farm population in favoured areas, but on the whole farm population is declining and farms are becoming larger and more highly mechanized.

## Manufacturing

Ontario is the greatest manufacturing province in Canada and by far the greater part of this production arises in the southern part of the province. That is not to say that a good deal of manufacturing, including pulp and paper making, sawmilling, metal refining and iron and steel working, is not done in northern Ontario. To a large extent, however, this is to be considered processing of raw materials which are manufactured into consumers goods elsewhere, notably in the cities of southern Ontario.

In recent years manufacturing has grown rapidly. In 1938, the last pre-war year, the total value of manufactures in Ontario was $1,712,496,000 (net $757,621,000). By 1942 it was twice as great. Following a slight post-war recession, the value rose again, reaching $9,616,000,000 (net $5,000,000,-000) in 1954. Manufactures employ 600,-000 workers, one-third of the labour force, and account for two-thirds of the total annual net production.

Among the most important industries are: automobiles and automobile supplies, smelting and refining of non-ferrous metals, primary iron and steel, electrical apparatus and supplies, slaughtering and meat packing, pulp and paper, rubber goods, machinery, flour and feed, butter and cheese. These are the leaders, both in peacetime and wartime, although their relative positions change somewhat from time to time. However, there are very few lines of everyday useful goods which are not produced somewhere in Ontario.

There are many reasons why Ontario has become a notable manufacturing region. At Niagara Falls and in the rivers of the Canadian Shield, a great wealth of hydro-electric power has been made available. Although lacking in coal and deficient in iron ore reserves, she has considerable wealth of other raw materials. She has an intelligent and industrious population with many skills and also with many desires to be satisfied. In other words, Ontario is her own best market and it is a normal thing for goods to be produced as close to market as possible. Finally, the excellence of transportation facilities, not only by land, but especially on the Great Lakes, makes it possible to obtain raw materials and to distribute finished goods very cheaply.

Some of the most important industries are very highly localized. Non-ferrous metal smelting and refining, for instance, are carried on in a few large plants. Nickel is refined at Port Colborne because of transportation facilities and power supply. A radium refinery is located at Port Hope.

The location of the primary iron and steel works at Hamilton is a good example of the balance of geographical factors. The ore comes by ship from ports on Lake Superior, coal from the Appalachian region also arrives by ship, limestone is quarried nearby and the product, steel, goes to many steel using industries in southern Ontario. From them, scrap metal goes back to the steel plant to be used again. It is natural, therefore, that many of these sec-

## Table 13    Leading Industries of Ontario 1951

| Industry | No. of Estab-lishments | No. of Employ-ees | Salaries and Wages $000,000 | Average Annual Wage $ | Cost of Materials $000,000 | Net Value of Products $000,000 | Gross Value of Products $000,000 | % of Cana-dian Total |
|---|---|---|---|---|---|---|---|---|
| 1. Motor Vehicles | 12 | 29,413 | 98.5 | 3,240 | 459.7 | 266.4 | 728.6 | 97.5 |
| 2. Pulp and Paper | 44 | 18,348 | 69.1 | 3,860 | 152.2 | 213.9 | 387.0 | 31.2 |
| 3. Primary Iron and Steel | 24 | 22,670 | 77.4 | 3,400 | 178.2 | 157.4 | 359.4 | 75.0 |
| 4. Slaughtering and Meat Packing | 61 | 8,073 | 24.2 | 3,000 | 304.1 | 49.8 | 355.6 | 39.7 |
| 5. Non-ferrous Metals | 7 | 9,539 | 31.5 | 3,300 | 176.4 | 161.5 | 353.4 | 41.0 |
| 6. Rubber Goods | 37 | 15,825 | 46.8 | 2,950 | 122.0 | 132.2 | 257.0 | 82.2 |
| 7. Motor Vehicle Parts | 94 | 20,205 | 62.8 | 3,100 | 139.0 | 113.0 | 255.2 | 97.0 |
| 8. Machinery, Heavy Electrical | 34 | 23,956 | 72.0 | 3,000 | 92.0 | 118.0 | 211.7 | 95.0 |
| 9. Agricultural Implements | 35 | 16,022 | 49.2 | 3,050 | 91.7 | 67.3 | 160.8 | 93.5 |
| 10. Petroleum Products | 14 | 4,907 | 17.5 | 3,680 | 104.0 | 41.3 | 153.5 | 25.6 |
| 11. Fruit and Vegetable Preparations | 214 | 10,269 | 20.1 | 1,960 | 75.8 | 58.9 | 136.5 | 68.7 |
| 12. Butter and Cheese | 594 | 7,831 | 18.7 | 2,400 | 98.9 | 31.4 | 132.9 | 35.5 |
| 13. Flour Mills | 61 | 2,196 | 6.4 | 2,900 | 114.0 | 15.8 | 130.6 | 46.3 |
| 14. Sheet Metal Products | 145 | 10,258 | 29.7 | 2,900 | 64.8 | 51.7 | 118.0 | 60.0 |
| 15. Iron Castings | 95 | 11,124 | 34.7 | 3,100 | 51.6 | 60.4 | 114.4 | 69.5 |
| 16. Miscellaneous Electrical App. | 91 | 9,023 | 25.5 | 2,840 | 53.4 | 55.2 | 109.6 | 49.5 |
| 17. Industrial Machinery | 171 | 11,438 | 35.1 | 3,080 | 38.4 | 68.8 | 108.3 | 53.7 |
| 18. Bread & Bakery Products | 878 | 14,379 | 30.9 | 2,140 | 49.3 | 50.7 | 103.4 | 42.5 |
| 19. Brass & Copper Products | 87 | 6,033 | 18.1 | 3,000 | 66.8 | 33.7 | 101.7 | 56.5 |
| 20. Miscellaneous Food Preparations | 127 | 4,373 | 10.4 | 2,380 | 71.0 | 28.5 | 101.1 | 39.0 |
| Twenty Leading Industries | 2,825 | 255,882 | 778.6 | 3,040 | 2,503.3 | 1,775.9 | 4,378.7 | 26.6 |
| Total, All Industries | 13,025 | 599,433 | 1,669.4 | 2,780 | 4,334.4 | 3,569.4 | 8,074.7 | 48.5 |
| Leading Industries as per cent of all Ontario Industries | 21.7 | 41.6 | 46.5 | 109.0 | 58.0 | 49.7 | 54.2 | |

Data from D. B. S. 1953.

ondary iron and steel industries find it convenient to locate in Hamilton or the Niagara Peninsula.

It was quite natural that Canadian automobile plants should be built in Windsor which is adjacent to Detroit, the location of the parent plants. At first, the motor cars built in Canada were assembled chiefly from imported parts. It was more convenient to do this as near as possible to the parent plant. Then, as time went on, Canadian plants became larger, more ef-

ficient and produced more and more of the parts themselves. The other concentrations of the industry in Oshawa and St. Catharines are not so easily explained. Oshawa has no geographical reason for becoming a city, let alone a major automobile centre. The answer, of course, must be sought in business initiative and acumen and in the accumulated skills of workers previously engaged in carriage building. Automobiles have little resemblance to buggies now, nevertheless the first car was simply a buggy with a motor, and the man who built one could build the other. The making of parts in St. Catharines utilizes skills of metal workers and machinists already there. The recent establishment of an automobile factory in Hamilton would seem to be entirely in accord with geographic principles.

The furniture industry is widely disseminated, being found in many small towns as well as larger centres. In the early days, native woods were fashioned by hand craftsmen who could compete against all imported goods because furniture is a bulky product, not easy to transport. Now much of the wood is imported, many more machines are used, the home market remains secure and the industry is able to compete outside its home territory. Thus we explain its importance in Stratford, Kitchener, Woodstock, Owen Sound and many smaller centres such as Hanover, Chesley, Clinton and Milverton, to mention a few.

Even more decentralized is the woodworking industry producing builders supplies. Practically every city, town and village has its planing mill and sash and door factory. Houses must be produced at the point where they are to be used. The fabricated parts are harder to transport than undressed lumber, hence the closer to the job they can be made, the better.

In the early days there were many small brickyards in the province. Nowadays a few large ones such as those at Cooksville, Milton and Toronto do most of the business. The nearer to a large city, the better for the brick industry.

Shipbuilding, for obvious reasons, is localized in ports. Toronto, Collingwood and Midland built many vessels during World War II.

Petroleum refining is localized in a few large plants, notably those at Sarnia, Toronto and Clarkson.

Food processing industries are an interesting group. The largest of these is slaughtering and meat packing. Meat is a perishable product and before modern refrigeration was developed it was necessary to have it produced as close as possible to market, hence the beginning of the packing industry close to large cities. Thus certain centres obtained a head start. Nowadays distant centres are beginning to cut into large city markets. This is particularly true of the poultry trade. It is much easier to ship frozen fowl from Atwood, Harriston or Mindemoya than to ship live birds all the way to Toronto. Flour and feed industries may be either decentralized or

D. F. Putnam.

Plate 55. The mill at Feversham on the Beaver River. Early mill sites often became the foci of important settlements.

centralized. In the early days hundreds of mills were established throughout the country to grind local grain. Many of these continue to operate, perhaps somewhat enlarged and using western wheat as well as local wheat. Other large plants have been established at lake ports such as Goderich, Midland and Toronto, to which western grain can be brought cheaply. Canning and fruit processing plants and wineries are always located near their sources of raw materials. Wineries are nearly all in the Niagara Peninsula. Canneries are found all the way from Essex county to Prince Edward county in the climatic belt in which it is possible to grow tender crops. Outside this belt there are isolated plants such as at Collingwood, which depend partly on local crops and partly upon fruits brought from a distance.

*D. F. Putnam.*
Plate 56. A cheese factory in Eastern Ontario.

Creameries and cheese factories are well scattered throughout the province. The cheese industry has been extremely decentralized within its own special areas. Milk is bulky and difficult to transport, it is therefore made into cheese, a much easier product to handle, as close to the farms as possible. Nowadays, however, larger factories, drawing by truck from wider territories, are being built. Cheese is also being given stiff competition by other plants making condensed and powdered milk.

As in other provinces, southern Ontario has a great number of small sawmills. Formerly there were a number of large ones in the Georgian Bay region and in the borders of the Shield. Nowadays, one or two large mills along the Ottawa are all that are left.

We usually think of pulp and paper as a northern industry but there are a number of mills in Old Ontario. The most important of these are located at Thorold, Corn-

## Table 14   Leading Manufacturing Centres in Southern Ontario Ranked in Order of Net Production 1949

| Centre | No. of Establishments | No. of Employees | Salaries and Wages $000,000 | Average Annual Wage $ | Fuel and Electricity $000,000 | Cost of Materials $000,000 | Gross Value $000,000 | Net Value $000,000 | Per Cent of Ont. Total |
|---|---|---|---|---|---|---|---|---|---|
| 1. Toronto | 4,005 | 158,562 | 368.5 | 2,320 | 17.0 | 837.1 | 1,579.2 | 725.1 | 26.8 |
| 2. Hamilton | 546 | 54,665 | 137.6 | 2,500 | 17.7 | 285.2 | 564.0 | 261.1 | 9.7 |
| 3. Windsor | 283 | 34,591 | 94.3 | 2,720 | 5.4 | 271.4 | 494.2 | 217.4 | 8.0 |
| 4. London | 270 | 15,153 | 32.9 | 2,180 | 1.7 | 62.4 | 139.3 | 75.2 | 2.8 |
| 5. Oshawa | 55 | 9,997 | 26.7 | 2,670 | 1.3 | 85.3 | 157.8 | 71.2 | 2.6 |
| 6. Kitchener | 197 | 14,821 | 31.9 | 2,160 | 1.5 | 75.5 | 141.7 | 64.7 | 2.4 |
| 7. Brantford | 156 | 13,650 | 31.8 | 2,330 | 1.7 | 66.9 | 129.4 | 60.8 | 2.3 |
| 8. Sarnia | 46 | 7,153 | 18.9 | 2,650 | 9.3 | 90.8 | 145.3 | 45.2 | 1.7 |
| 9. Welland | 63 | 8,061 | 22.3 | 2,760 | 3.6 | 43.4 | 91.9 | 44.9 | 1.6 |
| 10. St. Catharines | 104 | 9,899 | 25.2 | 2,550 | 1.2 | 39.8 | 85.7 | 44.7 | 1.6 |
| 11. Ottawa | 268 | 10,641 | 22.7 | 2,140 | 1.7 | 38.0 | 82.5 | 42.8 | 1.6 |
| 12. New Toronto | 39 | 6,407 | 17.4 | 2,720 | 1.5 | 55.5 | 99.6 | 42.6 | 1.6 |
| 13. Leaside | 51 | 7,873 | 19.3 | 2,450 | 1.0 | 40.7 | 83.7 | 42.0 | 1.6 |
| 14. Niagara Falls | 76 | 6,163 | 15.6 | 2,530 | 4.6 | 27.4 | 71.0 | 39.0 | 1.4 |
| 15. Peterborough | 99 | 9,591 | 23.6 | 2,450 | 1.1 | 61.6 | 100.0 | 37.3 | 1.4 |
| 16. Cornwall | 50 | 6,502 | 15.0 | 2,320 | 2.8 | 21.1 | 52.6 | 28.7 | 1.1 |
| 17. Kingston | 65 | 5,556 | 12.2 | 2,180 | 1.1 | 21.9 | 50.0 | 27.0 | 1.0 |
| 18. Guelph | 106 | 5,867 | 12.9 | 2,200 | .9 | 22.4 | 45.6 | 22.3 | .8 |
| 19. Galt | 86 | 6,030 | 12.8 | 2,120 | .7 | 17.7 | 40.2 | 21.8 | .8 |
| 20. Chatham | 71 | 3,572 | 8.5 | 2,380 | .9 | 42.4 | 62.4 | 19.1 | .7 |
| Twenty Centres | 6,636 | 395,854 | 950.1 | 2,400 | 76.7 | 2,206.5 | 4,216.1 | 1,932.9 | 71.5 |
| Twenty Centres as percentage of Ontario Totals | 51.2 | 71.5 | 73.0 | 102.5 | 55.4 | 67.5 | 69.0 | 71.5 | |

Data from D. B. S.

wall and Hawkesbury, in each case, where favourable transportation facilities exist.

The industrial pre-eminence of southern Ontario, then, seems due to its available power, excellent transportation, its head start in many lines and the sustaining influence of its large home market.

In Ontario there are 135 manufacturing centres which in 1949 had a gross annual production of more than $1,000,000. A somewhat fairer appraisal of manufacturing activity is obtainable by considering net value of production and number of workers employed. Table 14 gives the data for the twenty leading manufacturing centres of Southern Ontario, ranked in order of value of net production. Collectively they employ 71 percent of all the industrial workers and produce 71 percent of the net value. They produce nearly 70 percent of the gross value. It is notable also that most of these centres have average wage rates somewhat above that of the provincial average.

Figure 152 shows the general location of manufacturing activity in Southern On-

tario on the basis of net value. The leadership of the Toronto, Hamilton and Niagara Peninsula regions is quite evident. In addition to the leading centres already noted, these areas contain a number of smaller centres as well as many industries located outside the boundaries of incorporated places.

## Mining

Most of the important mines of Ontario are in the north but mineral wealth is obtained in Old Ontario also. Canada's first oilfield, still producing about 400,000 barrels per annum, is located around Petrolia in Lambton county. There are many natural gas wells in southwestern Ontario with an annual production of about $4,-000,000. Building materials including cement, brick, tile, lime, stone, sand and gravel, to the value of $80,000,000 in 1954, were produced in the province with much the larger share from Southern Ontario. Pleistocene clays are used for brick and tile making at a number of places but the shales of south-central Ontario supply the

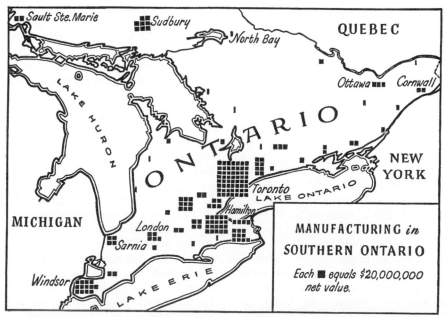

Figure 152. *Distribution of Manufacturing in Southern Ontario.* 1952. Manufacturing activity is strongly concentrated in the Toronto, Hamilton, Niagara and Windsor areas.

largest plants. Kames, eskers, spillway terraces and old beaches supply sand and gravel in great quantities for the building of
highways and concrete structures of all
kinds. Crushed limestone from the Niagara
Escarpment and other formations are used
for similar purposes. Limestone from Beach-
ville is used for flux in the steel industry.
Gypsum is mined from extensive beds near
Hagersville and salt is obtained near Windsor, Sarnia and Goderich.

Many mineral occurrences have been
noted along the southern margin of the
Canadian Shield. The smelter at Deloro in
Hastings county was once supplied with
ores from nearby mines. Now it treats ores
from Northern Ontario and even more distant points. Talc is obtained near Madoc.

Nepheline syenite, for use in the glass
and ceramics industries, is quarried and
ground at Nephton in Peterborough
county. Hematite iron ore is mined and
pelletized near Marmora in Hastings
county. It is shipped to American steel-
making centres from Picton on Lake Ontario. The need for light metals during
World War II led to the establishment of a
plant near Haley in Renfrew County where
magnesium and calcium are produced.
More recent still is the development of several uranium mines near Bancroft in the
northern part of Hastings county.

## Forestry

In the area underlain by Paleozoic rocks
and the Pleistocene deposits derived from
them, agriculture has almost completely
displaced the forest. In the rougher area
underlain by the Canadian Shield, sometimes known as the Huron-Ottawa Tract,
a large area of forest remains and wood
for various purposes is still of economic
importance. Lumber is obtained from both
deciduous and coniferous species. This is
the area that formerly contained the great
stands of white pine which were carried
to market via the Ottawa and its tributaries. The rivers emptying to Georgian
Bay were also noted for their log drives.

Lumbering is now on a much smaller scale
and there are few large mills. Instead the
forests of this region are dotted by hundreds of small logging operations supplying small portable mills. The motor truck,
in many areas, carries the logs to the mill
and stream driving is no longer practised
on the smaller water courses. It still has
its place, however, on the larger streams.

In the Huron-Ottawa region most of the
original settlement depended upon forest
exploitation with agriculture following
and establishing itself in the less rocky
areas. For the most part, however, it has
been part-time agriculture with lumbering
still remaining important. In recognition
of the fact that this area is primarily non-
agricultural two large forest preserves, Algonquin Park and Georgian Bay Provincial Forest, have been set aside. Along with
the great recreational development in this
forest area, a scientifically planned and operated "sustained yield" policy would provide the optimum in land use.

## Fisheries

Fish in commercial quantities have been
taken in the Great Lakes for at least a
century, but since 1930 the industry has
suffered considerable decline. About three-
fourths of the total amount comes from
waters adjoining Southern Ontario and
about 50% from Lake Erie alone. In Lake
Erie, which is a shallow lake, the most
important fish are herring, whitefish, blue
pickerel, doré and perch. Lake trout are
found in the deeper waters of Georgian
Bay and Lake Ontario. In 1950, a total
of 33,000,000 pounds of fish valued at
$7,000,000 was taken in Ontario.

While not bulking very large in the economics of the region, the commercial fishery forms an interesting phase of its human
geography. Among the fishing ports may be
mentioned Port Credit and Bronte on Lake
Ontario; Port Maitland, Port Dover, Port
Burwell and Port Stanley on Lake Erie;
Southampton on Lake Huron; Lion's
Head and Meaford on Georgian Bay. At

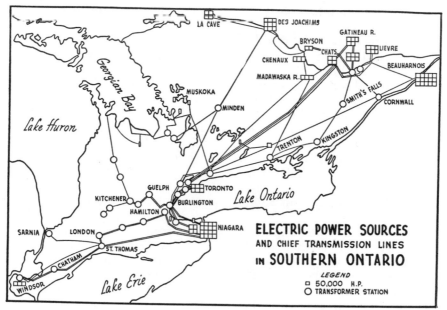

Figure 153. *Major Electric Power Sources and Distribution Lines in Southern Ontario.* The major power developments supplying Southern Ontario are those of the Niagara River and the Ottawa and its tributaries.

these places and others as well, various types of tugs, barges and motor boats may be seen together with ice houses, storage sheds and net drying reels which typify the landscape of the fishing village.

## Development of Hydro-electric Power

Southern Ontario produces no coal and only a small amount of other mineral fuels. In the pioneer stage power was produced by small water wheels and by wood-burning steam engines. The power which enabled the development of Southern Ontario as a great manufacturing region has come from the harnessing of the larger rivers, the Niagara, the Ottawa and the St. Lawrence. The energy of these streams is transmitted as electricity to all parts of the province. The production and distribution of electric power is almost entirely in the hands of the Hydro-electric Power Commission of Ontario, which was created in 1906 and is now the foremost publicly owned utility service on the continent.

During the year 1950 it supplied more than 2,800,000 H.P. of which over four-fifths was distributed by the southern Ontario System.

The greatest source of power is, of course, the Niagara River which falls a total of 327 feet from Lake Erie to Lake Ontario, including the straight drop of 158 feet at Niagara Falls. Four great generating plants, three on the Niagara River and one at De Cew Falls fed from the Welland Canal, produce a total of more than 1,000,000 H.P. Recent developments on the Ottawa River will permit the development of about 1,000,000 H.P. also. These include the earlier Chats Falls plant and those at Des Joachims, Chenaux and La Cave, which came into operation from 1950 to 1953. The Madawaska, Mississippi, Muskoka and Trent Rivers each have several power plants which, though much smaller than those of the Ottawa, supply important blocks of power. In addition to its own supplies, the Commission purchases about 950,000 H.P. annually. Most of this comes from the Beauharnois, Gatineau and other developments in the province of Quebec. The Ontario Hydro-electric System, by the end of 1952, was serving 1,244 municipalities in Ontario, including 27 cities, 136 towns and mining town sites, 324 villages and police villages and 757 townships and improvement districts. A few urban municipalities still have their own electric power systems. In order to supply the hundreds of local distribution systems over 10,000 miles of high voltage transmission lines must be maintained. About four-fifths of this total is in Southern Ontario.

Rural electrification is an important phase of the Hydro-electric programme. By 1950 rural municipal power lines totaled over 30,000 miles and slightly more than half of all Ontario farms were serviced as well as about two-thirds of all other rural residents. A further group of nearly 30,000 summer residences were also supplied, an indication of the importance of the summer cottage in Ontario.

The growth of the demand for power in Ontario has been phenomenal. It tends to double itself in a ten year period and new construction is hardly able to keep pace. The completion of the St. Lawrence power project at Cornwall adds a resource of 1,100,000 h.p. to the Ontario power supply but plans are being laid for other supplies. Steam plants have for some years been in operation at Windsor, Hamilton and Toronto and it is expected that new and larger steam plants will be built.

The widespread, publicly owned power systems of Ontario must be given a great deal of the credit for its development as the most important industrial area in Canada.

The Photographic Survey Corporation Limited

Plate 57. The DeCew generating stations of the Ontario Hydro-Electric Power Commission. Water from the Welland Canal operates turbines at the base of the Niagara Escarpment.

## Transportation and Communications

Southern Ontario occupies a strategic location with regard to transportation. It is almost surrounded by navigable rivers and lakes which in the early colonial days permitted peripheral settlement and created an almost maritime atmosphere. Jutting southward into the populous areas of the United States it serves as a bridge between the northeastern and midwestern sections of that country as well as being a node in the land transportation systems of Canada itself. The same locational factor has had much to do with the development of air transportation in recent years.

### Waterways

Due to its peculiar shape no part of southern Ontario is more than 100 miles from a lake or river port and the early settlement pattern in much of the area consisted in the establishment of lake ports and the building of long colonization roads into the hinterland. Kingston, Belleville, Cobourg, Port Hope, Bowmanville, Whitby, Toronto, Port Credit, Oakville and Dundas were such points on Lake Ontario. Port Dover, Port Burwell and Port Stanley on Lake Erie, Goderich, Kincardine, Owen Sound and Collingwood give evidence of similar development. The building of the railways brought an end to the activities of many lake ports, but others have become more important. Despite the fact that the St. Lawrence Deep Seaway has not yet been completed, the Great Lakes and their connecting canals constitute the greatest inland waterway in the world.

From the head of Lake Superior to the foot of Lake Ontario, a distance of 1,200 miles there is passage for vessels of 25 feet draught. This is made possible in Southern Ontario by the Welland Canal which connects Lake Erie and Lake Ontario. Re-

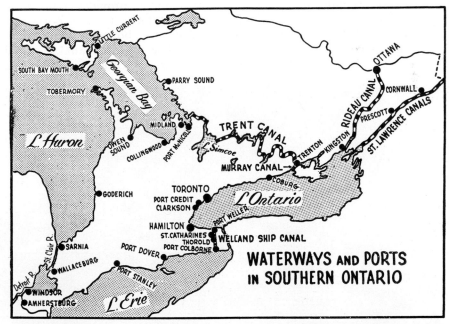

Figure 154. *Waterways and Ports of Southern Ontario.* The Great Lakes and the St. Lawrence give Ontario an extensive shoreline, along which numerous ports were developed in the early days. Only a few of them have grown into really important modern lake ports. The Welland Canal makes it possible for the larger vessels of the Upper Lakes to come into Lake Ontario, but only small boats can use the St. Lawrence canals.

placing earlier canals of smaller capacity the Welland Canal was completed in 1931 at a cost of about $140,000,000. Between the approaches at Port Weller and Port Colborne, it has a length of 27.6 miles. Eight great locks with a minimum length of 859 feet each make a total lift of 327 feet between the lake levels. Most striking is the triple flight at Thorold by which the canal traverses the face of the Niagara escarpment.

The Upper Lakes route which carries the commerce of both U.S.A. and Canada is the busiest waterway in the world with an annual tonnage of more than 140,000,000 tons, more than the combined tonnage of the Panama and Suez canals. The annual traffic of the Welland Canal is 10-15,000,000 tons, a figure which would be greatly exceeded upon the completion of the St. Lawrence Deep Waterway.

In the 40-mile stretch of the St. Lawrence between Prescott and Lake St. Francis there are nearly 24 miles of canals including Gallops, 7.36 miles from Cardinal to Iroquois; Rapide Plat, 3.89 miles near Morrisburg; Farran Point, 1.28 miles; and the Cornwall canal, 11.00 miles from Dick-

inson's Landing to Cornwall. These canals have locks only 270 feet in length and 14 feet deep. Between Lake St. Francis and Montreal Harbour are the Soulanges and Lachine canals with a total length of over 23 miles. Thus in Ontario and Quebec the St. Lawrence Canals have a total length of 47 miles and a total lift of about 200 feet. The St. Lawrence Canals carry 5-10,000,000 tons of shipping annually.

The St. Lawrence Seaway project is a plan to supersede this inadequate canal system by a 27 foot channel capable of carrying all but the very largest ocean liners. Great Lakes' ports such as Toronto, Buffalo, Cleveland, Chicago and the Lakehead will then become ocean ports as well. The development of the rapid section of the river will also provide more than 2,000-000 H.P. of electrical energy to be shared between Ontario and New York State.

There are other canals in Ontario. The Murray canal, 5.15 miles long, across Murray Isthmus, provides a short route from Lake Ontario to the ports on Bay of Quinte for boats drawing less than 11 feet. The Rideau canal, 126 miles from Kingston to Ottawa, connects Lake On-

*The Photographic Survey Corporation Limited.*
Plate 58. The Bluewater Bridge at Sarnia is a link between the highway systems of Michigan and Ontario. The St. Clair River is one of the busiest waterways in the world.

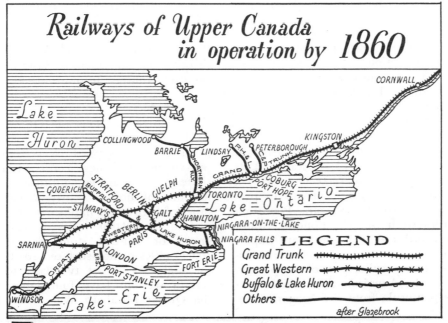

Figure 155. *Early Railway Lines in Southern Ontario*. The chief railways in operation by 1860 were the Grand Trunk, Great Western, Buffalo and Lake Huron and the Northern Railway.

tario with the Ottawa river which is navigable thus far by reason of canals on the Quebec side. The Rideau canal was built in 1827-32 by Col. By, the founder of Ottawa. It is navigable for barges of five feet draught only and is of little use except for pleasure craft at the present time. The Trent canal system connects the Bay of Quinte with Georgian Bay, a rather indirect route of 240 miles. For most of its length it has a depth of 6 feet. The harnessing of the Trent and Otonabee rivers in this system has provided a considerable amount of power, but the canal is of little use for the movement of freight.

The water-borne commerce of Ontario is greater than that of any other province, amounting to about 30,000,000 tons annually. Most of this is entered at southern Ontario ports. In 1951 the most active ports were Sarnia (3,800,000 tons), Toronto (3,-300,000 tons), Hamilton (2,500,000 tons), Port Colborne (2,000,000 tons), Windsor (1,100,000 tons), Kingston (900,000 tons),

Prescott (860,000 tons), Midland (800,000 tons), Thorold (750,000 tons), Port McNicoll (570,000 tons), Cornwall (430,000 tons), and Amherstburg (300,000 tons). Grain, coal, iron ore and oil are the chief water borne commodities. There are numerous smaller ports as well. Ontario had a total of 432,000 tons of registered shipping in 1951, more than any other Canadian province except Quebec.

## Railways

Southern Ontario has the most complete rail net of any area in Canada with over 6,000 miles of standard gauge track in operation. The total mileage is somewhat lower than it was in 1930 owing to the abandonment of duplications in the service. Most of the lines belong to either the Canadian Pacific or the Canadian National, but there are some other important lines including The New York Central, 370 miles; Ottawa and New York, 57 miles; Pere Marquette, 199 miles, and the Toronto, Hamilton and Buffalo, 104 miles in length.

Railways have been important in the economic life of Southern Ontario ever since the completion of the Northern Railway from Toronto to Collingwood in 1855 and the Grand Trunk from Toronto to Montreal in 1856. The geographic pattern of the southern Ontario rail net is definitely focused upon Toronto with lines giving direct service to nearly all parts of the country. Hamilton, also, because of its position at the head of Lake Ontario is a second nucleus, rivalling Toronto in providing service to the Niagara Peninsula and southwestern Ontario. London, Brantford, Stratford and St. Thomas are important junction points in southwestern Ontario. A rather peculiar part of the pattern consists of the American lines which traverse the peninsula from the Niagara fron-

tier to the Detroit River. Ottawa is the most important nodal point in the rail net of eastern Ontario and it, also, has direct connection with American lines. Most of the rail traffic in eastern Ontario, however, funnels into Montreal.

## Highways

The highway net of Ontario totals 74,000 miles, Southern Ontario being especially well supplied. Nevertheless, improvements and new construction necessitate a capital expenditure of many millions of dollars yearly. About 12,000 miles of highway is hard-surfaced while the surface on 52,000 miles is classified as gravel or crushed stone, leaving about 10,000 miles of non-surfaced road. Most of the highways are of two lane width but certain sections have four lanes, notably the Queen Elizabeth Way from Toronto

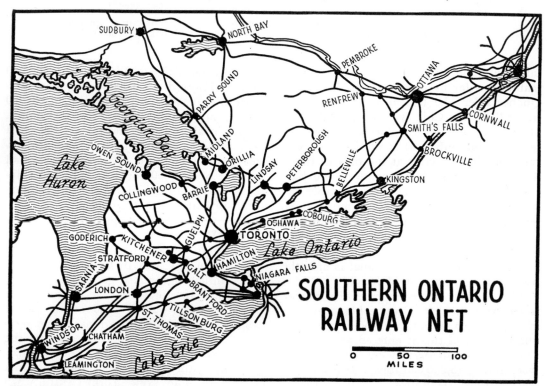

Figure 156. *Present Railway Net in Southern Ontario.* Southern Ontario is covered by a close network of railways and there is hardly any centre of population without their services. Note the concentration of lines at border-crossing gateways.

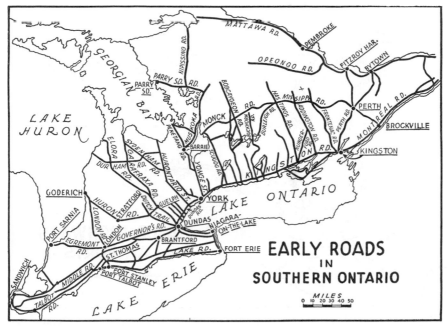

Figure 157. *Early Roads in Southern Ontario.* Besides the main road from Montreal to Windsor, many colonization roads were pushed northward into the forests to facilitate settlement.

to Fort Erie and the new highways from Toronto east to Newcastle and north to Barrie. These highways are constructed with grade separation at railway crossings and with cloverleaf intersections at other main highways. Surfaced highways now give more adequate coverage in southern Ontario than do railways, but it is noticeable that much the same nodes occur as in the railway net. The concentration is much in evidence around the western end of Lake Ontario and emphasizes the Niagara Peninsula as a traffic corridor. A somewhat similar situation exists at Windsor, the southwestern gateway. The nodal position of Ottawa in eastern Ontario is brought out by the radiating pattern of surfaced highways.

Ontario has nearly half the motor vehicles operated in Canada. In 1951 there were 958,000 passenger cars, 230,000 trucks, 4,000 buses and 13,000 motorcycles. Post war expansion has been rapid; motor traffic has become exceedingly congested on

many Ontario roads. Holiday traffic on the highways out of Toronto is especially heavy while the daily rush hour traffic in all the larger cities taxes the capacity of the streets which, in the older areas, are far too narrow. Apart from these congested areas, however, the highway system offers adequate and rapid access to all parts of southern Ontario. Most of the main highways are followed by scheduled bus lines.

**Airways**

Toronto is the centre of the greatest concentration of air routes in Canada with direct lines to Montreal, western Canada, Chicago, Cleveland, Buffalo, New York and Bermuda. The Toronto airport, located at Malton, thirteen miles northwest of the city, schedules more than 100 flights daily. Other important airports in southern Ontario are located at London, Windsor, and Ottawa. Besides these airports which are used by T.C.A. and other airlines, there are many others. Near Toronto are Barker

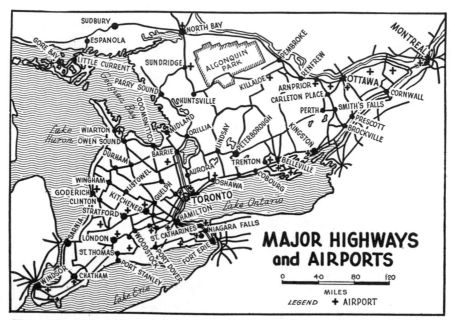

Figure 158. *Major Highways and Airports in Southern Ontario.* Southern Ontario has the most completely developed highway network in Canada. Busses and trucks offer serious competition to the railways and, in addition, reach many areas which do not have railway services. There are airports near all major cities.

Field, De Haviland and Toronto Island. Among other places, airports are located near Oshawa, Bracebridge, Hamilton, Brantford, Guelph, Kitchener, St. Catharines, Killaloe, Welland, St. Thomas, Trenton and Wiarton. Sea plane bases are found at Toronto Harbour, Goderich, Owen Sound, Orillia, Peterborough, Huntsville, Dorset, Midland, Parry Sound and Algonquin Park. It is possible, of course, to land or take off from almost any point along the shores of the Great Lakes, Muskoka Lakes, Kawartha Lakes, Rideau Lakes and many lakes in Algonquin Park and Renfrew county. All of southern Ontario is thus within easy reach by air and there are many small flying clubs and private owners.

### Telephone, Telegraph and Radio

Telephone service is almost universal in Ontario where over 1,600,000 phones are in operation. The telephone was invented by Alexander Graham Bell at Brantford, Ontario, in 1876 and the first long distance telephone conversation took place in the same year between Paris and Brantford, eight miles apart.

The Bell Telephone Company operates more than 80% of the telephones in Ontario while the remainder are divided amongst more than 500 small municipal company and government owned systems.

The first telegraph system in Canada was installed between Toronto and Hamilton in 1846. Most of the telegraph business is in the hands of the Canadian National Telegraph Company and the Canadian Pacific Railway Company since telegraph lines parallel all railway lines.

There are 40 radio broadcasting stations in Ontario, affiliated with the CBC networks. 25 of these are located south of North Bay. There are also many privately owned local stations. There are four powerful stations operating on 50,000 watts: CBL, CJBC, and CFRB at Toronto, and

CKLW at Windsor. The provincial forestry service operate an extensive network, most of which is in Northern Ontario. In 1949, Ontario had over 700,000 licensed radio receiving stations, slightly more than one third of the total for Canada, and averaging one for every six inhabitants.

## The Focus of Southern Ontario

A close appraisal of all the facts brought out in the various sections of this chapter makes it very clear that the economic core of Ontario is found in the nuclei clustered about the western end of Lake Ontario. Various reasons will be advanced to explain the rise and development of each of them but for the most part the factors may be named as *port, head start* and *corridor,* or to be accurate the junction of corridors which has been made permanent in the modern transportation pattern. Power, of course, is another factor, but power is now funnelled into rather than dispersed from this nucleus.

## Selected References

*A Conspectus of the Province of Ontario.* Department of the Provincial Treasurer. Toronto. 1947.

Dominion Department of Transport. *Power Possibilities of the St. Lawrence River.* Canadian Geographical Journal 36, pp. 70-71. 1948.

*Geographical Distribution of the Manufacturing Industries of Canada.* Department of Trade and Commerce. Ottawa. Annual.

Hoan, Daniel W. *The St. Lawrence Seaway—Navigational Aspects.* Canadian Geographical Journal 36, pp. 53-69. 1948.

Jones, R. L. *History of Agriculture in Ontario 1613-1880.* University of Toronto Press. Toronto.

*The Canada Year Book.* Annual. Dominion Bureau of Statistics.

*The Forty-First Annual Report of the Hydro-Electric Power Commission of Ontario for the year ending October 31st, 1949.* Toronto. 1950.

Whitaker, J. R. *Peninsular Ontario; a Primary Regional Division of Canada.* Scottish Geographical Magazine 54, pp. 263-283. 1938.

Whitaker, J. R. *Agricultural Gradients in Southern Ontario.* Economic Geography 14, pp. 109-120. 1938.

Whitaker, J. R. *Distribution of Dairy Farming in Peninsular Ontario.* Economic Geography 16, pp. 69-78. 1940.

# CHAPTER 12

# Regions and Cities of Southern Ontario

SOUTHERN Ontario is a land of cities and is steadily becoming more urbanized. Almost three-fourths of the people live in incorporated places. In 1956 there were more than 225 places of over 1,000 inhabitants including 40 with more than 10,000 and five exceeding 100,000. Many factors have contributed to city growth. Some cities, for instance Kingston, Toronto and Owen Sound were primarily lake ports; Ottawa and Peterborough were river towns; Welland has grown because of the canal; Windsor, Sarnia and Niagara Falls are gate-ways. Of course, all of them are manufacturing centres but very definite influences have caused industries to locate in them.

It is impossible to deal with each city at great length, but in the following pages considerable discussion will be devoted to the larger ones, and to some of the lesser ones which illustrate geographic principles or have important relations with the regions in which they are located. The reader who happens to live in a town, not herein discussed in detail, may use the same framework and organize his knowledge of his

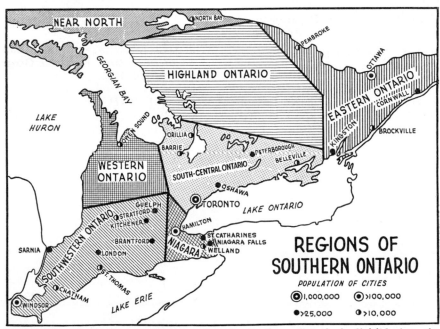

Figure 159. *The Regions of Southern Ontario*. Southern Ontario is divisible into six regions which tend to exhibit certain distinct regional characteristics. The boundaries however, are not sharp straight lines, but broad irregular zones, very difficult to map.

town into a coherent whole. In so doing he will become an urban geographer.

Cities developed rapidly during the first half of the twentieth century. Hard surfaced highways and motor transportation have enabled people to live at some distance from their work and suburbs have arisen around most large cities. Of the fifteen metropolitan areas recognized by the Bureau of Census in Canada in 1956, five are in Southern Ontario; they are, Toronto (1,358,028), Ottawa (345,460), Hamilton (327,831), Windsor (185,865), and London (154,453). They have all increased in population considerably since 1951.

Probably no two geographers would be able to agree upon the regional sub-divisions of Southern Ontario. Certain geomorphological lines are very clear, so are certain climatic lines but the two sets do not coincide. Still greater diversity is found when population, manufacturing and agriculture are taken into consideration. It is, therefore, hard to resist the tendency to cut Southern Ontario into very tiny areas in the hope of obtaining homogeneous regions. The accompanying map (Figure 159) is the result of many compromises. As a result the regions are bounded by broad bands indicating zones of transition rather than definite boundary lines. The six regions which will be briefly discussed are: Eastern Ontario, South Central Ontario, Niagara, Southwestern Ontario, Western Ontario and Highland Ontario.

## I. Eastern Ontario

Regional uniformity is an ideal which is rather closely approached over a large part of the area included in Eastern Ontario. A low, and in some places exceedingly flat plain, it has very definite borders in the St. Lawrence, the Ottawa and the edge of the Shield. However, the latter border is transgressed in a physical way by the waterlaid deposits in Renfrew, Leeds and Frontenac counties to form extensions of the plain. From the standpoint of human relations, also, an even deeper margin of the Shield is added to Eastern Ontario. There are many physical affinities between this area and the St. Lawrence Lowland in the province of Quebec. Moreover, the provincial boundary is only a political boundary and does not entirely separate the two great culture groups of Eastern Canada.

Agriculturally, Eastern Ontario is a unit, being almost entirely a dairy region. The only difference of note is that a small area near Ottawa acts as a milk-shed for that city while the rest of the region finds an outlet through cheese factories and condenseries. The methods of herd management vary greatly. The fluid milk shipper, either to a city market or to a condensery, must attempt to maintain a uniform supply. The traditional method in the cheese making districts was summer dairying and an attempt to winter the cattle as cheaply as possible on hay. To a certain extent this is still the method in submarginal areas of shallow soil. The larger cheese factory with a permanent staff is, however, requiring year-round production of cheese milk.

Tourists are attracted to Eastern Ontario by the scenic values of the Thousand Islands, Rideau Lakes and the Ottawa River as well as the possibilities for sport fishing. Water power developments of the St. Lawrence and of the Ottawa and its tributaries have given rise to the development of manufactures and the growth of towns and cities. Among those which may be mentioned are Ottawa, Kingston, Cornwall, Hawkesbury, Smith's Falls and Pembroke. Eastern Ontario also has a considerable number of small country villages which developed early but have remained small, although changing their functions to suit the demands of modern conditions.

### Ottawa

Ottawa, the capital city of Canada, had a population of 222,129, according to the census of 1956, ranking third among the cities of Ontario. Ottawa is also a metropolitan area, lying in two provinces, with a total population of 345,460 in 1956. Be-

Figure 160. *Eastern Ontario Landforms.* Although a region of little relief, Eastern Ontario has a variety of landscapes, characterized by specific landforms or associations of landforms.

side the city itself, Greater Ottawa includes the urban municipalities of Eastview (19,283) and Rockcliffe Park (2,097) in Ontario, and Hull (49,243), Aylmer (5,294), Deschênes (1,680), Gatineau (8,423), Pointe-à-Gatineau (6,175) and Templeton (2,475) in Quebec, and adjoining parts of rural townships in both provinces. Ottawa has been growing rapidly and has several times been forced to annex the built up areas of the neighbouring townships. The last adjustment of boundaries took place in 1949. The crowning glory of Ottawa, its chief claim to fame and its greatest economic activity belong to its function as the national capital of half a continent,

embracing a territory of nearly four million square miles. But, had the capital been located elsewhere, Ottawa would, nevertheless, have been a city, smaller it is true, but still interesting.

### History

Situated on the Ottawa River where it is entered by two large tributaries, the Gatineau and the Rideau, Ottawa was the natural meeting place and trading centre of the Indians. The name itself is derived from the Algonquin word for 'trade'. Samuel de Champlain, Nicholas de Vigneau and Etienne de Brule seem to have been the first white men to visit the spot, in 1613.

Champlain himself named the Rideau (Curtain) Falls and he translated the name Asticou (Kettle) to Chaudière — names which they still retain. No French settlements ensued, but the Ottawa continued for a century and a half to be the route of the voyageurs.

The father of Ottawa was Philemon Wright, who came to the Ottawa Valley in 1799 and, in the following March, brought a colony of 25 men and their families to the site of Hull on the north side of the river. Wright pioneered the timber trade, taking the first raft from Ottawa to Quebec in 1807. The first settler south of the river was Ira Honeywell who settled in Nepean township in 1808. In 1809, Bradish Billings appeared on the Rideau to cut timber. In 1812 he built a house about five miles from the mouth of the river and his descendants still live at Billings Bridge. In 1819 Nicholas Sparks located south of Sparks Street, his farm later becoming the most valuable real estate in the new city.

The town, however, did not materialize until Col. John By began to build the Rideau Canal in 1827, when the settlement which arose became known as the village of Bytown. Twenty years later, it became a town and, in 1854, it was incorporated as the city of Ottawa. In the meantime it had become the foremost centre of the lumbering industry of Canada. In 1858, Queen Victoria chose Ottawa as the capital of the province and, at Confederation in 1867, it became the capital of the Dominion of Canada .

**The Site**

Much depends upon the physical features of a city site. Ottawa is a focal point for a series of faults or huge cracks in the earth's crust which mark the St. Lawrence lowland. Upthrust blocks of resistant limestone are the cause of the waterfalls and of Parliament Hill, the miniature Quebec which overlooks the river. Interestingly enough, it was long known as Barrack Hill and fortifications were planned. Instead of a fort-

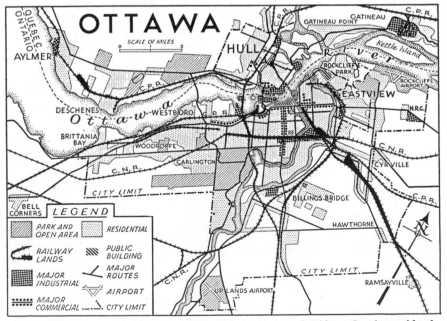

Figure 161. *Ottawa*. The Ottawa River, Rideau River and Rideau Canal provide the city with greater landscape variety than many Canadian cities possess. City planning is endeavouring to make the most of these possibilities.

ress, however, it now carries the chief administrative buildings of a nation. Apart from this hill, the site of Ottawa is relatively flat, the river and the canal offering the only resistance to the spread of the city.

### The Urban Landscape

As a city, Ottawa is beginning to take on the dignity which befits a capital. Confederation Square with its War Memorial, the great viaducts over the canal, the towering Chateau Laurier and the huge bulk of the Union Station, all combine with the Parliament Buildings in the background to form as impressive a city centre as there is on this continent. Westward along Wellington Street stand the Confederation Building, the Supreme Court and the Bank of Canada. Other structures are planned for sites which, during World War II, were occupied by temporary office buildings. Not all the government buildings are on Parliament Hill. Off to the south stand the Victoria National Museum and National Gallery. North, along the Ottawa River are the Royal Canadian Mint and National Research Council, while still farther north, beyond the Rideau River is Rideau Hall, the home of the Governor General. Southwest within the city limits, are the Dominion Observatory and the Central Experimental Farm. The latter occupies an area of a thousand acres devoted to agricultural research for the benefit of the whole country. Ottawa has many fine churches including the Anglican Christ Church Cathedral and the Roman Catholic Basilica Notre Dame. Ottawa is a city of bridges, four great structures carry road and rail traffic between Ottawa and Hull, a dozen bridges cross the Rideau River and six span the canal.

Ottawa also has its industries. The Chaudière Falls have been harnessed to provide power for mills turning out lumber, paper, matches and many other articles.

Much of the industrial development is on "the flats" near the falls, but many factories are located along the railways which, as in many other cities, cut the urban landscape in an unplanned and rather awkward fashion.

Ottawa has an excellent shopping district, extending along Sparks St., and Bank St. at right angles to it, and including, also, a number of nearby streets while just to the northeast of the city centre is found the Ottawa Produce Market. Ottawa has numerous up-to-date school buildings in various parts of the city. Ottawa University, just to the east of the Rideau canal, has an enrolment of over 2,000.

There are many fine residential areas including Rockcliffe Park in the vicinity of Rideau Hall and Sandy Hill, Ottawa's oldest residential district where the Prime Minister and many foreign ambassadors live. There are also many less pretentious areas of well built houses; the few poorer areas left as a legacy from old Bytown are fast disappearing.

Ottawa is noted for its park system including Rockcliffe Park, a scenic, natural area on the bank of the Ottawa, Landsdowne Park, where the Ottawa Exhibition is held, and the famous driveways that run for miles along the Rideau Canal.

Over it all stand the Houses of Parliament, impressive symbol, of Canadian democracy. The three original buildings were built between 1858 and 1865, of native Nepean sandstone and in Gothic style. In 1916 the central building burned and was rebuilt on a larger scale and with a higher tower. Known as the Peace Tower, it houses a carillon of 53 bells while below in the Memorial Chamber is the Altar of Remembrance preserving the book containing the names of Canadians who gave their lives in the first Great War. (See frontispiece)

### Population

The population of Ottawa in 1951 (202,-951) was almost ten times as great as in 1871, when the first census after Confederation was taken. Its growth has been remarkably steady but, during World War II, the city became greatly overcrowded. This was to some extent relieved by the expansion of 1949.

The chief ethnic groups in the city are: British (60%), French (28%), German (2%) and Jewish (2%). About 89% are native Canadians, but over 40% have come to the city from other parts of the country. The dominant religious affiliations of Ottawa citizens are: Roman Catholic (47%), United Church of Canada (20%), Anglican (18%) and Presbyterian (5%). In 1951, 88,000, 44% of Ottawa's population, were gainfully employed. Of these about 11% were engaged in manufacturing, 36% (32,000) found work in the service of the Dominion Government, 14% in trade, 6% in construction, 6% in transportation and communications, 4% in finance and 14% in other occupations.

## Economic Functions

The outstanding importance of the function of the capital city is shown by the foregoing figures for employment. In second place stands manufacturing, in which Ottawa is much behind other cities of its size. In 1954, the total value of goods was $106,-000,000, with a net value of $58,000,000. Among these industries there is a preponderance of printing, publishing, engraving and book-binding, accounting for one-sixth of the total; butter, cheese, bread and bakery products are about equally valuable. Planing mills, metallic products, textiles and chemicals are also important. Ottawa is an outstanding transportation centre with ten radiating railway lines and a radiating network of paved highways. Uplands airport is used by regular airlines and an important R.C.A.F. station is at Rockcliffe.

## Kingston

Kingston, county seat of Frontenac county, occupies one of the most historic sites in Ontario. Fort Cataraqui was founded by Frontenac in 1673 and was destroyed by the English in 1758. Kingston was founded by United Empire Loyalists in 1782, became a town in 1838 and was incorporated as a city in 1846. Fort Henry, now a national historic site, was completed in 1832. The capital of Canada was located in Kingston in 1841-44. An educational centre of note, Kingston contains the Royal Military College, for the education of officers of the three services, and Queen's University. The latter, founded in 1841, in the Scottish tradition, is the most noted centre of higher education in the eastern part of the province. Kingston is the seat of bishops of both the Anglican and Roman Catholic churches.

Kingston has long been noted as a lake port. In 1812 the first Great Lakes steamer was launched here and in 1827-32 the Rideau Canal was built, connecting this port to Ottawa. Kingston is still an important port and a growing industrial centre having locomotive shops, shipyards, a large aluminum plant, woollen mills and nylon factories. In 1954, the gross value was $76,-000,000, while the net value amounted to $38,000,000. Kingston has many old stone buildings. It is a pleasant place in which to live and is within easy reach of the scenic area around the Rideau Lakes. Most of the inhabitants are of British origin. The population in 1956 was 48,618, and the larger urban area had 58,290.

## Cornwall

Cornwall (18,000), and with suburbs containing nearly the same number, seat of the united counties of Dundas, Stormont and Glengarry, is located on the St. Lawrence River about 22 miles from the Quebec border. Its population is about equally divided between French and English. The chief products are paper, chemicals, rayon, cottons, furniture and clothing; total value in 1954, $76,000,000; net value $42,000,000.

## Brockville

Brockville (14,000), seat of the united counties of Leeds and Grenville, is located on the St. Lawrence River opposite Morristown, N.Y. It manufactures hats, hardware, abrasives, marine engines, boats and milk products; total value in 1950, $20,-000,000; net value, $9,000,000. During World War II an officers' training school was located here.

## Pembroke

Pembroke (15,500), county seat of Renfrew county, is located on the Ottawa River, 100 miles west of Ottawa. It produces lumber, matches and other wood products, office furniture, electrical goods, textiles, shoes and flour.

## Smiths Falls

Smith Falls (9,000) is located on the Rideau Canal at the entrance to the Rideau Lakes. It is an important divisional point on the C.P.R. and is important for the manufacture of farm machinery.

## Other Centres

Other centres in Eastern Ontario include *Gananoque,* a tourist centre of the Thousand Isles, the small manufacturing towns of *Perth, Carleton Place, Arnprior* and *Renfrew;* and *Hawkesbury,* site of a large pulp mill on the Ottawa River.

## II. South Central Ontario

South Central Ontario is the area that lies between Lake Ontario and the Canadian Shield. It is an area of no great relief; the highest points, with an elevation of 1200-1300 feet, are found along the Interlobate Moraine which forms the water divide between the tributaries of Lake Ontario and Georgian Bay. With the exception of the rougher parts of the moraine and the areas of shallow soil along the northern border, Central Ontario consists of good agricultural land. General crop and livestock farming was formerly the rule throughout the area, but a great deal of it is now included in the Toronto milk shed or in the smaller ones supplying the other cities. Along the shore of Lake Ontario where the frost-free season is longer and where, also, sandy loam soils are found,

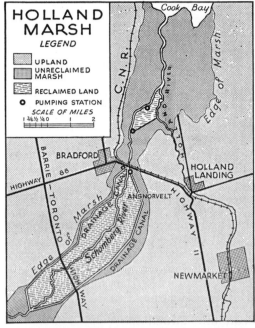

Figure 162. *Holland Marsh.* Approximately 7,000 acres of marshland have been reclaimed by draining and dyking. An area of about 12,000 acres of unreclaimed land remains north of Highway 11.

there is a belt in which orchards and canning crops are important.

Mention might also be made of the specialized truck crop section in the Holland Marsh about 32 miles north of Toronto. Holland Marsh is a shallow southward extension of the Lake Simcoe basin which through the centuries has become filled with peat. Drainage was begun in the 1920's, but for a number of years little land was cleared. Beginning about 1935 a colony of Dutch gardeners was established on the marsh. These have been joined by others until in 1950 about 500 families had over 6,000 acres under cultivation. The main crops are celery, onions and carrots. The old village of Bradford has been stimulated to new growth; large storage and packing houses have been built along the railway and highway. Besides the produce trucked directly to Toronto, over 1,000 refrigerator cars are loaded per season for distant points such as Winnipeg, Montreal, Halifax, St. John's and, in some seasons, to U.S. cities as well.

The influence of Lake Ontario as a means of transportation is indicated by the string of lakeside towns and cities. Only Toronto, however, has grown into an important modern port. Away from the lake shore, there are a number of small or medium sized towns but only Peterborough has reached the status of a manufacturing city.

South Central Ontario might almost be called the Toronto region since that city is now the most important factor in it. The concentration of roads and railways upon Toronto is a marked feature of the transportation map. Within 30 miles of Toronto one finds that all the small villages have become dormitory suburbs of the city with many people commuting daily by bus or private automobile. Commuting by rail is also common especially along the lake shore to the southwest where special suburban services have been provided for many years. Not only in the older villages,

however, but almost anywhere at random, small holdings and residential subdivisions are springing up in all the neighbouring townships which have been very slow to adopt any plan of development. Another important feature of the rural landscape of the Toronto region is the prevalence of country estates of city business men. Some of these consist mainly of large houses and extensive ornamental grounds while others are large, well equipped farms specializing in the breeding of purebred stock.

## Toronto

Toronto is the capital and largest city in Ontario and is the second most populous city in Canada, being outranked only by Montreal. Located on the north shore of Lake Ontario, it is 43 miles from Hamilton, 340 miles west from Montreal, 228 miles east from Windsor and 222 miles south of North Bay. It is thus very centrally located in Southern Ontario and is the focus from which radiate both railways and

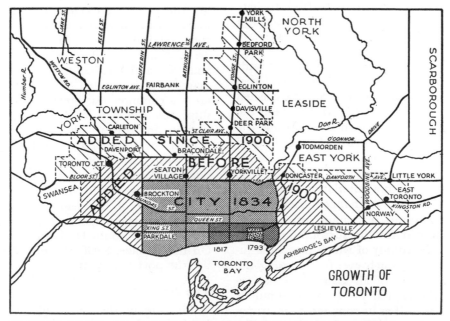

Figure 163. *The Growth of Toronto.* The city of Toronto has grown through a series of annexations of adjoining built-up areas. However, less than two-thirds of the population of the metropolitan area now live within the boundaries of the city.

provincial highways. From the Malton airport it has direct airline service, while in its harbour may be found large steamships from all parts of the Great Lakes, and smaller ones from all parts of the world. The census of Canada for 1956 records the population of the city as 667,706, and of the "greater city" as 1,358,028. Included in the metropolitan area are the towns of Leaside (16,538), Mimico (13,687), New Toronto (11,560), and Weston (9,543); the villages of Forest Hill (19,480), Swansea (8,595), and Long Branch (10,249); and the townships of York (117,553), North York (170,110), East York (64,616), Scarborough (139,744), and Etobicoke (103,621). Toronto is the political, commercial, industrial, financial, educational and cultural centre of the whole province.

## History

Toronto is a name of Indian origin, signifying "place of meeting". The vicinity was frequented by the Huron Indians and was the start of an overland route to Lake Simcoe and Georgian Bay. In 1615, the site was visited by Samuel de Champlain and Etienne Brûlé. A French fort was established in 1720 and abandoned ten years later. Again in 1749, Fort Rouillé was built near the Humber River but was evacuated in 1759. In 1793, Governor Simcoe selected the shore of Toronto Bay as the site of the settlement of York which soon became the capital of Upper Canada. It was burned by American invaders in 1813, but was rebuilt. It was incorporated as a town in 1817, and as a city with a population of 9,254 in 1834. Its name was changed back to the original Toronto, although York was the name retained for the surrounding township and the county of which it was the judicial seat. Although eventually losing the race for capital of all Canada, it has remained the capital of its most populous province as well as its commercial metropolis. Consequently, the population of Toronto has grown tremendously, causing the city to expand its boundaries a number of times to take in new suburbs. No new annexations have taken place since 1914.

In 1953, the municipality of *Metropolitan Toronto* was created to include the 13 municipalities of the "greater city"; they, however, still retain their own identities and local councils.

## The Harbour

The site of Toronto was determined by the presence of the harbour which is a small bay, about three square miles in area, shut in by a sandy hook which has been built from materials washed to the west from Scarborough Bluffs. Although it now has two entrances, it originally opened only to the west. Although its shores were shallow, there was a channel 2½ fathoms deep in the entrance and from 3 to 4 fathoms of water in the anchorage in the middle of the bay, making it the best harbour on the lake and one of the easiest to defend.

Over the years the harbour has been greatly changed. In 1853 and again in 1858 great storms broke through the bar, forming the eastern passage. Both it and the western gap have been provided with concrete retaining walls. The bay has been dredged and the shallow shores filled in and two and one-half miles of improved concrete piers erected. The filled-in land now accommodates great railway yards, shipyards, elevators, coal docks and miscellaneous industries. The island, which is reached by ferries, is a great summer resort with parks, cottages, hotels and, beside the Western Gap, a modern airport which, during World War II, was used for the training of Norwegian airmen. Since 1911, the harbour has been under the control of the Toronto Harbour Commission. On the average, 3,000,000 tons of shipping use the port each year.

## The Site

The site of the early city of Toronto, bordering the northern shore of Toronto Bay, lay entirely within the old bed of Lake Iroquois. The old lake plain, largely floored with sandy deposits, is about three miles in width and slopes gently northward at a rate of 50 to 60 feet per mile. Along its northern border are evidences of the old beach and a steep bluff about 75 feet in height representing the old shore cliff. Beyond this is an undulating till plain whose gently rounded summits reach 600 feet above sea level, or more than 350 feet above Lake Ontario. The Don River, which enters the head of Toronto Harbour, has cut a deep, but flat floored, valley through the eastern part of the city site. Its steep sides and those of the deep narrow tributary ravines have been great natural obstacles to the growth of the city. Beyond the Don, lies a triangular plain of sandy deposits cut off to the east by Scarborough Bluffs and somewhat dissected along its southern edge by narrow ravines. This plain was built by Lake Iroquois in the same manner as Toronto Island is being built by Lake Ontario. To the west the plain is cut by the Humber Valley and by the steep ravines in High Park and Swansea. Here also the old lake built a huge sandbar shutting off the Humber Valley so that, in the time of Lake Iroquois, there were two Toronto Harbours instead of one.

The site has furnished not only building room but much of the material of which the city was built. The old bars have furnished countless tons of sand and gravel, while in the ravines were exposed deposits of clay suitable for brickmaking.

## The Growth of the City

The geographical phenomenon of city growth can best be understood as a series of changes in the pattern of land utilization. They are the results of the pressure of economic and social or human factors upon the physical factors of the site. These at first are simple and Toronto had a very simple beginning. The village of York in 1793 consisted of a rectangular pattern of

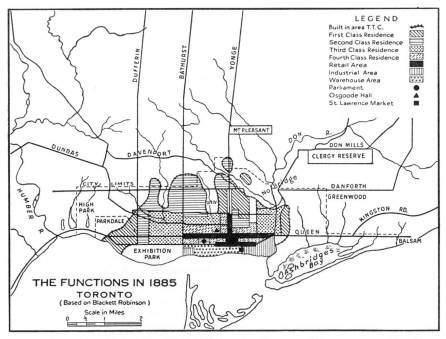

Figure 164. *The Functional Zones of Toronto in* 1885. Already a thriving city of the railway age, Toronto was expanding west and north to find room for 100,000 residents. East of the Don, the land remained unbuilt for lack of causeways across the valley. Rosedale ravine was also a barrier to the north.

streets covering about 100 acres near the head of the harbour and consisting of about a dozen blocks in all. Here as time went on were constructed barracks, storehouses, residences, a school, a church and parliament buildings. Growth was slow but eventually a new town was laid out west of Yonge Street. Here new barracks, parliament building and government house were built. In 1817 these areas were incorporated as the town. Having nearly reached 10,000 in 1834, a city was incorporated. The limits of the corporation were set far beyond the built up city and included about 8 square miles. This had not filled up by 1850, but the coming of the railways in the following decade was the cause of rapid expansion and soon the edge of the city was fringed with suburban villages. Beginning in 1883 and continuing until 1914, there was a series of annexations which brought the city to its present area of 34 square miles. Until after 1900 the city remained below "the hill", on the old lake plain. To the east only a small strip along the waterfront and Riverside, along the Don, had been incorporated. To the west Parkdale, Brockton, High Park and the lakeshore as far as the Humber River also came in. Bloor and Danforth were joined by bridges over the Don and Rosedale ravines in 1914. The double barrier of the old shore cliff and the C.P.R. just below were conquered by dugways and underpasses, and the various districts along St. Clair Avenue were incorporated. Along Yonge Street the city extends for three miles further north than anywhere else, taking in the old villages of Deer Park, Davisville, Eglinton and Bedford Park, all of which had previously been incorporated as North Toronto. Immediately adjoining North Toronto on the east is the town of Leaside, incorporated in 1913, while to the west is the village of Forest Hill which received its charter in 1923. Swansea, lying between the Humber and High Park, became a village in 1925. Except in the Don valley, however, the built up city extends far beyond all these

urban municipality boundaries, including at least 100 square miles. Over it all, with few exceptions, real estate subdividers have enforced the rectangular street pattern, regardless of the grain of the country. Moreover, the railways, taking the easiest grades to reach the water front, have added to the confusion of the pattern. Toronto, throughout, has emulated the celebrated Topsy who "just growed". Thus there are many gaps, many streets have dead ends against bluffs or ravines, and there are comparatively few through streets.

### The Pattern of the Urban Landscape

Despite the grid street pattern, Toronto displays a radial arrangement of its functional zones, albeit badly deranged. The waterfront and the railway facilities, which sought it in the early days, have attracted the chief wholesale and warehouse establishments. The new harbour area, created since 1911, has become the site of many industries. Immediately north of this, with Bay and Yonge Streets as its main arteries, is downtown Toronto. The concentration of business within this area has caused the erection of many tall office buildings. The Bank of Commerce Building is the tallest in the British Empire; the Royal York is the largest hotel. All this can be seen to advantage from Toronto Island, across the harbour, for the buildings of the waterfront are comparatively low structures. Downtown Toronto occupies about 400 acres, in and out of which there is a daily migration of 350,000 people including workers and others who may have occasion to visit the area on business or pleasure. Certainly no such massing of humanity was contemplated when the streets were laid out in 1817. Around this core area, and being gradually displaced by it, is the fourth class area, old and crowded. North of this, centred about the University and Queen's Park, is the old area of better residences, now the rooming-house district. Stretching away to the east and to the northwest are the massed rows of brick houses built between 1880 and 1910.

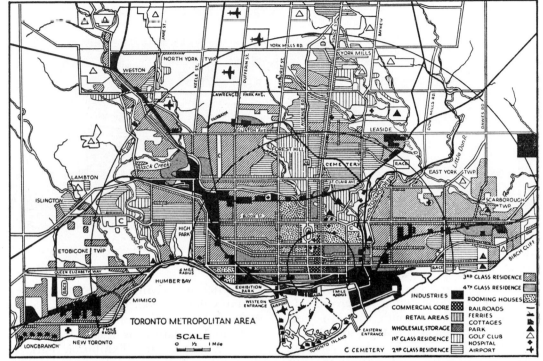

Figure 165. *The Functional Zones of Toronto in* 1940. (Based on survey by N. A. H. Deacon. **Can. Geo. Journal**, 1944). Present day Toronto has an extremely complicated land-use pattern. With the harbour and down-town area as a focal centre, the zones assume a roughly concentric arrangement which transcends all municipal boundaries. Much has been added to the built-up area since this survey was made.

Most of Toronto's streets were provided with fine rows of trees, but every year more streets are widened for use as thoroughfares and the trees are sacrificed. The more expensive houses are found some distance from the city centre or in areas dissected by the old ravines. Rosedale along the ravines just north of Bloor Street is the oldest of these. Others are Forest Hill and Lawrence Park in the north, High Park and the Kingsway in the west, to mention just a few. Beyond the city, at the present time, great areas of small homes are being built.

Toronto housing statistics are interesting. Brick is the most common material and has been used for 83% of all exteriors, second choice is stucco with 8%; 37% are single houses, 30% are semi-detached, while 25% are flats or apartments and 8% are in rows or terraces. 60% of all dwellings have 5 to 8 rooms and 94% have central heating with hot air, steam or hot water. Downtown is the centre of Toronto's retail business; here one finds the specialty shops and the great department stores. Along each main street stretch local shopping districts which supply their neighborhoods with most of their daily wants. One might mention Queen Street, Dundas Street, College Street, Bloor Street, Danforth Avenue, St. Clair Avenue and Eglinton Avenue, all prominent east-west thoroughfares, and Yonge Street which is almost a continuous shopping district for seven miles from north to south.

Beside the river valleys and ravines, already mentioned, the chief disturbing elements in the city pattern are the railways for, not only have they attracted many industrial plants, but they have caused many

*The Photographic Survey Corporation Limited.*

Plate 59. Exhibition Park, on the Toronto waterfront, where the Canadian National Exhibition is held every Autumn.

bottlenecks in street transportation, which it has taken a long time to overcome. In fact, so far as north-south transit is concerned, the problem is not yet solved. The modern tendency, however, is to establish new manufacturing plants outside the city. The war plants at Ajax, Scarborough, Leaside, Downsview, Malton and Long Branch are cases in point. Space in many of these plants has been converted to peace-time industry, while other new industrial buildings are being erected. An interesting case is the creation of the huge new oil refinery at Clarkson together with modern port facilities, sixteen miles away from the old site in Toronto Harbour. Outlying plants mean the creation of outlying residential suburbs. Many wartime houses were built, as at Ajax and Malton, but the village at Clarkson is of more permanent construction. In the outskirts of the metropolitan area, also, are found airports, golf courses, rifle ranges and many private estates of wealthy persons.

## Parks

Toronto has a number of fine parks within the city limits. High Park in the west end contains 406 acres, maintained as nearly as possible in a natural state. Riverdale Park, 109 acres lying in the Don Valley, contains the city zoo. Queen's Park, about 40 acres surrounding the buildings of the Ontario Legislature, is leased by the city from the University. Exhibition Park, in the southwestern part of the city, comprises 235 acres. It contains the buildings in which are held the Canadian National Exhibition each August and September and the Royal Winter Fair each November. During World War II, many thousands of Canadians passed through the military depots located there. There are many smaller parks in all parts of the city which serve as athletic and recreational grounds. Some of these, such as Christie Park and Eglinton Park, are located in enlarged ravines which for many years were used as brickyards. The total area of Toronto's park system is over 2,300 acres.

## Transportation

If transportation is the lifeblood of a community, Toronto suffers from high blood-pressure. In 1950, nearly 240,000 motor vehicles were registered in the city, of which 195,000 were passenger cars. They share the streets with the public transportation system which is owned by the city. On the average, over 1,000,000 passengers per day are carried. All main streets have double street car lines, and outlying areas are served by buses. Recently trackless trolley buses have been inaugurated and will probably spread to a number of routes. Nevertheless, the system is overtaxed, streets are too narrow for both public and private vehicles and a subway system at enormous cost has been begun to serve the main north-south and east-west routes. The daily movement of people to work is task enough, but special problems also arise. Crowds of 15,000 attend hockey games in the Maple Leaf Gardens, similar crowds attend the baseball games in the Maple Leaf Stadium, 25,000 spectators watch a football game in Varsity Stadium on a Saturday afternoon, 50,000 people may visit Toronto Island on a Sunday afternoon, 100,000 attend the Canadian National Exhibition in a single day. Public transportation takes care of most of them.

The first public transportation was an omnibus line between St. Lawrence Market and Yorkville by way of King and Yonge Streets, inaugurated in 1849. In 1861 rails were laid on Yonge Street and horsedrawn cars appeared. By 1891, 68 miles of track were in use. Electric cars were installed between 1891 and 1894. Though the city spread out, the privately owned street railway did not, and the city was forced to build outlying sections and to charge extra fares. Finally in 1921, the whole system within the city was taken over by the Toronto Transportation System. In March 1954, the Yonge Street subway was opened, giving rapid service for four and one-half miles on a north-south route from Eglinton Avenue to Union Station. Trolley and bus lines in the outlying municipalities are also operated by the T.T.C., but extra fares are charged. The T.T.C. also operates the Gray Coach Lines to Oshawa, Hamilton, Buffalo, Brantford, London, Owen Sound, Parry Sound, North Bay and all intermediate points.

## Economic Functions

Toronto is a financial, commercial and industrial metropolis. It contains the headquarters of five of the ten chartered banks in Canada, several trust companies, and insurance companies and numerous investment houses. Bay Street is sometimes called Toronto's Wall Street. The Toronto Stock Exchange, dealing in all manner of securities, is the largest market of mining shares in the world. Toronto is the chief headquarters for wholesale distribution of commodities in Ontario.

Toronto is second only to Montreal as a Canadian manufacturing centre. With 4,500 factories, employing 200,000 workers, the Toronto district production, in 1954, had a gross value of more than $2,500,000,000 and a net value of $1,200,000,000. Toronto has no raw materials, everything is brought in from the hinterland or from more distant places. Even the electrical energy, used so plentifully, is brought long distances from Niagara or the Ottawa. Among the more important industries are slaughtering and meat packing, electrical goods of all kinds, metal products, machinery, clothing, printing and publishing, confectionery and baking and oil refining. In addition there are hundreds of smaller industries. The keynote of manufacturing in the Toronto area is diversification.

## Other Functions

Toronto has numerous churches; it is the cathedral city, being the seat of an Anglican Bishop and a Roman Catholic Archbishop. It is the leading educational centre of the province by virtue of the presence of the University of Toronto which had an enrolment of over 17,000 students in 1946-47. Its numerous faculties include Arts, in which there are four federated colleges, University, Victoria, Trinity, and St. Michael's; Applied Science and Engineering; Medicine; Dentistry; Education; Household Science; Nursing; Forestry; Law; Music; the School of Chinese Studies and the School of Graduate Studies. Affiliated with it are Knox, Wycliffe, Trinity, and Emmanuel Theological Colleges, Ontario College of Pharmacy, Royal Conservatory of Music of Toronto and, located at Guelph but receiving degrees from Toronto, are the Ontario Veterinary College and Ontario Agricultural College. Hart House, a unique club for men, is the centre of student activity, housing dining halls, reading rooms, gymnasia and a theatre. The Soldier's Tower has a carillon of 52 bells. The city has many fine elementary schools, collegiates, technical and vocational schools. Toronto is an important medical centre. There are ten large public hospitals while medical research of world-wide fame is carried out in the Connaught Laboratories and Banting Institute. The Royal Ontario Museum, Toronto Art Gallery and Toronto Public Library with its many branches also offer cultural services to the city. There are two large auditoria, Massey Hall, built in 1894, seating 3,500, and the Maple Leaf Gardens seat-ing 12,600, devoted chiefly to hockey but available for other large gatherings.

## Population

Of Toronto's population of 675,754 in 1951, 400,000, or 59%, were born in Ontario and 67,000, or 10%, in other parts of Canada; 107,000, or 16% were born in the British Isles and 86,000, or 13%, in other European countries.

In the metropolitan area, with a population of 1,117,000, 700,000 or 62% were born in Ontario, 100,000, or 9%, in other parts of Canada; 185,000, or 16%, in the British Isles and 105,000 or 9%, in other European countries.

The origins of the people of the city are given as: British, 465,000 or 69%; Jewish 41,000 or 6.1%; Ukrainian, 23,000 or 3.4%; French, 22,000 or 3.3%; Polish, 21,-000 or 3.1%; Italian, 18,000 or 2.7 %; German, 12,000 or 1.8%; Asiatics, 8,300 or 1.2% and Netherlands, 6,700 or 1.0%.

In the metropolitan area, people of British stock number 812,000 or 73%; Jew-

The Photographic Survey Corporation Limited.
Plate 60. The University of Toronto.

ish, 59,000 or 5.3%; French, 32,000 or 2.9%; Ukrainian, 29,000 or 2.6%; Italian, 28,000 or 2.5%; Polish, 27,000 or 2.4%; Germans, 19,000 or 1.7%; Netherlands, 12,-000 or 1.1% and Asiatics, 10,000 or .9%.

The chief religious affiliations of the population of the city are: Anglican 171,118 or 25.4%, United Church of Canada 163,-809 or 24.2%, Roman Catholic 130,392 or 19.3%, Presbyterian 70,481 or 10.4%, Jewish 44,950 or 6.7% and Baptists 28,841 or 4.3%.

In the metropolitan area Anglicans number 307,980 or 27.6%, United Church of Canada 293,435 or 26.4%, Roman Catholic 187,262 or 16.8%, Presbyterians 116,789 or 10.4%, Jewish 66,773 or 6%, and Baptists 51,833 or 4.6%.

The most numerous age group in Toronto are those between 25 and 30 and one-third of the population is between 20 and 40. Children of school and pre-school age are somewhat deficient in numbers.

The active or gainfully occupied population of greater Toronto in 1951 was slightly over 368,000 or 33%. Of these 38%

were engaged in manufacturing, 9% in construction, 8.6% in transportation, 18% in trade, 4.5% in finance, 9% in professions, and 7.0% in public service.

## Geographical Significance of Toronto

While not the largest city in Canada, Toronto is the most outstanding example of the big city development and urban tendency of modern Canadian life. At first under the control of the simple factors of physical geography and political expediency, the city has developed until it is, itself, the most important geographical feature of its region, and in fact of the whole province of Ontario. Its influence as the political, financial, industrial, transportation and commercial centre is now so great that mere distance from Toronto has become a major factor in the physical geography of the region. Toronto has one-quarter of the population of Ontario. It is still growing rapidly. The "master plan", prepared in 1943, envisions a population of 1,500,000 within 30 years. This has been reached in only half the time, but Ontario would be in

*The Photographic Survey Corporation Limited.*
Plate 61. The General Motors Plant at Oshawa, Ontario.

a much sounder position if the future growth of Toronto were to be distributed amongst the smaller cities of the province.

## Oshawa

Oshawa, in Ontario county, thirty-three miles east of Toronto is famed for the manufacture of automobiles, although there is no obvious geographical reason for the growth of either the city or the industry at this point. It has a small harbour near which a French trading post was set up in 1752. The English settlement, however, developed a couple of miles north on the Toronto-Kingston military road about 1795. Known at first as Skae's Corners, it became the village of Oshawa in 1842, a town in 1889, and was incorporated as a city in 1924. At one time it was an important port for the shipment of timber and grain and it has always been a trading centre for a good farming district. On the foundations of a small local carriage shop it has developed into the second city in Canada in the automobile industry. Other factories produce brass and iron castings, sheet metal, leather, plate glass and textiles. In 1954, the 60 factories produced $300,000,000 in new goods. The population of Oshawa in 1956 was 50,412. Including Whitby and suburban areas the "greater city" had about 65,000, but all of it might well be considered part of Greater Toronto.

## Peterborough

Although spatially situated in the heart of Southern Ontario, Peterborough occupies a marginal position with respect to the more densely occupied area. One of the ten largest cities in Southern Ontario, its economic importance is even greater than its size would indicate. Located in the drumlin belt it is the nucleus of a general farming area. Its early settlement and its later development as an industrial town are both due to its location on the Otonabee River. Although a grist and sawmill had been in operation for three years, the real founding of Peterborough dates

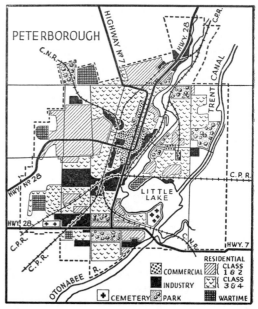

Figure 166. *The Functional Zones of Peterborough.* (Based on a survey by Mary Chamberlain. 1947). As in many other cities, the railway pattern poses a difficult problem in the logical development of the central zone.

from 1825, when Hon. Peter Robinson brought out 2,000 Irish settlers to the county. As the head of navigation, Peterborough became the natural supply point and, later, the judicial seat of the new county. About 1840 the town became an important lumbering centre, was incorporated as a town in 1850, and its position was enhanced by the building of a railroad to Cobourg in 1854. Other railways followed, including the Ontario-Quebec (now C.P.R.), completed in 1884. By 1900, the lumbering era was over and other industries began to develop, utilizing the waterpower of the Trent Canal System. In the ten miles above the city the Otonabee river falls 280 feet. The famous hydraulic lift locks at Peterborough take care of 65 feet, the rest is provided for in dams and locks on the river. Later much additional power has been obtained from the Ontario Hydro-electric System. The city has 100 factories which produced over $124,000,000 (net $59,000,000) in 1950. There are two very large plants producing electrical apparatus and cereal products, other important products are meats, carpets, dairy equipment, brake linings, yarns, clocks, watches, canoes and outboard motors. In addition to its industrial status and its natural position as a local trade centre, the city is also the headquarters of the Kawartha Lakes resort area. The city has grown rapidly since World War II. In 1956, the city itself has a population of 42,700, while that of the whole urban area was about 46,000.

## Belleville

Belleville (20,000), county seat of Hastings County, is located on the Bay of Quinte at the mouth of the Moira River. Its products are machinery, tools, radios, canned goods, paper boxes and clothing. Nearby are located a large distillery and a cement plant. The city is noted as the seat of Albert College and the Ontario School for the Deaf.

## Barrie

Barrie (18,000), county seat of Simcoe county is located at the head of Kempenfeldt Bay, western arm of Lake Simcoe. It is 14 miles from Camp Borden, the largest permanent military camp in Canada, and during World War II its population was swollen to over 15,000. It has railway shops, meat packing plants, tanneries, textile factories and boat works. There are numerous summer resorts nearby.

## Orillia

Orillia (14,000), situated at the narrows between Lake Simcoe and Lake Couchiching, is the gateway to a great summer resort region. it is also a manufacturing town producing machinery, marine engines, electrical appliances, stoves, castings, beverages and boats. It has increased in population considerably in recent years. A large mental hospital is located here.

## Georgian Bay Ports

There is an important group of ports at the southern end of Georgian Bay. *Midland* (8,500) is the largest town on the Penetang Peninsula and has large shipyards and flour mills. Near Midland is the site old Fort Ste. Marie and the Martyr's Shrine, commemorating the death of the Jesuit missionaries in 1649. *Penetanguishene* (5,500), *Victoria Harbour* (1,000) and *Port McNicoll* (1,000) are also lake ports on the peninsula. *Collingwood* (8,000) is a busy port with large grain elevators and shipyards. Eastward, along the south shore of the bay, lies Wasaga Beach, to which many Toronto people migrate each summer.

## Other Centres

South-central Ontario contains a number of small towns which act as local service centres and which have a certain amount of manufacturing activity. Almost any one of them might be the nucleus of a future industrial city.

*Trenton* (12,000) is situated at the outlet of the Trent River into the Bay of Quinte. Near it is a very large R.C.A.F. airport and training centre. *Cobourg* (9,500), *Port Hope* (7,500) and *Bowmanville* (6,500) lie along the shore of Lake Ontario between Trenton and Oshawa. *Whitby* (10,000) is an old market centre, with some industries, a few miles west of Oshawa. Nearby is *Ajax* which was founded as a munitions centre during World War II and is now developing a number of new industries. *Lindsay* (10,000) is adjacent to the Kawartha Lakes.

West of the Toronto Metropolitan Area are *Brampton* (13,000), having the largest concentration of green-houses in Canada, and *Oakville* (10,000), on the shore of Lake Ontario, near which is the site of a large automobile factory.

## III. Highland Ontario

Hardly elevated enough to deserve its name, this is a region of rocky hills, forests

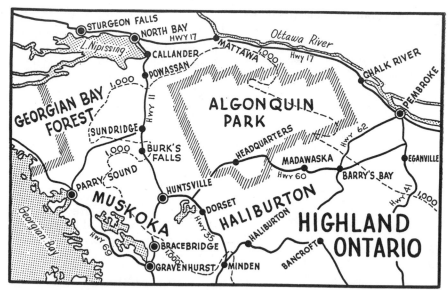

Figure 167. *Highland Ontario*. Much of this area is over 1,000 feet in elevation. Its heart is Algonquin Park, a completely forested tract, around which there is a fringe of sparse agriculture, forstry and recreational activity.

and scenic lakes which makes it a natural resort area for the people of the cities to the south. Once the scene of a great lumbering industry, its second growth forest still provides considerable amounts of both softwood and hardwood lumber. A sporadic agricultural settlement followed the lumbermen, but a great deal of land has been abandoned. In favourable pockets, however, considerable agriculture is still carried on. The dominant economic activity, in many areas, is catering to the wants of tourists and vacation guests.

The Muskoka Lakes were exploited at the beginning of the 20th century. They were made accessible to city people by the building of the railways and most of the old lumber settlements became resort towns. Small cruise steamers were put on the lakes as an added attraction. In recent decades most visitors come via the highway and do their cruising in their own cars. There are no large places; *Gravenhurst, Bracebridge* and *Huntsville* all containing about 3,000 inhabitants. *Parry Sound* (6,000), is the gateway to the 30,-000 islands of Georgian Bay.

Algonquin Park is the highest and most rugged part of this region. Here an area of 2,741 square miles of forest and lake has been set aside as a provincial park where game animals are protected. Railways and a highway cross the park and hotels and lodges are accessible from both, but a large part is still wilderness, accessible only by canoe.

## IV. The Niagara Region

The Niagara Region is small but it enjoys prominence as a corridor and gateway to the United States and because of the important economic activities for which it is the focus. Physiographically, it consists of two plains, a narrow lowland between Lake Ontario and the Niagara Escarpment and the wider plain between the brow of the escarpment and the shore of Lake Erie.

The Ontario plain is a zone of dense rural settlement with an intensive horticultural type of land use. Here are produced the bulk of the peaches and grapes grown in Ontario, as well as strawberries, raspberries and other small fruits. Some fruit growing and truck farming is found above the escarpment, most of this plain is occupied by dairy and general live stock farms.

The Niagara Region is the source of an immense supply of power which supplies its own manufacturing cities and those of all southwestern Ontario through the medium of the Ontario Hydro-electric Commission. Power is developed on the Niagara River and at De Cew Falls with water from the Welland Canal. The canal, by permitting the passage of large freighters, enables many of the industries of the region to import cheaply much needed raw materials. This is especially important to the paper industries of Thorold and the steel mills of Hamilton.

Niagara Falls has been a mecca for tourists for over a century and still draws its crowds of visitors. The shores of the lakes have many cottage colonies such as Burlington Beach, Grimsby Beach, Port Dalhousie and Crystal Beach. The first three are on Lake Ontario, the last named is on Lake Erie and functions as a suburb of Buffalo, being more frequented by Americans than by Canadians.

Many small early villages were established on the small creeks along the escarpment. Small ports also grew up on the Niagara River, Lake Ontario and Lake Erie. These early settlements have not all become modern cities because the railways and the canal have given the advantage to other sites. The cities of the river and canal section, however, are far outweighed by the development of Hamilton at the other end of the corridor.

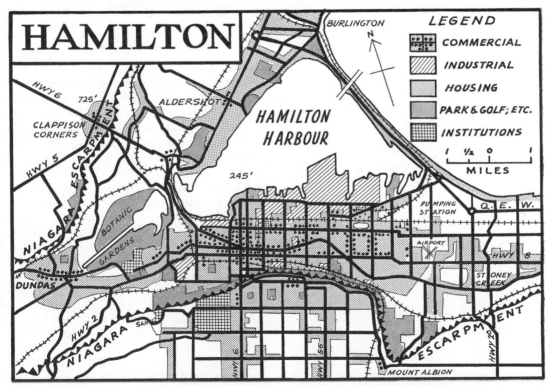

Figure 168. *Hamilton*. Wedged between the harbour and the escarpment, the city has been forced to expand east and west. Old independent settlements, now function as suburbs of the city.

*The Photographic Survey Corporation Limited.*

Plate 62. The Central section of Hamilton, Ontario, looking north over the Toronto, Hamilton & Buffalo Railway Station.

## Hamilton

Hamilton, the second city of Ontario, with a population of 239,625, in the city proper, and 327,831 in the "greater city", according to the 1956 census, is located on Hamilton Harbour at the head of Lake Ontario. It is sometimes called the "Pittsburgh of Canada" in recognition of the fact that it is the foremost centre of the primary iron and steel industry. It is the fifth city of Canada in terms of population and third in terms of industrial output. County seat of Wentworth county, it might almost also be called the regional capital of the Niagara Peninsula.

### History

The first settlers on the site of Hamilton were two United Empire Loyalists, Robert Land and Richard Beasley who took up land in 1778. Burlington Heights was an important base during the war of 1812. The actual founder of the village was George Hamilton, who, in 1813, laid

out his farm in town lots and named the streets after the members of his family. He also donated three parks, one of which, Gore Park, is still the centre of the city. The village was incorporated in 1816, in 1833 it became a town and, in 1846, achieved the status of a city. Its early growth was slow, being overshadowed by the earlier town of Dundas, which in addition to the Desjardins canal joining it to Lake Ontario, had important roads leading to London, Waterloo and Guelph, important trade centres in the interior. The real growth of Hamilton dates from the building of the railways in the 1850's.

### The Harbour

The harbour is now much more important than it formerly was. It is a landlocked bay, about 10 square miles in area, separated from Lake Ontario by Hamilton Beach, a sand and gravel strip four miles long and two to three hundred yards in width. Over it pass a railway and a highway which actually serve to by-pass the city. From end to end it is now solidly lined with cottages. The harbour must constantly be dredged in order to accommodate large ships, and access to Lake Ontario is by way of a concrete lined canal. The harbour has a frontage of over four miles, available for docks and industrial sites. Since the building of the new Welland Canal, Hamilton's harbour has assumed much greater significance.

## The City Site

Hamilton lies upon a gently sloping plain of lacustrine sediments, about two and a half miles in width, between the harbour and the Niagara Escarpment, which rises abruptly over 250 feet and is known as "the mountain". Toward the west the plain is broken by some rather difficult ravines while, to the east, it reaches unbroken into the fruit growing lands of the Niagara Peninsula. While sufficiently large for the early city, this site is proving too small for modern Hamilton which is stretching both east and west and, even to some extent, climbing the "mountain" to the south. The site of the early city was determined by the fact that all east-west traffic must pass this narrow plain, while all traffic from the north was restricted to the very much narrower Burlington Heights, the old bar across the head of Lake Iroquois.

## The Urban Landscape

There are few cities so easy to study because, from various vantage points on the "mountain", the whole city can be seen. The old city centre, where James crosses both King and Main Streets, is now a cluster of tall office buildings, about which are grouped hotels, theatres and shops of all kinds. The whole waterfront is given over to industry and there is also an industrial section west of the city centre. The whole lower part of the city plain, flanking the industries, is occupied by the homes of the workers, while the upper portion, just under the mountain, is the section in which the wealthy and middle class homes are found. On top of the mountain, modest homes are found again. It is interesting to note that Hamilton has grown so far eastward that a new business and shopping centre has sprung up along Ottawa Street to serve the east end. To the west beyond the creek valley, a new, almost detached suburb of Westdale has grown up. Here, also, is located McMaster University on the level terrace overlooking the Dundas Marsh, which has been set aside as a wild life preserve. The city pattern has some irregularities, mainly due to the location of the railways and their attraction of industries. Particularly noticeable is the position of the line to Buffalo which cuts through the residential district under the mountain. More praiseworthy has been the treatment accorded Burlington Heights. The railways are happily at the base of the ridge. The crest is followed by a broad thoroughfare flanked by well preserved old cemeteries, a national historical site dating from 1812, well kept parks and, at the northern entrance to the city, the slopes of the old gravel ridge have been transformed into a rock garden.

## The Population

Hamilton has grown steadily and rather rapidly from a small city of 26,000 to a metropolitan area of ten times that number in a period of eighty years. Amongst its population of 327,000 may be found migrants from all parts of the world who have come to work in its growing industries. More than 28% of the people enumerated in 1951 had been born outside Canada, about half of them being from the British Isles. People of British origin constitute about 70% of the population of Greater Hamilton. Italians, Poles, French, Germans, Ukrainians, Netherlanders and Hungarians are the largest European groups. The dominant religious groups are: Anglican (26%), United Church of

Canada (26%), Roman Catholic (21%), Presbyterian (12%) and Baptists (5%).

## Functions of the City

Hamilton is a highly industrialized city. According to the census of 1951, over 54% of the gainfully occupied found employment in manufacturing. The "greater city" ranks third among the great manufacturing centres of Canada. In 1954, there were over 650 factories, employing more than 57,000 workers, the products having a sale value of $784,000,000 and a net value of $405,000,000. Among the important industries are primary iron and steel, miscellaneous steel products, electrical apparatus and supplies, motor vehicles and parts, railway rolling stock, industrial machinery, textile and knitting mills, meat packing and miscellaneous food products, chemicals, soap, rubber goods, pottery, paper boxes, and other paper products.

About one-third of the industrial workers find employment in iron and steel. Hamilton is the greatest centre of blast furnace activity in Canada; coal is brought from Lake Erie ports and iron ore from Lake Superior, while the limestone required for flux is quarried from the Niagara Escarpment. Sault Ste. Marie is nearer to the source of iron, but Hamilton is closer to the coal and, above all, to the final market. Other important economic activities are wholesale and retail trade, construction, transportation and finance. There is also a fairly large professional personnel. McMaster University, with a faculty of 70 members and a student body of 1,100 is rapidly becoming a leading educational centre.

## St. Catharines

St. Catharines, "The Garden City" and county seat of Lincoln county is located in the midst of the orchards of the Niagara Peninsula. It was founded by Loyalists about 1790, was incorporated as a town in 1845 and as a city in 1876. Its growth and development have been closely associated with the Welland Canals, the first of

which was built in 1829, and with the development of electrical energy at Niagara Falls which is only twelve miles distant. Other towns are also associated with the canal and practically continuous with St. Catharines. Port Dalhousie at the Lake Ontario terminal of the old Welland Canal is a well-known lakeside resort, connected with Toronto by regular steamship service. Merritton is a small manufacturing town on the slopes of the Niagara escarpment while Thorold, slightly larger, sits upon the brow of the escarpment, over 300 feet above Lake Ontario. At this point the Welland Canal climbs the face of the slope by the Twin Flight Locks which have an aggregate lift of 139½ feet. St. Catharines and its satellite towns constitute an important industrial area producing automobile parts and machinery of all kinds, electrical apparatus and supplies, pulp and paper, tools, hardware, abrasives, wines and canned goods. In 1954 the gross value

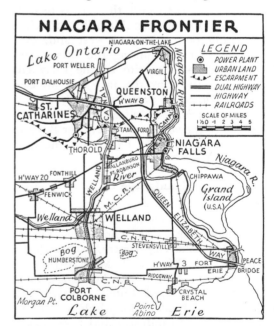

Figure 169. *The Niagara Frontier.* The concentration of land and water routes in this gateway has stimulated the growth of a number of cities and towns. Niagara power supplies a much larger area, including most of southwestern Ontario.

of this production was about $200,000,000 with a net value of $100,000,000.

In 1956 the St. Catharines urban area had a population of 85,000, including the city itself (39,700), Thorold (8,000), Merriton (5,400), Port Dalhousie (3,100) and the urbanized parts of the townships of Grantham (27,300) and Thorold (1,500). It constitutes one of the rapidly expanding sections of the important conurbation around the western end of Lake Ontario.

## Niagara Falls

Niagara Falls is located on the west bank of the Niagara River, overlooking the falls and directly opposite the city of Niagara Falls, N.Y., to which it is connected by both highway and railway bridges. It is famous as a tourist resort and for its great hydro-electric plants which supply most of the cities in southwestern Ontario. Its chief manufactured products include abrasives, beverages, chemicals, cereal products, canned goods, fertilizers, machinery, silverware and underwear; total value $100,-000,000, net value $50,000,000, in 1954.

In 1956 the population was 23,600, with 25,800 in adjoining Stamford Township.

## Welland

Welland, county seat of Welland county, is located on the Welland Ship Canal about 8 miles north of Lake Erie. A developing manufacturing centre, its factories produce steel products, machinery, tools, rubber goods, textiles and electrical appliances; in 1954 the gross value of production was $90,000,000 with a net value of $48,000,-000. In 1956 the city had resident population of 16,400 but the neighbouring township of Crowland had an urban population of about 15,000.

## Fort Erie

Fort Erie (8,700), at the outlet of Lake Erie into Niagara River, is connected with Buffalo, N.Y., by the Peace Bridge. At the Canadian end of the bridge is located a park which occupies the site of a French fort and settlement of 1750. From this point the four lane Queen Elizabeth Way leads to Toronto. Fort Erie manufactures aircraft, paints and chemicals; total value in 1950 was $16,000,000 with a net value of $10,000,000.

## Port Colborne

At the Lake Erie entrance of the Welland Canal, Port Colborne, including the formerly independent village of Humberstone, held a population of 12,870 in 1951. Grain elevators, blast furnaces, a nickel refinery and a cement plant are important industries. In 1947, the gross value of manufacturing was $132,000,000, with a net value of $26,000,000.

## V. Southwestern Ontario

Much of Southwestern Ontario consists of old lake plains bordering Lake Erie and Lake Huron where the sand, silt and clay plains form important agricultural regions. The sandy soils of Norfolk and Elgin counties have, during the past twenty-five years, become the tobacco belt of Ontario, specializing in flue cured cigarette tobacco. Fruits and canning crops are grown in the same areas. The clay plains of Kent and Essex counties form the "Corn Belt" of Ontario. Sugar beets and other cash crops are also grown. The far southwest with its early spring season, specializes in truck crops such as asparagus, early potatoes, sweet corn and tomatoes. Canning factories are numerous throughout the area.

The northeastern portion consists of undulating to rolling till plains and moraines, cut by great spillways in which the branches of the present Grand and Thames river systems now flow. The soils are mostly loams well suited for the production of grass and silage corn. This area is an important dairy region, producing milk for city delivery and to supply condenseries located in the region.

Both the Thames and Grand Rivers overflow their banks in spring floods causing much damage to the towns located on their flood plains. Valley conservation au-

The Photographic Survey Corporation Limited.

Plate 63. Paris, on the Grand River, is one of the most charming small towns of Southwestern Ontario.

thorities have been formed to build dams and undertake other remedial measures.

Southwestern Ontario has more cities than any other region, but none of them are found in lake shore locations. Lake Erie is a shallow body of water and its north shore is a zone of rapid wave erosion and has no first class harbours. There are no good harbours either, at the south end of Lake Huron. The Grand River basin contains a group of cities including *Kitchener-Waterloo* (80,000), *Guelph* (37,000), *Galt* (24,000) and *Brantford* (56,000) as well as the towns of *Paris, Preston, Hespeler, Elmira* and *Fergus,* all of which help to make this an important manufacturing area. Somewhat scattered through the body of the region are *Woodstock* (19,000), *Stratford* (20,000), *St. Thomas* (19,000) and *London* (155,000). In the southwest are *Sarnia* (52,000), *Chatham* (22,000) and *Windsor* (186,000).

## Brantford

Brantford, county seat of Brant county and located on the Grand River, was named for Joseph Brant, noted Mohawk chief. White settlement began here in 1818, the town was incorporated in 1847 and Brantford became a city in 1877. Alexander Graham Bell, inventor of the telephone, once lived in Brantford and the old Bell Homestead is still preserved. The manufactures of Brantford include farm machinery and other engineering products, hardware, tools, roofing, cordage, textiles, clothing, flour and feed. Total value in 1950 was $126,000,000 (net $63,000,000). The Six Nations Indian Reserve is nearby. During World War II, Brantford was an airforce training centre. The population of Brantford in 1956 was 52,000, (56,000 in the "greater city"), most of whom are Canadian born, whose ancestors came from the British Isles.

## Kitchener and Waterloo

Including Kitchener (60,000), Waterloo (16,500), Bridgeport (1,400), and the adjoining urbanized parts of Waterloo Township (2,500), the Kitchener-Waterloo conurbation in 1956 contained a population of over 80,000. Lying side by side, they are traversed by the same main street and the visitor is not conscious that there are two municipalities. The area was settled about 1805 by people of German ancestry from Pennsylvania. The village of Waterloo grew up around the Union Flour Mills established in 1816. The village was incorporated in 1857 and became a town in 1876. It was declared a city in 1947. As a small crossroads hamlet, Kitchener was early known as Sand Hills or Mount Pleasant. In 1830 it received a number of settlers from Germany and had its name changed to Berlin. It became a village in 1854, a town in 1871 and a city in 1912. Its name was changed to Kitchener in 1916. The ascendency of Kitchener probably arose from the fact that it was chosen as the county town and it received railroad service first. The "Twin Cities" constitute an exceed-

ingly well built and prosperous appearing urban area. More than 80% of the people live in single, detached dwellings, the majority of which are owned by their occupants.

The population is about 85% Canadian born, about 52% of German origin, 34% of British origin and most of the rest derived from other Europeans. The chief religious affiliations are Roman Catholic 29%, Lutheran 28%, United Church of Canada 9%, Anglican 8%, Mennonites, Presbyterians and Baptists about 5% each. 45% of the total population are gainfully employed, 59% of the latter being engaged in manufacturing and about 12% in trade.

A highly diversified manufacturing industry is found here. In Kitchener the most important lines are: tires and rubber goods, textiles and clothing, leather, footwear, furniture, beverages, machinery,

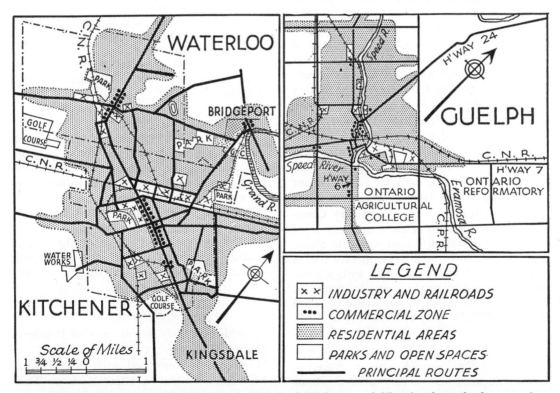

Figure 170. *Grand River Towns.* The "Twin Cities" of Kitchener and Waterloo form the largest urban and industrial centre of the area. Guelph, on the Speed River, is important for its institutions as well as its industries.

radios and electrical appliances. Waterloo has factories producing furniture, bedding, brooms, brushes, hardware, gloves, toys, threshing machines, footwear and beverages. The total annual value was about $220,000,000 in 1954 while the net value was over $115,000,000. Kitchener is an important distribution point while Waterloo is the headquarters of five nationally known insurance and trust companies. Waterloo College and Seminary (Lutheran) are also located here.

## Guelph

Guelph, county seat of Wellington county, located on the Speed River, was founded in 1827 by John Galt of the Canada Company. It was incorporated as a town in 1850 and as a city in 1879. Just south of the city, is located the Ontario Agricultural College, founded in 1874. This institution has trained several generations of noted Canadian scientists. Nearby is the Ontario Veterinary College. Guelph is a rather picturesque city with wide main streets and many stone buildings, including a fine Roman Catholic church which overlooks the city from the crest of one of its numerous drumlins. The flat floors of the old glacial spillways have provided excellent industrial sites. Its factories produce stoves, boiler machinery, electrical equipment, caskets, carpets, lime, leather goods, meats and dairy products. In 1941, the population was 23,273, mostly Canadian born of British origin while people of German and Italian origin comprise about 6% each of the total. Guelph city had a population of 34,000 in 1956, with a total of 37,000 in the urban area. It produced manufactured goods to the value of more than $66,000,000 (net $32,000,000) in 1954.

## Galt

Galt (24,000), second city of Waterloo county, located on the Grand River about 10 miles southeast of Kitchener, is noted for the manufacture of metal goods, chemi-

cals, shoes and textiles. In 1954, the gross value of manufactures was $56,000,000, with a net value of $28,000,000. Its position astride the Grand River has subjected the central part of the city to serious floods.

## Stratford

Stratford (20,000) county seat of Perth county, is an important railway centre. A provincial normal school is located here. It has packing plants and factories for furniture, flour, textiles and foundries for iron and brass; in 1956, the total value was $30,000,000, with a net value of $14,000,-000.

## Woodstock

Woodstock (19,000) county seat of Oxford county, situated in the valley of the South Branch of the Thames River, 25 miles east of London, is the centre of one of the most productive dairy districts of Ontario. It manufactures textiles, furniture, organs, fire engines, machinery, tubing, flour and feeds; the gross value, in 1954, was $50,000,000, with a net value of $21,-000,000.

## St. Thomas

St. Thomas (19,000) county seat of Elgin county, is located 18 miles south of London and 8 miles north of Port Stanley on Lake Erie. It is an important railway centre and has machine shops, flour mills and knitting mills; in 1954, the total value was $20,000,000, with a net value of $11,-000,000. A few miles south of the city is a large provincial mental hospital which during World War II was used as an airforce training centre.

## Sarnia

Sarnia (52,000) county seat of Lambton county is located at the outlet of Lake Huron. It is connected with Port Huron, Michigan, by the St. Clair Railway Tunnel, Ferry and Blue Water Bridge. It is an important lake port and has a 3,000,000 bushel elevator. Its industries include a large oil refinery, synthetic rubber plant, salt works, and boat building establishment. In 1954, the total value of manufactured goods was more than $290,000,000, with a net value of $135,000,000. A rapidly growing industrial area, its population has almost doubled in a decade.

## Chatham

Chatham (22,000) county seat of Kent county, is located on the Thames River about 16 miles from Lake St. Clair. Its manufactures include textiles, clothing, motor trucks, sugar, flour, tobacco, canned goods and chemical fertilizers. The total value in 1954 was $87,000,000 (net $27,000,000).

## London

London, "The Forest City", is situated at the forks of the Thames River, 115 miles southwest of Toronto, 114 miles northeast of Windsor, 23 miles north of Port Stanley on Lake Erie and 35 miles southeast of Grand Bend on Lake Huron; it is thus almost the geographical centre of southwestern Ontario. The county town of Middlesex county and located in the heart of a prosperous agricultural region,

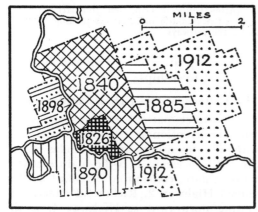

## EXPANSION OF LONDON

Figure 171. *The Expansion of London.* The last annexation to the city took place in 1912 and the built-up area extends beyond its boundaries in several directions.

it is the fifth city of Ontario in population and seventh in value of manufactures. It is also an important financial centre. In 1956, the population of the city of London was 102,000. Including the adjacent, built-up parts of London and Westminster townships, Greater London had a total population of about 155,000 and ranked twelfth among the "greater cities" of Canada. During the war and post-war periods, London has grown rapidly. In a 15-year period its population has increased about 70% to give it the fastest rate of growth among Ontario's greater cities.

### History

Governor Simcoe selected the "forks of the Thames" as the site for a city in 1793. Indeed he planned to make it the capital of Upper Canada but was forced to choose Toronto instead. The settlement of London was delayed until 1826 when Mahlon Burwell surveyed 240 acres as a town plot. In that same year, Peter McGregor became the first resident and the judicial centre of the district was transferred thither from Victoria. In 1840, with about 2,000 inhabitants, London became a village. It became a town in 1848 and, in 1854, with a population of 10,060 the city of London was incorporated. The Great Western Railway was opened in 1853; within a few years London became an important railway centre and by 1905 it boasted 120 trains per day. The locomotive on the civic coat of arms is no idle figurehead. With increased transportation facilities, including the development of its own port on Lake Erie (Port Stanley), London became a diversified manufacturing city and centre of wholesale distribution. As the headquarters of Military District No. 1, it was very active in the training of Canadian forces during World War II.

### The City Site and Development

London lies in a little basin, flanked by glacial moraines, into which the rivers from the melting ice brought great quantities of sediment producing a rather

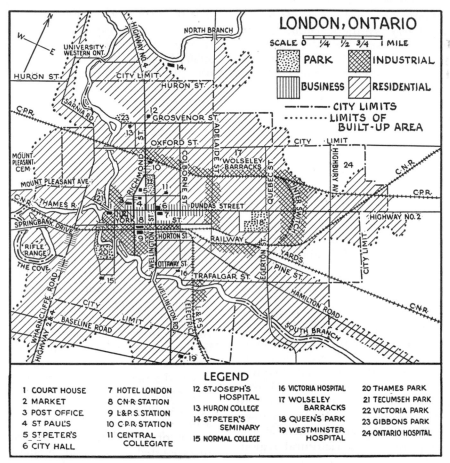

Figure 172. *The Functional Pattern of London.* (After Taube in Can. Geo. Journal).
The commercial areas are mainly in the old city centre and the main streets leading
from it. The manufacturing sites are strung along the railways.

smooth plain. Trenched by the Thames, it provides excellent, well-drained building sites. The flat-floored valley of the Thames itself with its abandoned "oxbows" and its liability to spring floods is not so well suited although, in later years, it too has been built upon. From the first, the river acted as a barrier, forcing the city to expand north and east; though, with the building of bridges, London South and London West also became parts of the city. Not quite all the land within the eastern part of the city is yet built up, but, toward the north, south and west,

the built-up area has overflowed into the adjoining townships.

## The Pattern of the Urban Landscape

The street pattern of London is the usual, conventional, rigid grid, oriented with the township lines. Dundas street, the old Concession I, is the main east-west thoroughfare, continuing eastward as Provincial Highway 2. Richmond street, continuing northward as Highway 4, is the main north-south route. Only a few, like Hamilton Road and Wellington Road, run diagonally. The railroad reaches the centre of the city, causing considerable interruption of the street plan. The city centre still lies within the original 240 acre survey. Here is the court house, built in the early years on the style of Col. Talbot's English home. Not far to the east are the Post Office, City Hall, Public Library, Hotel London and the Canadian National Railway Station. The C.P.R. Station is somewhat to the north. The financial institutions, the market place and chief retail houses are also located here. Subsidiary retail centres extend eastward along Dundas street, north along Richmond street, and on scattered corner locations elsewhere. Industrial plants are found chiefly along the railways and particularly eastern part of the city. London's best residential areas are in the north, while the industrial east contains the poorest. Small homes are also found on the flats of London South. London has two cathedrals, St. Peter's (Roman Catholic) and St. Paul's (Anglican) and many other fine churches. These and numerous excellent school buildings are scattered throughout the city. Parks and playgrounds are also numerous. Victoria Park, established in 1869, near the centre of the city, is the oldest; Queen's Park contains the Fair Buildings; Springbank Park, 325 acres in area, located about four miles down the river, is the largest. On the outskirts of the city are a number of large institutions such as Ontario Hospital in the east, Westminster Hospital to the southeast, the Sanitarium to the west; the Civic Airport to the northeast and the University of Western Ontario to the north. Golf courses and cemeteries also lie outside the city limits.

## Population

Greater London, in 1951, had a population of 121,516, of whom about 80% were Canadian born and 13% were from the British Isles. Russians, Poles and Italians also formed large immigrant groups. About 82% claimed to be of British origin; other important groups were: German (3.4%), French (2.4%), Netherlands (1.6%), Pol-

ish (1.4%) and Italian (1.1%). The dominant religious groups were: United Church of Canada (32.0%), Church of England (28.8%), Roman Catholic (14.4%), Baptist (8.7%) and Presbyterian (8.5%).

Numbering 54,000, the gainfully employed made up 45% of the total population. Of these, 32% worked in manufacturing, 17% in trade, 9% in professions, 8% in transportation, 7% in construction and 6% in finance.

## Urban Functions

London claims to be the "Commercial Capital" of Western Ontario by reason of its numerous wholesale and retail firms and its insurance, mortgage, savings and trust companies. London's position as a commercial centre has been aided greatly by its position in the highway and railway nets of the province. It has over 270 factories, employing 15,000 workers. A great diversity of products is produced including radios, refrigerators, sheet metal products and knitted goods, paper containers, machinery, printing, aircraft builders supplies, biscuits, breakfast foods and beverages. In 1954, the total value was $193,000,000 (net $107,000,000). London is an important educational centre containing a provincial normal college and the University of Western Ontario. The latter, founded in 1878, is located to the north of the city, overlooking the Thames River. It had 2,900 students in 1946-47. The medical faculty of the University and three large general hospitals give London prominence in medical affairs.

## Geographical Significance of London

London is the best example of a local regional capital in the province of Ontario. Centrally located in a comparatively uniform and relatively prosperous region, it is protected by distance and by natural barriers from its competitors. With the help of well established communications connecting all parts of its umland, it has developed industries and institutions which

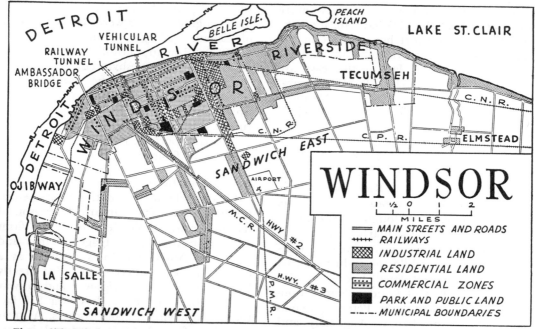

Figure 173. *Windsor*. Prior to 1935, the city of Windsor was composed of four separate municipalities, Sandwich, Windsor, Walkerville and East Windsor. The sprawling metropolitan area includes several other waterside municipalities and is invading the interior of the flat plain of Essex County.

dominate in their own constituencies and exert considerable influence, also, outside the immediate umland.

## Windsor

Windsor, "The Southern Gateway of Canada" is located on the Detroit River opposite the city of Detroit. It is thus part of the greater Detroit conurbation, as well as a metropolitan area in its own right and the fourth city in Canada in value of manufactures. The population of Windsor in 1941 was 105,311 living in an area of 12.89 square miles, a density of 8,170 per square mile. By 1956, the population of the city had passed 120,000. Greater Windsor, in 1941, had a population of 120,613 and, in 1956, it was found to contain a total of 185,865.

### History

Prior to the coming of the white man, Indian villages were located at the narrowest part of the river. In 1701, a French fort

was erected at Detroit and French settlement took place along both banks of the river. The settlers remained after the British took over the fort in 1763, and, when the fort was handed over to the Americans in 1796, many settlers removed to the Canadian side. Sandwich, slightly the older settlement, was the administrative centre. Windsor grew up at "the Ferry" opposite Detroit. Both were incorporated as towns in 1857. Windsor became the railway terminal and grew rapidly. In 1858, Walkerville was established and it became a town in 1890. Windsor became a city in 1892 with a population of 10,000. Ford City was founded in 1904, became a town in 1915 and was incorporated as the city of East Windsor in 1929. In 1935 the "Border Cities" were amalgamated as the city of Windsor with over 100,000 inhabitants. Due to the concentration of the automobile industry, Windsor ranks as fourth city of Canada in value of manufactures.

## Site and Situation

The site of Windsor is one of little relief, save for the declivity which marks the river bank. There are, therefore, no barriers toward growth inland. It is Windsor's situation in an international gateway, on the world's busiest waterway, which is Windsor's chief advantage. 118,000,000 tons of shipping passed through the Detroit River in its peak year, 1943. The Port of Windsor comprises a five mile frontage on this waterway, greatly facilitating importation of raw materials. Even more important to Windsor, is its position with regard to land traffic. Five great rail systems meet here, the Canadian National, Canadian Pacific, New York Central, Pere Marquette and Wabash. The Essex Terminal Railway connects all lines. A tunnel under the river serves the New York Central and Canadian Pacific, car ferries serve the others. Highway traffic may use either the Ambassador Bridge or the Detroit-Canada Tunnel. More than 1,500,000 visiting automobiles entered Canada at Windsor in 1946. Across the river, Detroit is the greatest centre of automobile manufacture in the world; Windsor could hardly have escaped becoming its counterpart in Canada. Other American manufacturers find it equally convenient to use Windsor as their Canadian headquarters.

## The Urban Pattern

The river front tends to impart a linear pattern to Windsor's development which has not been much affected by the early development of separate towns. Much of the river front is occupied by the railways which arrived early. Just behind the terminals, the commercial core of Windsor arose and has maintained its position. In addition to the downtown area, linear retail development is found westerly along London street and easterly along Wyandotte street. There are scattered smaller areas also such as those on Ottawa street and Sandwich street. Walkerville and East Windsor contain the largest concentrations of factories. Both Walker and Ford began their plants on the waterfront, east of the area already occupied by the railways. Railway spurs were built and other plants have been attracted to the same vicinity. Other industries are variously scattered along the railways or the river front below the city. Most of Windsor's residential streets are of modest appearance and with more wooden houses than in other large cities. Apartment houses are plentiful. Areas of more expensive houses are to be seen in East Windsor, Walkerville and Sandwich. Outlying portions of the metropolitan area, Riverside and Tecumseh to the east and West Sandwich and La Salle to the southwest are mainly residential. Several thousand wartime houses were erected in metropolitan Windsor to house the influx of workers during World War II.

## Population

The population of the metropolitan area was 157,672 in 1951. Of these 82,447 (52%) were of British origin, 33,072 (20.8%) were of French origin, 5,729 (3.6%) of German origin, 5,019 (3.2%) of Ukrainian origin, 4,974 (3.1%) of Polish origin and 4,942 (3.1%) of Italian origin. More than 75% were born in Canada while the largest groups of immigrants were from the British Isles, the United States, Poland, Russia and Italy.

The chief religious affiliations of Windsor's population were found to be Roman Catholic 67,343 (42.5%), Church of England 27,373 (17.2%), United Church of Canada 25,784 (16.2%), Presbyterian 12,498 (7.9%) and Baptist 5,974 (3.8%).

The greatest difference between Windsor and the other cities of Western Ontario is the large number of people of French origin, chiefly descendants of the first settlers.

The number of gainfully employed was reported to be 65,900, 41.5% of the population. Of these, 52% found work in manufacturing, 14% in trade, 7% in professions,

6% in transportation and 6% in construction.

## Urban Functions

Windsor is dominantly a manufacturing city, producing a larger value of goods per worker than any other large Canadian city. The automotive industry is the largest, but other machine shops, distilleries, breweries, salt works, chemicals, medicines, bakeries and dairy plants are important. The average annual value of manufactures, during the final years of World War II, was $335,000,000. In 1954, the total value of manufactured goods reached $700,000,-000, with a net value of $300,000,000. Windsor is an important port of entry and exit for international trade as well as a centre for wholesale distribution within its vicinity. Its local educational facilities are of high standard, particularly the technical schools. Assumption College, founded in 1855, is affiliated with the University of Western Ontario.

## Geographical Significance

Windsor exists because it occupies a 'crossroads' position on both land and water routes; such a location could not fail to produce a city. The fact that it is also on a political boundary has made it a smaller duplicate of Detroit rather than an integral part of the larger metropolitan area.

## The Towns

In addition to the cities, several larger towns are worthy of mention. *Preston* (9,400), site of numerous metal working industries, and *Paris* (5,500), with important textile plants, are located on the Grand River. *Simcoe* (8,000) is the Norfolk county seat and chief business centre of the flue-cured tobacco belt. *Ingersoll* (7,000), on the south branch of the Thames River, is an important dairy centre. *Leamington* (8,000), in the warmest part of the province, has large canning plants. *Wallaceburg* (8,000) is a growing industrial town, producing glass and metal goods.

## VI. Western Ontario

Western Ontario is bounded very definitely on three sides by the Niagara Escarpment, Georgian Bay and Lake Huron, but the fourth, or southern boundary, is a rather indefinite transition zone. Western Ontario represents old rural, agricultural Ontario. It has only one small seaport city, Owen Sound, with about 17,000 inhabitants, but a number of smaller towns which serve as local market centres and supply points. Among these may be mentioned Goderich, Kincardine, Walkerton, Hanover, Orangeville, Southampton, Wiarton and Meaford, none of which had 5,000 people in 1951.

Western Ontario consists of a high plain, 1,700 feet above sea-level, with an eastern hilly belt of moraines along the eastern border above the precipitous slopes of the Niagara Escarpment. From this high plain which occupies about half of Dufferin and Grey counties, long gentle slopes lead to the west and southwest. The long Bruce Peninsula stretching northward between Georgian Bay and Lake Huron is a limestone plain with shallow drift cover and much rock exposure.

Land use in Western Ontario varies with the different soil areas, but features spring grains, forage crops and pasture with most of the cash income derived from livestock. The limestone plains, rough moraines and hard clay soils are mainly devoted to grazing.

The shores of Georgian Bay constitute a small region quite distinct from the uplands. Here on the loamy soils of the Algonquin shorelines an important orchard area is found near Clarksburg, Thornbury, with lesser areas near Meaford and Collingwood. An attempt has been made to grow flue cured tobacco on the sandy soils of the old Saugeen delta near Port Elgin.

The Photographic Survey Corporation Limited.

Plate 64. Berkeley is a typical cross-roads settlement of rural Ontario, located a few miles south of Owen Sound.

## Owen Sound

Owen Sound with a population of 17,000 is located on a fine harbour opening into Georgian Bay. It was settled in the 1840's and soon became an important lumbering and shipbuilding centre. Later for a time it had important cement factories. Boat building, metal castings, stoves, ship propellers, furniture, electric light bulbs, paints, hosiery, tents and awnings are among the important manufacturing goods. Total value in 1954 was $22,000,000 (net $14,000,000.) The harbour is still important for shipping in the northern part of Lake Huron and in Georgian Bay. There is a 4,000,000, bushel grain elevator.

The city is picturesquely located on the flat floor of a deep valley indenting the Niagara Escarpment. Railways must enter the city by circuitous routes but springs along the Escarpment furnish a fine domestic water supply. Extensive waterfront locations are available as industrial sites.

Owen Sound also functions as a tourist headquarters for along the shores of Lake Huron and Georgian Bay there are many beaches and resort colonies. Among them may be mentioned those near Port Elgin, Sauble Beach, Lion's Head and Tobermory. From the last named point, ferries connect with Manitoulin Island which, also, has many resort areas.

## Southern Ontario

Southern Ontario is an area in which regional characteristics are still developing. The strong contrast between the Canadian Shield and the drift covered Paleozoic areas will always be of fundamental importance, but within these major divisions human patterns are taking shape. On the Shield there is a little agriculture, while forestry and recreation are major land use objectives. Further south, a rather uniform general farming economy is being replaced by many types of specialized agriculture, catering to nearby city markets. The most significant factor, however, is the growth of the industrial cities themselves. The majority of the population now live in cities, and Southern Ontario, along with Southern Quebec, has become part of the great industrial region of eastern North America.

# Selected References

*Business Year Book.* Ann. MacLean-Hunter Publishing Company Limited, Toronto.

*Canada Year Book.* Annual. Dominion Bureau of Statistics. Ottawa.

Deacon, N. A. H. *Geographical Factors and Land Use in Toronto.* Canadian Geographical Journal, 29, pp. 80-99. 1944.

*Decennial Census of Canada.* Dominion Bureau of Statistics, Ottawa.

*Geographical Distribution of the Manufacturing Industries of Canada.* Dominion Bureau of Statistics, Ottawa. Annual.

Harrington, Lyn. *Historic Rideau Canal.* Canadian Geographical Journal, 35, pp. 278-291. 1947.

Harrington, Lyn and Richard. *The Welland Canal.* Canadian Geographical Journal, 34, pp. 202-215. 1947.

Middleton, J. E. *Toronto's 100 Years.* The Centennial Committee. Toronto. 1934.

Robinson, J. L. *Windsor, Ontario. A Study in Urban Geography.* Canadian Geographical Journal, 27, pp. 106-21. 1943.

Taube, E. *The Growth of London, Ontario.* Canadian Geographical Journal, 33, pp. 102-16. 1946.

Watson, J. W. *Hamilton and its Environs.* Canadian Geographical Journal, 30, pp. 240-252. 1945.

Watson, J. W. *Mapping a Hundred Years of Change in the Niagara Peninsula.* Canadian Geographical Journal 32, pp. 266-283. 1946.

Wonders, W. C. *The Penetanguishene Peninsula.* Canadian Geographical Journal, 37, pp. 118-129. 1948.

Much of the information used in this chapter has been obtained through the courtesy of municipal clerks, boards of trade, and civic officials.

# CHAPTER 13

# Northern Ontario - Physical and Historical Background

## Land Forms

A HUGE sprawling area of 360,000 square miles, Northern Ontario, for the most part has monotonous landscapes, characterized by relatively few land forms.

### The Bedrock

Geologically it is made up of two large divisions; the southern and largest of which is underlain by Precambrian rocks of the Canadian Shield, while the area bordering Hudson Bay and James Bay is underlain by younger Ordovician, Silurian and Devonian rocks similar to those of southern Ontario. Near Lake Timiskaming and in the Manitoulin Islands, which lie along the northern shore of Lake Huron, similar rocks are found. (Figure 174).

The Precambrian rocks of Northern Ontario are very complex, consisting of very old sedimentary and volcanic beds which have been intruded by later magmas. Such conditions are favourable for the formation of mineral veins and Northern Ontario, in common with other parts of the Canadian Shield, is one of the richest mining areas in the world. The rocks commonly seen are granites, syenite, rhyolite, quartzite, schists, greywacke, slate and conglomerate. Probably dominant, however, are the great group of gneisses.

The rocks of the Paleozoic formations which overlie the Shield have been very little disturbed. They are mainly limestones, with some interbedded shale and sandstone formations. They were formerly

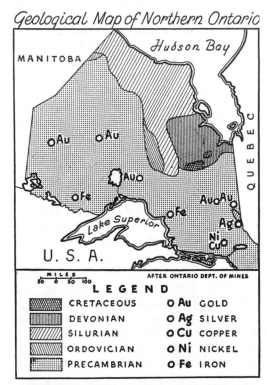

Figure 174. *Geological Map of Northern Ontario.* A very large part of Northern Ontario is underlain by crystalline Precambrian rocks. In some of these formations, rich finds of gold, silver, copper, nickel, iron and other minerals have been developed.

*Courtesy Canadian National Railways.*

Plate 65. Lake-of-the-Woods is studded with islands, typical of the rocky ridges of the Canadian Shield.

probably much more extensive but have been eroded from the areas which now show exposures of Precambrian rocks.

In the area south of James Bay there are small areas of much younger Cretaceous deposits which contain beds of lignite coals. Only a small part of Northern Ontario has actual solid rock at the surface. Over most of it there is a mantle of unconsolidated drift similar to the drift in Southern Ontario. This mantle is not deep and relief is influenced strongly by the underlying bedrock.

### Relief

Northern Ontario is a region of little over-all relief. The Paleozoic formations south and west of James Bay and Hudson Bay underlie a low flat plain which slopes toward the sea at about three or four feet per mile. The area of the Canadian Shield is more elevated, being for the most part over 1,000 feet above sea level. It also slopes slightly toward the north, so that the highest part and the water divide is not far from the southern margin of the Shield. Here the general elevation is about 1,500 feet but near the shore of Lake Superior there are isolated hills rising several hundred feet higher. Mount Batchawana (2,125′) is the highest point in the province of Ontario.

Although we speak of the Canadian Shield as an area of comparatively low relief, the traveller on the ground gets the impression of a rough and rugged terrain, particularly in the area bordering Lake Superior. Sometimes for miles there is no level land of any extent. Instead one sees a succession of steep-sided rock ridges with swamps or lakes between. From the highest hilltops, or from the air, the land appears as an ocean of rocky waves whose crests all rise to about the same height. The distant skyline is practically horizontal except for the occasional monadnock or rock knob.

While rocky ridges with shallow soils dominate the southern part of the Shield, the more northerly areas are covered by deeper drift which has a somewhat gentler relief. The least relief is found in the so-called *Clay Belts*, particularly those in which the deposits were laid down in the glacial lakes. There are also large areas of undulating to gently rolling ground morain or till plains. Sand plains also occur in old shore zones where broad deltas were built.

### Drainage

Since the highest part of the Canadian Shield is near its southern margin most of Northern Ontario drains towards Hudson Bay. The divide, however, is low and poorly defined and it has been possible

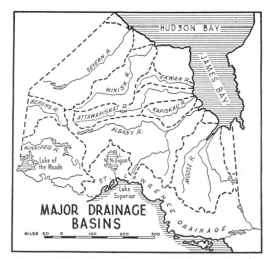

Figure 175. *Major Drainage Basins of Northern Ontario*. Most of Northern Ontario drains to Hudson Bay; the divide is not far from the northern shores of the Great Lakes, in the most rugged area of the province.

to divert northward flowing waters into the St. Lawrence system in order to provide extra water for power plants in Southern Ontario.

As a result of glaciation all of the preglacial drainage patterns have been disarranged and there has not been time for new ones to complete their development. The outstanding feature of the Canadian Shield is the abundance of lakes of all shapes and sizes. These lakes are formed in two ways. Either they occupy rock basins gouged out by ice, or they lie in old valleys which have been blocked by morainal deposits. Many of the lakes have been filled with peat and converted into bogs. Farther north there are fewer lakes and more and larger bogs.

River patterns are rather poorly developed and drainage basins are not yet completely known. The largest rivers include the Severn and Winisk draining into Hudson Bay and the Attawapiskat, Albany and Moose River systems emptying into James Bay. The Harricanaw empties into James Bay in the northeastern corner of Ontario, also, but most of its drainage area is in the province of Quebec.

These rivers all exhibit to a greater or lesser degree a peculiar combination of characteristics. Rising in the higher parts of the Shield, their headwaters spill haphazardly from one lake basin to another until the drift covered region is reached where a sizable river rapidly takes form. Gradients, particularly in the Clay Belt, are low and long stillwaters held up by rock ledges which the river has discovered below the unconsolidated mantle. Over

D. F. Putnam.

Plate 66. A log drive on the Sturgeon River in Northern Ontario.

these ledges the river may fall ten to fifty feet into another long stillwater. The greatest interruptions occur in the descent from the Clay Belt to the Coastal Plain and here the best power developments are possible. At Abitibi Canyon, for instance, there is a head of 297 feet and a total of 240,000 horsepower is developed.

In spite of the large rivers, neither the Clay Belt nor the coastal plain is well drained, except along the river banks, and all the interfluvial areas have water tables at, or very near, the surface of the ground.

### Development of the Present Surface

While the records of the rocks of Northern Ontario tell of ages of mountain building and erosion in Precambrian times, they have little effect upon the present land forms. It is probable that many periods of erosion took place before the one which developed the flattish skyline of the area along the height of land north of Lake Superior. It is probable that the abrupt southern faces of this upland are due to faulting. The old peneplain or erosion surface of the upland is tilted toward the north, apparently downwarped in the region of Hudson Bay. Furthermore, there are suggestions of two later stages of erosion. One formed the undulating rock platform underlying the Clay Belt deposits and a final one levelled the floor of the coastal plain. If the evidence of the Onakawana lignite beds is correctly interpreted, all this happened before the end of Cretaceous time.

Present day topography is a heritage of glaciation. Undoubtedly there were several successive ice sheets which helped to shape the bedrock surface and to accumulate the unconsolidated deposits. The last of these to cover Northern Ontario was a great lobe of the Labradorian ice sheet which radiated from James Bay. In consequence, the borders of the Shield are everywhere covered by calcareous (limy) drift derived from the limestones of the coastal plain.

As this ice sheet melted a great lake, or rather series of water bodies, stood in front of it. These are collectively referred to by geologists as Lake Barlow-Ojibway. In them the varved clays and other deep water deposits of the Clay Belt were laid down. When finally the sea gained entrance to the Hudson Bay basin, the land stood much lower than it does at present. Indeed the whole coastal plain seems to have been inundated. It has gradually recovered since, and uplift is still going on. Very clear evidence of this is given by the series of abandoned beaches at the southern end of James Bay.

## Land Form Regions of Northern Ontario

Much exploratory work remains to be done before the land forms of Northern Ontario are fully known and mapped. It is possible, however, to outline a scheme of land form regions or geomorphic divisions, which, while not so accurate as those of Southern Ontario, will serve the purpose of

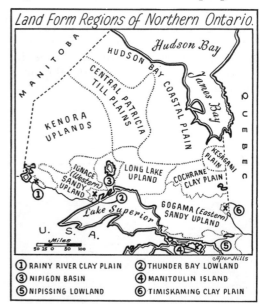

Figure 176. *Land Form Regions of Northern Ontario.* Although not by any means completely studied, Northern Ontario may tentatively be divided into a number of land form regions according to the patterns of surface formations and materials.

differentiation. These regions are shown in the accompanying map (figure 176) and briefly described in the following paragraphs.

### The Hudson Bay Coastal Plain

This low flat area is underlain by horizontally bedded limestones covered by varying depths of drift. The most prominent features of this plain are the old beach ridges of the high sea levels of the post glacial period. Between these low ridges are long quaking bogs. The plain is cut by shallow river valleys about at right angles to the ridges. Drainage is poor everywhere except on the ridges and along the river banks. From the air these are clearly marked by the development of forest in contrast with the scrub and bog of most of the area.

### The Kesagami Plain

A small area in north-eastern Ontario can be differentiated from the coastal plain by its shallow covering of drift and the presence of many open lakes as well as muskeg. The largest, Lake Kesagami, gives its name to the region.

### The Central Patricia Till Plains

Adjoining the coastal plain in the west and for the most part covered by glacial till in which limestone is abundant, Central Patricia is an area of loamy till ridges and intervening bogs.

### The Kenora Uplands

The old district of Kenora is entirely underlain by Precambrian rocks. The surface is cut by innumerable lakes and rivers. The drift over the bedrock is somewhat deeper than that on other rocky uplands in Northern Ontario and has a moderate content of limestone fragments derived from the Paleozoic rocks of the Hudson Bay Lowland. There are deposits of deeper silt and clay, notably in the area extending northward from Dryden, which may prove suitable for agricultural development.

*D. F. Putnam.*

Plate 67. A soil profile in the Clay Belt of Northern Ontario. Note the peatty surface and the varved clay parent material.

### The Long Lake Upland

Between the north shore of Lake Superior and the expanded southern portion of the coastal plain lies an upland composed of rocky ridges and drift hills. The till cover here is of variable depth and contains a great deal of limestone from the north east. Typical drumlins are found near Geraldton and probably occur elsewhere as well. Drainage is considerably better than in the adjoining areas, north and east.

### The Cochrane Clay Plain

Commonly known as the Great Clay Belt of Northern Ontario, this area is often referred to as being covered with clay and silt laid down in glacial lakes Barlow and Ojibway. Actually, however, there is a mosaic of deposits including lake laid material, glacifluvial sands and gravels and ground moraine or till. Much of it is extremely flat but other areas are gently sloping where the unconsolidated mantle overlies low bedrock domes and ridges. There are few lakes here in comparison with the areas to the south and west, but there are large areas of treeless muskeg. Drainage has not been established, only the main rivers have cut into the plain and their influence extends only a short distance from the valley side.

## The Timiskaming Clay Plain

Sometimes known as the 'Little Clay Belt' this area is found between the head of Lake Timiskaming and the gold mining region. The overburden is more dominantly water laid clay than in the Great Clay Belt and stream development somewhat more advanced. In this vicinity there are found some outliers of Paleozoic limestone.

## The Gogama (Eastern) Sandy Upland

Extending from Lake Superior to the Ottawa River and the Little Clay Belt is a large rocky upland covered by sandy drift. This is especially heavy along the southern margin which seems to have been the position of the ice front during a long period corresponding with the high levels of Lake Algonquin. There are a large number of lakes contained in rocky basins, Lake Timagami being the largest and best known. Two large areas of forest have been set aside by the provincial government, the Mississagi and Timagami Forest Reserves. There is very little soil suitable for agriculture.

## The Nipigon Basin

The Nipigon Basin with its adjoining ridges contains the largest lake in Northern Ontario (1,870 square miles). This basin contains some clay and sand plains laid down in Lake Superior and serves as the link through which water is now transferred from the James Bay watershed to that of the St. Lawrence.

## Thunder Bay Lowland

Thunder Bay Lowland is also filled with lacustrine deposits on which some reasonably good agricultural land is found.

## Rainy River Lowland

Rainy River Lowland is floored with clay laid down in Lake Agassiz; it, also, has some good agricultural land.

## Ignace (Western) Sandy Upland

The Western Sandy Upland lies between these two clay filled basins and has rather rough topography and sandy soils.

## The Nipissing Lowland

This low area forms the southern boundary of the region under discussion. Probably a down-faulted area, it collected a great deal of sand and clay during Algonquin time and now has considerable agricultural land. Bordering it are bedrock hills from which the overburden has almost all been washed away. There are also extensive plains of coarse gravel.

## Manitoulin

Consisting of several islands in the northern part of Lake Huron, this region differs greatly from the adjoining mainland in that it is underlain completely by horizontal Paleozoic rocks. The Niagara Escarpment which figures so strongly in Southern Ontario is here also the most prominent feature. A good deal of the area consists of almost bare rock plains, but there are areas of glacial and lacustrine materials of sufficient depth to form arable soils.

# Climate, Vegetation and Soils

## Climate

Northern Ontario is a large area without any great relief hence the climate varies gradually in all directions in obedience to the general continental controls. These are modified somewhat by the presence of Hudson Bay and James Bay to the north and the Great Lakes to the south while the high lands north of Lake Superior also have some climatic effect.

## Temperature

Isotherms of mean temperature for January, April, July and October are shown on the accompanying maps. In January (Figure 177) there is a general and fairly uniform gradient from south to north, from 10°F. at North Bay to —15° F. near the shores of Hudson Bay. Lake Superior serves to raise the temperature slightly along its shores but its influence does not extend far inland. The isotherms for April (Figure 178) have a general trend from north-

July isotherm map (Figure 179) is the "cold loop" including the highlands and the north shore of Lake Superior.

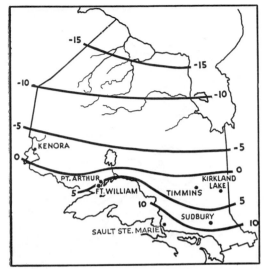

Figure 177. *January Mean Temperature.* Midwinter in Northern Ontario is cold, with mean temperatures ranging from 10° above zero to North Bay to 15° below zero on the shores of Hudson Bay.

west to southeast, showing the influence of the more rapid warming of the interior and the retarding effect of the cold water and ice of Hudson Bay.

July temperatures range from 66° F. at North Bay to 56° F. along the shores of Hudson Bay. The peculiar feature of the

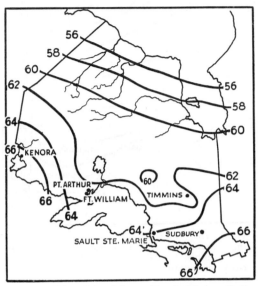

Figure 179. *July Mean Temperature.* Both Hudson Bay and Lake Superior tend to lower the summer temperatures of Northern Ontario.

The October mean temperatures (Figure 180) range from 45° F. in the south to 30° F. along Hudson Bay. James Bay, Lake Huron and Lake Superior all serve to raise the temperature slightly at this time of year.

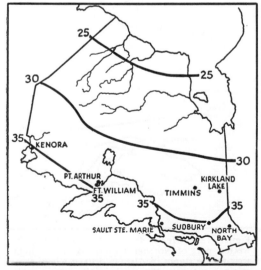

Figure 178. *April Mean Temperature.* Spring comes first in the southwest corner.

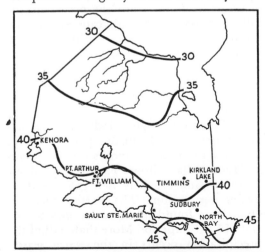

Figure 180. *October Mean Temperature.* Water bodies tend to keep the temperature slightly higher in the autumn months.

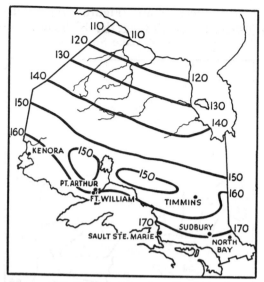

Figure 181. *The Average Length of the Growing Season.* The growing season is calculated as the number of days during which the mean daily temperature remains above 42°F.

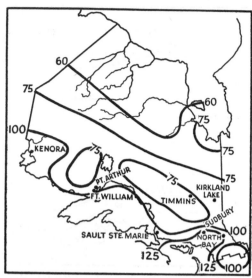

Figure 182. *Average Length of the Frost-free Period.* The average number of days between the last killing frost in the spring and the first killing frost in the fall. This period is, of course, much shorter than the one in which the temperature normally permits plant growth.

Growing temperatures (above a mean of 42° F.) are experienced for about 175 days in the south and about 110 in the far north. (Figure 181). The highland areas north of Lake Superior show a shorter season than the Great Clay Belt. The frost-free period shows an even greater variation. (Figure 182). The presence of all the large bodies of water tends to retard the occurrence of killing frosts in the fall, causing the isopleths to bend sharply northward. Even these favoured localities, however, have a much shorter season than any place in Southern Ontario.

**Precipitation**

Precipitation (Figure 183) varies generally from about 30 inches per annum at Sudbury to about 15 inches on the shores of Hudson Bay. Moose Factory gets about 20 inches and the Clay Belt gets about 26 inches per annum. The wettest place in Ontario is found along the slopes to the east of Lake Superior. More than half of the precipitation occurs in the warm season but the maximum in the west is in mid-summer, while in the east it comes in late

summer and fall. This extra moisture at harvest time is a handicap to agriculture in the Clay Belt.

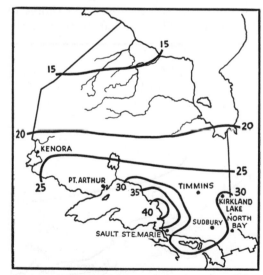

Figure 183. *Mean Annual Precipitation.* The wettest part of Northen Ontario is on the high, west-facing slopes in Algoma district where some stations get over 40" per year. The least moisture is received in the far north.

Most of the inhabited part of Northern Ontario gets from 80 to 100 inches of snow each winter. (Figure 184). The northern half, in general, gets less than 60 inches.

### Climatic Regions

The climatic data for Northern Ontario is not yet good enough to enable us to draw

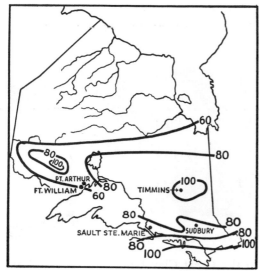

Figure 184. *Mean Annual Snowfall.* Some parts of Northern Ontario get more than 100 inches of snowfall per winter.

Figure 186. *Forest Regions of Northern Ontario.* (After Halliday). The three main vegetation belts, mixed forest in the south, the coniferous forest or *taiga* of the main body of the region, and the treeless area of the Hudson Bay coast, may be divided into a number of subregions.

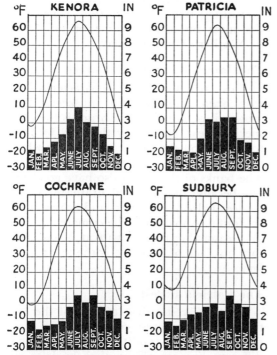

Figure 185. *Climatic Diagrams for Four Selected Northern Ontario Stations.* The chief difference shown here is the tendency for greater autumn rainfall in the eastern part of the province.

satisfactory regional boundaries. The accompanying diagrams represent the climatic conditions in four districts, Kenora, Patricia, Sudbury and Cochrane. (Figure 185). They show sufficient differences to justify thinking of them as representative of climatic subregions.

### Vegetation

Northern Ontario is for the most part a forested region; only along the shore of Hudson Bay do the trees finally give way to the barren tundra. The forest shows considerable variation from place to place. The accompanying map (Figure 186) has been

D. F. Putnam.

Plate 68. An Ontario Department of Lands and Forests fire rangers station in the Cochrane District.

taken from that of Halliday published some years ago. It divides Northern Ontario into useful forest regions.

## Great Lakes Mixed Forest

The southwestern and southeastern areas, separated by the great northern embayment of Lake Superior, are regarded as part of the Great Lakes Forest. Pines were the most characteristic tree of the original forest, east of Lake Superior. The present mixed cover consists of yellow birch, balsam fir, white spruce, white pine, sugar maple and red pine. After fires new stands of aspen, white birch and jack pine occur. The swampy areas contain black spruce and tamarack with some white cedar. West of Lake Superior, white and red pine are abundant with red pine most prevalent. Neither of these species, on the average however, are quite so tall as in the eastern section. There is a similar mixture of hardwood and softwood species. In both sections one of the most characteristic sights is the growth of jack pine on the dry sand plains. The Great Lakes Forest is the source of most of the saw timber in Northern Ontario.

## The Central Coniferous Forest

The most characteristic tree of this region is black spruce which grows in dense stands in the Great Clay Belt. With better drainage mixed stands occur, including other trees such as tamarack, white spruce, balsam fir, aspen and white birch. On dry sand plains and rocky ridges jack pine is the prevailing tree. This section constitutes the most important source of pulpwood in Northern Ontario today.

## The James Bay Coastal Forest

This large flat area is characterized by vast open marshes and muskegs. Tree growth is poor and black spruce is the chief species. Near James Bay the only forest is to be seen on the raised sea beaches which parallel the coast for some miles inland. The banks of the rivers also have good forests because of improved drainage. White spruce, balsam fir, aspen and white birch are found. Apparently, the climate will permit reasonable tree growth at Moose Factory but lack of drainage is the great problem.

## The Patricia Forest

This is a westward extension of the central coniferous forest containing the same species. Growth conditions are somewhat different because of the slightly drier climate. Little exploratory work has been done but it is thought to contain considerable pulpwood.

## The Northern Transition Forest

In this zone the forest becomes stunted and thinner, interspersed with open bogs. Near the shore of the bay it gives way to open tundra. Black spruce, white spruce, white birch and tamarack are the common trees with some jack pine along the southern boundary.

## The Soils

The soils of Northern Ontario have been assigned to three soil zones. Those of the southern border normally belong to the Brown Podzolic soil group while the great body of the region has an environment suitable to the development of true Podzols. A narrow strip of Tundra adjoins Hudson Bay. These soil zones correspond closely with the vegetation zones, Brown Podzolic soils occurring normally under mixed hardwoods and pine forests, Podzols under the uniform coniferous forests while the tundra is without trees. Actually, however, there are vast areas in which poor drainage has prevented normal soil forma-

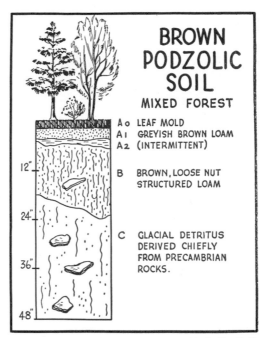

Figure 188. *Profile of a Brown Podzolic Soil in Northern Ontario.*

Figure 187. *Soil Regions of Northern Ontario.* Northern Ontario soils have not been fully surveyed but, under the prevailing coniferous forest cover, podzolic leaching tends to occur. Many areas, however, do not develop normal profiles.

tion, producing bog and half-bog soils; there are large areas of bare rock or of shallow covering over rock as well as deep coarse sand plains, all of which are too dry for normal soil development.

Generalizing very broadly then we may draw up a map of the region as in figure 187. On it, we have a very narrow band in the south in which Brown Podzolic soils occur. They are shallow with only two horizons; a brownish gray surface soil, in which there is a considerable admixture of organic matter, and a coffee brown, somewhat nut-structured subsoil. There is no strongly leached horizon (see figure 188). Intermixed with these types and extending a considerable distance northward are the Podzols. These are illustrated in figure 189. Under a mat of spruce, fir and pine needles there is usually an inch or two of dark grey soil underlain in turn by a light grey or almost white, highly leached horizon, which may be several inches in depth. The B horizon or subsoil appears very much like

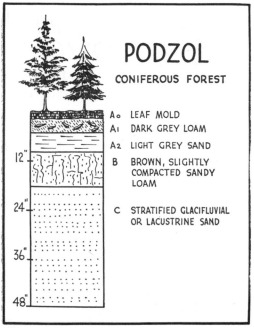

# PODZOL
## CONIFEROUS FOREST

A₀  LEAF MOLD
A₁  DARK GREY LOAM
A₂  LIGHT GREY SAND
B   BROWN, SLIGHTLY
    COMPACTED SANDY
    LOAM
C   STRATIFIED GLACIFLUVIAL
    OR LACUSTRINE SAND

Figure 189. *Profile of a Podzol Soil in Northern Ontario.*

that of the Brown Podzolic soils. Such soils are best developed in the better drained upland regions.

Farther north and in other areas where drainage is poor these profiles do not develop. Instead there is a tendency for greater accumulation of organic matter on the surface while in the subsoil a clay like substance, which is known as *glei*, accumulates. The Clay Belts of Northern Ontario lie in the Podzol zone but, because of their flatness and heavy clay texture, only small areas are well enough drained to have a Podzol profile. The remainder is covered with peat of varying depth. In general the peat is shallowest near the shoulders of the shallow river valleys but it gets deeper as one goes away from the stream and may be six feet or more on the interstream divides. Consequently the best lands of the Clay Belt, and the only ones which can be farmed economically are those situated near the large streams. More than three feet of peat usually prevents agricultural settlement. Within the clay belt there are narrow ridges and sometimes wider areas of sandy materials which have better internal drainage than the clay. On these mineral soil with a fair admixture of organic matter has developed. Such soils are sought after for special agricultural use such as the growing of potatoes for which the climate of the clay belt seems well suited.

Northwestern Ontario is the only part of the north for which a soil survey report is available. Here the Thunder Bay Area, the Rainy River Clay Plain and the Dryden area were surveyed on a reconnaissance basis. Here also the well drained soils are Podzols or Podzolic, with large areas of poorly drained soil. In the Rainy River area soils are described which resemble very closely the Grey Wooded and Degraded Chernozem Soils of the Prairie Provinces.

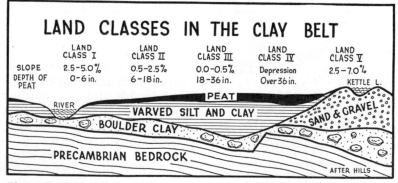

Figure 190. *Physical Land Classes in the Clay Belt.* The chief criteria in the classification of land in the Clay Belt are drainage and depth of peat. As a rule the best lands are near the rivers.

## Historical Development

Oddly enough, the oldest settlement in Ontario is Moose Factory at the southern end of James Bay. Here in 1671 the second post of the Hudson's Bay Company was founded. It did not, however, lead to any expanded settlement for its hinterland was much too forbidding. The wilderness effectively served to protect the British company from the French colony of the St. Lawrence. Only d'Iberville was able successfully to penetrate this seclusion.

When the province of Ontario was constituted in 1867 its northern and western boundaries were indefinite. After some debate with Manitoba the line between them was fixed by arbitration in 1877 in its present location. The English River and the Albany River to James Bay were proclaimed the northern boundary in 1889. Finally the present boundary was established in 1912.

Settlement approached from the south. French fur traders and later those of the North West Company had forts in the Lake Nipissing, Sault Ste. Marie and Lakehead areas. The earliest settlement of the lumbering period was founded at Mattawa in the 1850's but Mattawa had been a trading post since 1784. In the 1850's, also, colonization reached Lake Nipissing from the south via the Muskoka Road.

In 1882 the C.P.R. reached North Bay and continued on its thousand-mile course across the province. A second railway made connection with Toronto in 1886.

Settlers went ahead of the railway. In the 1880's they began to drift into the "Little Clay Belt" at the head of Lake Timiskaming and within a few years were asking for a railway. In order to open up the northeastern area, the Ontario Government, between 1902 and 1905, built the Timiskaming and Northern Ontario to New Liskeard. It was continued to Cochrane in 1908 and finally to Moosonee in 1932. Branches serve the mining area. A second railway across the rocks of Northern On-

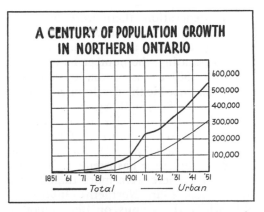

Figure 191. *A Century of Population Growth in Northern Ontario.* The rapid growth of population in Northern Ontario has been largely the result of urban expansion at mining camps and transportation nodes.

tario was completed in 1911 by the Canadian Northern Railway Company and in 1913 the National Transcontinental was built through Cochrane and the Great Clay Belt. Thus Northern Ontario acquired three transprovincial railways linking eastern and western Canada.

## Population

A century ago there were few people in Northern Ontario. By 1871, the first census

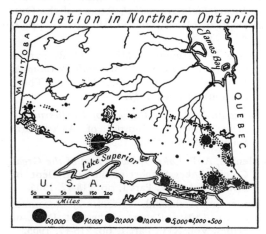

Figure 192. *Distribution of Population in Northern Ontario.* The population of Northern Ontario is found largely in favoured pocket locations while most of the area is without settlement.

after confederation, there were less than 8,000, mainly in Algoma, Manitoulin and Nipissing. By 1891, after the first wave of railroad building, the number had risen to 55,000; by 1901 it was almost 100,000. During the next decade the developments at the Lakehead, the Soo, Sudbury and the discovery of three mining fields in northeastern Ontario shot the total to 238,000. There was little increase during World War I but since then the curve has risen steadily (see figure 191). There were more than half a million people in Northern Ontario in 1951, while the census of 1956 reported more than 625,000.

The population of Northern Ontario is of mixed origin; 45% of the people stem from the British Isles and 25% from France while 3½% are of native Indian descent. A mixture of other people, mainly of European stock, make up the remaining

26½%, including Finns, Scandinavians, Italians, Ukrainians, Poles and Russians in large numbers.

With less than 1.5 persons per square mile, Northern Ontario is a sparsely populated land. Its population is not, however, thinly and uniformly scattered over its vast surface. Instead it is concentrated in certain favourable pockets, while most of the area remains without settlement.

Less than half the people may be classed as rural dwellers. Northern Ontario has some fairly large cities such as North Bay, Sudbury, Sault Ste. Marie and the Lakehead. It also has many smaller urban settlements based upon pulp and paper mills and mining developments. Only about ten per cent of the population lives on farms, a proportion considerably smaller than that to be found in Southern Ontario.

## Selected References

Burrows, A. G. et al. *The Porcupine Gold Area.* Rept. of the Ont. Dept. of Mines. Vol. XXXIII. Part III, pp. 1-105. 1924.

Burrows, A. G. and H. C. Rickaby. *Sudbury Nickel Field Restudied.* Report of the Ont. Dept. of Mines. Vol. XLIII. Part II, pp. 1-45. 1934.

Canada Department of Mines and Resources. *Geology and Economic Minerals of Canada.* Economic Geology Series No. 1. (Third Edition). Ottawa. 1947.

Chapman, L. J. *The Climate of Northern Ontario.* Canadian Journal of Agricultural Science 33, pp. 41-73. 1953.

Coleman, A. P. *Lake Ojibway; Last of the Great Glacial Lakes.* Report of the Ont. Dept. of Mines. Vol. XIV. Part I, pp. 213-47. 1905.

Henderson, Archibald. *Agricultural Resources of the Abitibi.* Report of the Ont. Dept. of Mines. Vol. XIV. Part I, pp. 213-47. 1905.

Hills, G. A. *Pedology, "the Dirt Science" and Agricultural Settlement in Ontario.* Can. Geog. Jour. 29, pp. 106-27. 1944.

Hills, G. A. and F. F. Morwick. *Reconnaisance Soil Survey of Parts of Northwestern Ontario.* Guelph. 1944.

Hurst, M. E. *General Geology of Ontario.* Canadian Mining Journal. Vol. 71:11, pp. 102-6. Nov. 1950.

Moore, E. S. *Elementary Geology for Canada.* J. M. Dent & Sons. Toronto. 1944.

Nichols, D. A. *The Geographic Setting of Northern Ontario.* Canadian Geographical Journal 18, pp. 147-151. 1939.

*Report to the Ontario Legislature from the Select Committee on Conservation.* Toronto. 1950.

Satterley, J. *Geology of the Dryden-Wabigoon Area.* Report of the Ont. Dept. of Mines. Vol. L. Part II, pp. 1-62. 1941.

Sharp, J. F. and J. A. Brodie. *The Forest Resources of Ontario. 1930.* Ont. Dept. of Lands & Forests. Toronto. 1931.

# CHAPTER 14

# Economic Geography of Northern Ontario

## Forest Industries

THE forest area of Northern Ontario is roughly 100,000,000 acres or 155,000 square miles, not counting any which may be in the central Patricia region or upon the coastal plain. The accessible forests of Ontario are estimated to contain over 30,000 million cubic feet of softwood which may be thought of as 40,000 million f.b.m. of saw timber and 270 million cords of smaller material. Most of this is in the region discussed as Northern Ontario. A considerable portion, also, of the 26,000 million cubic feet of hardwood in the province is found in the southern portions of this region. It should be said, however, that these figures are just estimates and a much better knowledge will have been gained on the completion of the forest inventory which was initiated soon after the close of World War II.

For the most part, the forest land of Ontario is Crown Land; only 6.0% is under private ownership. In this it is similar to Quebec where private owners control 7.2%. Over 12,000,000 acres have been set aside as Provincial Forests to be handled in a scientific manner by the Department of Lands and Forests. The Kawartha, Eastern

D. F. Putnam.

Plate 69. The Spruce Falls Pulp and Paper Mill at Kapuskasing, Ontario.

307

and Georgian Bay areas are in Southern Ontario; the Timagami, Wanapitei, Mississagi, Nipigon and Sibley Forests are in Northern Ontario.

Timber cutting operations are carried on by private or corporate enterprises who obtain permits or licenses to cut in specified areas. The chief uses for timber are as sawn lumber or as pulpwood but there are others such as plywood, veneer, fuelwood, matchwood, etc. Strictly speaking, only the securing of the logs from the forest can be regarded as primary industry, sawing, grinding and all other forms of processing being classed as manufacturing. Since they are often under the control of the same operator, and usually geographically related, timber cutting and processing will be discussed together.

The importance of forest industries in Ontario can be judged from these figures. In 1945 woods operations employed 29,500 workers, mostly seasonal, who earned more than $44,000,000. There were 42 pulp and paper mills employing 12,000 with a payroll of $26,500,000 in wages and salaries; and 1,147 licensed saw mills with 7,000 workers, also mostly seasonal earning $7,-000,000. It was estimated also that there were 2,000 plants in the province using pulp, paper, lumber or other wood as the primary raw material. These secondary industries employed 51,000 people and paid them $75,000,000. The significance of forest industries in the economic life of the province is not confined to the localities in which men are employed in the woods. Many farm labourers and fishermen find seasonal employment and it is estimated that the camps use about $16,000,000 worth of farm produce. Lumber and pulp and paper mills also use a great deal of electric power and their product furnishes freight for railways and trucking concerns.

The relative importance of the two main forest industries has changed greatly. In 1908, for instance, about 1,250,000 M.f.b.m. of sawn lumber were produced; this declined steadily to about 200,000 M.f.b.m. in

1932 but rose again to 600,000 M.f.b.m. during World War II. Pulp on the other hand was relatively insignificant in 1908 with a production of about 100,000 tons, this had increased in 1932 to 800,000 tons and to 2,400,000 tons in 1954. Most of the pulp is converted into paper, though often at other mills.

The relative importance of pulp and paper tends to increase. There are now (1950) 45 pulp and paper mills in the province of which 17 are located in Northern Ontario. These are all relatively large mills representing great outlay of capital since the cost of erecting a mill is from $30,000 to $40,000 per ton of daily capacity.

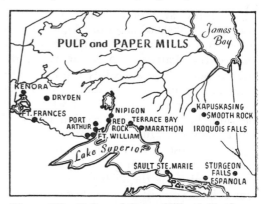

Figure 193. *Pulp and Paper Mills of Northern Ontario.* Pulp and paper mills are found in all the geographic regions of Northern Ontario, except the very far north. The factors to be balanced in locating a mill are power resources, transportation facilities and pulpwood reserves.

The location of mills in Northern Ontario is shown in figure 193. Those producing pulp only are found at Smooth Rock Falls, Marathon, Terrace Bay and Nipigon. Pulp and paper mills producing newsprint are found at Iroquois Falls, Sault Ste. Marie, Kapuskasing, Port Arthur, Fort William (2), Fort Frances and Kenora. Other types of paper are produced at Sturgeon Falls, Espanola, Kapuskasing, Red Rock, Port Arthur and Dryden. Approximately 50,000 square miles of forest land is set aside for the supply of these mills under agreements with the companies concerned.

In addition the cutting of pulpwood for export is permitted from several large areas.

There are several hundred sawmills in Northern Ontario but only a few are of any size, only about 50 having an annual cut of more than one million f.b.m. Of these 15 are located in the Near North between Sault Ste. Marie and the Ottawa River, 20 are located in the Clay Belts and mining areas of Northeastern Ontario, about 10 in the central section along the C.N.R. and C.P.R. and five in the western part of the

## Fur and Fish

Neither the fur trade nor the fishing industry bulk very great in the total economy. The fur trade, however, had a great deal to do with the early exploration of the area. The first furs exported from Northern Ontario probably went down the Ottawa River to the fur traders established at Montreal in 1642. A few years later (1668), the first English fur trading ships came to Hudson's Bay. From that time on the fur trade of the northern part

D. F. Putnam.

Plate 70. A Lumber Camp in Northern Ontario.

province, including the very large operations at the Lakehead. Sawmills are usually temporary features of the landscape, only a few persisting from year to year and forming the nuclei of settlements. Only a few small areas in Northern Ontario are leased for saw timber only, and most of the saw logs must be secured from concessions under lease to pulp companies.

The Kennedy Report (1947) points out that there is much land in Northern Ontario that will always be forest land. Some of it is capable of growing saw-timber, other areas can produce only pulpwood. Therefore, the forests need careful management in order to see that both kinds of wood are produced in an orderly fashion, so that both the pulp and paper industry and the lumber industry may continue to operate.

was in the hands of the English although the southern area continued to trade with Montreal.

Over 13,000 trapping licenses are taken out each year in Ontario and the total value of fur taken ranges from $5,000,000 to $7,000,000. The largest part of this activity is in northern Ontario. Muskrat, mink, beaver and fox are the most important species.

Commercial fishing is carried on in the Great Lakes and in many inland waters. In recent years there have been 1,800 to 2,000 licensed fishermen and the total catch has averaged 30,000,000 pounds per year. Whitefish, pickerel, herring and lake trout are the most important species. Roughly 70% of the provincial total is caught in the waters of Southern Ontario, Lake Erie being the leader with over 50%. In Northern Ontario the inland waters are the largest producers with about 5,000,000 pounds per year or 16% of the total. The rest are credited to Lake Superior and the North Channel. The annual value of the fish produced in Ontario is about the same as the value of the trapped fur but a smaller portion of it comes from the north.

## Agriculture

In Northern Ontario agriculture is a minor industry. Less than 13% of the total population live on farms and in some districts less than 10%. Even of those who live on farms, only a small proportion are full-time farmers. The agricultural areas are small, widely scattered patches making up only 1.2% of the whole region. According to the census of 1951, there were 12,900 farms comprising an area of 2,412,-000 acres, an average of 185 acres each. This is larger than the average southern Ontario farm (135 acres) but only 60 acres is improved land.

Throughout much of Northern Ontario, low temperature, the shortness of the growing season and unfavourable harvest weather vigorously limit the choice of crops. The problems of soil fertility and drainage are a further handicap. The region cannot compete with the Prairies in the production of wheat nor with the southern parts of Ontario in other field crops. It is therefore difficult to establish an extensive commercial type of agriculture. In suitable areas adjacent to the large cities there are moderately well developed dairy farms. Manitoulin Island, more like southern Ontario in many ways, has developed a grazing specialty with the sale of young beef cattle for finishing elsewhere. Manitoulin also raises a large number of turkeys. Potatoes of a high quality are a cash crop on some Sudbury farms, while the New Liskeard area or "Little Clay Belt" is a livestock area. For the most part, however, the farms of Northern Ontario do not produce much for sale and most of the food consumed in the towns and cities is brought from dis-

tant places. This economic weakness is emphasized by the fact that in 1941, three-fifths of all the abandoned farms in Ontario were in the north, particularly in the "Great Clay Belt" or Cochrane District.

For forty years the Great Clay Belt was extolled as an area of 14,000,000 acres of potential farm land. An area of over 1,000,-000 acres has been settled and manhandled. Pulpwood cutting rather than agriculture was the chief occupation of the settler and when the last stick was gone the pioneer also moved on to start over again somewhere else. Only a few were able to turn their "first crop" of trees into permanent farm improvements. It is argued by many that a more effective form of government aid, such as it practiced in Quebec, would have promoted more successful settlement. It is also argued that the failure of unsubsidized agricultural settlement is proof positive of the unwisdom of any form of agricultural occupance. It is probable that the best use of the land will in future be promoted by a combination of agriculture and forestry. Soil surveys are proving that a great deal of the land is unsuitable for agriculture without a great expense for drainage and amelioration. There is as yet no lack of food from the agricultural areas of Canada and there is a great demand for pulpwood. It would seem logical for Northern Ontario to promote forest settlement in which the main endeavour would be wood production. At the same time on suitable soils and in economic locations agriculture might be a small but profitable sideline.

## Mining

The mines of Northern Ontario normally produce 30 to 40% of Canada's mineral wealth. In less than 50 years, this industry has produced $5,000,000,000 of new wealth and is currently adding to it at the rate of $500,000,000 per year. Great as it is, however, mining is Ontario's third ranking source of income standing well behind the diversified agriculture of the southern part

## ONTARIO MINERAL PRODUCTION
### (*MILLIONS OF DOLLARS*)

ONT DEPT. MINES

Figure 194. *Mineral Production in Ontario.* The annual value of mineral production in the province reached $295,000,000. in 1948. By far the greater part of this is produced by the mines of Northern Ontario.

of the province. The most important minerals are gold, nickel, copper, silver, platinum, cobalt and iron, if ranked in terms of long-time total production. In terms of production in 1951, they ranked: nickel, $151,000,000; gold, $91,000,000; copper, $71,000,000; platinum, $22,000,000; iron ore, $21,000,000; silver, $4,000,000; calcium and magnesium, $3,600,000; cobalt, $2,000,-000.

## Gold

Although sometimes displaced by nickel from first place in recent annual statistics, gold has provided one third of all the mineral production of Ontario. Gold has also contributed more than anything else to the glamour and romance of the north country. Gold mining camps are scattered across the whole expanse of the Shield from the Quebec boundary to that of Manitoba. Gold is found mainly in association with basic volcanic and intrusive rocks, hence much barren granitic country lies between the gold producing areas. The more notable fields are Porcupine, Kirkland Lake, Larder Lake, Matachewan, Michipicoten, Long Lac, Red Lake and Pickle Crow.

The Porcupine discovery was made in 1909, uncovering the richest series of mineralized quartz veins in Northern Ontario. More than half the gold production of the province has come from fifteen large mines in this belt. Hollinger Consolidated Gold Mines Limited with approximately 920 acres of mining claims is the largest producer in Canada. Mine shafts extend to depths of over 5,000 feet and there are many miles of underground workings. More than 2,200 men are employed, about 1,000,-000 tons of ore are hoisted per year and $9,000,000 worth of metal sold. The mill on the main property has a capacity of 5,000 tons per day but during the war years it was not operated to capacity because of labour shortage.

McIntyre Mines Limited was one of the original producers in the Porcupine camp, beginning in 1912. Present holdings include more than 1,300 acres along the ore zone in Tisdale township. Its shafts are more than 4,000 feet in depth.

Dome Mines Limited began to produce in 1910. The main property includes 2,650 acres in Tisdale township and its mill has a capacity of 1,700 tons per day. Its deepest shaft is more than 4,000 feet.

There are several other large mines now operating, but the three mentioned above have together paid more than nine-tenths of the dividends from the Porcupine Camp, which, up to 1946, had amounted to more than a quarter of a billion dollars. The area had produced over $900,000,000 worth of gold by 1948.

The Kirkland Lake Area lies about 60 miles southeast of Porcupine field. The chief producing mines are found in an area about three-quarters of a mile wide and 3 miles long centred about the town of Kirkland Lake. The largest mines are Lakeshore, Wright-Hargreaves and Kirkland Lake. The Kirkland Lake Area has produced over $500,000,000 in gold. Several mine shafts in the area are over a mile deep with one at Wright-Hargreaves reaching 7,200 feet.

Larder Lake camp is located on the Quebec border east of Kirkland Lake. Claims were first staked in this area in 1906. It has produced gold worth over $100,000,000 since 1918. The chief mines are Kerr-Addison and Chesterville.

The Matachewan area south of Kirkland Lake has produced about $25,000,000. It has one producing mine.

The Long Lac area is about 50 miles north of Lake Superior and 50 miles east of Lake Nipigon. Gold was discovered here in 1931 and production began in 1934. About ten mines are in operation here of which the most important are Little Long Lac, Macleod-Cockshutt and Hardrock. In 15 years this field produced about $70,000,000.

The Red Lake Camp is located in the Patricia district in northwestern Ontario, about 100 miles north of Kenora. Gold was discovered here in 1897, but no production followed at that time. Discoveries in 1925 brought about a boom which was notable from the fact that airplane transport came into general use in this isolated area. Today a highway makes connection with the outside world. The important mines are Madsen, Cochenour Willans, Hasaga and McKenzie Red Lake. The original Howey mine has been abandoned. The Red Lake Camp has produced over $50,000,000.

The Pickle Crow camp is another very isolated spot, 170 miles east of Red Lake and nearly 100 miles north of the Transcontinental railway. Since production commenced in 1934 over $40,000,000 has been won from this field. The two important mines are Pickle Crow and Central Patricia.

Gold mining, which to the end of 1948 has won about $1,700,000,000 from the hard rocks of northern Ontario and paid over $500,000,000 in dividends, has become an important factor in our economic geography. About 15,000 men are employed in the mines. Timmins and Kirkland Lake each have more population than some incorporated cities in Southern Ontario.

## Nickel, Copper and Platinum

The Sudbury area has been for many years the source of most of the world's supply of nickel and, to the end of 1945, over $1,000,000,000 had been produced. Along with it the Sudbury ores have yielded over $500,000,000 in copper and $155,000,000 in platinum as well. The producing area is a syncline or structural rock basin, roughly oval in shape, about 35 miles in length from east to west and 16 miles from north to south. The nickel-copper ore is found in the intrusive basal layer of the syncline which outcrops around the edge of the basin. The producing mines are found on both the north and south flanks of the syncline.

When the Canadian Pacific Railway was built in 1883 copper ore was exposed and was worked for several years before its content of nickel was discovered in 1887. The first smelter was built in 1888 at Copper Cliff. From these small beginnings has grown the great International Nickel Company of Canada with a huge concentrator and smelter at Copper Cliff employing 4,300 persons; a smelter at Coniston, formerly the Mond Nickel Company, 470; the Frood-Stobie mine, 2,000; Creighton mine, 1,570; Garson mine, 760; Levack mine, 600; Murray mine, 340; Frood-Stobie open pit, 380; the Copper Cliff refinery, 680; and the Port Colborne Nickel refinery, 1,330. Beside these, the company and its subsidiaries operate hydro-electric plants at High Falls, Big Eddy, Wabageshik and Nairn Falls, Ontario; refineries at Acton, England and Clydach, Wales; rolling mills at Birmingham, England; Huntington, West Virginia and Glasgow, Scotland; a colliery at Pontardawe, Wales; and a foundry at Bayonne, New Jersey. This company mines an average of 10,000,000 tons of ore per year and sells about 200,000,000 pounds of nickel, 200,000,000 pounds of

D. F. Putnam.

Plate 71.  The head frame of the Levack Mine in the Sudbury District.

copper and considerable quantities of gold, silver and platinum metals.

Falconbridge Nickel Mines Limited operates a nickel-copper mine, concentrator and smelter at Falconbridge, about 12 miles northeast of Sudbury, and a refinery at Kristiansand, Norway. The company employs nearly 1,000 men and handles about 900,000 tons of ore annually.

Since it produces practically all of the nickel, copper, and platinum metals in Ontario, as well as quantities of other metals, the Sudbury district yields nearly two thirds of the total annual mineral production of the province and is the richest mining district in the country. In 8 mines, 3 smelters and 2 refineries, the nickel-copper industry employs from 15,000 to 18,000 persons and pays out $50,000,000 to $60,000,000 in salaries and wages per year. About $40,000,000 in dividends are paid each year (1951) with a total of over $500,000,000 in 50 years.

## Silver and Cobalt

Silver ore was discovered at Cobalt, Ontario, during the building of the railway in 1904 and in a short time a booming mining camp arose. In 1911 it reached its peak production of more than 30,000,000 ounces but dwindled to 10,000,000 ounces by 1926 and by 1939 yielded less than 1,000,000 ounces. During that time the output of silver, cobalt, arsenic and minor quantities of other minerals amounted to nearly $300,000,000. For years Cobalt was a ghost town but has experienced some revival during post war years.

## Iron

Iron is mined by the Algoma Ore Properties Limited at the Helen Mine in the Michipicoten area. Siderite ore outcrops at the top of the highest hill in the vicinity, 1700 feet above sea level. It is worked by a combination of open pit and tunnels. The ore is sintered and shipped by water from Michipicoten to Sault Ste. Marie.

Steep Rock Lake in Rainy River District, 135 miles west of Port Arthur, is the location of an important iron discovery, now operated by Steep Rock Iron Mines Limited. The ore was discovered on the floor of the lake by drilling through the ice in 1937. The lake, 15 miles long and 150 feet deep was pumped out and three ore bodies are now worked as open pits. The ore of high grade, being low in phosphorus and silica, is taken by rail to the Lakehead where it is dumped into large ore carriers for shipment to the smelters.

In 1951, these two mines produced about 2,800,000 tons of iron ore, valued at $20,000,000. They furnished employment for about 1,200 men, supporting the towns of Wawa (2,000) and Atikokan (2,800).

## Hydro-electric Power

Northern Ontario contains some very large hydro-electric power developments which provide power for the operation of great mines, pulp and paper mills and other manufacturing industries of the northern towns and cities. Including those plants which are integral parts of pulp and paper mills, nearly one-third of Ontario's hydro-electric installations are in the north.

Among the earliest installations were those at Sault Ste. Marie, the Lakehead and the mining areas of Sudbury and Cobalt. The first development on the Spanish River for use at Copper Cliff was completed in 1905 and in the same year the town of Sudbury obtained power from the Wanapitei River. Cobalt was supplied with power from the Matabitchuan and Montreal Rivers in 1910 and the Porcupine area began to get power from Sandy Falls on the Mattagami River in 1911.

Since it assumed the operation of the Abitibi Canyon generating station in 1933

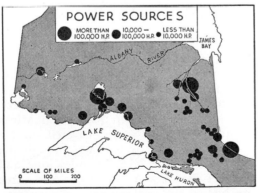

Figure 195. *Hydro-Electric Power Developments.*

the Ontario Hydro-Electric Commission has been the largest producer and distributor of power in Northern Ontario. Most of the development is in northeastern Ontario. Abitibi Canyon with a capacity of 248,000 H.P. is still the largest single development in the north. Its power is supplied to the Cochrane district, Porcupine mining area and to the Sudbury district, a distance of 250 miles. Nearly 25,000 H.P. is developed from the Mattagami River for use in the Porcupine area while the Montreal and Matabitchuan Rivers contribute about 35,000 H.P. In the Sudbury district, three stations on the Wanapitei develop 16,500 H. P. and Crystal Falls, on the Sturgeon River, 10,700 H.P. Power from Crystal Falls is supplied to North Bay to supplement a supply of 5,000 H. P. from the South River. The newest and largest of the Ontario Hydro-Electric Commission stations in the Sudbury region is Tunnel on the Mississagi River with a capacity of 56,500 H.P. Developments on the Spanish and Vermilion Rivers, operating as a subsidiary of International Nickel develop 33,000 H.P. for use in the Sudbury area. The Great Lakes Power Company of Sault Ste. Marie also develops power on the Montreal and Michipicoten Rivers.

In the Thunder Bay region the Alexander, Cameron Falls and Pine Portage stations on the Nipigon River have a capacity of 225,000 H.P. and the Aguasabon development is rated at 53,000 H.P. Tied by long transmission lines these constitute the Thunder Bay System supplying the gold mines of Beardmore and Little Long Lac, the pulp mills of the Nipigon Region, the Lakehead and the Steep Rock iron mining area. Power is also obtained from the Kaministiquia and Rainy Rivers.

Ear Falls on the English River has a capacity of 26,200 H.P. and Rat Rapids on the Albany, 3,300 H.P. These supply the mines of the Patricia region.

The value of electrical power used in 1952 in Northern Ontario was approximately $18,000,000, only a small portion of the production costs in the industries which are served. Lacking coal, the area is indeed fortunate in its wealth of water power, much of which has yet to be harnessed.

## Manufacturing

Manufacturing bulks large in the economic statistics of Northern Ontario where a surprisingly large percentage of Ontario's wealth is located. For the most part the manufactures are closely tied to the raw materials of the region, particularly wood and metals. Thus, in previous sections, we have already mentioned the production of pulp and paper, sawmilling, the refining of copper and other metals. Transportation routes account for the development of other industries such as flour milling at Kenora and the Lakehead. Cheap transportation also influences the iron and steel industry at Sault Ste. Marie, which has operated for periods of years without any Ontario iron ore whatsoever. The other factor which often has a great influence is the supply of power. This has also been pointed out already in connection with the wood-using industries.

The Lakehead cities constitute an area of very diversified manufactures including pulp and paper, sawmilling, flour milling and transportation equipment, including railway rolling stock, trolley cars, buses, planes and ships. Such diversity leads to a high level of income and in recent years Fort William has claimed to rank second among Canadian cities in wage rates, being surpassed only by Sudbury.

The gross value of manufactured goods in 1954 was 735 million dollars, with a net value, after accounting for the cost of fuel, electricity and raw materials, of 385 million dollars. In figure 196 is shown the distribution of net production in the various districts of Northern Ontario.

## Transportation

The transportation network of Northern Ontario is for the most part not closely knit

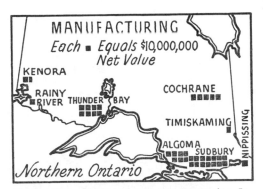

Figure 196. *Distribution of Manufacturing Industries by Districts in Northern Ontario,* 1952. (Data from D. B. S.) Important manufacturers in Northern Ontario include pulp and paper, sawmilling, primary iron and steel and non-ferrous metal smelting and refining.

but it is made up of exceedingly varied components. Canoe routes, steamship routes, railways, highways and airways all have a part in it, and, in order to reach many destinations one finally has to go on foot.

### Water

Lake Superior, Lake Huron and the connecting links, St. Mary's River and the canals at Sault Ste. Marie, give unexcelled water access to a large part of the southern zone. The Lakehead ports and Sault Ste. Marie are well known as points on the busiest waterway in the world. Port Arthur and Fort William, the combined Lakehead port, handle about 7,000,000 tons of shipping per year, to rank among the busiest ports in Canada. The important commodities shipped from the Lakehead are iron and western grain.

Lake transport serves many smaller ports also such as Michipicoten and its iron ore, and Little Current through which coal reaches the mining areas.

### Rail

Northern Ontario has over 4,000 miles of railways including three complete east-west transprovincial lines of the C.N.R. and C.P.R. as well as the Ontario Northland System and the Algoma Central. All the important settlements except the far north-

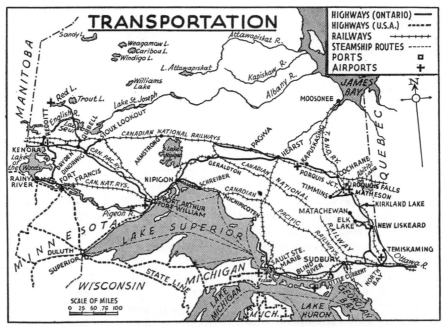

Figure 197. *Chief Transportation Routes in Northern Ontario.*

western mining areas thus have adequate rail service.

## Highway

Throughout most of Northern Ontario railways were built first and roads were feeders extending for short distances from railway stations. Most of them were mere bush trails impassable for much of the year. Slowly the connecting links and main gravelled roads were constructed—from North Bay to Sault Ste. Marie, North Bay to Cochrane and thence to Hearst, and from the Lakehead to various parts of Northwestern Ontario. In 1943 the final connecting link in the Ontario Highway system was built from Hearst to Geraldton. This was also the last link in the Trans-Canada Highway. The final route of the Trans-Canada Highway, however, will follow Highway 17 which is projected along the north shore of Lake Superior and will join Sault Ste. Marie directly to the Lakehead area. Highway construction in Northern Ontario is difficult and costly because

of the rugged terrain and necessity for rock excavation in many places, and the lack of drainage and abundance of muskeg in others. It will therefore be some time before an adequate highway net is completed. Many of the secondary roads are surprisingly good but they do not always run through the populated areas. Quite often one finds a good road flanked by abandoned farms while a few miles away a poor road is well settled.

## Air

Air transport year by year continues to increase in importance. Northern Ontario, by virtue of its innumerable lakes is the natural habitat of the pontoon plane but there are also many airports for wheeled aircraft. The daily transcontinental flights of Trans-Canada Air Lines have since 1947 followed the Great Lakes route from Toronto via Sault Ste. Marie and the Lakehead. A large intermediate airport is located near Gore Bay on Manitoulin Island. Northeastern Ontario which formerly was on the transcontinental route is now provided with a local service from Toronto to North Bay, Porquis and Kapuskasing.

The Ontario Department of Lands and Forests maintains a fleet of patrol aircraft with headquarters at Sault Ste. Marie and a Western Divisional Headquarters at Sioux Lookout. Aircraft are allocated to twenty other stations during the flying season.

There are numerous "bush fliers" available for the use of prospectors, timber cruisers, trappers, sportsmen and others who need to travel to otherwise almost inaccessible parts of the north.

## Communications

For a large and sparsely occupied area the communication services are well developed. Telephone and telegraph lines follow the transportation routes as they do in the southern part of the province. Radio broadcasting stations are located in Sudbury, Timmins, Kirkland Lake, Sault Sainte Marie, Fort William, Port Arthur and Kenora, thus covering the inhabited areas, Public commercial radiotelephone services operate in the Sioux Lookout-Pickle Lake and Kenora-Red Lake areas. The provincial government operates a widespread network of more than 300 radio stations in connection with the forest protection service.

## Economic Summary

Northern Ontario has a total area of 360,000 square miles, of which less than 15,000 square miles are occupied by somewhat more than 600,000 people. The *ecumene* is small, but relatively rich if judged by its population density. Northern Ontario is not an agricultural country, it produces less than 5% of the agricultural wealth of the province. On the other hand it produces most of the mineral and forest wealth, an average of about $500,000,000 per annum in recent years. Secondary industries, however, outrank primary production, despite the fact that many materials such as pulp, lumber, steel and nickel are marketed in a condition of partial manufacture. Located between east and west, Northern Ontario may yet obtain a larger share of the Canadian market for fully manufactured goods.

## Selected References

Brodie, J. A. *Timber Management in Ontario.* Can. Geog. Journal 42, pp. 100-17. 1951.

Canada Department of Mines and Resources. *Geology and Economic Minerals of Canada.* Econ. Geol. Ser. No. 1. (3rd Ed.) Ottawa. 1947.

*Conspectus of the Province of Ontario.* Department of the Provincial Treasurer. Toronto. 1947.

Gosselin, A. and G. P. Boucher. *Settlement Problems in Northwestern Quebec and Northeastern Ontario.* Canada Department of Agriculture, Technical Bulletin 49. Ottawa. 1944.

Hills, G. A. *An Approach to Land Settlement Problems in Northern Ontario.* Scientific Agriculture 23, pp. 212-16. 1942.

*Statistical Review of the Mineral Industry of Ontario.* Annual Report of the Ontario Department of Mines.

Kennedy, Howard, *Report of the Ontario Royal Commission on Forestry.* Toronto. 1947.

*Report to the Ontario Legislature from the Select Committee on Conservation.* Toronto. 1950.

# CHAPTER 15

# Regions and Cities of Northern Ontario

NORTHERN Ontario has considerable variety in its surface features but, for the most part, it offers little encouragement to the spread of human population. Consequently a map of geographical regions exhibits a great deal of neutral or unorganized space. The recognizable regions are small areas upon which man has placed the impress of a cultural landscape. They are not to be considered as static regions, however, for in some cases they are quite capable of enlargement and may even now have developed a considerable sphere of influence in the neutral territory.

In sparsely populated areas, such as Northern Ontario, a site must have great geographical advantages to attract sufficient population to form a city. Such advantages

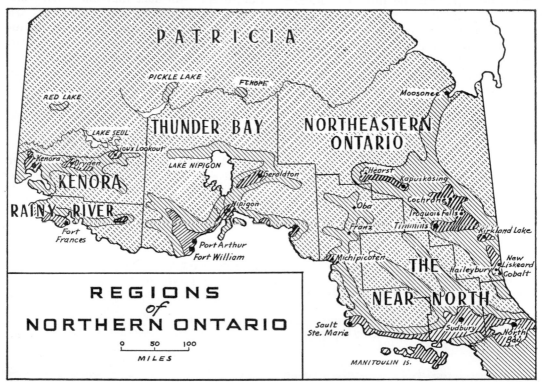

Figure 198. *Regions of Northern Ontario.* With the exception of the huge and empty north, the regions of Northern Ontario are focused upon small populated areas, sometimes containing fair-sized cities. The administrative divisions agree fairly well with the zones of influence of these centres. (Density of shading is approximate to population density.)

318

are to be found at important transportation nodes, such as railway junctions or points of transfer between land and water carriers. Cities may also develop in important mining fields. Forest exploitation may be the mainstay of small towns and may contribute to the development of large cities, but no large cities have arisen solely as a result of lumbering or pulp manufacture.

According to the census of 1956 the populations of the largest urban centres were: Greater Sudbury (96,000), the Lakehead (Fort William-Port Arthur 85,000), Sault Ste. Marie (51,000), Greater Timmins (39,-000) and Greater North Bay (30,000). Kirkland Lake (16,000) is part of the township of Teck. Smaller urban centres include Kenora (10,000), Fort Frances (9,000), Atikokan (6,100), Sturgeon Falls (5,900), Kapuskasing (5,500), New Liskeard (4,600), Dryden (4,500), Elliott Lake (4,000), Blind River (3,700), Cochrane (3,700), Geraldton (3,300), Mattawa (3,200), Haileybury (2,700), Sioux Lookout (2,500), Marathon (2,400), Cobalt (2,400), Hearst (2,200), Wawa (2,000) and Red Lake (2,000).

All of these towns and many smaller ones tie within the confines of the small regions of Northern Ontario. Some of them, especially the larger ones, may be considered as regional nuclei or capitals. In some cases there may be some doubt as to which city is the actual centre of influence in the region, for, as regions and cities mature, certain adjustments take place. There are also some towns and many smaller settlements which lie within the great outer region of Northern Ontario. Such centres may have arisen at railway division points, ports, mines or centres of forest exploitation. Their ties may be less with the nearest regional centre than with the distant cities of Southern Ontario.

## I. The Near North

The "Near North" or southern fringe of Northern Ontario is a strip of lowland stretching for 300 miles from the Ottawa River to Lake Superior. This is probably the most clearly definable region of all, since it can be distinguished from all the rest of the north on the basis of land forms, climate, vegetation, soils and settlement pattern and furthermore it is spatially separated from its nearest neighbour region by a wide stretch of rock and forest.

It is well knit together by a system of communications which includes both a railway and a highway from end to end, with adequate branches to its component parts, as well as corridors binding a large part of the hinterland to it. Its economic importance may be judged from the fact that it contains one third of the total population of Northern Ontario in about 3% of the total area. Even with the politically attached hinterlands it has only 54,000 square miles or 1/6 of the total area. It has a pattern of urban and rural settlement which, although not developed uniformly, is recognizably similar throughout the region. The climate is relatively favourable to agriculture and numerous pockets of arable soils exist and have been developed. In spite of all this it tends to fall apart because it is trinucleate, the settlements being grouped around three large cities. Each of these is the administrative headquarters of a political district and each has a different major economic function and a different regional influence.

## North Bay

*North Bay* (30,000) is known as the "Gateway to the North". Located on the shore of Lake Nipissing, 221 miles north of Toronto and 240 miles west of Ottawa it is an important rail centre, served by the Canadian National and Canadian Pacific as well as the Ontario Northland Railway for which it is the southern terminus. Provincial highways 11 and 17 cross at North Bay.

The Nipissing lowland (Figure 199) has always been a travelled route. Champlain passed that way in 1615 on his journey from Montreal to Lake Huron and it was important in the days of the fur trade. The actual

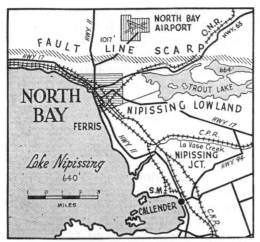

Figure 199. *The Nipissing Lowland.* The concentration of transportation routes through the Nipissing lowland has caused the rise of the city of North Bay almost on the site of the fur trader's portage.

site of North Bay, however, seems not to have been used, the fur traders' forts having been located about four miles south at the mouth of LaVase Creek.

In 1882 the site of North Bay contained a single log shack. The C.P.R., then building from Mattawa to Sudbury, selected the flat shore of Lake Nipissing for railway yards and the city began to grow. In 1886 the area was reached by a railway from Toronto.

The city area of 2,100 acres contains 21,000 people but the adjoining rapidly growing communities of Widdifield and Ferris which contain about 9,000 more. The shore of Lake Nipissing is lined by a closely built development of summer cottages and tourist accommodations. The business section of North Bay is compact, confined chiefly to one street of brick structures. The residential areas which lie around this in a semicircle consist mainly of small frame dwellings, often resting on solid rock foundations. The industrial plants and warehouses tend to cluster along the railways. Some of the industries are fur processing, planing mills, mining equipment, a bronze foundry, a frozen food plant and two pub-

lishing houses. A large new lumber yard is on the northwestern margin of the city. There are two large and several smaller hotels. The North Bay Airport is about four miles outside the city, to the north and above the escarpment which bounds the Nipissing lowland. The dominant functions of the city are wholesale and retail trade and providing service for travellers. Manufacturing is secondary. The city is also an educational centre with a provincial normal school, technical and high school. Here also is the administrative centre of Nipissing District.

North Bay lies in the transition or shatter-belt between the English and French culture areas of Canada, the population of Nipissing District being almost evenly divided. In 1951, of 17,944 inhabitants almost three-fifths claimed British origin, about 27% French, with Italian and German peoples most numerous among the many others.

## The Umland of North Bay

*Sturgeon Falls* (5,000), twenty-five miles west of North Bay, is the second town in size in the Nipissing lowland. It is located about five miles upstream from Lake Nipissing at the head of navigation where the Sturgeon River drops about 40 feet and at the same time narrows so that it is easily bridged by both railway and highway. Sturgeon River House, a fur trading post, was located about two miles from the lake and there were a few settlers before the railway was built. In 1898 a pulp mill was built, making use of power from the falls. Later another large generating station was built at Crystal Falls, a few miles upstream. The river drains a large forested area and is very useful for log driving. The best wood was used up and the mill closed in 1931. It reopened again in 1947 using inferior wood (tamarack, aspen, jack pine and some spruce) for the manufacture of kraft paper. Other manufactures in the town include cooperage, broom handles and abrasives. There are a number of commercial fishermen and caviar is obtained from the local sturgeon.

*Cache Bay* (1,000) about three miles west of Sturgeon Falls has a large saw mill.

While depending chiefly upon forestry and forest products, Sturgeon Falls lies in the centre of a closely settled agricultural area of about 25 square miles and is a headquarters, also, for recreation, hunting and angling.

Most of the inhabitants of this area, both rural and urban, are of French origin.

*Mattawa* (3,200), at the junction of the Mattawa and Ottawa Rivers is an old settlement. Mattawa House was a trading post in 1784 and Mattawa had become an important lumbering centre by 1855. It is the only town for many miles along the river. Stretching for 50 miles to the east is the lake impounded by the Ontario H.E.P.C. dam at Des Joachims, while a few miles upstream another large dam provides additional water storage.

*Callander* (800), on the southeast bay of Lake Nipissing was once an important sawmill town with 2,000 inhabitants. During the 1940's only one mill remained in use.

Between Callander and Mattawa there is rather an extensive agricultural area with about 4,500 rural inhabitants and 120,000 acres occupied as farms. Farming is of a general and part time nature.

## Sudbury

*Sudbury* (47,000), is the sixth city of Ontario, the largest city in Northern Ontario and sometimes dubs itself "the capital of the north". Within fifteen minutes drive from Sudbury post office, the "greater city" has a population of over 96,000. Although it has neither a mine nor a smelter within the city boundary, Sudbury is the population nucleus of the mining field which has produced more than one third of Ontario's mineral wealth and has over 4,000 men engaged in mining.

Sudbury was founded in 1883 as a collection of log shacks on Federal Government land, a mile north of Lake Ramsay. It was a C.P.R. construction camp and the railway controlled the townsite until the camps were moved to Biscotasing in 1885. Overnight the population dropped from 1,500 to 300 leaving only those who were interested in mining and lumbering. In

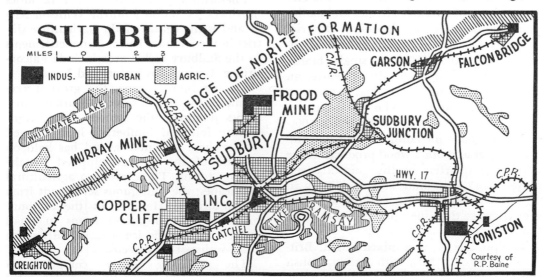

Figure 200. *Sudbury*, Sudbury, itself, contains neither mines nor smelters, but it is the trade centre and largest residential area for the oldest and most important mining district in Northern Ontario. Most of the agriculture lies in the basin to the northwest.

1887, the C.P.R. began to build the Soo line and Sudbury began to grow again. It was incorporated as a town in 1893 with 2,000 inhabitants. Its early growth was steady, reaching 8,000 in 1920 but, since then it has been one of the fastest growing towns in Ontario. It was incorporated as a city in 1930. The census of 1951 reported a population of 42,410, and the city is still growing rapidly.

Modern Sudbury is a well-built city with more than 20 miles of paved streets. It has an extensive business section with many stores, hotels and large office buildings. Sudbury has many fine churches and schools. The Sudbury Mining and Technical School, Sudbury High School and Sacred Heart College are noteworthy educational institutions. St. Joseph's Hospital serves the entire district. The Inco Club is a recreation centre erected at a cost of $250,000. The city hall and the Sudbury District judicial buildings are also near the centre of the city. Bell Park is located on the shore of Lake Ramsay. The finest residential areas are located near the park and again on the heights north of the city centre. Most of Sudbury's homes are smaller than the average for Southern Ontario, but only 35% of the dwellings have wooden exterior and 45% are single family dwellings. Sudbury is a railway centre, an administrative and commercial headquarters and a labour pool. The few industries in the city produce $5,000,000 to $9,000,000 worth of goods including mining machinery, lumber and other wood products. More than three-quarters of the gainfully employed work in mining and metallurgy in the surrounding district, earning a higher average wage than the workers of any other Canadian city.

The population is of mixed origin: British 42%, French 34% with Italian, Polish and Ukrainian as important minor groups. A large proportion of the rural population of the district is French speaking.

## The Sudbury District

*Copper Cliff* (3,800), four miles west of Sudbury, was founded in 1885, when the Canadian Copper Company reopened its mine nearby. The mine has long since been closed but the town is the headquarters of the International Nickel Company and the site of its huge smelter. In earlier years, the sulphur fumes from the roasting ores destroyed the vegetation for miles around. This has been controlled by building three tall stacks the largest of which is 512 feet high with an inside diameter of 45 feet at the top. Nearby is a large refinery to treat the copper produced here, but the nickel is sent to Port Colborne for refining. The town is completely controlled by International Nickel and its citizens are nearly all company employees.

*Coniston* (2,500), is about 8 miles east of Sudbury. It is a railway junction and the site of another smelter formerly operated by the Mond Nickel Company.

*Capreol* (2,400), about 20 miles north of Sudbury is a railway junction and division headquarters on the Canadian National Railway.

*Chelmsford* (2,200), is located 12 miles northwest of Sudbury on the Whitson River and is the centre of the agriculture district in the Sudbury basin. Mine settlements in the Sudbury nickel area include Falconbridge, Garson, Creighton and Levack.

Mining is, of course, the greatest economic factor and mining and urban landscapes dominate the Sudbury area. Agriculture followed lumbering here, as well as elsewhere in Ontario, and has held on because of the market supplied by the mining towns. There are two agricultural landscapes; the contiguous settlement from Chelmsford to Hanmer in the Sudbury basin and the dispersed farms in small pockets among the ice scoured hills south and southwest of the city.

The *Sudbury Basin* comprises a boatshaped area about 23 miles long and 8 miles in width at its widest. It is floored by clay, silt and sand deposited in an ancient glacial lake. Parts of this plain are too sandy or gravelly for good farming, there are some outcrops of rock, and the lowest part occupied by the meandering Vermilion River is too wet. However, about 500 farms, with an agricultural population of 2,500, are to be found here. The farmers are mostly French speaking people. In spite of the square system of the Ontario Land Survey, the farms are narrow strips and the rural homes are concentrated along the main gravel roads with six to twelve houses per mile. Fields are small and the crops are chiefly hay and oats with potatoes becoming an important crop specialty. Pasture is important, both in the improved area and the rough clearings. Although there are about 4,500 dairy cows in this basin, milk production is insufficient to supply the demand in Sudbury. Even so, in the more isolated districts, some cheese is produced.

In the dispersed settlements south of Sudbury there are large numbers of Finnish settlers. The farms are larger and there are some good dairy herds. Much of the land, however, is fit only for poor subsistence or part-time agriculture.

## Sault Ste. Marie

Situated on the St. Mary's River which connects Lake Superior and Lake Huron, *Sault Ste. Marie* (51,000) is a growing city and an industrial "island" at the centre of the world's busiest water-way. Serving two great nations, the locks of the "Soo" canals accommodate more waterborne freight each year than the combined tonnage of the Suez and Panama canals. The "Soo" is also the only possible gateway for land traffic in 600 miles of water-located international boundary. It is a "twin city", not an uncommon occurrence on the international boundary, but unique in the fact that the Canadian city is much larger than its American counterpart.

Sault Ste. Marie was known to the French explorers from the time of Etiènne Brûlé who visited it in 1611. He found an Indian settlement located on the south bank which subsisted mainly on whitefish caught at the Falls. From 1630 on, it was a centre of the fur trade and a mission station. In 1797, the North West Fur Traders built a post on the north shore and two villages came into being. They also built the first lock around the rapids. In the 1840's two

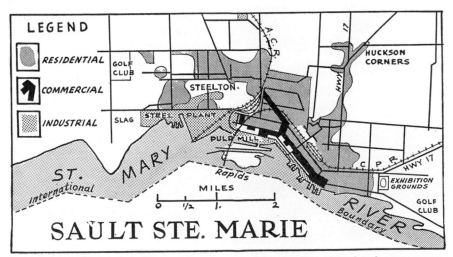

Figure 201. *Sault Ste. Marie.* At this gateway and intersection of land and water routes, twin towns have arisen. A rather unusual case along the international boundary, here the Canadian city is larger than its American counterpart.

commercial towns came into being, based on the exploitation of the Lake Superior timber and mining resources. In 1859, the district of Algoma was organized and Sault Ste. Marie became its judicial centre. In 1887 the first C.P.R. train arrived and, in the same year, the town was incorporated. In 1891 it had 2,400 people, only half as many as its Michigan neighbour. It was then an important saw milling centre. Canalization and control of the river flow made possible the development of a large supply of electric power and a paper mill was established. In recognition of the geographical advantages of the area a steel mill was erected in 1901 and the population jumped to 7,000. In 1911 it was 10,000 and a separate suburb of Steelton had grown to more than 4,000. Later they were amalgamated to form a single city. During both World Wars the "Soo" has been a very important Canadian steel producing centre.

In keeping with its riverine location the city is rather elongated, stretching for nearly five miles beside the river. The incorporated area is 4,900 acres but it is not all built up. The steel mills and the pulp and paper mill have water-side locations

The Photographic Survey Corporation Limited.
Plate 72. The Algoma Steel Plant at Sault Ste. Marie, Ontario. Its annual capacity is over 1,000,000 tons.

above the falls. The business section is down stream from the falls and contained between the railway and the riverside along which the docks are located. Parks, golf courses and other recreational lands are, for the most part, located at the eastern end of the city.

Although the "Soo" is a district town, a market centre of some importance and an international gateway, it is pre-eminently a seat of heavy industry. Fifty-five per cent of the gainfully employed are engaged in manufacturing, four-fifths of whom are in iron and steel. Pulp and paper, lumber, chemicals and many small industries employ the remainder. In 1950, the gross value was $110,000,000, with a net value of $43,-000,000. Here also are found the headquarters and shops of the Algoma Central Railway and the home base of the Ontario Provincial air service which patrols the vast forest area of Northern Ontario.

Tributary to the city is a small dairy farming area on the Algonquin Lake plain. Behind it at a distance of about four miles from the river rises a steep fault line scarp which marks the edge of the forested upland of the Canadian Shield. The summit elevations are more than 1300 feet above sea level and 700 feet above the surface of Lake Superior. Garden River Indian Reserve lies about five miles east of the city. River location and nearness to the wilderness make the "Soo" a notable tourist headquarters.

## The North Shore of Lake Huron

Between Sudbury and the "Soo" a narrow belt of settlement extends along the north shore of Lake Huron. *Desbarats, Bruce Mines, Thessalon* and *Blind River* (3,700) are small towns or villages in this area. Founded as headquarters for forest exploitation they now have much smaller populations than formerly.

Nearer Sudbury, there are several settlements along the Spanish River. Espanola (2,000) is the site of a large pulp and paper mill on the river. It is also the gateway to

Manitoulin Island by both railway and highway. Farther downstream, *Webbwood* and *Massey* are villages which were formerly important lumbering centres. Upstream at *Turbine* there is a large hydroelectric installation.

The tourist industry becomes more important each year throughout the whole region. Cottage colonies and fishing lodges are found along the shores of Lake Nipissing, French River and the north shore of Lake Huron. Smaller inland lakes are being developed also. The activity carries over into the fall because the fringes of this partially settled area constitute one of the best deer hunting grounds in North America.

The Near North is a region of transition. It is the beginning of the north with its emphasis on forests, mining, small part time bush farms and tourist resorts. At the same time its large cities are an important outpost of the south. In spite of their great size the three districts in which this region lies are approximately 60% urban. Even the rural population is strongly nucleated into hamlets at cross roads points and railway stations.

## II. The North Huron Islands

Lying in the northern part of Lake Huron are several large islands and a number of smaller ones. Three of the large islands, Manitoulin, Cockburn and St. Joseph belong to Ontario. Drummond, Neebish and Sugar belong to Michigan, U.S.A.

Climatically these islands resemble the Near North, but tend to have lesser extremes of temperature and a lower rainfall. The vegetation is much like that of the northern part of peninsular Ontario and the soils normally have Brown Podzolic profiles.

Physiographically the islands are part of the Niagara Cuesta, the rim of the great dolomite saucer that underlies the Michigan Basin. If it were not for a few low places this rim would form a long land arc from the Bruce Peninsula to Northern Michigan and divide Lake Huron in two.

### Manitoulin

Manitoulin, (Figure 202), the largest of these islands has an area of 1,073 square miles—it is said to be the largest "freshwater" island on earth. It is dotted with

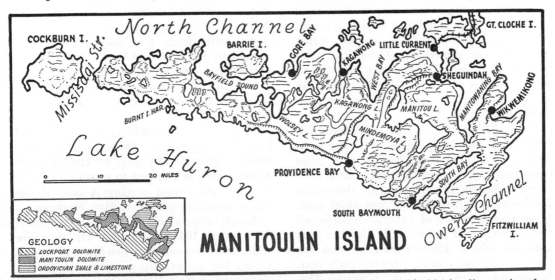

Figure 202. *Manitoulin Island.* The largest "freshwater" island in the world, Manitoulin carries the Niagara Escarpment and several lower escarpments which, closely ranked, face the quartzites of the Canadian Shield across the North Channel.

more than 100 inland lakes, the three largest of which are Kagawong, Mindemoya and Manitou.

Manitoulin is underlain by limestones and shales which dip southward under Lake Huron. The structure of the island may be compared to a giant stairway with three broad insloping treads separated by two north facing escarpments as risers. The upper member, Lockport dolomite, covers the southern two-thirds of the island and toward the north forms several plateaux about 500 feet above Lake Huron. Most of the northern part of the island is underlain by Manitoulin dolomite which also is bordered on the north by a steep escarpment at the foot of which is a narrow lowland plain underlain by older limestones. A large part of the surface on all three levels consists of scoured rock plains, unbelievably flat, covered with only a few inches of soil. In some places there is deeper drift, consisting of till plains, drumlins, moraines and lake-laid sands, silts and clays.

The population of the island is somewhat over 11,000, of whom 2,000 are Indians. The eastern end of the island, about one fifth of the total area, is known as "Manitoulin unceded" as it was retained by the Indian inhabitants in 1862, when a treaty was signed providing for white settlement of other parts of the island. The population is almost completely rural, the two incorporated towns having less than 2,000 inhabitants.

*Gore Bay* (750), is the administrative centre and the shopping place for the western end of the island. Nearby is a large Canadian Government airport. *Little Current* (1,500), is the gateway to the mainland, only railway contact and chief port. It is a rendezvous of yachtsmen from all the upper Great Lakes. It is also the port through which 450,000 tons of coal for the mining districts is imported each year. White quartzite, quarried at nearby Sheguindah, is exported.

956 farms occupy 290,000 acres, or 40%

of Manitoulin, with 53,000 acres in crop and 110,000 acres devoted to pasture. The emphasis on grazing is confirmed by the livestock figures—20,000 cattle and 14,000 sheep. There are two main patterns of agriculture. On the deeper soils a mixed crop and livestock economy prevails, while the shallow and stony soils are given over to grazing.

Many farmers own 100 acres in the areas of better soil on which they grow crops and keep small herds of breeding stock. In addition, they have several hundred acres of "range" on which they pasture their growing animals during the summer. Hereford cattle dominate because of their adaptability to range conditions. The island cattle are in good demand among the farmers of Southern Ontario who finish them for market. Dairying is of minor importance but there are a few good dairy herds which supply the towns and the two creameries. There are several large fur farms, one of which is the largest in Ontario. The raising of turkeys has become very important in recent years.

Agriculture is the most important economic activity on the island. More than 40% of the people reside on farms. It is, however, a marginal and extensive type of agriculture with few specialties, conditioned by isolation and lack of good arable land. The area of occupied land remains about the same, but over the years farm population and number of farms continue to decrease.

Much of Manitoulin remains in forest but all the good saw-timber has been removed. Spruce and poplar are cut for pulpwood which is shipped to outside mills by steamer. Pulpwood cutting is one of the main activities of the Indian workers.

Manitoulin, at one time, had important fisheries. In 1931, the total catch was more than 3,000,000 pounds, two-fifths of it lake trout, but in recent years it has greatly decreased. South Bay in the eastern part of the island is being used as an experimental area by the Ontario government in the hope of finding out how to revive the industry.

The island is becoming increasingly popular as a summer resort. Lodges and cottage camps are widespread but they are especially attracted to the shores of the inland lakes. On the south shore the villages of Providence Bay and South Baymouth attract some visitors but otherwise the 80 mile coast line is almost uninhabited even in summer. Although some come from Southern Ontario, the summer guests of Manitoulin are mostly Americans, with a noticeably large representation from the cities of Ohio.

In addition to the northern road and railway entrance at Little Current, the island may be reached from the south. A large steam ferry makes several trips daily between South Baymouth and Tobermory on the Bruce Peninsula. Regular steamship service is also maintained from Owen Sound to Little Current and Manitowaning.

Cockburn Island, although having deeper soils than much of Manitoulin is largely forested and there is very little farm land. There is one small village of about 50 people.

St. Joseph Island also has considerable deep drift and a large part of the island is occupied as farm land. It has a population of 840 about two-thirds of whom live on farms. Its agriculture is similar to that of Manitoulin except that a small acreage is devoted to the growing of fruits and vegetables for sale in Sault Ste. Marie. The island also has a number of summer resorts.

## III. Northeastern Ontario

Northeastern Ontario (Figure 203) is a large and composite region contained entirely within the administrative districts of Timiskaming and Cochrane. Like the Near North it is an extremely tenuous region, for the most part adhering very close to its communication lines, the Ontario Northland and C.N. Railways and Highway Number 11, which extend for nearly 300 miles from Cobalt to Hearst. Here and there, however, small areas of settlement occur as in the Timiskaming or Little

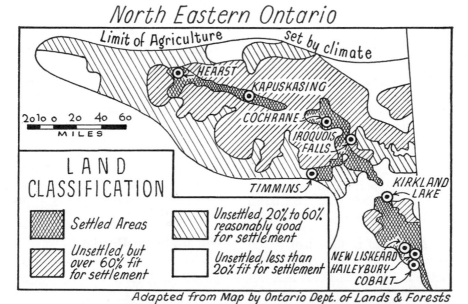

Figure 203. *Northeastern Ontario.* A narrow ribbon of farmland, groups of mining settlements and isolated pulp mill towns make up the settled area of Northeastern Ontario. All the rest is unbroken forest.

Clay Belt, Kirkland Lake Mining Camp, Matheson District, Porcupine Mining Camp and the Cochrane, Kapuskasing and Hearst settlements along the Transcontinental Railway in the Great Clay Belt. North of this there stretches to the shore of James Bay a wilderness across which the northern branch of the Ontario Northland finds its way to Moosonee.

The districts of Timiskaming and Cochrane cover about 58,000 square miles, but the combined area of the townships containing settlements is little more than 3,600 square miles. The population in 1956 was about 137,000, an average density of 36 per square mile. Such a figure has little meaning, however, since there are city-sized agglomerations of people in the mining areas and very sparse populations in the agricultural settlements.

## Timiskaming

Because it was believed that Northeastern Ontario offered land for colonization the Ontario government in 1903 began to build the Timiskaming and Northern Ontario Railway. During its construction the silver ores of Cobalt were discovered and a great mining camp sprang up. Settlers also spread into the clay lands at the head of Lake Timiskaming, where about 20 townships, or 720 square miles, soon became pretty solidly taken up. It still remains the best of the agricultural areas of Northern Ontario, and, in 1951, had about 1,600 farms containing over 296,000 acres of which 125,000 or 42% was classed as improved land. Hay, oats, barley, mixed grains, wheat and potatoes constitute the chief crops. Of the 8,000 people on farms in the district about one-third are French speaking.

*Cobalt* (2,300), said to have had 10,000 people in its boom days as a silver camp is now a ghost of its former self with a few mines producing small quantities of ore.

*Haileybury* (2,700), was founded in 1883 but had few settlers before the Cobalt strike in 1903, when it was made the location of the mining recorder's office. In 1912 it was chosen as the judicial centre for the new district of Timiskaming.

*New Liskeard* (4,600), located on Wabi Bay at the head of Lake Timiskaming was founded in 1895. It is a well built town which functions as the market and supply point for much of the nearby area. It has a woodworking plant, dairy product plant and canning factory.

## Kirkland Lake

The town of *Kirkland Lake* is the largest of the settlements located in the important gold mining area which extends for thirty miles across the northern part of Timiskaming District from Swastika to the Quebec boundary. Swastika and Larder Lake, toward the east, were both staked by prospectors in 1906, but it was not until 1911 that Bill Wright made the great discovery at Kirkland Lake. Since then twelve mines have developed along the "Golden Mile" with an annual production of $15,000,000.

Although containing a population of 16,000 (1956) Kirkland Lake has never been incorporated and remains part of the municipality of Teck township. It is an extremely haphazard urban agglomeration in which mines, business district and residential areas are closely intermixed. The physical difficulties of the site are great for sewers and water pipes must often be laid in solid rock. Rail transportation is provided by the Nipissing Central Railway which connects with the Ontario Northland at Swastika. Larder Lake (1,500) is located 18 miles east of Kirkland Lake. Its mines are not as productive as formerly.

## The Matheson District

The southernmost settlement of the Great Clay Belt is an area about two townships (12 miles) in width along the Ontario Northland Railway for 40 miles from Ramore to Potter, with lateral extensions toward the southern extension to-

*Courtesy Canadian National Railways.*

Plate 73. Two views of the Mines at Kirkland Lake.

ward Iroquois Falls in one direction and the Porcupine gold field in the other. A large part of this area is drained by the Black River and its tributaries. This area has a fair proportion of reasonably good silt and clay soils and is favourably situated with respect to markets in the mining fields. It contains about 600 farms with an occupied area of 95,000 acres of which about 35,000 are classed as improved land. A number of dairy farms are being developed and potatoes are a crop specialty, especially on lighter soils.

*Matheson* (800), is a centrally located village which serves as the business centre for most of the area. Here also are located the district offices of the Ontario Departments of Agriculture and Lands and Forests. An asbestos mine nearby began operation in 1950.

During World War II a large prisoner of war camp was located at Montieth.

Porquis is a junction on the O.N.R. with branches leading to Timmins and Iroquois Falls. A large airport is nearby.

*Iroquois Falls* (1,500), on the Abitibi River, is the site of a large pulp and paper mill. It is a well planned town controlled by the paper company. Alongside stands Ansonville, an unincorporated village of crowded nondescript frame buildings contrasting strongly with the planned town and containing a larger population.

Considerable land fit for settlement lies between Matheson and the Porcupine gold field but it has all been staked as mining claims.

## The Porcupine Mining Camp

The Porcupine gold field is the richest in Canada and as a mining camp is second only to Sudbury. Its mines are located mainly in the southern part of Tisdale township, but important mines are found in adjoining townships as well. (Figure

204). The whole landscape may easily be seen from the Lands and Forests lookout on the "back road". A dozen or so huge shaftheads are the most conspicuous landmarks. Nearby are water tanks and the lower structures of the stamping mills. Between the mines lies a sea of green shrubbery for the urban settlements are not closely associated with the mines, as in Kirkland Lake, but give the impression of having been more definitely designed as business and residential areas. The central mining area itself contains few farms but, to the west in Mountjoy township and to the east in Whitney, considerable areas of cleared land may be seen.

*Timmins* (27,700), was founded in 1911 by Noah Timmins in order to house the employees of Hollinger mines. However it is not a company town. Work was begun in September and its incorporation as a town dates from January 1, 1912. Laid out in grid fashion on sandy terraces overlooking the Mattagami River, it had from the first its regularly designated business centre along Third Avenue and its first class residential section on the "Hill" which was the highest terrace. Unfortunately some of the later expansion of Timmins has been northward down the hill

onto wet flats of clay and peat, rather than south onto the sand plains.

Timmins is larger than many cities but takes pride in being "the largest town in Canada". It has many substantial brick business buildings and its workmen's homes though smaller than many in the south appear well designed for comfort in the long cold winters. There are numerous well built schools and churches. Eastward between the town and the mine is a large green space. Once a small lake, it was filled with mine "tailings", over which soil was placed to make a municipal playground and park. Other huge piles of tailings are to be found to the south of the town. To the west, on the banks of the Mattagami River, are large mills which make lumber from the logs brought down the river. About one-fifth of the people of Timmins are of foreign extraction, mainly Europeans. The remainder are about equally divided between French and English speaking Canadians. Hydroelectric plants at Wawaitin Falls and Sandy Falls furnish energy for the town and the mines. Power lines also bring electricity from the Abitibi River.

Tisdale township (8,400) has two chief settlements, *Schumacher* and *South Porcupine*. Neither of these are incorporated

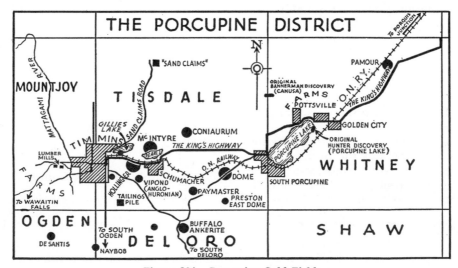

Figure 204. Purcupine Gold Field.

*National Film Board.*

Plate 74.   The Golf Course at Timmins, Ontario, with the Hollinger Mine in the Background.

though each appears as a full-fledged town of several thousand people.

Schumacher, the town of the McIntyre mines, has a population of 4,000. Although only about two miles from Timmins it is built on very rocky land. South Porcupine (4,000) on the shore of Porcupine Lake is the "capital" of the township. It has a modern appearing business section, good schools and many blocks of neat small homes. The lake which is about two miles long and half a mile in width is the local air base for Provincial Government planes and those of commercial airlines. In winter the planes are equipped with skis to operate from the ice.

The people of Tisdale township are about 50% of British origin, less than 10% are French and the remainder include many Finns, Italians, Croats, Poles and Ukrainians.

The Porcupine district contains about 155 farms with about 9,400 acres of improved land. Nearly all of this is found in Mountjoy township where the Mattagami valley contains fine loamy soils. Dairy products, poultry products, potatoes and other vegetables are sold in nearby markets. Some very good farms are to be seen.

### Cochrane District

The Cochrane community comprises the town of Cochrane and the agricultural set-tlement in ten surrounding townships. In 1951 the total population was 6,400, of whom more than 3,400 resided in the town.

*Cochrane* (3,700) was founded at the terminus of the T. and N. O. Railway in 1908. By 1911 it had 1,700 people. When the transcontinental line was built it became an important junction and division point. In 1922 it became the judicial and administrative centre for a district of 52,000 square miles. By 1931 it had nearly 4,000 inhabitants. The decrease since then is in large part due to decrease in railway employment. The town is the headquarters for a number of lumber and pulpwood operators and a market for surrounding farmers. A creamery, cold storage and egg grading station and a potato storage are found here. There are two parks, one of which surrounds a small kettle lake.

The agricultural area embraces about 600 farms and 100,000 acres of which about 25% may be classed as improved land. The area immediately north of the town contains a number of fine dairy farms. There are one or two small cheese factories. The crops are mainly hay and oats, but potatoes are successful on the lighter and better drained soils. The Cochrane areas is undoubtedly one of the best in northeastern Ontario, yet one sees many abandoned farms.

*Smooth Rock Falls* (1,100) is an important pulp mill town on the Mattagami River about halfway between Cochrane and Kapuskasing. The adjoining townships have little agricultural settlement.

From Cochrane the Ontario Northland Railway extends northward 187 miles along the Abitibi and Moose Rivers to Moosonee which lies on the estuary about 12 miles from the open water of James Bay. Thus a great portion of Northern Ontario is tributary to Cochrane. Along the railway are a number of pulpwood and sawmill operations as well as the important hydro-electric developments at Island Falls and Abitibi Canyon. The lignite mines at Onikawana are now abandoned and the pits are filled with water.

Abitibi Canyon is an interesting place which may be regarded as typical of the outlying power plant settlements of Northern Ontario. The site itself is noteworthy, being located at the point where the Abitibi River makes its swift descent to the James Bay lowlands. A head of 297 feet is obtained making available about 250,000 H.P. Here surrounded by the wilderness is a community of 40 homes, a church, school, store, dispensary and recreation centre. The buildings are all heated by electricity. In summer the situation is not unpleasant but in winter the isolation is complete. The undisturbed quiet of the present is in extreme contrast to the bustle of construction days when 2,000 men found employment. Energy from the Abitibi station is transmitted by great power lines to pulp mills and mines far to the south.

*D. F. Putnam.*

Plate 75. Hudson's Bay Company Post at Moose Factory, Ontario.

*Moose Factory* and *Moosonee* are interesting and contrasting outposts. Their combined populations numbered 523 in 1951. Moose Factory is located on an island in the estuary of Moose River and was the second post of the Hudson's Bay Company being founded in 1671. It was captured in 1686 by a French war party from Montreal but was later reoccupied. The old "Factory" is a huge wooden structure, the ground floor of which is occupied by trading space whilst upstairs in the old storage lofts is a small museum containing many interesting relics of the fur trade. The village contains mission schools, Anglican and Catholic churches, the R.C.M.P. headquarters and a doctor's office. Stretched out along the river bank is a row of whitewashed Indian houses each with a small vegetable garden.

Moosonee, founded in 1932, is located about four miles away on the western bank of the estuary. It is entirely new and modern with a small tourist hotel and a new Hudson Bay store, railway station and dock. The port, however, is so shallow that it can be used for small craft only.

### Kapuskasing

The founding of the town of *Kapuskasing* may be said to date from 1914 when this way station was selected as the site of an internment camp during World War I. Later an experimental farm was established and a number of soldier settlers located near the town. During the 1920's a huge pulp and paper mill was erected and a new company town of neat painted houses replaced the tar paper shacks of construction days. By 1931 the town contained 3,800 people. In 1941 it had dropped to 3,431, but 1,000 more lived in the suburbs. In 1956, Kapuskasing contained 5,500 people. The mill which has a capacity of about 500 tons per day produces sulphite pulp and a fine grade of sized paper. It employs about 900 men. A small amount of power is obtained at the site but the most of it comes from Smoky Falls, about 50 miles down the river. A railway, built to facilitate the construction of the power plant, now serves to haul pulpwood. The mill owns rights to 5,000 square miles of forest, north and south of the transcontinental railway. Hundreds of men find work in the pulpwood camps. Kapuskasing has a large airport from which T.C.A. maintain direct daily service to Toronto. Pontoon planes for local flights are based at Remi Lake near Moonbeam.

Although not a regional capital like Cochrane, Kapuskasing may be regarded as a nucleus of the Clay Belt settlement extending for about 50 miles along the railway. Rural population in eight townships totalled more than 6,300 in 1951. Only 38% of these lived on farms, however. The 500 farms contained 60,000 acres of land, of which about 34% was improved. The crops are mostly hay and oats but potatoes are important on lighter soils near Moonbeam.

## Hearst

The most westerly settlement in the Great Clay Belt is found in the townships near Hearst. In 1951, this area contained over 6,000 people including those in the town. A farm population of more than 2,300 were living on 440 farms comprising 67,700 acres, of which 19,250 (28.5%) were classed as improved land.

*Hearst* (2,200) is a railway divisional point and the terminus of the Algoma Central Railway which connects with Sault Ste. Marie. It was also the terminus of the Provincial Highway until 1943, when the section to Geraldton was opened. In consequence, there are a considerable number of hotels and restaurants. Many woods workers make it their home during off-seasons.

## Results of Settlement

The Great Clay Belt of Northern Ontario has been regarded as a field for agricultural colonization for over 40 years yet the results to date are not impressive. In 1951, 2,200 farmers operated 125,000 acres of improved land while over 1,000,000 acres had been manhandled, the pulpwood re-

moved and the land abandoned. The greatest contribution to economic welfare in the area, apart from the mines on its southern border, comes from the three great pulp and paper mills. Ontario does not yet have sufficient population pressure to force even the best land of this area into agricultural production or even to ensure an economic return on the land which had been cleared. Compared with Southern Ontario, even the best land of the Clay Belt is of mediocre quality, despite the success of the occasional outstanding farmer. On the other hand the demand for wood seems to be constantly increasing and the best lands for agriculture are also the best for tree growth. Forest-crop management should be the keynote of land management, with enough subsidiary agriculture to supply home markets with the foods which may be easily produced.

The geographic realities of the Clay Belt indicate that a multiple use husbandry should be adopted in which wood and food shall both be seen in true perspective as products of the soil. From such a basic assumption a geographic pattern and a programme of settlement might be worked out.

## IV. Thunder Bay

Thunder Bay, with an area of 52,471 square miles is larger than the three Maritime Provinces or the whole of Southern Ontario. Its population in 1956 was 123,000 giving a density of two per square mile. Two-thirds of this population is urban however, and concentrated in the twin cities of the "Lakehead", Fort William and Port Arthur (Figure 205), and most of the remainder is found in a few settled townships, the area of which is less than 600 square miles.

Like Sault Ste. Marie, the Lakehead may be considered as an industrial island far removed from its chief market in Southern Ontario but tied to it by the nation's chief transportation routes. During World War II its expanded facilities produced ships and planes in great numbers. In peace time it supplies street-cars and buses for the whole country.

Figure 205. *The Lakehead Cities.* The largest urban area in Northern Ontario, the twin cities of Port Arthur and Fort William constitute the largest lake port in Ontario and one of the more important ports in Canada.

## Fort William

*Fort William* (40,000) is the second city of Northern Ontario and ranks eleventh in the province. Located in the shadow of Mount McKay at the mouth of the Kaministiquia River, it has undoubtedly been the site of Indian encampments for many centuries, and for more than 250 years has been known to white voyageurs. French explorers built the first fort there in 1678. New Fort was built here in 1803 by the North-West Company and renamed Fort William in 1804 after William McGillivray, Governor of the company. Under the Hudson's Bay Company, from 1821 to 1881, it was one of their most important fur trading posts. Since that time it has become an important lake port. The city extends along the dredged out estuary for about five miles. The Kaministiquia enters Thunder Bay through a broad delta by three channels, each of which is lined with docks. The port has 22 miles of protected frontage, 13 miles of which is dredged to 25 feet; 1,000 ships, totalling 2¾ million tons use the port each year. The waterfront area is lined with industries including car works, oil refineries and storage, pulp and paper mills, grain elevators, flour mills. In 1954, the total value of manufactured goods reached $54,-000,000, with a net value of $30,000,000.

## Port Arthur

*Port Arthur* (38,000) is located on the shore of Thunder Bay, immediately north of Fort William. Its harbour is protected

*Courtesy Canadian National Railways.*

Plate 76. Huge terminal elevators at the Lakehead handle the wheat crop of the Canadian Prairies. Pool Terminal 7 is reputed to be the largest grain elevator in the world.

by nearly five miles of breakwater behind which lie several miles of berthing space; 1,300 ships totalling 4¼ million tons enter Port Arthur each year. Along the waterfront are fifteen large elevators, two pulp and paper mills and the largest Canadian dry dock on the Great Lakes. The gross value of manufactured goods was $42,000,-000 in 1954, with a net value of $21,000,000.

### Agricultural Settlement

Most of the agricultural land in Thunder Bay district is within a few miles of the Lakehead cities but there is a small pocket around Nipigon, about 60 miles to the northeast, and another at Upsala about 70 miles northwest. Possibly there are 400,000 acres of clay and loam soils suitable for agriculture. In 1951, over 278,000 acres were occupied and over 75,000 acres reported as improved land on 1,800 farms. Hay, oats, potatoes, barley and wheat are the chief crops. Dairying is important in the townships immediately adjoining the cities. The farm population numbers 8,800 or 7% of the total population of Thunder Bay.

### The Mining Area

The mining field between Long Lac and Lake Nipigon contains the second largest group of people in Thunder Bay district. The census of 1951 reported over 6,000 inhabitants, of whom 3,200 were in the town of *Geraldton*. *Beardmore* at the western end of this mining district has a population of over 1,000.

### Nipigon

Lake Nipigon has an area of 1,870 square miles and is the largest lake in Ontario, exclusive of the Great Lakes. Its elevation of 852 feet places it 250 feet above Lake Superior into which it drains by the Nipigon River. This short river is the source of power for the whole Lakehead district and for the Beardmore-Geraldton mining areas. In order to increase the water supply the Ontario Hydro-Electric Commission divert-

ed the Ogoki River from the Hudson Bay drainage.

The Nipigon watershed is an important forest area and the wood is utilized by the mills at *Nipigon* (2,300), and *Red Rock* (1,600), near the mouth of the rivers.

The Nipigon region has long been known for its hunting and fishing resources.

*Marathon.* Located on Peninsula Harbour, 184 miles east of Port Arthur, is the new pulp mill town of Marathon. Construction of a sulphite pulp mill of 300 tons daily capacity was begun in 1944. In order to house the workers a new town was built which in 1956 had a population of 2,400. Wood for the mill comes from 2,500 square miles of lease hold and is driven down the Pic River to Lake Superior and towed to Peninsula Harbour.

*Terrace Bay* (1,500). Another pulp mill town, constructed in the post-war period, is located on the north shore of Lake Superior about 70 miles east of Nipigon. The mill will produce 300 tons of sulphite pulp daily and maintain a town of several hundred population. In order to supply power to this mill the Ontario Hydro-Electric Power Commission has undertaken the development of 53,500 H.P. from the nearby Aguasabon River. Near its mouth the river falls nearly 300 feet and by means of a tunnel diversion the water is conveyed to a power house at Terrace Bay. In order to increase the water supply, Long Lake and the headwaters of the Kenagami River have been diverted into the Aguasabon River.

## V. Rainy River

The administrative district of Rainy River has an area of 7,276 square miles and in 1956 contained a population of 25,500. About three-fifth of the population lives in towns and about one-fifth on farms. There are a number of small rural villages. There are only two towns. *Fort Frances* (8,000) is the administrative centre. It has a pulp and paper mill and numerous retail stores. *Rainy River* (1,350) is a railway di-

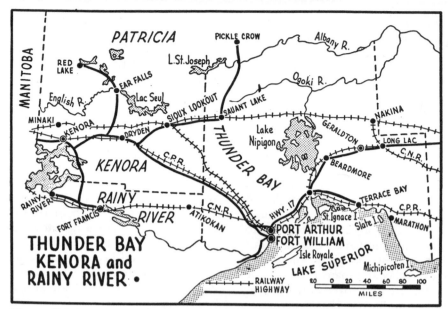

Figure 206. *Northwestern Ontario.* Northwestern Ontario, including Thunder Bay, Rainy River, Kenora and Patricia, has a large area, but a relatively small occupied zone. The largest part of the population is found in the twin cities of the Lakehead, Port Arthur and Fort William.

visional point and is located in an agricultural area.

Agriculture in Rainy River is encouraged by the presence of clay soils developed on the deposits of glacial Lake Agassiz. There are about 400,000 acres of soils suitable for agriculture. The climate is also favourable being much more like that of the prairies than the rest of Northern Ontario. Over 312,000 acres are occupied by about 1,400 farms. Hay, oats, barley, flax and wheat are the chief crops.

Steep Rock Lake Iron Mine is located in Rainy River District. By draining the lake a rich deposit of iron ore was made available. About 3,000,000 tons per annum are being raised from open pit and underground mines. *Atikokan* (6,000) has grown rapidly in recent years to accommodate the hundreds who now find employment in the area.

## VI. Kenora

The district of Kenora, including Patricia, is by far the largest and least densely populated administrative unit in Ontario, containing 153,000 square miles and 47,000 people (1956). The original district of Kenora had an area of 18,000 square miles and in 1956 its population was about 36,000. These people live in the region from Sioux Lookout to the Manitoba border and this area of less than 2,500 square miles may perhaps be considered as a unit in the human geography of Ontario, although it is certainly not densely populated. Four towns contain an urban population of 20,000; 3,800 people live on 550 farms, and the remainder in scattered rural hamlets. The area of occupied farm land is 117,000 acres, with 28,000 acres listed as improved.

*Kenora* (10,300) is the administrative and business centre and tourist headquarters as well as an important railway division point. *Keewatin* (2,000) is the site of a large flour mill. *Dryden* (4,400) situated in an extensive clay plain is the most important agricultural centre and also has a pulp mill. *Sioux Lookout* (2,500) is the headquarters through which the Patricia mining areas get much of their supplies.

## VII. Patricia

The district of Patricia, added to Ontario in 1912 is estimated to have an area of 135,070 square miles. Its total population in 1956 was less than 12,000 and apart from the mining camps it has no population nuclei. To the geographic region, however, one must add nearly all of Northern Ontario beyond easy reach of the railway lines thus making an area of at least 175,000 square miles in which the dominant activity is hunting and trapping. Perhaps we should now use the term wild life management since, for the most part, trap-lines and areas have been registered, so that the owner may be assured of the returns from the use of conservational methods in handling the wild life resource. Most of the trappers are Indians, native to the region.

### The Patricia Mining Camps

The mining camps at Red Lake, central Patricia and Pickle Crow are good examples of isolated development. Discovered in 1925, Red Lake was for years accessible only by airplane or canoe in summer or dog team in winter. Temporary winter frcighting roads wcrc built and latcr an all-year highway was constructed linking Red Lake with Vermilion, a point on Highway 17, about 25 miles west of Dryden. A similar road is to link Pickle Crow to Sioux Lookout by way of Savant Lake. A hydro-electric power plant at Ear Falls on the English River supplies energy to Red Lake, Pickle Crow and Sioux Lookout. Several thousand people live in these Patricia areas and there are always possibilities for new mining camps in the future.

### Geographic Reality

Map shape and space relations make it easy and, in fact, necessary to deal with Northern Ontario as a unit apart from the older and more densely settled areas of the province. The geographer, however, finds it somewhat difficult to demonstrate that the area possesses true regional unity, either from the standpoint of homogeneity or through the development of complementary and reciprocal human relations. On a smaller stage, unity may be demonstrated

*The Photographic Survey Corporation Limited.*

Plate 77. Steep Rock Iron Mine. Ore is obtained from a huge open pit in the floor of a dewatered lake.

in the emerging settlement areas discussed in this chapter but, apart from similarities in certain major problems, they have little coherence. They have not, for instance, been able to get the Ontario Government to construct adequate transprovincial highways. Northwestern Ontario often feels more akin to Western Canada than to the eastern and southern parts of the province. There are even those who advocate the secession of this region to form a new province to be named *Aurora*. Professor Lower (1948) advocates the creation of two new provinces and the abandonment of the far north to the care of the federal government. No doubt northern resources have received some unwise and short-sighted administration from the provincial capital. This has, in no small measure,

been the direct result of ignorance of the geographical realities. The major natural resources are forests, minerals and water power but they are by no means uniformly distributed. Processing and manufacturing, based upon mine and forest products, are important and will become greater in the future. All of these activities tend toward a highly nucleated urban type of settlement. Agriculture is and will continue to be a minor industry. Combined with primary forestry, however, it may help to support dispersed settlement in certain areas. Ontario may be a province in spite of geographical differences, but it can develop fully only when these differences are recognized and understood. At present, however, Northern Ontario stands in need of intensive geographical research.

## Selected References

Brodie, J. A. *Timber Management in Ontario.* Canadian Geographical Journal 42: 100-117. 1951.

Burrows, A. G. et al. *The Porcupine Gold Area.* Report of the Ontario Department of Mines, Vol. XXXIII. Part II, pp. 1-105. 1924.

Burrows, A. G. and H. C. Rickaby. *Sudbury Nickel Field Restudied.* Report of the Ontario Dept. of Mines, Vol. XLIII. Part II, pp. 1-45. 1934.

Coleman, A. P. *The Sudbury Nickel Region.* Report of the Ontario Dept. of Mines, Vol. XIV. Part III pp. 1-183. 1905.

Coleman, A. P. *Lake Objibway; Last of the Great Glacial Lakes.* Annual Report of the Ontario Bureau of Mines, Vol. XVIII. Part I, pp. 284-293. 1909.

Douglass, D. P. *Hydro-Electric Development for the Mining Industry of Northern Ontario.* Ontario Dept. of Mines. Bulletin 46, pp. 1-36. Toronto 1944.

Gosselin, A. and G. P. Boucher. *Settlement Problems in Northwestern Quebec and Northeastern Ontario.* Canada Department of Agriculture, Technical Bulletin 49, pp. 1-54. 1944.

Henderson, Archibald. *Agricultural Resources of Abitibi.* Report of the Ontario Department of Mines, Vol XIV. Part I, pp. 213-247. 1905.

Henderson, Archibald. *Agricultural Resources of the Mattagami.* Report of the Ontario Dept. of Mines, Vol. XV. Part I. pp. 136-155. 1906.

Hills, G. A. *An Approach to Land Settlement Problems in Northern Ontario.* Scientific Agriculture 23, pp. 212-216. 1942.

Hills, G. A. *Pedology, "the Dirt Science" and Agricultural Settlement in Ontario.* Canadian Geographical Journal 29. pp. 106-127. 1944.

Hills, G. A. and F. F. Morwick. *Reconnaissance Soil Survey of Parts of Northwestern Ontario.* Guelph. 1944.

Horwood, H. C. *Geology and Mineral Deposits of the Red Lake Area*. Ontario Dept. of Mines Report, Vol. XLIX. Part II. pp. 1-219. 1940.

Kennedy, Howard. *Report of the Ontario Royal Commission on Forestry*. Toronto. 1947.

Kerr, H. L. *Explorations in the Mattagami Valley*. Report of the Ontario Dept. of Mines, Vol. XV. Part I. pp. 116-135. 1906.

Lower, A. R. M. and H. A. Innis. *Settlement in the Forest and Mining Frontier*. Macmillan Company of Canada Limited. Toronto. 1936.

Lower, Arthur. *What This Country Needs is 10 New Provinces*. Maclean's Magazine, Vol. 61, No. 19. Oct. 15, 1948.

Mackay, Corday. *Great Rendezvous. Kaministikwia*. Canadian Geographical Journal 36, pp. 9-15. 1948.

McMillan, J. G. *Explorations in Abitibi*. Report of the Ontario Dept. of Mines. Vol. XIV. Part I. pp. 184-212. 1905.

Nichols, D. A. *The Geographic Setting of Northern Ontario*. Canadian Geographical Journal 18, pp. 147-151. 1939.

Ontario Research Foundation. *A Technical and Economic Investigation of Northern Ontario Lignite*. Report of the Ontario Department of Mines Vol. XLII. Part III, pp. 1-45. 1933.

Putnam, D. F. *Manitoulin Island*. Geographical Review, Vol. XXXVII, pp. 649-662. 1947.

Randall, J. R. *Agriculture in the Great Clay Belt of Canada*. Scottish Geographical Journal, Vol. 56, pp. 314-317. 1940.

*Report to the Ontario Legislature from the Select Committee on Conservation*. Toronto. 1950.

Rumney, G. R. *Settlement of the Nipissing Passage*. Transactions of the Royal Canadian Institute. Vol. 28, pp. 65-120. 1949.

Satterley, J. *Geology of the Dryden-Wabigoon Area*. Report of the Ontario Dept. of Mines. Vol. L. Part II, pp. 1-62. 1941.

*Statistical Review of the Mineral Industry of Ontario 1948*. Annual Report of the Ontario Dept. of Mines. Vol. LVIII, Part I. 1949. pp. 1-51. Toronto. 1950.

Todd, E. W. *Kirkland Lake Gold Area*. Ontario Dept. of Mines Report. Vol. XXXVII. Part II, pp. 1-167. 1928.

Whitaker, Russell. *Sault Ste. Marie, Michigan and Ontario: A Comparative Study in Urban Geography*. Bulletin of the Geographical Society of Philadelphia. XXXII, pp. 88-107. 1934.

# CHAPTER 16

# The Physical Geography of the Prairie Provinces

Mᴀɴɪᴛᴏʙᴀ, Saskatchewan and Alberta are known as the "Prairie Provinces" because they include the Canadian section of the vast grass-covered interior plains of North America. Their southern margin is the International Boundary, or 49th parallel of north latitude, and they extend northward to the 60th parallel, roughly a distance of 760 miles. From the Ontario boundary on the east to the crest of the Rocky Mountains on the west the average distance is about 1,000 miles. The total area is 753,497 square miles or about 20 percent of the area of Canada. The three provinces are almost the same size, the actual areas being: Manitoba 246,512 square miles; Saskatchewan 251,700 square miles; Alberta 255,285 square miles. The surfaces of freshwater lakes amount to more than 47,000 square miles. Lake Winnipeg covers 9,000 square miles while Lakes Athabaska, Reindeer and Winnipegosis are all

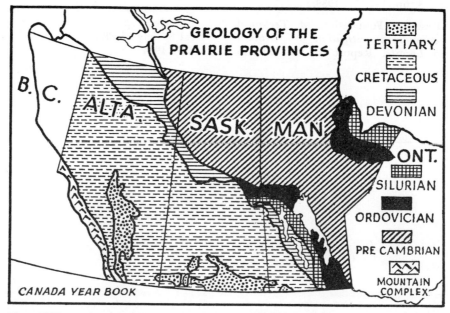

**Figure 207.** *Bedrock Geology of the Prairie Provinces.* There are two great areas, the Canadian Shield underlain by old crystalline Precambrian rocks, and the Great Plains underlain very largely by Cretaceous marine sediments.

more than 2,000 square miles in extent. Both Northern Saskatchewan and Northern Manitoba have hundreds of smaller lakes. Saskatchewan and Alberta are inland provinces but Manitoba has a salt water shoreline on Hudson Bay of more than 400 miles, including the harbour and seaport of Churchill. This portal is open for a short time only each year and does not greatly affect the geographic personality of the Prairie region.

## Geological Formations

In the Prairie Provinces, as in most parts of the world, a fundamental reason for geographical differentiation is to be found in the characteristics of the bedrock. Figure 207 is a simplified geological map adapted from one prepared by the Canadian Geological Survey. A large area in the northeast is underlain by very old Precambrian rocks, an extension of the Canadian Shield which comprises so much of Ontario and Quebec. As in the adjoining portion of Northern Ontario, this area is largely composed of gneisses, granites and other acidic intrusive rocks. There are also mineralized belts in which important discoveries are made from time to time, giving rise to rich mining camps such as Flin Flon, Sherrit-Gordon and Goldfields.

Adjoining Hudson Bay are areas of Paleozoic rocks of Ordovician and Silurian ages, forming an extension of the Hudson Bay lowland. These rocks are mostly limestones and dolomites with undisturbed and almost horizontal bedding.

Along the western margin of the Canadian Shield is found a narrow strip of country underlain by limestones of Ordovician, Silurian and Devonian ages, somewhat like those found in Southern Ontario. In Manitoba all three are well represented, but in Saskatchewan and Alberta, the Devonian is most widespread and, apparently, lies directly upon the Precambrian. The Silurian of Manitoba contains gypsum beds.

Upon these Paleozoic rocks, but separated from them by a great erosional disconformity and a hard sandstone formation, lie enormous masses of shale of Cretaceous age accumulated in a great downfold. The upper formations of this system contain the great coal deposits of Alberta.

Finally there were great areas of Tertiary rocks, chiefly sandstones and conglomerates which were, apparently, spread out upon the plain by debris laden streams issuing from the Rocky Mountains. In pre-glacial times these rocks suffered erosion until only remnants of the formation remain. They are fairly extensive in Southern Saskatchewan and Central Alberta and a small area is preserved in Southern Manitoba.

Here, as in Eastern Canada, the bedrock is covered by many feet of glacial drift which has obscured the old drainage pattern and given a very young appearance to the surface of the plain. While, as yet, little detailed glacial geology has been done, there seems to be good evidence for more than one ice age. Here, too, there were enormous lakes during the melting of the ice, leaving great flat plains of stratified clay.

## Land Forms

The area of the Prairie Provinces includes portions of several of the great physiographic provinces of Canada, the outlines and some of the major features of which are shown in Figure 208. From west to east these are: the Cordilleran Region, represented by the Rocky Mountains and the Foothills; the Interior Plains; the Canadian Shield and the Hudson Bay Lowland.

The mountain building activities of the Laramide Revolution disturbed only the southwestern margin of the area, elsewhere the sedimentary rocks underlying the plains have remained nearly horizontal. Nevertheless, the geological history includes many cycles of deposition, uplift and erosion since the formation of the Canadian Shield. The records of the last three, which

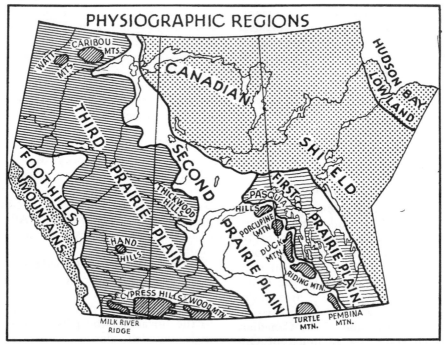

Figure 208. *Physiographic Regions of the Prairie Provinces.* The Prairie Plains fall naturally into three areas on account of elevation and relief. Above them, elevated tablelands remain as remnants of a former widespread surface of erosion.

have taken place since the Tertiary period, remain in the three levels of the Prairie Plains although somewhat obscured by the effects of Pleistocene glaciation. The work of the present or post-glacial cycle of erosion has hardly had time to make much impression upon the land form regions.

## The Shield and Hudson Bay Lowland

The characteristics of these northeastern regions are much the same as those of their counterparts in Ontario and Quebec. In general, the elevation and relief of the Shield is less than in Ontario but the surface is just as thoroughly dotted with small lakes which are a heritage from the great ice age. There are also some very large ones such as Lake Athabaska (3,058 sq. mi.) and Reindeer Lake (2,440 sq. mi.). In Northern Manitoba, also, there are clay plains of considerable extent somewhat similar to those of the Great Clay Belt of Northern Ontario and Quebec.

## Regional Landforms of the Prairie Plains

Canadian physiographers usually divide the plains into three areas of roughly uniform altitude separated by sharp topographic breaks. From east to west these are, as shown in Figure 208: the Manitoba Lowland or First Prairie Level, with an elevation of less than 1,000 feet above sea level; the Manitoba Escarpment, a narrow belt of hilly terrain with a total relief of about 1,000 feet; the Saskatchewan Plain or Second Prairie Level, with an average elevation of about 2,000 feet above sea level; the Missouri Coteau, which is a second narrow hilly belt with a total relief of about 500 feet; the Alberta Plain or Third Prairie Level, which rises gradually from about 2,500 feet above sea level to nearly 4,000 feet at the foothills of the Rocky Mountains.

## The Manitoba Lowland

Lying between the edge of the Shield and the foot of Manitoba Escarpment this area forms a great natural basin, the lower parts of which are occupied by large fresh-water lakes including Lake Winnipeg (9,398 square miles), Lake Winnipegosis (2,086 square miles), Lake Manitoba (1,813 square miles), Cedar Lake (537 square miles), Moose Lake (525 square miles), Lake Dauphin (200 square miles) and many smaller ones. These, however, may be regarded merely as modern remnants of the huge glacial Lake Agassiz which occupied all of this lowland and adjacent portions of the Shield as well. At its maximum, it is estimated that the area of Lake Agassiz was 110,000 square miles or more than that of the five Great Lakes. A great deal of clay and silt accumulated on the floor of this lake and today form the fertile soil of the Red River Valley, as the southern portion of this lowland is known. The area farther north was not so fortunate, the Interlake region between Lake Winnipeg and Lake Manitoba having rather shallow soils interspersed with depressions filled with peat and muck. The base of the Manitoba Escarpment is marked by numerous sand and gravel ridges built by the waves of old Lake Agassiz.

In the southern part of the Red River Valley, flowing wells are found, the water having been trapped in sandy deposits lying beneath the heavy capping of lacustrine clay.

## The Manitoba Cuesta

The steep face of the Manitoba Cuesta and the hilly eastern borders of the Saskatchewan plain constitute a narrow but distinct physiographic region. It is not continuous, however, being cut by wide, deep valleys, the largest of which is occupied by the Assiniboine River. South of the Assiniboine River, between the edge of the Manitoba Escarpment and the Pembina Valley, lies the upland known as Pembina Mountain. North of the Assiniboine River are the Riding Mountains, Duck Mountains, Porcupine Mountains and Pasquia Hills, the latter overlooking the Carrot River Valley in Saskatchewan. None of them show very great relief when viewed from the west but they have precipitous eastern slopes. The tops of these isolated uplands are remnants of a very widespread Tertiary erosion surface, represented elsewhere in the Prairie Provinces by Turtle Mountain, Wood Mountain and the Cypress Hills. The rough nature of the surface is the result of the deposition of great quantities of morainic debris during the waning of the ice sheet. Riding Mountain National Park and Duck Mountain Forest Reserve possess a great many small lakes contained by depressions in the moraine.

Eastward from Brandon, the wide Assiniboine Valley is composed of sand plains representing an extensive delta of the river at the time of Lake Agassiz.

## The Saskatchewan Plain

The second prairie level, or the Saskatchewan Plains, is much more extensive than the Manitoba Lowland. It comprises the dip slope of the great Cretaceous formation which terminates so abruptly at the Manitoba Escarpment. For the most part it is an area of gentle relief, the surface being composed of glacial boulder clay or ground moraine interspersed with wide flat areas of clay plain, representing the floors of glacial lakes. The Souris Basin in southwestern Manitoba, the Regina Plains from Regina to Weyburn, the clay plains from Yorkton to Quill Lakes and the plains of the Carrot River and Saskatchewan River Valleys were all laid down in post-glacial lakes. Rather prominent belts of terminal moraine are found along Moose Mountain and in the Touchwood, Allan and Thickwood Hills farther north. Some of these morainic deposits are very stony, as can be seen about 20 miles east of Saskatoon. The river valleys, also, are major relief features of the Saskatchewan plain. Some of these, having carried the drainage from the melt-

*Courtesy Canadian National Railways*

Plate 78.  The typical Prairie landscape has little relief; grain elevators mark the skyline while grainfields have replaced the original sod.

ing ice sheet, are much larger and deeper than could have been cut by the small streams now flowing in them. The Pembina Valley which once carried the drainage of Lake Souris, and the Qu'Appelle Valley, which carried the Saskatchewan drainage to the Assiniboine, are good examples of this type of misfit. Both these valleys are occupied by series of long narrow lakes resulting from the damming of the waters by alluvium, carried in by fast flowing tributaries. The Qu'Appelle Lakes, a few miles northeast of Regina, form a very pleasant resort area. There are numerous other lakes, occupying shallow depressions on the Saskatchewan plain, the largest of which are the Quill Lakes; there are also many small depressions or 'sloughs'. The existence of these undrained depressions is evidence of the youthful nature of the landscape.

## The Missouri Coteau

The Missouri Coteau is a hilly belt separating the second from the third prairie level. It is neither so abrupt nor so high as the Manitoba Escarpment but it repre-

sents a similar break between old erosion levels. The Coteau was also a barrier to the continental ice sheet and is paralleled by two belts of terminal moraine, one along the crest and one a few miles to the west. Old drainage courses having the same general direction are represented today by Lake of the Rivers and the valley of the Big Muddy. Tramping Lake and the upper valley of Eaglehill Creek represent a similar old spillway further to the northwest.

## The Alberta Plain

The third prairie level, or the Alberta plain, stretches from the Missouri Coteau to the foothills of the Rocky Mountains and embraces about two thirds of the area of Alberta as well as the southwestern quarter of Saskatchewan. It is more elevated and shows more relief than the other prairie plains. The various tributaries of the Saskatchewan River system flow in deep valleys which would almost justify the classification of this area as a plateau. Standing high above the plateau surface are remnants of an earlier (Tertiary) erosion surface, including such uplands as Wood Mountain,

Cypress Hills, Milk River Ridge and, far to the north, the Watt and Caribou Mountains. The southern uplands now constitute the drainage divide between the Saskatchewan and Missouri River systems but there are numerous, abandoned, high-level valleys which carried meltwater southward during the recession of the ice sheets. Verdigris, Etzikom and Chin coulees represent the old glacial drainage across the Milk River Ridge. The Gap and other breaks in the Cypress Hills had a similar history and may possibly be remnants of a still older, preglacial drainage system. Farther north on the Alberta plain, there are long valleys which once carried the waters of the North Saskatchewan system toward a more southerly outlet. There are several belts of terminal moraine also, containing deposits of the great Keewatin ice sheet and, along the western margin of the plain, material from the Rocky Mountain ice.

The outstanding features of the Alberta plain, however, are the deeply entrenched valleys in which flow the main tributaries of the Saskatchewan River system. The valleys of the South Saskatchewan and of the Red Deer are from 300 to 400 feet deep. Extensive bad lands have developed along the Red Deer River, exposing fossil beds in which are found the skeletons of dinosaurs and other extinct animals. These deeply cut valleys also expose valuable coal seams, such as those at Lethbridge, Drumheller and Edmonton. Farther north, the plateau is trenched by the deep valley of the Peace River.

## The Rocky Mountains and Foothills of Alberta

Viewed from the plains, the Rocky Mountains appear as an immense, abrupt, snow-capped wall to the westward. Closer approach reveals that between the plains and the mountains there lies a rolling foothill region which, though fairly narrow in the south, widens considerably in the north.

The Rocky Mountains are young, high mountains which were upthrust, probably, during early Tertiary times. The rocks of the region are strongly folded and faulted. The abruptness of the eastern wall in Southern Alberta is due to thrust faulting

*D. P. Kerr*

Plate 79. The Rocky Mountains near Banff, Alberta.

whereby older rocks were pushed over the Cretaceous shales of the Prairie Plains. This can be clearly seen in Waterton Lakes Park and again at Crowsnest Mountain. As mountain ridges rose, a complex pattern of river erosion was etched upon them and further complicated by glaciation. The highest peaks, which are ten to twelve thousand feet in elevation, are snow capped at present but, during the glacial period, ice action was much greater and all the major valleys were filled with ice.

They are, therefore, broad, deep U-shaped valleys instead of narrow V-shaped canyons cut by river erosion. The valley of Waterton Lakes and the Bow Valley are good examples. The pyramidal mountains of Waterton Lakes Park are due to the effects of the glaciers which wore away their flanks. Small lakes, also, are found high up in the mountains, occupying 'cirques' or rocky basins hollowed out by ice. Some of the most marvellous, glaciated mountain scenery in the world is found in Waterton Lakes, Banff and Jasper National Parks.

The glaciers and mountain lakes are of economic as well as scenic importance for they constitute the sources of mountain streams which furnish water power and irrigation for the plains below.

The rocks of the foothills have been much more gently folded but some of the higher ridges exceed an elevation of five thousand feet above sea level. Here there has been no intense mountain glaciation and the crests are rounded, but the valleys of the major streams have all been cut to a depth of several hundred feet. The topography thus may be generally characterized as rugged.

## Rivers

The waters of the Prairie Provinces drain three ways: north to the Arctic Ocean by way of the Mackenzie River system, northeast to Hudson Bay and, from a very small area only, south to the Mississippi and the Gulf of Mexico.

The chief branches of the Mackenzie are Peace River and Athabaska River.

The Peace River is 1,054 miles in length from the head of its longest tributary, the Finlay, to its confluence with the Slave, some miles below the outlet of Lake Athabaska. It drains a large area of mountainous country in Northern British Columbia and is well entrenched throughout much of its length.

The Athabaska River is 765 miles long, from its source in Jasper National Park to Lake Athabaska. Its course is entirely within the province of Alberta but it receives some tributaries from Saskatchewan. It forms an important link in northern transportation routes from Waterways and Fort McMurray to its mouth.

Churchill River, flowing into Hudson Bay, is about 1,000 miles in length. Its longest tributary, the Beaver (305 miles), rises near Lac la Biche in Alberta and flows into Lac Ile à la Crosse which is regarded as the source of the Churchill. Most of the area drained by the Churchill is underlain by Precambrian rocks and the courses of the river and its tributaries are highly irregular, consisting of innumerable lakes with intervening stretches of rapids. The area drained is estimated to be about 180,000 square miles. This is over three times as large as the area drained by the Ottawa River in Ontario and Quebec, yet the volume of water carried by the Churchill is considerably smaller. A power plant at Island Falls near the Saskatchewan-Manitoba boundary supplies the mining area of Flin Flon.

The Nelson River system, from the source of the Bow River in the Rocky Mountains to its entrance into Hudson Bay, is over 1,600 miles in length. Through its tributaries in the Saskatchewan, Red and Winnipeg systems, the Nelson drains over 450,000 square miles, including about half the area of the Prairie Provinces and considerable areas in Ontario and the United States as well. Like the St. Lawrence, the Nelson has a system of great natural reservoirs which serve to maintain a regular flow throughout the year. On a comparative basis, the flow is much smaller because of the much lower rainfall in the interior of the continent. Conditions vary greatly, however, since the annual run-off from some Ontario tributaries may equal 15 inches of rainfall, and over 20 inches from rivers in the Rocky Mountains, yet it averages only a fraction of an inch from many Prairie streams. A good example may be taken from the North Saskatchewan. Measurements taken at Prince Albert and at Edmonton show that nine-tenths of the flow originated in the headwaters and represented the run-off from one-fifth of the area of the watershed. Even more striking is the situation on the South Saskatchewan. About 5,250,000 acre-feet of water flow past Medicine Hat each year, representing the drainage from over 20,000 square miles, yet the drainage from 15,000 square miles of headwater area pours more than 6,500,000 acre-feet into the system, according to measurements taken on the Red Deer, Bow and Oldman Rivers. The difference is represented by irrigation water evaporated from the land and not returned to the river. The Milk River in Alberta and Frenchman River in Saskatchewan are the most important streams draining into the Missouri.

The rivers of the Prairie Provinces are not only important physical features but they constitute a source of power, furnish means of transportation, and provide water for irrigation, domestic and industrial purposes.

## Climate, Vegetation and Soils

### Climate

Situated in the northern interior of the continent of North America, the Prairie Provinces have a continental climate. It is one of great range in its annual temperature regime, with average winter temperatures at, or below zero and average summer temperatures above 60° F. While not

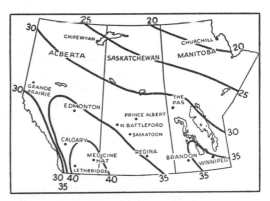

Figure 209. *Mean Annual Temperature.* Mean annual temperature in the Prairie Provinces varies from 20°F. to 40°F. in a regular fashion from northeast to southwest.

as warm as Southern Ontario, nevertheless, the southern part of the Prairie Provinces may be said to have a short warm summer. The rainfall regime is also of the continental type. Most of the rain comes in the warm half of the year and only a small portion of the total precipitation falls in winter. Because of the low temperatures this is nearly all in the form of snow which remains on the ground for a long time.

Mean annual temperatures (figure 209) vary from about 18° F. in Northern Manitoba to 42° F. in Southern Alberta. In general the isotherms trend from northwest to southeast across the plains, though, of course, the elevated ranges of the Rocky Mountains also have low tem-

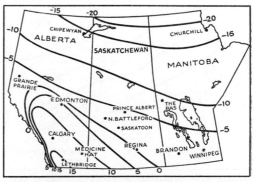

Figure 210. *January Mean Temperature.* Winter is cold, only the southwestern section has January mean temperatures above 0°F.

peratures. It is interesting to note, also, that the lowlands of Manitoba appear as a warm loop on this map.

Winter temperatures, as shown by the January isotherms (figure 210), vary from 20° below zero in the northeast to 15° above zero in the southwest. The high plains of Southern Alberta owe their advantage to the effects of the chinook winds which, from time to time, sweep down from the mountains raising the temperature 20° to 40° in a few hours. The summer temperatures show much less variation (figure 211). The 60° F. isotherm bends far to the northwest to enclose most of the area. Only the coasts of Hudson Bay and the elevated stations in the Rocky Mountains have July mean temperatures of 55°F. The southern parts of the plains have over 65° F., a few

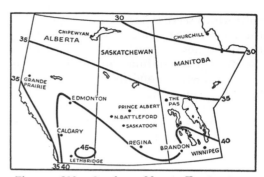

Figure 213. *October Mean Temperatures.* There is a north-south gradient of more than 15°F. in October as cold air moves in from the north.

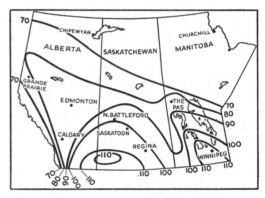

Figure 214. *Average Length of the Frost-free Period.* The frost-free period varies from less than 70 to more than 110 days each summer. Cereals, of course, can grow even while there is danger of spring frost.

Figure 211. *July Mean Temperatures.* There is little variation in midsummer temperatures, only the extreme northeastern section has a July mean below 60°F.

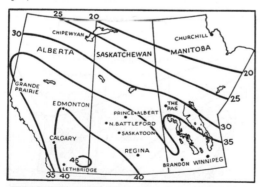

Figure 212. *April Mean Temperatures.* A gradient of more than 25°F. in April, from northeast to southwest serves to demonstrate the fact that spring comes first in the southwest.

stations in Southern Alberta reaching 68° F. and 69° F. Note that the 65° isotherm shows a "cold loop" on the crest of the Manitoba Cuesta and a corresponding "warm loop" in the adjoining lowland.

Spring temperature conditions may be represented by the records for April (figure 212). A temperature of 42° F. is often selected as marking the beginning of the growing season for ordinary farm crops such as cereals. This occurs around the middle of April in Southern Alberta and progressively later as one goes north and east.

Isotherms of mean temperatures for October are shown in figure 213. The critical limit of 42° F. may again be regarded as the close of the growing season. This does not occur until mid-October or later in most of Southern Alberta, Southern Saskatchewan and the extreme southern parts of Manitoba. Temperatures in the north do not fall off so rapidly toward Hudson Bay as in April.

Figure 214 shows the length of the frost-free period. This varies from more than 110 days in the southern parts to about 80 days in the Peace River area. There is very little variation throughout a large part of Central Alberta. This is perhaps of less importance in the Prairie Provinces than in eastern Canada. Cereals and forage crops are less affected by frost in the spring than tender fruits and vegetables such as are grown in Southern Ontario.

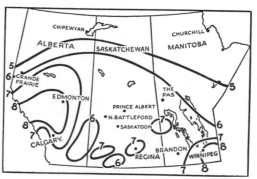

Figure 216. *Rainfall in the Months of May, June and July.* The months of May, June and July constitute the growing period for cereals, hence rain at this time is of most value.

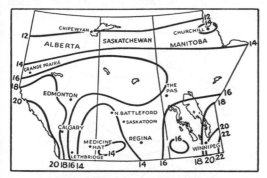

Figure 215. *Mean Annual Precipitation.* The moisture supply varies from 12 to 20 inches per year. Areas with less than 15 inches lie both north and south of the central humid belt.

Figure 215 is a map of isohyets of mean annual precipitation. It shows that the moisture supply of the Prairie Provinces varies from less than twelve inches to more than twenty inches of rainfall per year. The least precipitation is experienced in the far northwest and in the "dry belt" of Southern Saskatchewan and Southern Alberta. The foothills of the Rocky Mountains have about 20 inches per year while southeastern Manitoba gets slightly more. The effect of elevation is seen in the increased precipitation of the Cypress Hills area in southwestern Saskatchewan. The general pattern, however, seems to show a crescent shaped area of higher precipitation

extending from southeastern Manitoba to Central Alberta, with areas of lesser precipitation both north and south.

So far as agriculture is concerned, the rainfall coming during the crop growing season is most important. For cereals this means May, June and July. This is shown by isohyets in figure 216. In the far north where, of course, cereals are not important, there is less than five inches of rainfall in this period. In the "dry belt" of the southwest there is also very little rainfall in the growing season. Most of the Prairie region has between six and seven inches but, in Central Alberta, there is, on the average, over eight inches of rain in this season.

Another way of looking at seasonal

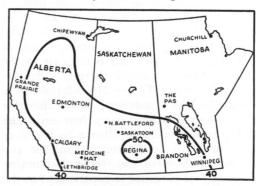

Figure 217. *Percentage of Total Precipitation Falling During May, June and July.* Grassland climates are characterized by a concentration of rainfall in the early summer.

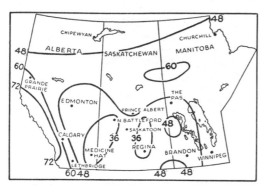

Figure 218. *Mean Annual Snowfall.* Snowfall varies from 36 to 60 inches, being much lighter than in most of Eastern Canada.

rainfall is presented in figure 217. Here it is seen that the three grain-growing months receive over 40% of the rainfall throughout the Prairie region and in a large part of Northern Alberta. In south-central Saskatchewan the proportion rises to more than 50%.

Figure 218 shows the distribution of snowfall. The central parts of the Prairies average about three feet of snow, which is the equivalent of 3.6 inches of rainfall; while farther north, some areas receive as much as five feet. The foothills of Western Alberta get over six feet of snow. From this map, it is seen that much of the extra moisture of the humid crescent comes in the colder season of the year.

Temperature and precipitation are important but so is evaporation which, being the result of the application of heat, is closely tied to temperature. In some climates there is more moisture than the atmosphere can take up again, while in others there is less. This is the case in the Prairie Provinces where there is a definite water deficiency. Figure 219, adapted from a map by Mrs. Sanderson,[1] shows that this deficiency varies from more than ten inches per year in Southern Alberta to less than two inches in northeastern Manitoba and in the foothills of the Rocky Mountains. This lack of moisture is experienced in the

[1] Sanderson, Marie (1948). *The Climates of Canada, according to the New Thornthwaite Classification.* Scientific Agriculture 28: 501-517.

summer season since the winter, even though it has low precipitation, has very little evaporation.

### Climatic Divisions

Despite the very obvious differences in climate from place to place in the Prairie Provinces, it is not easy to make exact subdivisions. The pattern is simplest in Saskatchewan where our various climatic maps and, as we shall see, vegetation and soils, all suggest a five-fold division (Figure 220). These might for convenience be labelled: The *Semi-arid* or *Dry Belt,* the *Sub-humid Prairie,* the *Sub-boreal, Boreal* and *Sub-arctic.* In the west where the pattern is interrupted by elevation, there is the Foothill and Mountain Region which has a series of climates all its own. In

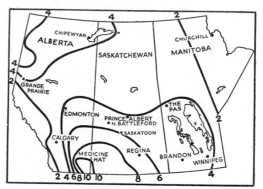

Figure 219. *Average Annual Moisture Deficiency.* The Prairie Provinces constitute an area of moisture deficiency which may vary from 2 to more than 10 inches of rainfall. (After Sanderson).

southeast Manitoba, greater availability of moisture and higher summer temperatures suggest that a small area with a *humid* climate be recognized.

While a number of the boundaries depend upon moisture relationships, especially in the south, those in the north depend very largely on temperature. Several of the maps show important temperature lines running from Central Manitoba to the northwest corner of Alberta, suggesting a division in the broad Boreal zone. When we see that this boundary is also recognized

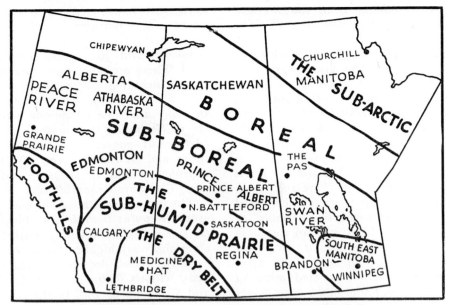

Figure 220. *Climatic Subdivisions of the Prairie Provinces.* Temperature and moisture vary in the same direction, delimiting five main climatic belts.

by foresters we can have little doubt about it. Minor subregions may be recognized on minor criteria. The Edmonton district, for instance, has a higher summer rainfall than the Peace River. Swan River and Prince Albert have much the same climates but they are separated by a hilly and somewhat cooler belt. The Athabaska River area has distinctly more rain in the summer than the Peace River, but a little less snow in winter. However, for the purposes of broad scale regional geography such minor divisions are unnecessary.

## Vegetation

While the Prairie Provinces take their well known name from the great area of grassland which they contain, this in actuality comprises only about one third of the total area. To the north and northeast of this somewhat triangular area are found several belts of forest and, in the far northeast, even treeless tundra. The forests, then, might be said to form a transition zone between the regions that are too dry and those which are too cold for forest growth. Both grassland and forest regions, however,

can be further subdivided as shown in figure 221.

The short grass prairie, or true steppe formation, occurs in the more arid southern parts of Alberta and Saskatchewan and is, of course, just a small northern extension of the semi-arid grasslands of the Great Plains region of the United States. This is the heart of Palliser's "triangle", the area which he judged to be too arid for agricultural settlement.

The characteristic species of the short grass association are: June grass (*Koeleria cristata*), blue grama grass (*Bouteloua gracilis*), common spear grass (*Stipa comata*), western wheat grass (*Agropyron Smithii*), Sandberg's blue grass (*Poa secunda*) nigger wool (*Carex filifolia*), pasture sage (*Artemisia cana*) and prickly pear cactus (*Opuntia polyacantha*). As well as being short, such vegetation is sparse, with considerable bare soil to be seen between the plants. The root systems, however, are very extensive, invading practically the whole soil mass in their search for available water.

Completely surrounding the "shortgrass" area, lies the crescent of the mixed grass formation, extending from southwestern Manitoba to southwestern Alberta. The vegetation includes the same species mentioned previously, together with such taller ones as northern wheat grass (*Agropyron dasystachyum*), green spear grass (*Stipa viridula*), rough fescue (*Festuca scabrella*) and side-oats grama grass (*Bouteloua curtipendula*). In some natural depressions and stream valleys, small groves of poplar, willow and various shrubs may occur.

Between the open prairie and the forest lies the aspen grove or "Parkland" belt. This is a tall grass formation interspersed at frequent intervals with small "bluffs" or groves of trees, indicative of an increased moisture supply. Continuous strips of woodland are found in most of the river valleys of this region. Isolated areas of parkland are to be found in the Peace River district of Alberta, far to the northwest of the main belt.

Some of the important grasses in this zone are: awned wheat grass (*Agropyron subsecundum*), slender wheat grass (A. *pauciflorum*), fringed brome grass (*Brom-*

*us ciliatus*), marsh reedgrass (*Calamagrostis canadensis*), northern reed grass (*C. inexpansa*), Hooker's oat grass (*Avena Hookerii*) and June grass (*Koeleria cristata*). There are, also, numerous flowering plants, including: plains cinquefoil (*Potentilla bipinnatifida*), hairy cinquefoil (*P. strigosa*), anemone (*Anemone canadensis*), crocus (*Pulsatilla ludoviciana*), milk vetch (*Astragalus goniatus*), baneberry (*Actaea rubra* and *A. Alba*), sweet pea (*Lathyrus ochroleucus* and *L. venosus*) and golden pea (*Thermopsis rhombifolia*).

The woody vegetation is made up of: aspen (*Populus tremuloides*), black poplar (*P. tacamahacca*), Saskatoon bush (*Amelanchier alnifolia*), highbush cranberry (*Viburnum trilobum*), dogwood (*Svida instolonnea*), willows (*Salix discolor, S. Bebbiana* and *S. petiolaris*) and, in the southeastern section, bur oak (*Quercus macrocarpa*), Manitoba maple (*Acer negundo*), elm (*Ulmus americana*), and green ash (*Fraxinus campestris*).

The "Mixedwood Belt" occupies the southern portion of the forested zone, hav-

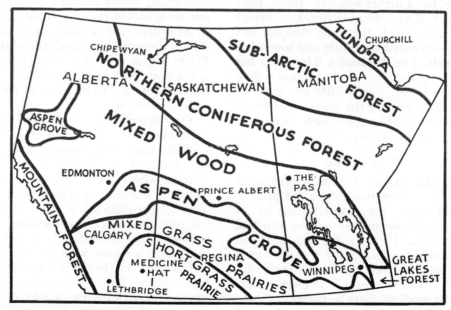

Figure 221. *Vegetation Belts of the Prairie Provinces.* Vegetation belts, in general, parallel the climatic belts from southwest to northeast, ranging from shortgrass prairie to tundra.

ing a breadth of one hundred and twenty-five to one hundred and fifty miles in Central Saskatchewan, broadening out considerably in Alberta and becoming narrower in Manitoba. The northern boundary of this belt is rather indefinite but seems to coincide fairly well with the border of the Canadian Shield.

As the name implies, this woodland consists of a mixture of deciduous, broad-leaved trees and evergreen, coniferous

(*Petasites palmatus*). Mosses are not abundant.

The second or "Open Poplar" association is found on sandy or gravelly soils. The poplars are widely spaced, short and branching; willows (*Salix Bebbiana*) are present but no spruce. The undercover consists of rose, blueberry (*Cyanococcus canadensis*), bear berry (*Arctostaphylos Uva-ursi*), wild rye (*Elymus innovatus*) and other grasses.

Courtesy Exp. Farms Service

Plate 80.   A "Texas gate" in the rangeland of the Dry Belt.

types. The mixture, however, is far from uniform and, in Saskatchewan at least, three forest associations may be identified.

The first, designated as "Normal Poplar", is characterized by fairly dense stands of aspen (*Populus tremuloides*), in which distinct age classes, usually in separate areas, may be recognized. Spruce is scanty and is represented by a few small trees and seedlings. The underbrush consists of hazel (*Corylus rostrata*), cranberry (*Viburnum*) *eradiatum*), and rose (*Rosa acicularis*). The ground cover includes twinflower (*Linnaea americana*), dewberry (*Rubus pubescens*), sarsaparilla ( *Aralia nudicalis*), disporum (*Disporum trachycarpum*) and coltsfoot

The third type is the "Poplar-Spruce" association. It is regarded as the normal or climax forest of the region and it develops in locations where the spruce (*Picea glauca*) has had sufficient protection from fire. The other two associations are regarded as fire induced, by inference from the occurrence of areas of uniform stands of different ages. In the normal forest, cranberry and buffalo berry (*Shepherdia sp.*) are the principal shrubs, while mosses and lichens are common.

Poplar and spruce are, also, the chief trees reported from the wooded districts west and north of Edmonton and in the Peace River district. The same species are reported in the Manitoba Lowlands with jack pine (*Pinus Banksiana*) on the limestone outcrops and bur oak (*Quercus macrocarpa*) on the old Lake Agassiz beaches. Here, also, are large areas with poor drainage in which tamarack (*Larix laricina*) and black spruce (*Picea mariana*) are the common trees. Some rather extensive jackpine stands are found in Saskatchewan.

Apart from the continuous belt just described, islands of mixed woods occur on isolated elevations on the plains, such as Cypress Hills in Southwestern Saskatchewan, Turtle Mountain in Southern Manitoba and in the Duck Mountains and Riding Mountains along the Manitoba Cuesta.

North of the "Mixedwood" lies the northern "Coniferous Forest" in which very few broadleaved trees are found. Besides white spruce, the types to be found include balsam fir (*Abies balsamea*), black spruce (*Picea mariana*), larch or tamarack (*Larix laricina*), jack pine (*Pinus Banksiana*) and white birch (*Betula alba*). For the most part, the trees are small and it is a rather scrubby forest. Black spruce and tamarack especially are trees of wet or swampy habi-

tats and there are also large areas of open bog or muskeg. This forest is not regarded as of much economic significance, except as a habitat for game and fur bearing animals.

Northward of the "Coniferous Forest", in northeastern Saskatchewan and northern Manitoba, lies the "Subarctic Forest", sometimes known as "the land of little sticks". Here the species are much the same as in the above mentioned belt but the trees are fewer and much smaller and slower growing. There is also more open ground, rock and muskeg. It is, of course, a transition to the Arctic Tundra or great barren ground which comprises so much of Northern Canada. This latter formation extends far southward along the shores of Hudson Bay and includes a considerable area of lowland in northeastern Manitoba.

The "Mountain Forest" belt along the eastern flank of the Rocky Mountains is somewhat different from the forests of the plains. Here are found such trees as Engelmann spruce (*Picea Engelmanni*), lodgepole pine (*Pinus contorta*), Alpine fir (*Abies lasiocarpa*), white bark pine (*Pinus albi-*

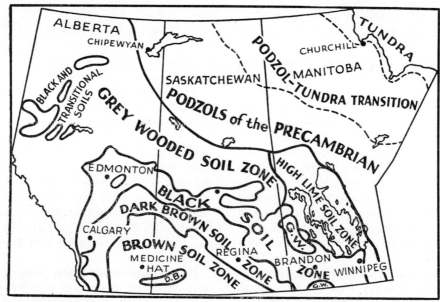

Figure 222. *The Soil Zones of the Prairie Provinces.* (After Ellis, Wyatt, Mitchell, Leahey and others).

*caulis*), Alpine larch (*Larix Lyallii*) and even Douglas fir (*Pseudotsuga taxifolia*).

The "Great Lakes Forest" belt is also quite different from the chief forest areas of the Prairie Provinces. It occupies only a small area in southeastern Manitoba, an extension of the much larger areas in Ontario and Minnesota. Here, on appropriate sites, are found a large number of tree species including white cedar (*Thuja occidentalis*), white spruce (*Picea glauca*), white pine (*Pinus strobus*), red pine (*P. resinosa*), balsam poplar (*Populus tacamahacca*), large toothed aspen (*Populus grandidentata*), white elm (*Ulmus americana*), basswood (*Tilia glabra*), Manitoba maple (*Acer negundo*), and bur oak (*Quercus macrocarpa*).

## The Soils of the Prairie Provinces

Soil geography and, indeed, the whole of modern soil science is of comparatively recent development. The pioneer explorers, who investigated the suitability for settlement of the Canadian Prairies, said very little about soils, and they reported their observations upon the relief of the land and upon its vegetative cover with an occasional note about sand, clay or stones.

Modern soil survey work was started in Alberta and Saskatchewan by the respective agricultural colleges in 1921, after a period of widespread crop failure. Manitoba Agricultural College began organized soil surveys in that province in 1927. In the 1930's the Dominion Department of Agriculture began to co-operate in the work. Many maps and survey reports have been published by these agencies and from them we can obtain a reasonably accurate picture of the soils of the Prairie Provinces (see figure 222).

### The Brown Soil Zone

The Brown Soil Zone comprises the southwestern part of Saskatchewan and the southeastern part of Alberta. Brown Soils are found, also, in many places in the interior valleys of British Columbia.

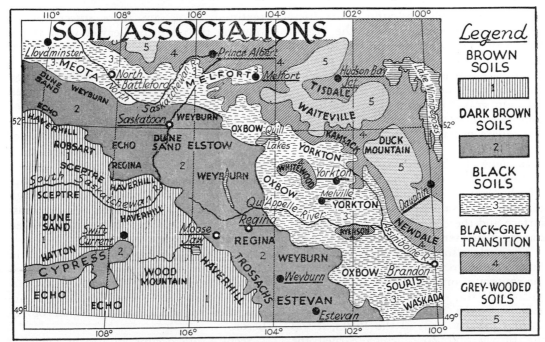

Figure 223. *Soil Association of Southern Saskatchewan.* (After Mitchell *et al*). Each landscape area is characterized by an association of soil types which is mapped under the name of the district in which it was first described.

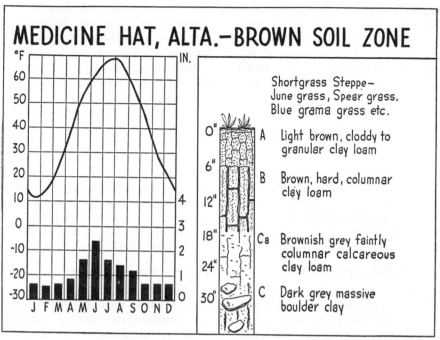

Figure 224. *Environment of the Brown Soil Zone.*

The Brown Soils are found in the driest part of the treeless prairie, the region which the explorers agreed was too dry for agricultural settlement. The climate, as we have already seen, may be classed as semi-arid and the vegetative cover, a typical short grass formation. The area of this zone is estimated at 32,500,000 acres (51,000 square miles) of which about 25% is arable land.

In general, the Brown Soils have the shallowest profiles of the grassland soils. The horizon of accumulation of lime, and often of other salts as well, is closer to the surface and the concentration of these substances is greater.

The surface soil is light in colour, sometimes almost grey rather than brown, and the content of organic matter is low. When cultivated, the organic matter is rapidly exhausted and soil drifting takes place. During the dry years of the 1930's, it was the Brown Soil Zone which earned the title of the "Dustbowl" of Western Canada. Naturally, the sandy soils and lighter

textured loams are more susceptible to blowing than are the heavier soils. Water erosion is also a problem in the areas of greater surface relief.

Brown Soils are of a reasonably high degree of natural fertility and, when enough rain falls, they produce wheat of the highest quality. It is in this region that large irrigation projects are under way in both Alberta and Saskatchewan. A great deal of this zone is grazing land or range, and, in spite of the recurrent temptation to plough it up in periods of high wheat prices, it should be left in grass since it furnishes excellent pasture when properly managed.

Some of the more widespread soils in this zone in Saskatchewan are comprised in the Sceptre, Haverhill and Echo associations. Similar soils, but not named, are described in the adjoining region of Alberta.

Sceptre soils occupy an area of 2,000,000 acres along the South Saskatchewan River, from the Alberta boundary to Elbow. They are developed upon post-glacial lake deposits and are of heavy texture although the surface soils are quite granular in structure. They occupy areas of gentle relief and are free of stones, hence well suited to tractor farming. These soils resist drought well, have good natural fertility and are used for wheat growing by alternating with summer fallow in a two-year rotation.

Haverhill soils are found on rolling morainic uplands, occupying about 8,500,-000 acres in Saskatchewan. The texture ranges from clay loam to light loam and stones are sometimes abundant. Drainage is fair but alkaline sloughs are not uncommon. The lighter soils drift readily after cultivation but wheat may be grown on the heavier soils. Water erosion is common on slopes.

The Echo soil association occurs south and west of the Frenchman River, south and southwest of Kerrobert and in the Central Butte district, occupying about 1,500,000 acres. The parent material is a glacial till containing a great deal of Cretaceous marine shales and thus heavily charged with "alkali" salts. The soil profile is of the solonetz type with a heavy, impervious B horizon. The agricultural value of these soils is limited by wind erosion of the surface soil with the formation of numerous "burnt-out" areas.

## The Dark Brown Soil Zone

The Dark Brown Soils are also found under open grasslands, but with better moisture conditions and a heavier cover of vegetation. They occupy an area of about 35,000,000 acres, mainly contained in a belt, 50 to 100 miles in width, surrounding the region of Brown Soils. About 18,500,000 acres are in Saskatchewan and the rest in Alberta. To the casual observer there seems little difference in the landscapes of the two zones and there is no sharp boundary. Both areas were included in Palliser's "triangle".

In comparison with the Brown Soils, the surface is somewhat deeper as well as

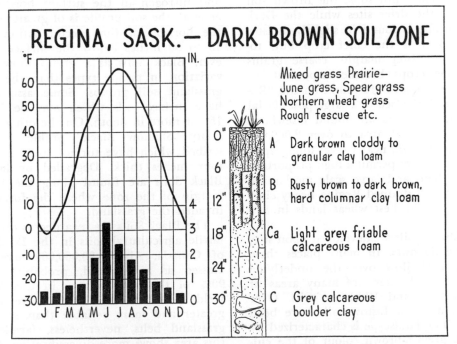

Figure 225. *Environment of the Dark Brown Soil Zone.*

darker, and contains more organic matter. The horizon of lime accumulation is usually found at a depth of 10 to 18 inches.

The agricultural resources of this zone are much greater than those of the Brown Soil Zone. The organic matter content, natural fertility and moisture holding capacity are higher and, consequently, the productivity of these soils is much greater. Over 60% (21,000,000 acres) of this zone is regarded as arable land, most of which is now in use. The chief crop is wheat and this belt is recognized as the one in which the most reliable high quality is to be obtained.

The Weyburn association is the most widespread in the Dark Brown Soil Zone, occupying an area of more than 7,750,000 acres in Saskatchewan. There are also large areas of similar soils in Alberta. These soils have developed upon glacial till with a somewhat more favourable topography than the Haverhill soils, but stones are a problem. Along the zone boundary there are mixed areas of Weyburn and Haverhill soils, the Brown soil occupying the drier sites while the Dark Brown profile is found in slightly moister areas. Wheat is the chief crop but, toward the moister margin, coarse grains and forage crops become important.

The Regina soils are found on the "Regina Plains", the bed of a large post-glacial lake. Smaller tracts are found elsewhere, bringing the total area to over 2,000,000 acres. The smooth, nearly level topography and lack of stones permit a high proportion of arable land and large scale mechanization. The well drained Regina heavy clays are rated as the best wheat lands in Saskatchewan.

The Elstow soils are developed upon silty lacustrine deposits. In many places these are rather shallow over the underlying glacial till and there are many areas of mixed Elstow and Weyburn soils. Over 2,250,000 acres of Elstow soils have been mapped. The landscape is characterized by the dark greyish-brown colour of the cultivated soil, spotted with light grey, limy patches and darker grey, leached, solonetzic areas. There are relatively few stones and little waste land except around the saline lakes and sloughs which, however, are less common than in the Weyburn association. Farms are well developed and wheat is the dominant crop.

The Cypress association is found on the Cypress Hills plateau which, although well within the Brown Soil Zone, constitutes an enclave of Dark Brown Soil because of its elevation and resultant more humid climate.

## The Black Soil Zone

The Black Soils are found beneath the "tall grass" cover of the "Park" belt which lies between the open prairie and the forest in all three Prairie Provinces. The area of the Black Soil Zone is estimated to be 42,000,000 acres. In keeping with their more favourable moisture supply, these soils are characterized by a darker colour and a higher content of organic matter and nitrogen in the surface horizon. In general, the soil profile is of greater depth, the horizon of lime accumulation lying 15 to 30 inches below the surface. However, Black Soils as a group show more variation in profile types than the other grassland soil groups. Some associations have surface soils which may be 12" to 15" or more in depth. On the other hand, many "Shallow Black" profiles are described which have surface soils less than four inches thick. Degraded or leached Black Soils are found along the humid margin of the zone where the forest has invaded the grassland.

The Black Soils are regarded as the most fertile agricultural soils in the Dominion of Canada. About 30,000,000 acres are classed as arable and, probably, about 90% of this area is now in use. While yields of wheat in this belt are always greater and more reliable than in other grassland belts, nevertheless, farming in this area shows more diversification. Other

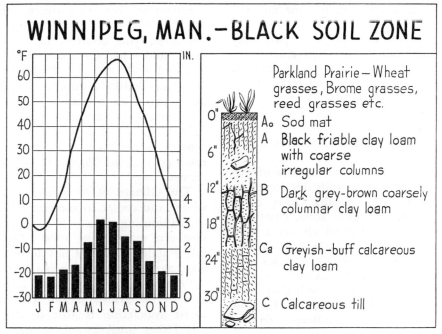

Figure 226. *Environment of the Black Soil Zone.*

grains and forage crops are grown as the basis of a livestock economy and farm incomes may be more largely derived from the sale of hogs and dairy products. The excellence of these soils is shown by the fact that, whereas the size of farm in the Dark Brown Soil Zone is about one square mile and about 1,000 acres in the Brown Soil Zone, most of the farms in the Black Soil Zone have an area of about 320 acres.

The transitional Degraded Black Soils are regarded as intermediate in agricultural value between the Black Soils and the Grey Wooded Soils. They are very widespread, however, extending from Eastern Manitoba to the Peace River and are found even in the Hay River area of northwestern Alberta.

Some members of the Black Soil group are described below in greater detail.

The Oxbow association is the most extensive group of Black Soils, covering an area of 6,750,000 acres in Saskatchewan and a large area of southwestern Manitoba as well. Certain areas in Alberta, too, while

not named, must certainly be correlated with the Oxbow soils identified just to the east of them. These soils, as was the case with the Haverhill and Weyburn, are developed upon "undifferentiated glacial till" and the surface has the characteristic 'swale and swell' of ground moraine. The surface texture is commonly a loam, but ranges from a light loam to a clay loam. Stones are present in all Oxbow soils and in most places must be removed from cultivated land. The rolling areas contain considerable waste land in the form of slough and rough upland. Much of the uncultivated land is covered with trees and scrub and its value for pasture is lowered. However, the trees supply fuel and fencing, afford shelter to livestock and add greatly to the appearance of the farmsteads.

The Yorkton association occupies over 1,800,000 acres of undulating land in which small depressional areas are of frequent occurrence. The parent material is glacial till, modified somewhat by having been submerged around the margins of glacial lakes. The soils are high in lime and the A horizon is unusually deep, often 14 inches or more. For the most part they are only moderately stony. The chief drawback of this association is that it contains large areas of low, wet, non-arable land. The farms have small acreages under cultivation and the fields are irregular in shape. Mixed farming is carried on and, in the Yorkton district itself, dairying is important.

The Melfort association consists of medium to heavy textured soils developed on heavy, glacial lake deposits. They cover an area of about 600,000 acres, chiefly in the Carrot River Valley which was a western extension of extinct Lake Agassiz. The surface soil is stone free, deep, black and fertile, producing high yields of both grain and forage crops. Farms are well developed and the Melfort district is one of the most attractive agricultural landscapes in the province.

## The Grey Wooded Soil Zone

As defined by officials of the Dominion Department of Agriculture, the Grey Wooded Soil Zone covers about 150,000,-000 acres, lying between the Rocky Mountains and the Canadian Shield. Grey Wooded Soils are also found in the interior of British Columbia. Though very large, this zone appears to have a rather low percentage of arable land and much of the best of it is already occupied by pioneer agriculture. It is estimated that eventually about 25,000,000 acres may be farmed.

The climate of this zone is colder in winter and cooler in summer than that of the adjoining Black Soil Zone. At its southern margin the mean annual rainfall is about 16 inches but decreases northward as the temperature falls. The climate is, therefore, slightly more humid than that of the grassland and a mixed wood forest association is able to maintain itself. Lakes, muskegs and streams are characteristic of the zone.

Under such a vegetation, the surface is normally covered by 1 - 4 inches of forest

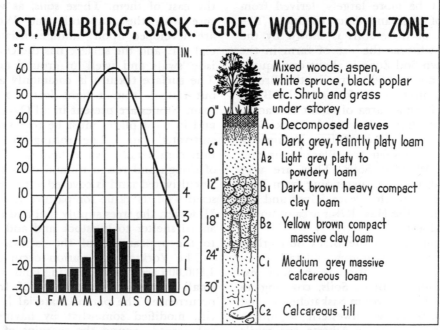

Figure 227. *Environment of the Grey-wooded Soil Zone.*

litter and mould. Under this is a shallow, dark grey surface soil overlying a grey, leached horizon which may be several inches in depth. This leached zone or $A_2$ horizon is the hallmark of forest soils everywhere and shows the relationship of these soils to the Podzols of Eastern Canada. The Grey Wooded Soils differ, however, in having a zone of lime accumulation at the base of the profile, thus resembling grassland soils. The surface soils, also, are only slightly acid while the eastern Podzols are much more so. They are considerably lower in natural fertility than the grassland soils.

Mixed farming, with emphasis on livestock and the growth of clover, seems necessary in order to utilize these soils advantageously, since they do not produce wheat of a high quality.

The Waiteville association is the most extensive yet mapped in the Grey Soil Zone of Saskatchewan. It occupies about 1,750,000 acres but there are large areas of very similar soils in Northern Alberta. The parent material is a stony till, the surface relief being undulating to rolling with sloughs, muskegs and marshy depressions quite common. Most of the surface soils are loams, but clay loams and light loams occur. Waiteville soils are typically podzolic, or leached, forest soils but the association includes many mixed areas with degraded black soils. Though slightly acid on the surface, a zone of lime accumulation occurs at a depth of about 30 inches.

These soils are low in organic matter, nitrogen, phosphorus and sulphur. The low initial productivity may, however, be greatly increased by the use of manure, commercial fertilizers and crop rotations including leguminous crops.

Grey wooded loam to the extent of over 300,000 acres has been mapped in the St. Ann area, west of Edmonton. It is the largest single class of soil in the area and is representative of the wooded soils of Alberta. The topography varies from gently rolling to quite hilly and the surface, in some places, is quite stony. The area was at one time covered by heavy poplar growth but forest fires have removed a large part. Poplars up to 12 inches in diameter are found. Within the area are depressions containing peat and black spruce; such areas are of little value for agriculture. On the uplands, under normal conditions, the forest litter and mould are from 2 to 4 inches in depth, the leached horizon is from 4 to 12 inches and the horizon of lime accumulation is found at a depth of about four feet. The surface soil is acid. These loams constitute the main agricultural resource of the wooded areas but they have a low level of natural fertility and require careful handling in order to produce good crop yields.

## The High Lime Soil Zone

The High Lime Soils are intrazonal soils which have not developed normal characteristics because of the great amount of limestone in the parent material. They are found in many places in the Prairie Provinces, but in Central Manitoba, particularly in the Interlake district, they occur to the practical exclusion of the normal Grey Wooded Soils that we would expect to find there. This area has therefore been called the High Lime Soil Zone. The soil profile is very shallow and is characterized by a dark coloured surface horizon, which is finely granular and friable, over a marly lime accumulation of a rather crumbly consistency. Toward the north where moisture supply is greater, there is a tendency to greater leaching of the surface soil. Where stone-free or reasonably so, these are good agricultural soils, but owing to the high content of lime they need phosphate fertilizers. Coarse grains, roots and grasses are suitable crops on these soils and they are outstanding for the production of alfalfa seed, which, along with barley, ranks as a cash crop. Livestock and mixed farming, on the whole, are more successful than the production of cash grains. There are large areas which have been farmed at one time but are now abandoned and it is felt that agriculture should not be greatly expanded, especially on the shallow and stony soils of this area.

## Significance of the Physical Background

Rocks, landforms, climate, vegetation and soils constitute the physical background. They cannot be said to impart any widespread uniformity but rather tend to break the area into a number of small natural regions. In terms of human geography, however, we shall see that a stage has been set on which settlement may take place.

It is true that climate imposed a distinct hazard upon agriculture until suitable crop varieties were found but, apart from this, the Prairie Plains with their favourable topography, fertile soils and lack of an impeding forest cover, formed a desirable area for the settlement of European peoples. Lack of the physical basis of support for close permanent settlement in the adjoining zones means almost inevitably that they become integrated as part of a larger human use region. By the provision of timber, minerals, fish and furs they afford a broader resource base for the provinces concerned, although at the same time giving them additional administrative problems. Lastly, it must be said that the more the physical background of this great region is studied, the less justification there is for the interprovincial lines which make of it three provinces instead of one.

## Selected References

Alden, W. C. *Physiographic Development of the Northern Great Plains.* Bull. Geol. Soc. Am. vol. 35, pp. 385-424. 1924.

Allen, John A. *Geology.* Research Council of Alberta. Report No. 34. Edmonton. 1943.

Antevs, Ernst. *Late-Glacial Correlations and Ice Recession in Manitoba.* Geological Survey Memoir 168. Canada Department of Mines. Ottawa. 1931.

Connor, A. J. *The Climate of Manitoba.* Manitoba Economic Survey Board. Winnipeg. 1939.

Ellis, J. H. *The Soils of Manitoba.* Manitoba Economic Survey Board. Winnipeg. 1938.

Johnston, W. A. *Moraines and Glacial Lakes in Southern Saskatchewan and Southern Alberta.* Trans. Roy. Soc. Canada. 3rd series, Vol. 25, Sec. 4, pp. 29-44. 1931.

Johnston, W. A. *Surface Deposits and Groundwater Supply of Winnipeg Map-area.* Geological Survey Memoir 174. Canada Department of Mines. Ottawa. 1934.

Mackintosh, W. A. *Prairie Provinces: The Geographic Setting.* The Macmillan Company of Canada Ltd. Toronto. 1934.

Mitchell, J., H. C. Moss, J. S. Clayton and F.H. Edmunds. *Soil Survey of Southern Saskatchewan, Townships 1-48.* Saskatchewan Soil Survey Report No. 12. Saskatoon. 1944.

Rawson, D. C. *et al. The Big River Survey.* University of Saskatchewan. Saskatoon. 1943.

Stevenson, H. I. *The Forests of Manitoba.* Manitoba Economic Survey Board. Winnipeg. 1938.

Wallace, R. C. *The Geological Formations of Manitoba.* The Natural History Society of Manitoba. 1925.

Williams, M. Y. *The Physiography of the Southern Plains of Canada.* Trans. Roy. Soc. Canada. 3rd Series. Vol. 23, Sec. 4, pp. 61-79. 1929.

Williams, M. Y. and W. S. Dyer. *Geology of Southern Alberta and Southwestern Saskatchewan.* Geological Survey Memoir 163. Canada Dept. of Mines, Ottawa, 1930.

# CHAPTER 17

# Patterns of Settlement and Economic Activity in the Prairie Provinces.

THE patterns of human geography in the Prairie Provinces are interesting because they are the result of a comparatively brief period of development. Having been created in the modern period, they reflect clearly the nature of man's adjustment to the environment in a technical and scientific age, without the added handicap of having to overcome historical inertia. There were, of course, human patterns before the building of the railway but they have been completely submerged by the wave of settlement which followed. The present marks the end of the colonization phase and the beginning of urbanization and is, therefore, an opportune moment to take stock.

## Population

### Distribution

The population of the Prairie Provinces,

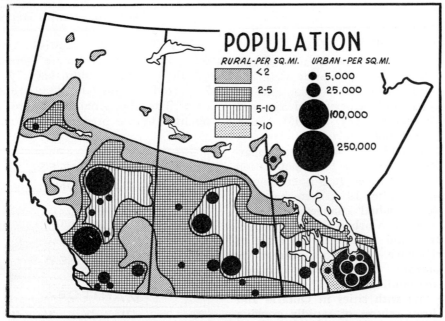

Figure 228. *Population Distribution in the Prairie Provinces.* (Based on the 1946 Census of the Prairie Provinces) The density pattern of rural population has a tendency to agree with that of precipitation.

according to the census of 1951, was 2,853,-821. The average population density, therefore, is about 3½ per square mile. Actually, the population is nearly all in the southern half of the area, making an effective density of 7 per square mile in the settled regions. Even here it ranges from 2 to 10 per square mile as shown in Figure 228. This, of course, is sparse compared with 100 per square mile in Southern Ontario or even the 22 per square mile of the Maritime Provinces. Both of these regions, it must be remembered, also have their unoccupied areas.

in progress. While the total population has fallen slightly, that of the urban places has begun to rise. The change is more evident in Saskatchewan and Alberta, particularly the latter, because the cities of Calgary and Edmonton have both grown to over 100,000 while Winnipeg has not increased at the same rate.

### Ethnic Origin

The population of the Prairie Provinces is derived from many ethnic groups. In 1951, less than 46% claimed to be of British origin, including about 22% English,

| Table 16 | | Population Growth in the Prairie Provinces | | | |
|---|---|---|---|---|---|
| Year | Total | Rural | % | Urban | % |
| 1901 | 419,512 | 316,277 | 75.5 | 103,235 | 24.5 |
| 1911 | 1,328,121 | 858,699 | 65.0 | 469,422 | 35.0 |
| 1921 | 1,956,082 | 1,252,604 | 64.0 | 703,478 | 36.0 |
| 1931 | 2,353,529 | 1,468,147 | 62.5 | 915,482 | 37.5 |
| 1936 | 2,415,545 | 1,547,898 | 64.0 | 877,647 | 36.0 |
| 1941 | 2,421,905 | 1,496,300 | 61.8 | 923,605 | 38.2 |
| 1946 | 2,362,941 | 1,354,454 | 57.4 | 1,008,847 | 42.6 |
| 1951 | 2,547,770 | 1,406,045 | 55.0 | 1,141,725 | 45.0 |
| 1956 | 2,853,821 | 1,385,411 | 48.6 | 1,468,410 | 51.4 |

Data from Census Reports.

### Population Growth

During the first three decades of this century, the Prairie Provinces were the fastest growing parts of Canada; since at its beginning, both Alberta and Saskatchewan were almost empty. By 1931, apparently, all the immediately useful territory was filled up and there has been comparatively little change in total population in the last two decades. It is interesting to note, also, that after 1911, there has been only a very gradual change in the relationship between urban and rural populations. It would seem that the cities of the Prairies have, up to now, been pretty closely controlled by the service demands of their surrounding areas. They have not, as is the case with cities in Ontario and Quebec, been centres of rapidly growing manufacturing industries. The figures for 1946, however, indicate that a change is

10% Irish and 13% Scottish. Among the other European origins are German 12%, Ukrainian 10%, Scandinavian 7%, French 7%, Netherlandic and Polish about 4% each. The aboriginal inhabitants, as represented by the present Indian and Metis

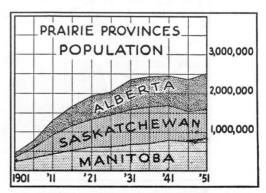

Figure 229. *Population Growth in the Prairie Provinces.*

people amount to a little less than 3% of the total population, or about 65,000.

## Settlement Patterns

### The Indian Period

There were several tribes of Indians in the territory now known as the Prairie Provinces and, while they did not have established territorial boundaries, usually they kept to their own regions. In the north and northwest lived two tribes of forest hunters and trappers, the Chipewyan and Beaver. They were fairly tall, broad headed people who spoke the Athapascan language. The Saracees of Central Alberta also spoke Athapascan but their culture was otherwise more like that of the Plains Indians. In Southern Manitoba and Southern Saskatchewan were the Stoney or Assiniboine peoples who were part of the great group speaking the Sioux language. In the territory between these southern and northern groups, comprising the grasslands and eastern forest area, were various tribes speaking the Algonkian tongue. These included the Blackfeet, Blood, and Piegan of southern Alberta and the Crees of Central Saskatchewan and Manitoba.

The aborigines can hardly be said to have had any true settlements before the white men came. In both the forest and the grassland environments they lived by hunting and they were forced to be as migratory as the game animals which they followed. There were, of course, many favorite camping sites, situated at river crossings or on portages and to these the tribes might return with great regularity year after year. They did not build permanent villages in the same way as the agricultural Indian tribes of the Great Lakes region.

With the coming of the white fur trader, the pattern changed. At first the Indians set up temporary encampments at the traders' forts for a short period during the summer when they brought in their winter catch of furs. Gradually the settlements became more permanent. Then too, many of the voyageurs in the employ of the fur trading companies married native women and the Metis race was founded. These people usually regarded the settlement as home rather than the tribal lands of their mothers' kinfolk. Many, though not all, of the voyageurs were French Canadian and the little settlements along the Red and Saskatchewan Rivers resembled those along the St. Lawrence.

### The Geographic Pattern of the Fur Trade

The annals of the fur trade are usually related against a vague and shadowy territorial background known as Rupert's Land or the Great Northwest, most of the details of which remain unmapped. But as well as a history there is also a geography of the fur trade in which the forts, routes and fur producing areas can be given precise locations. True it was a changing geography, as new areas were tapped, new routes traversed and new forts built by new groups of traders. Perhaps, rather than a changing geography, we should regard it as a series of geographies, one after the other. Just as each area of the earth's surface may have a section of history devoted to the activities of man in that area, so each period of history may have a geography relating the pattern of those activities to the surface

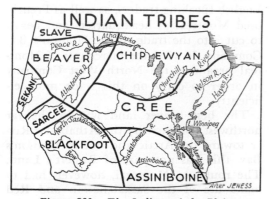

Figure 230. *The Indians of the Plains.*

Figure 231. *Routes of the Rival Fur Traders.* The routes of the Hudson's Bay Company led to the Bay and by ship to England. The routes of the North West Company led to Winnipeg and Lake Superior and thence to Montreal.

of the earth. The study of these geographical patterns of the past is known as Historical Geography and from it we gain much insight into the origins of present day patterns.

For approximately two centuries, the fur trade was the chief and almost the only economic activity of the Prairie Provinces. The Hudson's Bay Company was founded in 1670 and Rupert's Land was purchased by the Dominion of Canada in 1869. There are many points in this long history which might be chosen for study but we cannot do so now. One of the most interesting periods, undoubtedly, is the one at the beginning of the nineteenth century when rival companies were competing for the trade.

The French in Canada were also interested in the fur trade of the west. Using the corridor of the St. Lawrence and the Great Lakes the La Verendrye's, from 1731

to 1743, became the "Pioneers of the Plains". They were, very likely, the first white men in the Red River country, and the first to sight the Rocky Mountains. Thus Montreal, already the greatest fur trading centre on the continent, began to extend its influence into Rupert's Land. After Canada passed into British hands, English speaking traders, as well as French, used Montreal as headquarters and began to cut into the trade of the Hudson's Bay Company. In 1784 the merchants of Montreal organized the North West Company in order to carry on this trade more efficiently.

The best beaver land was in the far northwest. Drained by the Athabaska River toward the Arctic and not to Hudson's Bay, this was not part of Rupert's Land. The routes to Montreal, however, had to make use of the Saskatchewan and Red River systems. Within a few years the rival companies covered the disputed territory with a network of forts. Sometimes, as at Winnipeg, Fort Qu'Appelle, Cumberland Lake and Edmonton, the forts of the two companies were quite close together and the rivalry was intense. In the far northwest and in British Columbia, the Hudson's Bay Company had few outposts, while the North West traders did not attempt to establish themselves close to the Bay.

With their North American headquarters at York Factory the Hudson's Bay Company enjoyed a great geographical advantage over their rivals in Montreal. To offset this, the latter established an intermediate headquarters at Fort William on Lake Superior. Brigades of voyageurs or canoemen came from Montreal each summer bringing supplies and taking back the furs brought in by brigades from the outposts. The latter returned home with the goods from Montreal. The men were thus not required to be away from home over winter as they certainly would have been had they made the complete journey from Montreal to Lake Athabaska.

Eventually, the two companies were amalgamated and, from 1821 onward, the fur trade was in the hands of an expanded Hudson's Bay Company. Instead of canoes they began to use York boats which were stronger than canoes and could carry heavier loads. York boat brigades required more than two months to make the journey from Edmonton, or from Lac la Loche, to either Fort Garry or York Factory. Overland routes were also established, along which the fur brigades travelled by oxdrawn Red River carts. One such route was the 500 mile trail from Fort Garry to Fort Carlton, about 40 miles southeast of Prince Albert on the North Saskatchewan River. About 300 Red River carts travelled this route each summer. A second brigade of about 500 carts made two trips each year from Fort Garry to St. Paul in Minnesota, where they made connection with American systems of transportation.

With the building of the Canadian Pacific Railway, however, the use of overland brigades came to an end. On the rivers too, the company began to use small steamers driven by a paddle wheel at the stern. The first of these was placed on the Red River in 1861, later others were placed on the northern rivers.

The fur trade is still of importance in the northern part of the Prairie Provinces and is the source of livelihood for many Indians and Metis. Furs travel to market much more quickly now, often by airplane. The Hudson's Bay Company is still in business, not only in its scattered outposts but also in its large department stores in Winnipeg and other Prairie cities.

The geography of the fur trade deserves extended study by the students of western Canada since many important points in the pattern of settlement originated as fur trading posts or as nodes in the early system of transportation.

## The Selkirk Settlement

The fur trading companies were not interested in promoting settlement of the country; they wanted it left as it was. The first agricultural settlement was that fostered by Thomas Douglas, third Earl of Selkirk, a young Scotsman who was interested in finding new homes for Scottish crofters. Unable to buy land in the Red River Valley from the Hudson's Bay Company, he and his friends purchased a controlling interest in the company and were thus able to compel the directors to sell the land.

The first colonists arrived at York Factory late in the summer of 1811, reaching the Red River the next summer. Others came out during the following years. They had a hard time at first. Food was scarce and their first crops, being unsuited to the environment, resulted in failure. Plagues of grasshoppers attacked their crops. The Red River, also, overflowed its banks, flooding their farms. Although the Indians were not hostile, the colony was harried by the Metis and the men of the North West Company. Twenty-two settlers were killed at the battle of Seven Oaks. Only after the union of the fur trading companies in 1821, were the colonists left in peace.

The settlement was laid out along the river, the farms being long narrow strips. Only a small amount of land was cropped and each family tried to grow everything they needed for themselves. They also had to make everything they used including furniture, clothing, household utensils and farm implements since they were completely isolated from the markets of the world. Not for many years could wheat from the Red River Valley be transported to European markets in exchange for manufactured goods.

In spite of all hardships, however, the population of the colony continued to increase. In 1870 the descendants of the Red River settlers, the fur traders and the Metis numbered 12,000, and the district which Lord Selkirk had purchased became the province of Manitoba.

## Exploring the Agricultural Resources

The treaty of 1818 established the 49th parallel as the southern boundary of British North America from the Lake of the Woods to the Rocky Mountains. During the next 40 years many settlers entered the American West but, under the control of the Hudson's Bay Company, Rupert's Land remained empty. As Canada continued to grow there were many Canadians who felt that the western lands should belong to Canada. They were apprehensive that if they remained empty too long they might fall into the hands of the United States. Indeed, transportation to the west was already much easier by American routes.

In 1857 the British Colonial Office sent Captain John Palliser to examine and report upon the area. During the years 1857 to 1860, he travelled from Lake Superior

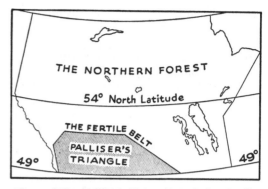

Figure 232. *Palliser's Triangle and the Fertile Belt.* Palliser's Triangle includes most of the open prairie. He believed that only the wooded land was fit for agricultural occupation.

to beyond the Rocky Mountains. As a result of his explorations, he divided the plains into two parts, a "fertile belt" and the "true prairie" which he regarded as a semi-arid desert. The latter area, according to him, embraces most of what is now the southern parts of both Saskatchewan and Alberta. In spite of the fact that it is an irregular, five-sided area, it is often referred to as "Palliser's triangle".

During the same years the Government of Canada also dispatched explorers to the west. Professor H. Y. Hind was commissioned to report on the country of the Assiniboine and the Saskatchewan. In general he agreed with Palliser, stating that the treeless prairie was unsuitable for settlement but that millions of acres of arable land were available in "the wooded area", as he termed the Park Belt.

Later, Professor John Macoun accompanied the engineers of the Canadian Pacific Railway across the prairies. He disagreed with Palliser and Hind, allowing only 20,000 square miles for the arid country of Palliser's triangle. He was the first to point out that most of the rainfall came during the summer months, and also that warm summer conditions extended to the sixtieth parallel in the northwest.

Professor Hind had reported that there were 11,000,000 acres of arable land and an equal additional area suitable for pasture. Professor Macoun estimated that there were 150,000,000 acres fit for crops and pasture. The total amount of occupied land, according to the census of 1946, was 117,000,000 acres of which 65,000,000 acres were improved and 42,000,000 acres were classed as prairie or natural pasture.

## The Railway Pattern

The settlement and economic development of the Prairie Provinces might almost be said to have been under complete control of the railways. It is important, therefore, to make a careful study of the railway pattern.

At the time of Confederation, British North America consisted of a series of small, disconnected, settled areas along the southern border of a great wilderness. Anyone of them might have, and did have, more dealings with its neighbour on the south, than with its fellows. The first railroad reached Winnipeg in 1878, providing connections with St. Paul and Chicago.

If the new nation were to function at all it would have to be knit together; consequently the building of a transcontinental railway was the first task of the Dominion Government. In fact, it was a pledge to the new provinces of the west, particularly to British Columbia which was separated from the rest of the country by the uninhabited prairie.

In spite of the adverse reports of Palliser and Hind upon the character of the country, the railway was built along the shortest route and directly across the semi-arid grasslands. Much of the land received as subsidy by the Canadian Pacific Railway company, however, was located further north in the fertile belt.

The C.P.R. was completed across the prairies in 1885. Within a few years, branch lines were built from Regina to Saskatoon and Prince Albert and from Calgary to Edmonton. Southern Manitoba also saw a number of short lines built in its settled territory (see figure 233).

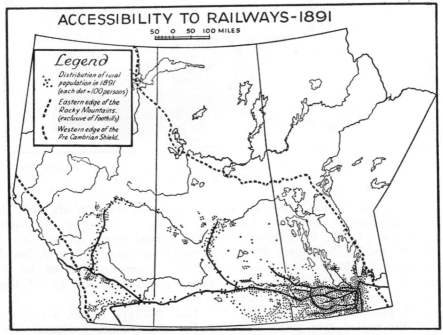

Figure 233. *Accessibility to Railways in 1891*. (After Mackintosh). There was one trans-prairie line, a loose net in southern Manitoba and branches to Saskatoon and Edmonton.

Aided by these railways, settlers poured north into the "fertile crescent" while relatively few located in the semi-arid south. A close net of railways, however, began to appear in Manitoba and eastern Assiniboia. After the formation of the provinces of Saskatchewan and Alberta, two more trans-prairie lines were completed. These were the Canadian Northern and the Grand Trunk Pacific, both traversing the fertile crescent to the north

Under the conditions of early settlement, with horse drawn vehicles and poor prairie trails, the distance from the railway was highly important. While of necessity, hauls of 50 miles might be undertaken, yet studies have shown that it was not economical to haul grain more than 12 to 15 miles. Thus the railways needed to be about 20 miles apart, with stations or sidings every seven to ten miles.

With the coming of motor vehicles and

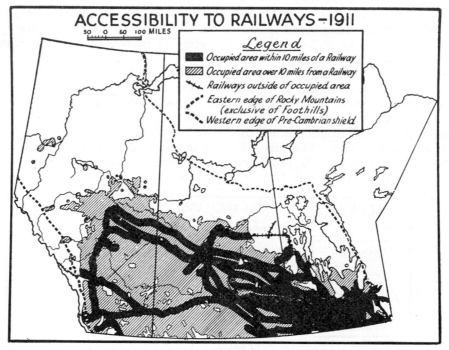

Figure 234. *Accessibility to Railways in 1911.* (After Mackintosh). Western Saskatchewan and Alberta had large areas still untouched by railways.

of the open grassland. At the same time, most of the prairie was occupied, save for small scattered areas in the most difficult parts of the dry south. (See figure 234).

During the period of World War I both railway building and land settlement were less rapid but, during the twenties, further expansion took place. By 1931 there was very little of the settled area which was not within ten miles of a railway. (See figure 235).

the improvement of roads, these distances are not so important but the pattern had become established. As we view it now, railways were overbuilt and, indeed, during the depression years of the thirties a number of unprofitable branch lines were removed.

The railways almost completely controlled the smaller nucleated settlements in the prairie provinces. The other factor of importance being water supply, the best

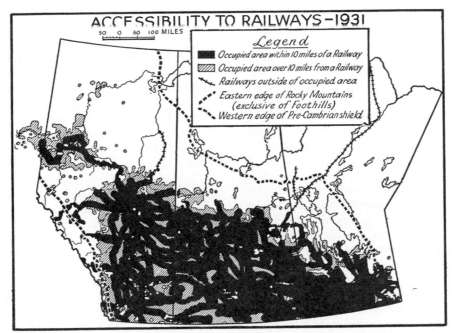

Figure 235. *Accessibility to Railways in 1931.* (After Mackintosh). By 1931 the railway net of the Prairie Provinces was practically complete.

locations are at creek and river crossings. In some cases, towns have outgrown their water supply as, for instance, Moose Jaw which now has to get water from the distant Saskatchewan River.

## The System of Land Survey

With the exception of a few early settled areas such as the Red River and Saskatchewan River settlements, the land of the Prairie Provinces is divided into practically square townships, each containing thirty-six sections of as nearly one mile square as is permitted by the convergence of the meridians.

For convenience in surveying, certain meridians were designated "principal meridians". The first of these is located a few miles west of Winnipeg at longitude 97° 27′30″ W, the second is 102° W, forming part of the Manitoba-Saskatchewan boundary, the third, at 106° W, is approximately in the middle of Saskatchewan while the fourth, at 110° W, forms the boundary between Saskatchewan and Al-

berta. The fifth principal meridian, at 114° W, passes through the eastern outskirts of Calgary and the sixth, at 118° W, bisects the Peace River district.

Base lines are surveyed east and west, the first base line being the 49th parallel of latitude, which is also the southern boundary of this part of Canada. Base lines are numbered consecutively from south to north and are 24 miles apart.

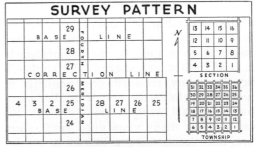

THE PATTERN OF LAND SURVEY
IN WESTERN CANADA

Figure 236. *The Pattern of Land Survey in Western Canada.* The country was covered with an astronomical grid of square-mile sections and six-mile townships.

Along each base line, points are established at six mile intervals and from them lines are surveyed 12 miles due north and 12 miles due south. These lines, 24 miles in length, are true meridians and converge toward the north; consequently, they are not directly in line with corresponding offsets from the next base line. Thus all north-south lines have a jog every 24 miles. The line along which these jogs occur, lying midway between the base lines, is known as the "correction line". Townships are numbered from south to north, beginning at the International Boundary. Each meridional row of townships is called a "range" and these are numbered from east to west, beginning at each principal meridian.

Each township is divided into sections of 640 acres or one square mile. Road allowances are provided every mile, east and west, and every second mile from north to south (see figure 236). Each section is divided into quarter sections of 160 acres each and into 16 legal subdivisions of 40 acres each. Both sections and subdivisions are numbered, beginning in the southeast corner. From these references exact locations may be given. Thus, Catherwood Station is in legal subdivision 4, section 6, township 35, range 11 west of the third meridian, which places it 38 miles west, and 11 miles south, of the centre of the city of Saskatoon.

## Land Grants

The ownership of land in the Prairie Provinces has had some important geographical consequences, more particularly in local settlement patterns. The Hudson's Bay Company retained one-twentieth of the land in the fertile belt, a total of more than 6,000,000 acres. A great deal of this was held for many years until land values rose, thus constituting a barrier to continuous settlement. The Canadian Pacific Railway Company received title to 25,000,-000 acres in the Prairie Provinces. Since, by contract stipulation, these lands must be "fairly fit for settlement", the C.P.R. became owner of a large area in the fertile belt. The C.P.R. lands were not continuous blocks for the company held only every other section. Other railway systems also received large grants of land which they offered for sale or disposed of to land companies which sold them to settlers. Another factor in the land pattern was the reservation of certain parcels as school lands.

The land which remained in the public domain after all reserves had been set aside was made available as free homesteads of 160 acres each. While not always the case, nevertheless, the tendency was for free land to be settled first and other lands to be purchased later. In this way a very loose pattern of rural settlement resulted with much land unoccupied at first. While this was a drawback at first, particularly in the provision of roads and schools, it has not been entirely detrimental. The size of farms on the prairies has continued to increase. There is now, in most sections, more occupied land than ever, but fewer farms. Had close settlement been the rule the rate of abandonment would have been higher.

## The Economic Development of the Prairie Provinces

In 1954, the Prairie Provinces produced about one fifth of the net national income. In Saskatchewan agriculture is the most important industry, but in Manitoba manufacturing is the largest industry and in Alberta both manufacturing and mining are important. Normally, 50% of the production is provided by agriculture.

## Agriculture

As we have already noted, the natural environment of the prairie region is quite different from that of the earlier settled regions of Eastern Canada. That difference is expected to be reflected in different crops and methods of agriculture. The east pursues diversified agriculture of many kinds, the prairies for the most part are devoted to grain growing and, in fact, have almost completely replaced the farms of the east in the production of wheat for export.

## Cereals

It is easy to say that because the prairie environment produces grass naturally, it should be the natural habitat for cereal crops which belong to the grass family. However, the cereals which the earliest settlers had available were poorly adapted, since they had for generations been selected for their fitness in the moister habitats of western Europe and eastern North America. Even those varieties suited to the subhumid central parts of U.S.A. did not suit the Canadian prairie because of its shorter growing season. The success of the west as a wheat growing region became possible only when new varieties were found. The first of these, Red Fife, though developed commercially in Ontario, undoubtedly came originally from the prairies, or steppes, of southern Russia. Through the use of Red Fife, Manitoba became a leading exporter of wheat and "Manitoba No. 1 Hard" became the standard of excellence on the world's wheat markets.

Much of the prairie area, however, had too short a growing season even for Red Fife Wheat. The Canadian Department of Agriculture, therefore, set plant breeders to work to develop new varieties. In 1911, Dr. Chas. E. Saunders (later Sir Charles) introduced Marquis which ripened a week earlier than Red Fife. With this new variety, successful wheat culture spread over the whole of the prairie region. It also became popular in the United States where, at one time, about 12,000,000 acres of this variety were grown. Later, newer varieties such as Garnet and Reward, which ripen several days earlier than Marquis, were produced. Thus the wheat belt was extended farther north.

Marquis wheat is not very resistant to stem rust which, in some years, has done more than $100,000,000 damage in Western Canada. In order to combat this menace, new rust resistant varieties, such as Thatcher, Apex and Renown, have been developed and they have largely replaced Marquis on the western wheat farms. The area devoted to wheat has grown to more than 25,000,000 acres and the annual crop ranges between 300,000,000 and 600,000,-000 bushels, ranking as the most important single crop produced by Canadian farmers.

The other important cereal crops are oats, grown on about 10,000,000 acres, and barley, on about 6,500,000 acres per year. Minor crops are rye, on 500,000 acres and flaxseed on about 1,000,000 acres.

## Changing Techniques

Great changes have taken place in the methods of growing grain in the Canadian West. The pioneers of the Red River colony dug their fields by hand, later using an oxdrawn wooden plough with an iron point. They cut their crop with scythes and sickles and bound the sheaves by hand. Threshing was done with the flail and the chaff removed by winnowing in the wind.

The great wave of settlement came after special machinery had been developed to suit prairie conditions in the United States. Steel ploughs drawn by horses were the rule Usually they were gang ploughs turning two or more furrows, drawn by four, six or eight horses. Sometimes steam tractors were used. Harrowing and seeding were also done with large machines. Nearly everyone has seen photographs of western threshing scenes. The large threshing machine, driven by a tractor, is equipped with a long pipe through which the straw is blown into a huge stack. The grain runs from a pipe into a waiting wagon box or, just as often, into a portable wooden granary from which it will be hauled to the elevator later in the season. Finally, grouped about the outfit will be four or more teams of horses drawing flat-floored stook wagons. Included in the picture are perhaps a dozen men. Harvest time was the busy season. For many years, thousands of extra labourers were brought from the east each summer on special trains. They operated the binders, stooked the grain, loaded the wagons and fed the sheaves into the threshing machine. When harvest was over most of them returned home, but many remained in the west, either making farms of their own or taking up residence in the growing cities.

The scene is changing rapidly. The harvest excursion is a thing of the past. The great gangs of men are no longer needed, nor the teams of horses. Tractor drawn combines now cut and thresh the grain in a single operation. Two men do the work; one to drive the tractor, the other to operate the combine. The grain is run into trucks which travel beside the combine until fully loaded when they are driven directly to the elevator.

### Agricultural Gradients

Prairie agriculture is by no means uniformly developed. The natural differences of soil and climate are reflected in differences in land use, creating landscape patterns which, in some areas, may be quite intricate and involved. A general idea of some of these differences, on a regional scale, may be obtained from the accompanying isopleth maps which are based on the census of 1946.

### Occupied Land

Figure 237 shows the occupied farm land as a percentage of total area. In the central prairies, the land is fully occupied, except for rough or wet areas and land put to other uses such as city sites, highways and airports. Around the margin lies a belt in which there are gradients. To the north there is a broad pioneer fringe but the transition from wilderness to agricultural landscape is quite abrupt on both eastern and western boundaries. The relationship to relief may be inferred

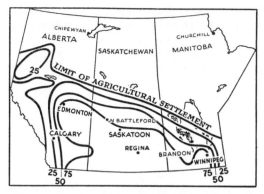

Figure 237. *Occupied Farm Land in the Prairie Provinces.* This map is based on the census figures for 1946, calculated as per cent of total area.

from the fact that the Regina Plains and the Red River Valley, both flat areas, have over 90% occupied land.

### Improved Land

The pattern of improved land in Figure 238 shows some correlation with that of occupied land, thinning out toward the

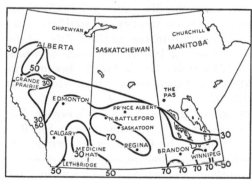

Figure 238. *Distribution of Improved Land in the Prairie Provinces.* The figures for 1946 are plotted as per cent of occupied farm land.

pioneer fringe in the north. It shows much greater obedience to climatic control, however, since throughout the dry belt there is less than 40% of improved land although over 80% is occupied.

### Crop Land

In Figure 239, the percentage of farm land devoted to crop varies from below

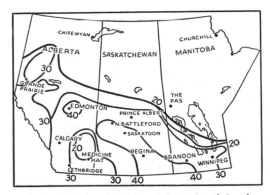

Figure 239. *Distribution of Crop Land in the Prairie Provinces.* Crop area is calculated as per cent of occupied farm land in 1946.

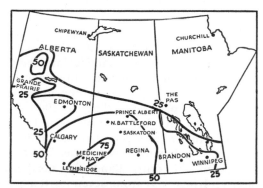

Figure 241. *Importance of Wheat in the Prairie Provinces.* The area in wheat is plotted as per cent of total crop area in 1946.

20% in the dry belt and in the pioneer fringe to over 40% in southeastern Saskatchewan and southwestern Manitoba. In the Edmonton district, also, 40% of the land is devoted to crops.

## Wheat

Two maps help us to visualize the distribution of wheat which is the most im-

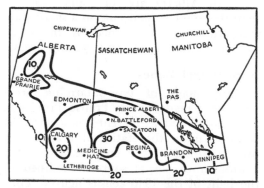

Figure 240. *Distribution of Wheat in the Prairie Provinces.* Land in what is plotted as per cent of occupied farm land in 1946.

portant crop of the Prairie Provinces. The first map, Figure 240, shows wheat land as a percentage of total farm land. Here we see that the density is greatest (over 30%) in the south central part of Saskatchewan and that it decreases toward both the dry and the cold margins of cultivation. The second map, Figure 241, showing wheat

land as a percentage of the crop area, has quite a different pattern with the greatest relative concentration in the dry area, thinning out in the areas with greater moisture supply.

## Pasture

Pasture distribution is shown in Figure 242. Except in the wooded regions, pasture is the alternative to cropping as a land use. Over 60% (and as high as 70% in some sections) of the occupied area in the dry belt is used as pasture. This falls to 35%, or less, in the regions where wheat is the most important crop. The wooded pioneer areas have 40%, or over, of their occupied land in pasture. Only a very small part of the pasture land of the Prairie Provinces is classed as improved.

Figure 242. *Pasture Land in the Prairie Provinces.* Land in pasture is plotted as per cent of total occupied farm land.

## Livestock

Figure 243 shows the density of live-stock population in terms of animal units per thousand acres of occupied farm land. An animal unit means the equivalent, in feed consuming capacity, of one horse or one cow, five pigs, seven sheep or 100 hens. The central dry belt is thus seen to be very low in livestock population, the Swift Current area having only two per hundred acres. On the other hand the northern pioneer fringe has from seven to ten per hundred acres of occupied land. Cattle

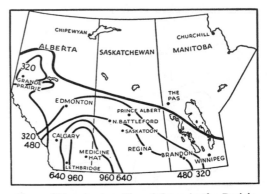

Figure 244. *Average Size of Farm in the Prairie Provinces.* Farms are largest in the driest areas and smallest in the northern pioneer fringe.

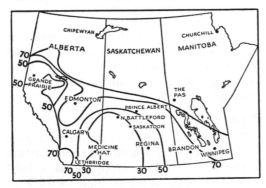

Figure 243. *Density of Livestock Population in the Prairie Provinces.* The density is plotted in terms of animal units per thousand acres of occupied farm land in 1946.

are by far the most numerous but sheep are important in Southern Alberta while swine and poultry are more numerous in Central Alberta.

## Size of Farm

Figure 244 indicates the gradation in the size of farms. Farms in the Prairie Provinces more commonly occur as quarter sections or multiples thereof, because of the type of land survey used in laying out the country and because, under the homestead laws, a man was permitted to take up one quarter section or 160 acres. As time has passed there has been a process of consolidation. Farmers have purchased adjacent railway or company land or have bought out their neighbours who wished to give up farming. Consequently there

are now fewer farms than formerly and they are much larger. The map shows that there is a rough correlation with the moisture factor. Farms in southeastern Alberta average over 1,000 acres in area while toward the pioneer fringe they are less than 300 acres. Only in the extreme eastern part of Manitoba is the average size below 200 acres. The irrigated farms of southern Alberta are, of course, smaller than the non-irrigated but, on a small scale map, they are outweighed by the extra size of the dry farms and grazing areas.

## Agricultural Zones

Many maps of type-of-farming areas have been made of the Prairie Provinces, each with slightly different boundaries, depending upon the statistical information used. Figure 245 has been generalized from a number of official sources, modified in the light of the 1946 census figures. Thus the outline of the grazing areas is determined by the fact that most of the included townships have 50% or more of the occupied land in pasture. The wheat belt is the area in which wheat occupies 50% or more of the crop land. Mixed farming is found in the pioneer belt as well as in the mixed farming belt but the amount of occupied land is generally less than 25% of the total and the percentage of improved land is also low.

Figure 245. *Agricultural Zones in the Prairie Provinces.* This map is based on one published by the Department of Agriculture, modified in the light of the returns of the census of 1946.

## Irrigation

The semi-arid climate of the Great Plains makes irrigation advisable wherever water and suitable land can be brought together. These possibilities are greatest in Western Alberta where glacial streams from the Rocky Mountains flow into the plains. The first irrigation ditch was constructed in 1879 near Calgary. In 1894 the Parliament of Canada passed the Northwest Irrigation Act to encourage and control irrigation and, according to the first report on Canadian Irrigation Surveys in 1896, there were 79,000 acres then under ditch. Estimates for 1949 show that large scale projects have under ditch about 727,000 acres in Alberta and 65,000 in Saskatchewan while small individual projects, authorized under provincial statutes, include another 130,000, making a total of 922,000 acres of irrigable land. It has been estimated that, during the dry years of the 1930's, the irrigated farms produced nearly 10% of the gross agricultural wealth of Alberta.

The major irrigation districts are shown in Figure 246. The largest project is that of the Eastern Irrigation District on the main line of the C.P.R. between Medicine Hat and Calgary. This region has an average precipitation of 11.5" and the evaporation from a free water surface amounts to 33" per year. Pioneer work by the C.P.R. was begun in 1906 and, by 1917, they had spent over $10,000,000. At that time there were about 200 farms in the area with 10,000 acres under irrigation. By 1921, under the influence of post-war prices, 1,140 farms were in operation but by 1924 over 400 had been abandoned, involving over 26% of the acreage. Although it was designed to serve 400,000 acres, no more than 90,000 acres were irrigated in any one year. In 1935, the Eastern Irrigation District was established by the Alberta Government and the company transferred the whole project which, up to that time, had cost $25,000,000. Under C.P.R. management the land was sold at $50 per acre and carried a fixed annual charge of $1.25 per acre for water service. The district revalued the land at about

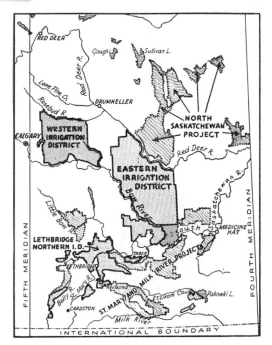

Figure 246. *Major Irrigation Districts.* Most of the irrigated land of the Prairie Provinces is in Alberta, and is supplied from the headwaters of the South Saskatchewan. Future projects have been suggested to utilize water from the North Saskatchewan to irrigate land in both Alberta and Saskatchewan.

1/5 the former price and raised the water service charge to $1.75. By 1937 over 125,-000 acres were under irrigation and, since 1943, the area has increased to over 167,000

acres. Included in the district there is an area of more than 1,000,000 acres of range, sufficient to provide summer pasture for 20,000 head of catttle. Winter feed for such a herd would require 10,000 acres of alfalfa. Dairying is being encouraged, as is also the growing of various crop specialties, in order to build up a diversified agriculture in the area.

Other important irrigation projects are the Western Irrigation District near Calgary, which was also begun by the C.P.R.; the C.P.R. Lethbridge section; Lethbridge Northern Irrigation District; United Irrigated District and Canada Land and Irrigation Company. It is interesting to note that the pioneer irrigators in Southern Alberta were Mormon settlers from Utah who began to use water from the St. Mary River in 1898. Today this area appears as one of the most prosperous in the province and is noted for its production of sugar beets.

### Future Development of Irrigation

The basin of the Saskatchewan River continues to be the most important area with possibilities for development. Its area in three provinces is over 150,000 square miles or 96,000,000 acres. The total yearly flow of the river in Manitoba is about 18,000,000 acre feet. Of this more than 13,000,000 acre feet originate in Alberta,

*Courtesy Exp. Farms Service*
Plate 81. An irrigation canal in Southern Alberta.

mostly from the Rocky Mountains. This is enough to irrigate 9,000,000 acres but, of course, only the water which can be conserved in reservoirs or diverted during the growing season may be used. It is believed that about 1,661,000 acres in Alberta and 925,000 in Saskatchewan may be irrigated. To do this requires storage capacity of 3,250,000 acre feet. Since most of this land is in the basin of the South Saskatchewan which is already supplying a large amount of irrigation water, it will be necessary to divert about 2,218,000 acre feet from the North Saskatchewan. This would be done by way of the Clearwater, the Red Deer, Buffalo Lake and a long canal to Central Saskatchewan. Its cost would be great (in excess of $100,000,000), but it would permit greater diversification of farm enterprise in the areas concerned.

The South Saskatchewan project proposes to irrigate 500,000 acres near Saskatoon.

Other schemes of less magnitude are proposed for the south. All told, there is said to be possible storage for 5,964,000 acre feet, including that already in use. The total possible acreage of irrigable land is placed at 3,334,000 acres. This is less than 10% of the crop acreage of the two provinces but, if brought into production, it would have the effect of stabilizing agriculture in the driest part of the Prairies.

## Prairie Farm Rehabilitation

As a result of the low price for wheat and low yields due to the droughts of the early 1930's, the agricultural prosperity of the Prairie Provinces reached a low ebb. The Dominion Parliament passed the Prairie Farm Rehabilitation Act in 1935. It authorized the Dominion Government to appropriate funds "to provide for the rehabilitation of drought and soil-drifting areas in the provinces of Manitoba, Saskatchewan and Alberta". Later the scope of the act was broadened to include the whole problem of land utilization and land settlement. The Prairie Farm Rehabilita-

tion Authority was set up to carry on the work. Its headquarters are in Regina.

The P.F.R.A. program involves three main phases: (1) It aims to improve farm practices so as to conserve moisture and prevent soil drifting. Strip cropping, contour cultivation and trash cover are some of the soil conservation methods advocated. (2) By means of a water development program the flow of the prairie streams is being conserved and the water used for stock-watering and the irrigation of crops. Aid has been given to the construction of hundreds of small dams as well as to large irrigation projects. Thousands of dugouts have been constructed to conserve surface run-off on individual farms. (3) Under the land utilization program the poor grades of land have been retired from cultivation, regrassed and made available for grazing. Over 3,000,000 acres have been designated as community pastures in which the farmers of the various districts may rent pasture rights. The community pastures are usually in blocks of 20,000 acres or more, each under a resident manager. Many of these pastures are in the rough land along the Missouri Coteau.

The farmers who formerly lived in the pasture areas were aided to move to new land. Some of them went to the northern forested districts while others were established on irrigated land.

## Land Classification

In addition to providing aid for the soil survey, the P.F.R.A. instituted a program of land classification in order to determine those areas which should be retired from cultivation. Since wheat is the most important crop, the classification is based on ability of the land to produce wheat for market. Five land classes were set up:

Land Class I — Quarter sections (160 acres) not capable of producing more than 350 bushels of wheat available for sale.

Land Class II — Quarter sections capable

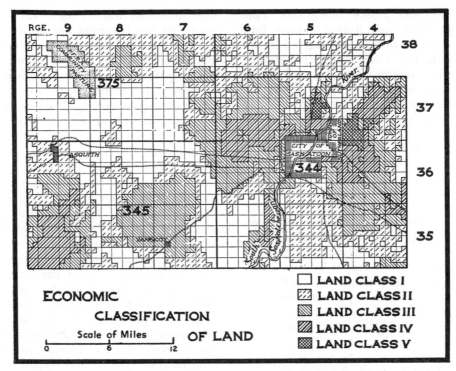

Figure 247. *Land Classifications in Southern Saskatchewan.* (After Stutt). A sample section of a map of economic land classes in the vicinity of Saskatoon.

of producing 351 to 475 bushels of wheat for sale.

Land Class III—Quarter sections capable of producing 476 to 720 bushels of wheat for sale.

Land Class IV—Quarter sections capable of producing 721 to 900 bushels of wheat for sale.

Land Class V—Quarter sections capable of producing more than 900 bushels of wheat for sale.

Land class II was considered to be marginal for wheat production, land class I definitely sub-marginal and to be returned to grazing. Land classes III to V, on the other hand, were considered suitable for wheat production.

The great variation in the productivity of prairie farm land is illustrated by the results of this survey. In 65 municipal districts of Southern Saskatchewan, with a total area of 13,500,000 acres, land class I comprised 39.4%; land class II, 18.1%; land class III, 28.5%; land class IV, 11.3% and land class V, 2.7%. The diversity, even within relatively small areas, is shown in Figure 247, which is a reproduction of a portion of the official land classification map. It is maps such as this, studied in conjunction with contoured topographical maps and soil maps, which enable us to understand the geographical details of settlement and agriculture within small areas of the country.

## Cattle Ranching

Ranching has been carried on in the Prairie Provinces since 1874 when range cattle were brought into the Wood Mountain area from the United States. Dominion Government regulations of 1882 permitted the leasing of tracts up to 100,000 acres in size, and the industry expanded rapidly until about 1900. After that the

*Courtesy Exp. Farms Service*

Plate 82.   Beef Cattle on the Range Lands of the Foothills in Southern Alberta.

increase in agricultural settlement forced the breaking up of large ranches.

Commercial cattle ranching is regarded by economic geographers as a pioneer type of land utilization in grassland environments. Where conditions are favourable it usually gives way to commercial grain growing, but persists in areas which have greater hazards. The ranching belt, therefore, lies mainly in the southern parts of Saskatchewan and Alberta in the Brown and Dark Brown Soil zones, often referred to as the "Shortgrass Plains". In addition, ranching is carried on in the Cypress Hills, the Rocky Mountain Foothills and the Northern Prairie area centring about Wainright, Alberta, and extending a short distance into Saskatchewan. The climate of these areas permits a long grazing season, winter feeding being required for less than 100 days in all except the Northern Prairie area which requires about a month longer. Hereford cattle are preferred by most ranchers as they seem more able than the other beef breeds to take care of themselves on the open range. Water supplies are limited and range animals must often travel one to two miles or more between watering places and grazing grounds.

More than 200 ranches are in operation, with an average size of over 10,000 acres. About 2,000 acres, on the average, are owned by the rancher and constitute his headquarters area. The remainder of the range is held under lease and consists mostly of provincial lands. Herds average from 200 to 500 head of cattle in the various districts.

**Forestry**

Although the Prairie Provinces have relatively small areas of commercial forest, it is, nevertheless, of some importance. In recent years the forests of this area have produced an annual cut of approximately 270 million cubic feet of wood, or about 10% of the total for Canada. The value of the products of woods operation, chiefly logs and pulpwood bolts, varies from $16,-000,000 to $19,000,000 per year. In Saskatchewan and Alberta the bulk of the production is devoted to the manufacture of saw mill products while in Manitoba pulpwood is as important as saw logs. Railway ties, telephone poles, fence posts and pulpwood are made in quantity in all three provinces.

The rough Rocky Mountain and Foothills Forest region, west of Edmonton, is the most important lumber producing area in Alberta but considerable logging is also done in the Peace River and Athabaska districts. In Saskatchewan the most productive area is in the east, centring on Hudson Bay Junction. The forests of the Porcupine and Pasquia Hills have in recent years produced nearly two-thirds of the spruce and jack pine logs in the province. The Torch River area, northeast of Prince Albert, is also important. Big River, Waterhen, Candle Lake and Meadow Lake forests account for most of the production in the western part of the Saskatchewan forest belt. A small amount of pulpwood is cut in the Porcupine and Pasquia areas. In Manitoba most of the lumbering is carried on near the large lakes and along the lower part of the Saskatchewan River. The forests along the Manitoba Cuesta, particularly toward the north, are also productive.

The lumbering industry in the prairie provinces is made up of hundreds of small operations and a few larger ones. As virgin forest reserves become depleted, the tendency is for larger outfits to drop out and to be replaced by small operators who work isolated patches of forest which were not easily accessible to larger operators.

The Pas, in Northern Manitoba, has been for many years one of the chief sawmilling centres. The logs which supplied the mills came not only from the surrounding district but, in even greater volume, from the forests of Eastern Saskatchewan. Carrot River, Torch River, the Saskatchewan and its many smaller tributaries have provided cheap transportation for logs to the mills which were naturally located where rail transportation was available for their products. The sawmilling industry of Calgary uses logs cut in the forests of the Rocky Mountains and floated down the Kananaskis and Bow Rivers. Other important mills are located in the vicinity of Edson on the north Saskatchewan River and near Whitecourt on the Athabaska River.

Many mills in the Prairie Provinces, however, are not located on large rivers and logs must be brought to them by land. Trucks are used but much hauling is done in the winter by tractor train, either directly to the mills or to railway sidings.

Lumbering is, largely, part-time and seasonal work. This has been so even during the years of great market demand and highest levels of production. Approximately 800 saw mills produce an average of half a million board feet of lumber each, per annum. Each mill employs about five men.

A large pulp and paper mill is located at Pine Falls on Winnipeg River in eastern Manitoba. Established in 1926 it has a capacity of 250 tons of newsprint per day. In 1954 a pulp mill was constructed at Hinton on the Athabaska River in Alberta.

## The Utilization of Wild Life

Trapping, hunting and fishing are important in the sparsely settled parts of the Prairie Provinces. Before the white man came, these were the only means of maintaining life and, for long after the first Europeans appeared, the fur trade was the major commercial enterprise. The herds of bison which roamed the grassy plains have entirely disappeared, to be replaced by wheat fields and domestic cattle, but furbearers are still found in the forest. The most important of the wild furbearers is the muskrat which is especially plentiful in the marshes of the Saskatchewan River delta. Mink, weasel, squirrel and beaver are also important. The total value of the furs produced in a recent year (1946-47) was over $9,000.00. Not all of this is trapped fur, however, for there are numerous fur farms on the prairies. These produce about one third of the total value. Some types of fur are more easily produced in captivity than others. The 1948 statistics for Saskatchewan, for instance, show that about 2,100 fox pelts were trapped while 13,000 were produced on fur farms. About 9,500 mink pelts were trapped and 62,000 raised on farms.

Big game animals in the Prairie Provinces include woodland and barren land caribou, antelope, moose, deer and elk. they are carefully protected by closed seasons and hunting regulations. Bounties are paid for the destruction of predators, particularly timber wolves and coyotes.

The great numbers of lakes in the Shield areas of Manitoba and Saskatchewan are the breeding grounds of waterfowl. In recent years there has been a great decline in the numbers of ducks and geese. Conservation organizations such as Ducks Unlimited, the P.F.R.A., the various Fish and Game Leagues and government departments, are endeavouring to provide protection and to study the problems of wild life management in the hope of increasing the supply.

Commercial fishing is important in all three provinces. The total value of the fish landed in 1951 was over $10,000,000. About two thirds of this was produced in Manitoba. Whitefish, lake trout, pike, pickerel and tullibee are the most important species. During recent years fishing has been extended into the more remote lakes of the north through the use of airplane transportation. Besides the great lakes of Manitoba (Winnipeg, Winnipegosis and Manitoba) large quantities of fish are taken from other lakes, including Athabaska, Reindeer, Wollaston, Long, Churchill, Peter Pond, Doré and many others.

Properly managed, the wild life of the north is a source of wealth. It constitutes the entire livelihood of the Indian and Metis population. For this reason, Dominion and Provincial government departments are initiating research projects and setting up conservation areas in which the variations of wild life populations may be carefully watched.

## Mineral Wealth

The mineral wealth of Ontario and Quebec is to be found in their sections of the Canadian Shield. In the Prairie Provinces, on the other hand, while important metal mines exist on the Shield, the greater part of the mineral production consists of coal, oil and natural gas from the Great Plains and the foothills of the Rocky Mountains. The value of mineral production in 1954, in the three provinces was over $380,000,000, and Alberta replaced Quebec as the second ranking province in mineral industry. Manitoba produced about $7,200,000 in copper, $4,500,000 in gold, $3,600,000 in nickel, $3,900,000 in zinc, $5,600,000 in petroleum, and $9,000,000 in cement and other structural materials. Saskatchewan mined about $21,000,000 in copper, $11,000,000 in uranium, $12,000,000 in zinc, $12,000,000 in mineral fuels, and $3,000,000 in structural materials. Alberta produced $26,000,000 in coal, $8,000,000 in natural gas, $228,000,000 in petroleum and $16,000,000 in cement and other structural materials. More than 20,000 persons are gainfully employed in mineral industries, of whom 15,000 are in Alberta, about 4,000 in Manitoba and 2,000 in Saskatchewan.

## Metals

The most important metal mines are at Flin Flon, on the boundary of Manitoba and Saskatchewan. They are operated by the Hudson Bay Mining and Smelting Company. The town and the smelter are in Manitoba but much of the underground work is in Saskatchewan. The Flin Flon discovery was made in 1915. The ore was very valuable, containing gold, silver, copper and zinc. It was nearly 100 miles from the nearest railway and for years remained undeveloped. In 1928, a railway was built from The Pas and operations commenced. Electric power was obtained from Island Falls on the Churchill River, about 60 miles to the north. Open pit mining was carried on to a depth of more than 300 feet. Underground workings now have a depth of over half a mile. On the average about 2,000,000 tons of ore are mined per year and $25,000,000 worth of refined metals sold. The company employs over 2,000 persons, while the city of Flin Flon has a population of over 10,000.

Another important area is found at Lynn Lake where the Sherritt Gordon Company is mining copper and nickel. The nickel is sent to Fort Saskatchewan for refining; the copper goes to Noranda. Two new development areas are in the vicinity of Moak Lake where the International Nickel Company is at work, and Snow Lake, where new base metal mines are being opened by the Hudson Bay Mining and Smelting Company.

The Beaverlodge area, centred on Uranium City in Northern Saskatchewan was for some years the most important source of uranium in Canada. Even with the Ontario mines in full production, it will still provide 20% of the Canadian output.

## Coal

The Cretaceous rocks of the Prairie Provinces contain vast amounts of coal. The accessible resources of Alberta are estimated at 48,000,000,000 tons, those of Saskatchewan are about 24,000,000,000 tons, Manitoba 100,000,000 tons. The coal of Alberta is largely bituminous but there is a small quantity of anthracite. The coal of Saskatchewan and Manitoba is almost entirely lignite. In 1954 Alberta produced over 4,850,000 tons of coal worth over $26,000,000; Saskatchewan mined 2,200,000 tons worth $4,000,000. There are more than 35 different coal fields in Alberta, with nearly 200 operating mines. The most productive fields are at Crow's Nest, Drumheller, Mountain Park, Coalspur, Lethbridge, Cascade and Nordegg. Cascade, Crow's Nest, Mountain Park and Nordegg produce high grade bituminous coal; the coal of Coldspur is sub-bituminous coal, while Drumheller, and Lethbridge produce low grade domestic fuels.

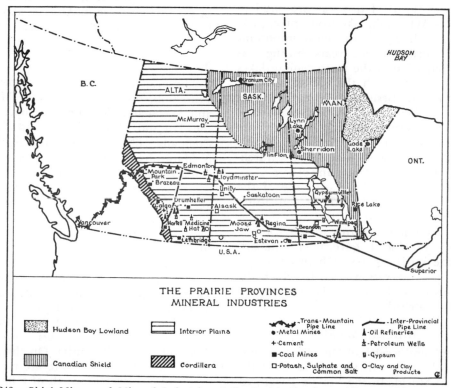

Figure 248. *Chief Mines and Mineral Industries of the Prairie Provinces.* Alberta, with great resources of coal and petroleum, has the largest share of mineral production.

*Courtesy Canadian National Railways*

Plate 83. A coal mine near Drumheller, Alberta.

The railroads normally use about half the coal mined in Alberta and about 25% is sold for domestic and industrial use in the province. The remainder finds markets in British Columbia, the other Prairie Provinces, the adjoining parts of the United States and in Eastern Canada.

Nearly all the lignite produced in Saskatchewan comes from the Estevan field where it is obtained by stripping. Some of it is used in a large central electrical power plant while the rest is shipped to other parts of the province.

## Petroleum and Natural Gas

Oil was discovered in the Turner Valley by Dingman in 1914. In 1924, the field's most spectacular well, Royalite 4 came in. During a six-year period it yielded 900,000 barrels worth $3,000,000. For some time Turner Valley was the second largest field in the British Empire, producing 90% of the Canadian output. At its peak it yielded 10,000,000 barrels per year. The city of Calgary profited greatly, becoming the business centre of the industry and the site of large oil refineries. Other smaller fields were developed in the south at Taber and Del Bonita, and further north at Princess, Wainwright, Vermilion and Lloydminster.

Since 1947, the major developments have been at Leduc and Redwater near Edmonton and, by the middle of 1949, the daily production in the province had passed 70,000 barrels. In that year a refinery began operations at Edmonton. Its history is interesting. During the war it was built at Whitehorse, Yukon, to refine the oil transported from Norman Wells by Canol Pipeline. When, during the post-war period of

*National Film Board*

Plate 84. An oil well in a wheat field near Leduc, Alberta.

steel shortages, the need for a refinery developed at Edmonton, the one at Whitehorse was carefully dismantled and transported via the Alaska Highway to its new site where it was soon in operation. More refineries have since been built. Pipe lines carry crude oil from the central Alberta fields to refineries in Regina, Moose Jaw, Winnipeg, Sarnia and the Pacific coast. In 1956, the Prairie Provinces produced 170,-000,000 barrels, worth $400,000,000.

Another great source of petroleum exists in the tar sands along the banks of the Athabaska River in the northeastern section of Alberta. Here, in an area of 30,000 square miles, there is estimated to be 250,-000,000,000 barrels of oil. The oil soaked sands lie at the surface and may be mined easily by the open pit method. High octane gasoline and other products may be refined from this oil but the cost of separation from the sand is too great for competition with liquid crude oil drawn from wells. This resource, therefore, remains for future development.

Natural gas occurs in great abundance. The total production in 1956 was over 170,-000,000 M cubic feet worth about $17,000,-000. The province of Alberta provides more than 80% of the total annual production.

All the large cities of Alberta are served with natural gas. The Viking-Kinsella field supplies Edmonton, Turner Valley supplies Calgary and the Medicine Hat-Redcliff field supplies southeastern Alberta. A pipe line to eastern Canada is in prospect.

The province of Saskatchewan also has possibilities for oil and gas. The major producing field at Lloydminster is an extension of the Alberta field. Natural gas is used also at Unity and Kamsack.

### Other Non-metallic Minerals

Salt occurs in all three Prairie Provinces, in beds 200 to 500 feet in thickness. Salt is produced at McMurray and Elk Point in Alberta, at Unity in Saskatchewan and at Neepawa in Manitoba. Sodium sulphate is recovered from the alkali lakes of Southern Saskatchewan; plants are located at Alsask, Bishopric, Ormiston and Chaplin. The chief markets for this salt are the Kraft Paper mills in Ontario and Quebec and the copper-nickel refinery at Sudbury, Ontario.

Gypsum is quarried at Gypsumville and Amaranth near Lake Manitoba.

Building stone is quarried at various points in Manitoba and Alberta. Tyndall limestone is especially famous.

Clay and limestone for the manufacture of cement are available in both Manitoba and Alberta.

## Manufacturing

The Prairie Provinces are not considered to be one of the manufacturing regions of Canada, yet in 1954 the gross value of manufactured products was about $1,430,000,000, with a net of $545,000,000. Manufacturing ranks next to agriculture as a producer of wealth. For the most part manufacturing is confined to the processing of raw materials produced within the region. Quite frequently it is very closely associated. This is the case when mining and smelting are done by the same company, as they are in the Flin Flon field. Logging, sawmilling and wood working may also be associated under the same management, as may also limestone quarries, clay pits and cement factories. Economic geography is therefore somewhat unreal when we try to divide the subject along the traditional lines of the economic statistician.

Some types of manufacturing are carried out in geographical locations removed from the place of origin of the raw materials, even though within the same region. Such are the leading manufacturing industries of the Prairie Provinces, slaughtering and meat packing and the milling of grains into flour and feed. The markets for the products are partly local or regional and partly outside of the region. Both are concerned with the disassembly of complicated raw materials and the sale of simpler

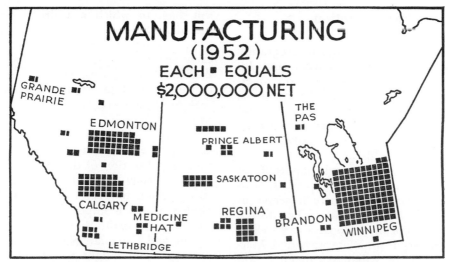

Figure 249. *Manufacturing in the Prairie Provinces.* Winnipeg is the great manufacturing centre of the Prairie Provinces, but Calgary and Edmonton are gaining momentum.

standardized goods. Slaughtering and meat packing are centralized largely in Calgary, Edmonton and Winnipeg. The milling industry is found in these centres and in Saskatoon, Regina, Moose Jaw and Brandon.

Petroleum refining is naturally situated in Calgary and Edmonton, which are close to raw materials, but also found in Moose Jaw, Regina and Winnipeg.

Butter and cheese manufacture is also one of the leading industries, carried on in many widely distributed plants.

The four chief industries, viz., slaughtering and meat packing, milling, butter and cheese, and petroleum products, account for over 50% of the value of manufactured goods. Other important industries, in order, are: railway rolling stock, breweries, miscellaneous foods, bakery products, sawmills and printing and publishing.

Metropolitan or "greater" Winnipeg is the most important manufacturing centre. Industries are of necessity associated with transportation facilities and Winnipeg had the advantage also of an early start. A further advantage is the reliable supply of electrical power. The manufacture and repair of rolling stock is located here. Raw materials come from Eastern Canada or the U.S.A. to be used in servicing a transportation industry at a transportation node. The growth of the Winnipeg market itself provides the reason for establishing breweries, bakeries and clothing trades. The presence of a large labour force made Winnipeg the logical location of wartime industry in Western Canada and is also a factor in attracting peace time industry.

The cities of Alberta, also, have good sources of power including coal, natural gas and hydro. They have nearly as good access to most raw materials as Winnipeg with the addition of large petroleum resources. It is reasonable to expect that Alberta will eventually surpass Manitoba as a manufacturing province.

Saskatchewan has fewer advantages for manufacturing than either of its neighbours. Power is not so easily obtained nor does it have a wealth of petroleum or coal equal to that of Alberta. It does have large northern forests, deposits of sodium sulphate, common salt and other minerals. In time other industries may be developed to supplement the present program of processing farm products.

## Transportation

The geography of transport is just as important a part of regional geography as types of productive industry and location and nature of natural resources. The Prairie Provinces were the last areas of Canada to be settled because they lacked transportation facilities. They were settled quickly once they were given railway links to the outside world.

Water transport, although important in earlier times, is not so now. It persists, however, in the far north where it serves as a link with the Northwest Territories. Steam and motor driven boats carry freight and passengers from Waterways and Macmurray down the Athabaska to Fitzgerald at the head of the rapids on the Slave River. Here the river falls 109 feet in 16 miles and goods are transferred by motor vehicles over two parallel roads. There is commercial navigation, also, on Lake Winnipeg between Selkirk and Norway House.

Ocean transportation facilities touch the Prairie Provinces at Churchill on Hudson Bay, to which a railroad was completed in 1930. Here a large safe harbour is open from mid-July to mid-November each year. The port has an elevator of 2,500,000 bushel capacity and is as near to the ports of the British Isles as Montreal or New York. With the use of improved navigation aids in Hudson Strait, this route will become more important. Churchill also serves as the gateway to the central section of the Canadian Arctic.

Over 19,000 miles of steam railway are in operation in the Prairie Provinces. Included are such important transportation links as the main lines of the Canadian Pacific and Canadian National, with many passenger and freight trains per day, strategic links with the north such as the Hudson Bay line and the Alberta and Great Waterways, and many small prairie lines whose only function is to haul wheat in the fall. Saskatchewan with nearly 9,000 miles, stands second to Ontario in total mileage, and well ahead in mileage per capita.

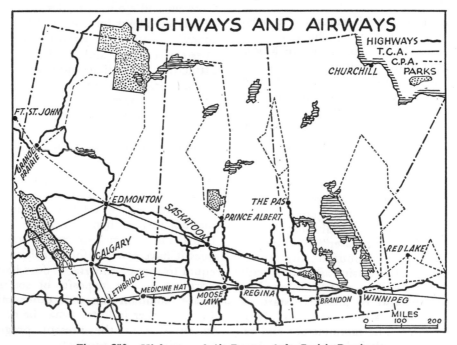

Figure 250. *Highway and Air Routes of the Prairie Provinces.*

The close relationship between railway building and settlement has already been stressed. Settlers followed rail lines or tried to locate in advance of them. Strategic railway junctions have become large cities. The railway net on the map indicates the extent of settled territory. Nowadays, other means of transport have robbed the railway of some of its prestige but it is still the most economical way to move bulk commodities. Each year in the Prairie Provinces, the railways carry ten to fifteen million tons of grain.

Most of the railway mileage belongs to either the C.N.R. or the C.P.R. system. The Northern Alberta Railway, serving the Peace River district, is jointly operated by the two systems. Short branches of American roads enter the southern sections.

Land transport, apart from railways, nowadays, is a matter of motor vehicles and highways. The Prairie Provinces, for their population, possess an incredible road system, totalling 385,000 miles, which is 70% of the total for the Dominion. In 1951 only 40,000 miles, or 11%, was surfaced and only 3,700 miles had pavement. Motor vehicle registrations in the three provinces numbered 765,000, of which 235,000 were commercial vehicles. The latter figure, it should be noted, is about equal to that of Ontario and shows to what extent the movement of goods depends upon highway trucking.

The extensive road net and sparse population constitute a great problem for the Prairie Provinces. They cannot hope to put hard surfaces on any but the main roads connecting the larger towns. On the other roads, spring and fall conditions constitute a hazard and unsurfaced prairie sideroads become impassable.

The great distances of the Prairie Provinces make their people, naturally, air-minded. During World War II many airfields were established to aid in the Commonwealth Air Training Plan. Since the war they have largely been converted to civilian use. Trans-Canada Air Lines provide daily service between Winnipeg, Regina, Swift Current, Medicine Hat, Lethbridge, Calgary, Edmonton, Saskatoon and points in other parts of Canada. American air lines provide service from Great Falls to Lethbridge and from Fargo to Winnipeg. Canadian Pacific Air Lines operate from Edmonton to Northern Alberta, Northwest Territories and Yukon. The Saskatchewan government operates its own air services in the northern part of the province.

## Communications

Manitoba, Alberta and Saskatchewan have large provincially owned telephone systems. There are hundreds of small co-operative telephone companies in Alberta and Saskatchewan. Edmonton operates the largest municipal telephone system in Canada. The Canadian Broadcasting Corporation has three 50,000 watt stations at Winnipeg, Watrous and Edmonton. There are thirteen other stations in the CBC networks. With more than 16 per hundred persons, there are more radios than telephones. Wireless communications are important in the northern regions of all three provinces.

## Summary of the Human Geography

In the span of a single lifetime the Prairies were transformed from an almost unoccupied wilderness to a fully settled modern agricultural community. There is now little space left which will support new pioneer farms.

The next stage of development has already begun. Great cities such as Winnipeg, Calgary and Edmonton are beginning to be known as industrial centres. Most of the manufacturing of the past has been concerned with processing farm products. Utilization of coal, oil, natural gas and other mineral resources forms the basis of further industrialization which is the only means by which an increasing urban population may be maintained.

# Selected References

*Alberta Facts and Figures.* Bureau of Statistics. Alberta Dept. of Industries and Labour. Edmonton. 1950.

Britnell, G. E. *The Wheat Economy.* University of Toronto Press. Toronto. 1939.

Earl, L. F. *Industrial Manitoba in 1949.* The Monetary Times. August. 1949.

Hedges, James B. *Building the Canadian West.* The Macmillan Company. New York. 1939.

Innis, H. A. *The Fur Trade in Canada.* Yale University Press. New Haven. 1930.

Johnson, C. W. *Relative Decline of Wheat in the Prairie Provinces of Canada.* Economic Geography. Vol. 24, pp. 209-16. 1948.

Long, H. G. *Prairie Irrigation.* Canadian Geographical Journal. XXXIII. pp. 152-159. 1946.

Martin, Chester. *Dominion Lands Policy.* The Macmillan Company of Canada Ltd. Toronto. 1938.

Morton, A. S. *History of Prairie Settlement.* The Macmillan Company of Canada Ltd. Toronto. 1938.

Patterson, H. L. *Dairy Farm Business in Alberta 1939-43.* Canada Dept. of Agriculture. Publication 812. Ottawa. 1948.

Patterson, H. L. *Dairy Farm Business in Manitoba. 1942-7.* Canada Dept. of Agriculture. Publication 829. Ottawa. 1949.

*P.F.R.A. A Record of Achievement.* Canada Dept. of Agriculture. Ottawa. 1943.

Province of Saskatchewan. *The Natural Resources of Saskatchewan.* Dept. of Natural Resources and Industrial Development. Regina. 1947.

Spence, George. *Soil and Water Conservation on the Prairies.* Canadian Geographical Journal. XXXV. pp. 226-41. 1947.

Spence, C. C., and E. C. Hope. *An economic classification of land in fifty-six municipal divisions, south-central Saskatchewan.* Canada Dept. of Agriculture. Publication 728. Ottawa. 1941.

Spence, C. C., B. H. Kristjanson and J. L. Anderson. *Farming in the Irrigation Districts of Alberta.* Canada Dept. of Agriculture. Publication 793. Ottawa. 1947.

Spence, C. C., and E. C. Hope. *An economic classification of land and its relation to farm types and income, Blucher-Colonsay Area, Saskatchewan. 1940-41.* Canada Dept. of Agriculture. Ottawa. 1948.

Stewart, A., and W. D. Porter. *Land Use Classification in the Special Areas of Alberta.* Canada Dept. of Agriculture. Publication 731. Ottawa. 1942.

Stutt, R. A. *An economic classification of land in the Elrose-Rosetown-Conquest Area. 1944.* Canada Dept. of Agriculture. Ottawa. 1948.

Stutt, R. A. *A farm business study with particular reference to the relation of farm types and land classes, Cory-Asquith-Langham area, Saskatchewan. 1943.* Canada Department of Agriculture. Ottawa. 1949.

Vrooman, C. W., G. D. Chattaway and Andrew Stewart. *Cattle Ranching in Western Canada.* Canada Dept. of Agriculture. Publication 778. Ottawa. 1946.

# CHAPTER 18

# Regions and Cities of the
# Prairie Provinces

Rᴇɢɪᴏɴᴀʟ differentiation is by no means complete in the Prairie Provinces. While man has occupied the area, the processes of human adjustment to the environment and human adaptation of the environment are still going on. When those processes have advanced somewhat further, geographic or human use regions will appear. Already, however, we see nuclei and also certain boundaries which are apt to be permanent. Elsewhere the trends are vague and apt to change. With these reservations, nine geographic divisions have been outlined on the accompanying map. (Fig. 251).

Urban centres are interesting to the geographer on two counts. First of all, cities are geographical phenomena whose place in the region must be examined and evaluated with care, and secondly, there are the internal forms and functions of the city itself which make up what is

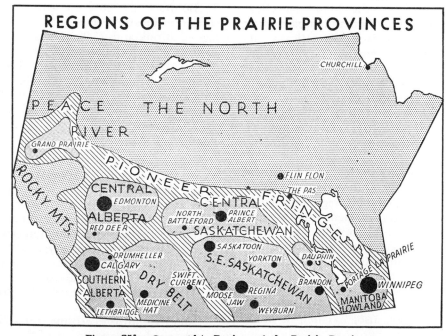

Figure 251. *Geographic Regions of the Prairie Provinces.*

usually called urban geography. The former is probably the most important aspect of our study of the Prairie cities, but we shall not entirely neglect the other.

Most of the urban centres in the Prairies are quite small, being railway stations around which have clustered a few hundred people, including merchants, tradesmen and retired farmers. Five larger centres will be examined in detail: Winnipeg, the capital of Manitoba; Regina, capital of Saskatchewan, and Saskatoon, seat of the provincial university; Edmonton, capital of Alberta, and Calgary, the metropolis of the foothills. Briefer attention will be given to smaller centres.

## I. The Manitoba Lowland or Winnipeg Region

Although it is the smallest, this region is, perhaps, the most important. It is well marked out by physical factors such as land form, climate and soil. Its eastern boundary is the edge of the Canadian Shield; its western one, the Manitoba Cuesta. Its basin-like form is emphasized by the presence of the Manitoba Great Lakes, with several thousand square miles of fresh water surface. Climatically, its moisture supply, averaging 20 inches per year, is better than that of any other part of the plains. The park vegetation and black soils are also characteristic, indicating the transition from grassland to forest conditions. On these grounds, G. Taylor ([1]) recognizes it as a natural region.

It is more, however; for the patterns of human settlement and activity mark it out as a true geographic region. It has a strong population nucleus in Greater Winnipeg (410,000), to which all parts are held by a close transportation net. Though overshadowing all others, it has not completely prevented the development of smaller local centres, among which might be named Portage la Prairie and Dauphin. History, also, has helped in re-

[1] Taylor, G. *Canada* p. 115.

gional definition since this basin held the earliest permanent white settlement. Even catastrophes, such as the floods of the Red and Assiniboine rivers, although they do not involve the whole area, tend to have a regional significance.

Agriculturally, it is part of the mixed farming belt, but its adjustments appear to be more permanent. Dairying is well established because of the importance of the city market.

## Winnipeg—The Gateway to the West

Winnipeg, the capital of Manitoba, is the largest city in the Prairie Provinces. Located 1,409 miles west of Montreal and 1,473 miles east of Vancouver, it has some claim to be considered the geographical centre of Canada. The census of 1956 enumerates a population of 257,000 in the city itself, but the metropolitan area had a total of 410,000, thus ranking fourth among the "greater cities" of Canada. The urban area around Winnipeg includes the city of St. Boniface (29,000); the towns of Transcona (8,300) and Tuxedo (1,200); the village of Brooklands (3,900); and the municipalities of Assiniboia (3,500), Charleswood (5,000), Fort Garry (13,000), Kildonnan E. (18,600), Kildonnan N. (4,400), Kildonnan W. (15,000), Old Kildonnan (1,000), St. James (26,000), and St. Vital (24,000).

### Historical Note

None of the prairie cities can be said to be very old, but Winnipeg, as well as being the largest city, is also the oldest. The first habitation of the white man on this site was Fort Rouge, erected by La Verendrye in 1738, although it was later abandoned. Part of the city is called Fort Rouge today, and the statue of La Verendrye stands near the Manitoba Legislative Building to commemorate this early explorer.

Later Winnipeg became the scene of bitter rivalry between the North West

Company from Montreal and the Hudson's Bay Company. The "Nor'westers" built Fort Gibraltar in 1806 and the Hudson's Bay traders built Fort Douglas near by. In 1821 the two companies merged, and a second and larger Fort Garry was built in 1835.

The real birth of the city, however, was the Selkirk settlement. Lord Selkirk, concerned over the displaced crofters of the Scottish highlands, conceived the idea that the Red River Valley offered possibilities for their re-establishment. Securing control of the Hudson's Bay Company, he proceeded to carry his scheme into effect. Beginning in 1811, several hundred immigrants arrived to make their homes in Manitoba, and in spite of incredible hardships the settlement was established.

Winnipeg continued to be the centre of the fur trade for many years. At first the furs were taken by York boat down the Red River, down Lake Winnipeg to Norway House and thence down the Hayes River to York Factory where they were placed in ships for England. Later the famous Red River Carts were used to carry furs south to St. Paul in Minnesota. In 1861, the Hudson's Bay Company began using steamers on the Red River.

In 1870, the Province of Manitoba entered the Dominion of Canada, and Fort Garry became the capital with its name changed to Winnipeg. In the Cree language, *win nipiy* means murky water—a fitting name for the Red River. In 1873 Winnipeg was incorporated as the first city on the prairies, with less than 2,000 inhabitants.

The completion of the C.P.R. in 1885 stimulated Winnipeg to active growth; overnight it became the gateway to a vast

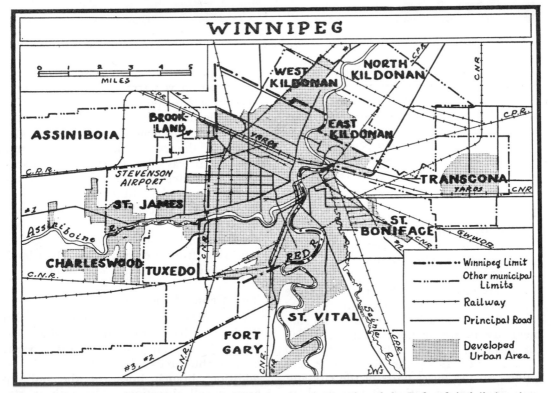

Figure 252. *Greater Winnipeg.* From its original focus at the junction of the Red and Assiniboine rivers, the urban development has spread in all directions.

Plate 85.   The urban landscape of Winnipeg with the Red River in the background.

inland empire. All the business of the Northwest Territories became centralized there. All goods from the east are distributed from this point and goods from the west are assembled for shipment. The railroads created Winnipeg which arose in a strategic location, somewhat similar to those of Chicago, Illinois, or Hamilton, Ontario.

## The Site

The city is situated at the junction of the Red River and its largest tributary, the Assiniboine. The site is not impressive — a wide, featureless, flat plain over which the rivers meander in channels which are very little entrenched below the general level. Such a location is exposed to submergence in spring floods. That of 1950, for instance, created a lake of over 600 square miles along the Red River, engulfing all the lower parts of the city and requiring the evacuation of tens of thousands of people.

In a period when rivers were highways, this junction was strategic and the North Westers seized upon it to tap the fur trade which formerly went to Hudson's Bay. The early settlement, rather naturally, clung to the river. Main Street is very crooked; it was once a settler's trail paralleling the river. Portage Avenue is the beginning of the old overland route to Edmonton. The early village grew where these trails met. Numerous bridges are necessary to hold the greater city together but, away from the rivers, the urban landscape may spread in all directions.

## The Urban Landscape

Created by the railways, Winnipeg is also dominated by them. The Canadian Pacific and Canadian National Railway yards contain hundreds of miles of track. In addition, branch lines cut the built-up area in all directions. The railway stations are imposing buildings, so are the great railway hotels, the Canadian National "Fort Garry" and the Canadian Pacific "Royal Alexandra". There is a larger "down-town" shopping district centred about Portage Avenue and Main Street and smaller ones in outlying neighbourhoods. The Manitoba Legislative Building, topped by the famous "Golden Boy", stands in a spacious park, overlooking the Assiniboine River; not far away are the Law Courts and the Civic Auditorium. The City Hall, a most ornate structure, stands on Main Street in the centre of the down town district. St. John's Anglican Cathedral stands in the northern part of the city while across the river in St. Boniface stands St. Boniface Roman Catholic Cathedral, the largest church in Western Canada.

The Legislature and many other buildings are built of Tyndall limestone, quarried a few miles from the city. There are also many brick buildings for stores, offices and apartments, but more than half of the houses of Winnipeg are built of wood. Forty-four per cent of the homes are occupied by their owners.

## Population

Winnipeg has a very mixed population. In 1951, nearly one-third of its people were from countries outside Canada while, of those born in Canada, large numbers were of other than British descent. In greater Winnipeg there were 52% of British origin, 12% Ukrainian, 7% French, 7% German, 5% Jewish, 5% Polish, and 4% Scandinavian.

The chief religious denominations rank as follows: United Church 28%, Roman Catholic 20%, Anglican 18%, Greek Catholic 8%, Lutheran 6%, Presbyterian 6%, and Jewish 5%.

In 1951, about 46% of the population of Winnipeg reported gainful employment. The chief categories were: manufacturing 25% (greatly increased since 1941), trade 23%, services 18%, transportation 12%, professional 7%, construction 6% and financial 5%.

## Economic Functions

Winnipeg is primarily a market which operates to exchange the products of Western Canada with the rest of the world. It is the financial and commercial headquarters for Western Canada.

Winnipeg is also an important manufacturing centre; its chief industries include slaughtering and meat packing, flour and feed mills, printing, publishing and bookbinding, manufacture of clothing, brewing, baking and other food processing. Metropolitan Winnipeg ranks sixth among the manufacturing cities of Canada, producing, in 1953, a total value of $505,000,000 ($200,000,000 net) and employing 35,000 workers. This was more than double the value of the pre-war industrial output. The Winnipeg manufacturing district includes about six-sevenths of all the industrial development of Manitoba and approximate-

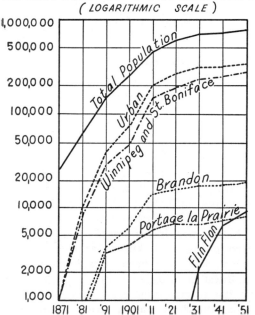

# MANITOBA CITY POPULATION
### ( LOGARITHMIC SCALE )

Figure 253. *Growth of Population in the Cities of Manitoba.*

ly two-fifths of the total for the Prairie Provinces, so great have been the advantages of its location and head start.

Manufacturing in the Winnipeg district is facilitated by municipally operated hydro-electric plants on the Winnipeg River about 80 miles to the east. Municipal water supplies are also obtained from a distance, through an aquaduct from Shoal Lake on the Ontario boundary.

Founded as a trading post, Winnipeg retains this function today. It takes care of more than half of the consumer buying of the province. As the centre of the grain trade it was the logical location for much of the wholesale business of Western Canada. Winnipeg is the capital and quite a large number are employees of the provincial government, there are also many members of the Dominion civil service since the city is the regional headquarters for many branches of the federal government.

The University of Manitoba, with over 6,000 students, is located along the Red River to the south of the city, while normal schools, colleges and other educational institutions in the city and in St. Boniface add considerably to the student population.

## The Geographical Significance of Winnipeg

Because of its peculiar nodal position in the national transportation system, Winnipeg has been for half a century the focus of economic life in Western Canada. Its importance is enhanced because it is the capital of a large province, but it is, itself, the most important part of that province, having over one third of the total population, and more than half the total wealth. Despite its key position, however, the population of Winnipeg has not increased greatly in the past two decades. Winnipeg has been surpassed by the port city of Vancouver in the far west, while in Alberta, Calgary and Edmonton are growing rapidly.

## Other Urban Centres

Greater Winnipeg includes the city of St. Boniface, while the town of Transcona lies immediately to the east. Both are discussed briefly in the following paragraphs. Other centres have arisen, also, in response to local influences in various parts of the Lowland. Only Portage la Prairie has attained city status. Some of the smaller towns, however, have almost equal significance as local regional centres.

### St. Boniface

St. Boniface (29,000), situated on the east bank of the Red River, is part of the Winnipeg metropolitan area. The site was visited by La Verendrye in 1738 and settled by French people in 1775. It was incorporated as a town in 1883 and as a city in 1908. It has the largest and most beautiful cathedral in Western Canada and is the centre of French and Roman Catholic culture. As part of the Winnipeg industrial area, it has packing plants, flour mills, paint and soap works and oil refineries. In 1954, 4,500 people were employed in manufacturing, with an annual return of about $135,000,000.

### Portage la Prairie

Portage la Prairie (10,500) is an important junction point for both the C.N.R. and C.P.R., situated on the north bank of the Assiniboine River, 56 miles west of Winnipeg. It is only 15 miles south of Lake Manitoba and was the southern terminus of an important portage during the fur trading days. It was the site of Fort La Reine, built by La Verendrye in 1728, and of a Hudson's Bay Post built in 1832. The city was incorporated in 1907. The surrounding area, known as the 'Portage Plains', has long been considered one of the finest farming areas in Manitoba. The city has several large grain elevators, dairy plants, machine shops, brick works and an overall factory. Its manufactures are worth about $1,800,000 annually.

## Transcona

Transcona (8,300) lies seven miles east of Winnipeg. It is an important railway centre having large yards and repair shops of the C.N.R. It has, also, several important manufacturing industries.

## Selkirk

Selkirk (7,400) is on the west bank of the Red River, 24 miles northwest of Winnipeg. One of the old Red River settlements, it is the port through which products from Northern Manitoba are handled. In the 1870's it was a strong rival of Winnipeg and for several years it was believed that the C.P.R. would cross the Red River at Selkirk. The town has sawmills, a box factory, a boat building plant and other small manufacturing plants.

## Dauphin

Dauphin (6,000) is situated on the plain between Lake Dauphin and the Riding Mountain, 122 miles northwest of Portage la Prairie. The settlement was founded when the C.N.R. reached the site in 1896 and it was incorporated as a town in 1901. It is a railway divisional point and has several industries including flour mills, lumber mills, creameries and a machine shop. It is an important provincial administrative centre. The surrounding area is a good mixed farming district and about one-third of the population are of Ukrainian origin.

## Neepawa

Neepawa (3,100) is on Neepawa Creek, 123 miles west of Winnipeg. In the Cree language the name signifies "abundance", and the settlement was thus called by its founders in 1873. It is a railway divisional point and the centre for a grain and mixed farming district. Elevators, creameries, a machine shop, a sash and door factory and numerous retail establishments serve the district.

## Morden

Morden (2,200) on the C.P.R. 82 miles southwest of Winnipeg, in the midst of an important wheat producing area, is the site of a Dominion Experimental Farm. Here scientists are attempting to produce varieties of horticultural plants which will withstand the Prairie environment and help to make farm gardens more productive.

The Manitoba Lowlands contain many small villages also. Characteristically they have tree-planted residential streets thus adding to the parklike landscape of the region.

# II. Southeastern Saskatchewan or The Assiniboine Region

Decisively separated from the region to the east by its elevation and by the sharp slopes of the Manitoba Escarpment, this region includes the southwestern part of Manitoba as well as southeastern Saskatchewan. The climate is drier and the vegetation grades from park to treeless steppe. The characteristic portions of this region are the plains which extend from Weyburn to Regina and continue northward to Saskatoon. Most of this area is drained by the Qu'Appelle and Souris Rivers, both tributaries of the Assiniboine River. Similar plains around Yorkton and Kamsack are drained by the Assiniboine itself. For the most part open prairie, they are now devoted to wheat growing.

While, from the viewpoints of physical geography and general land use, there is considerable uniformity throughout this region, it is probable that, in future, geographic differences will become more apparent. In particular, the growth of several cities in different parts of the area tends to create patterns of commerce and communications, which become the most important geographic influences. Thus, Brandon, Regina and Saskatoon may be thought of as emerging regional nuclei.

The Photographic Survey Corporation Limited

Plate 86.   A sector of Regina, showing the Saskatchewan Legislative Building and the landscaped grounds along Wascana Lake.

## Brandon

Brandon (25,000), on the main line of the C.P.R., 133 miles west of Winnipeg, is situated in the valley of the Assiniboine River. A Hudson's Bay Post was founded in 1794. After the building of the C.P.R. the settlement was made a city in 1882. It is now served by a radiating net of railway lines and provincial highways linking it with the surrounding smaller centres of this important agricultural area. The city has flour mills, meat packing plants, tanneries, dairies, breweries, woollen mills, steel works, and oil refineries. The gross value of manufactures in 1954 was $14,200,-000, with a net value of $4,000,000. The regional importance of the city is increased by its educational institutions, including Brandon College and a provincial normal school for training teachers. A Dominion Experimental Farm is located nearby. During World War II, a Royal Canadian Airforce Training station was located here; while at Shilo, a few miles east, there is an important army training camp.

## Regina

"The Queen of the Plains", Regina is centrally located with respect to the populated portion of the Prairie Provinces, being approximately 360 miles west of Winnipeg and 460 miles east of Calgary. The capital of the Province of Saskatchewan, it is a modern city of 90,000 people (89,755 in 1956).

### Historical Note

Before the white man came, Indian buffalo hunters frequented a camping site beside the small creek which flows through the city. Buffalo bones accumulated and the Indians gave the name Wascana (Pile of Bones) to both the creek and the camp site. Later it became a white man's trading post. In 1882, when the Canadian Pacific Railway reached it, the new settlement became the capital of the Northwest Territories and its name was changed to Regina in honour of Queen Victoria. The next year it became the headquarters of the newly formed Northwest Mounted

Police. A tented city at first, it soon became a wooden one and was for some years the most important city in the Northwest Territories, a trading centre from which buffalo bones and hides were shipped east. Soon a branch line was built to Saskatoon, and Regina became an important junction and distribution point. In 1905 the city, with about 6,000 inhabitants, became the capital of the newly formed province of Saskatchewan. On June 30, 1912, the city was laid in ruins by the most devastating tornado ever experienced in Canada, but it was quickly rebuilt.

### The City Site and Urban Landscape

Regina is located on the flat treeless plains of Southern Saskatchewan, broken hereabouts only by the shallow valley of Wascana Creek which winds through the city. A dam across this valley creates a lovely winding lake along which spacious parks have been laid out, providing a wonderful recreation resource for the citizens. On the south shore of the lake, stand the Saskatchewan Legislative Buildings, constructed of Tyndall limestone and surrounded by landscaped gardens.

Although laid out in the familiar gridiron pattern, (Fig. 254) Regina is not so planless as some other cities. Entering the city at the Union Station, which serves both Canadian National and Canadian Pacific Railways, one is quite close to the business section and civic centre which lie to the south. Here, near a small park, are grouped the Post Office, City Hall, Public Library and the Federal Building, containing the offices of the Dominion Government. To the north of the railway yards, lies an area of 300 acres, supplied with railway sidings, which is set apart for industries and warehouses. The abattoirs and stockyards are located in the eastern part of the city while to the north, and just outside the city limits, is a large oil refinery. To the west of the railway yards lies the exhibition grounds while the

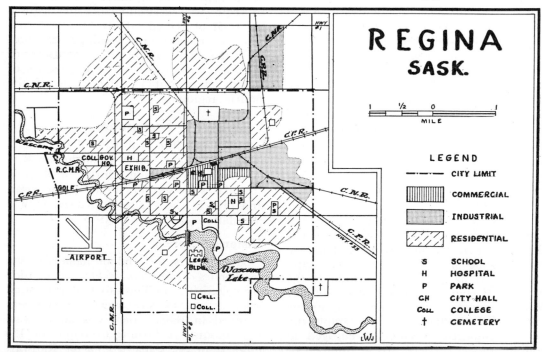

Figure 254. *Regina.* The functional zones of the city are more or less centred on the original railway junction. Note that the urban development is now extending beyond the original civic boundary.

Municipal Airport is located on the south-western edge of the city.

The city contains an area of 19.22 square miles, its boundaries having been extended to include the northern suburbs. Older residential areas are closely packed with small houses, about half of which are of frame construction and the other half about equally divided between brick and stucco. The city parks and most of its streets are lined with trees which, from the air, make a great contrast with the treeless plains outside.

## Population

Regina grew very rapidly at first, reaching a population of 30,000 within 30 years (1911); since then its population has tripled. Approximately half the population are Regina-born while about 78% are native Canadians. Of the remainder, the largest group, 9%, was born in the British Isles and about 8% of the total are from European countries. People of British descent make up 56% of the total, others include 16% of German origin and smaller groups of French, Ukrainian, Roumanian and Hungarians. The dominant religious groups include: United Church 34%, Roman Catholic 23%, Anglican 15%, and Lutheran 9%. In 1951 approximately 32,-000 people, or 43%, were gainfully employed. Of these, manufacturing employed 25%, construction 3%, transportation 4%, trade 27%, services 35%, and financial institutions 2%.

## Urban Functions

Regina has, from its inception, been a combined trade and administrative centre. Its trading area embraces more than one third of the province. As provincial capital, Regina has a large proportion of the provincial civil service and there are also many Dominion officials stationed in the city as well. Including the city employees, several hundred persons are engaged in public service. There are a number of educational institutions, including Regina College which is a junior branch of the provincial university.

Manufacturing is of growing importance. Some of the larger industries are, slaughtering and meat packing, flour milling, brewing, petroleum refining, cement, clay products, paper products, and steel pipe. In 1954 the gross value of manufactured goods was $82,000,000, with a net value of $32,-000,000. Natural gas from newly opened fields in Southern Saskatchewan will provide cheap power for future expansion.

## Geographical Significance

As a trade and administrative centre, Regina grew rather steadily in response to the influences of the railways and the government. In 1940, its planners foresaw a possible population of 90,000 at the end of thirty years. This mark was reached in about half the time, indicating a radical change in the rate of city growth in response to new forces in the post-war era. These forces are connected with the rise of the manufacturing industries which find in Regina well serviced factory sites, a growing pool of skilled labour, new and convenient sources of power and, perhaps most important of all, a centrally located base of distribution, not only for the province of Saskatchewan but for the whole of the prairie region.

## Saskatoon

Saskatoon, "the Hub City of the West", is located on the South Saskatchewan River about 150 miles northwest of Regina. It ranks as the second city in Saskatchewan and fifth in the Prairie Provinces, with a population of 72,858 in 1956.

### Historical Note

Saskatoon is the Indian name for the red berries of the *Amelanchier* bush which the colonists from Toronto, Ontario, found growing on the site when the city was founded in 1883. There was no railway, the colonists had come overland for 150 miles from the Canadian Pacific Railway. Later their supplies were brought down by boat from Medicine Hat where the railway crosses the river. Saskatoon grew slowly, for, without a railway, the surrounding prairie could be used only for ranching. In 1890 a branch line was built from Regina, but the real growth of the city did not begin until the building of the Grand Trunk Railway (now C.N.R.) at the beginning of the twentieth century. In ten years a village of 100 people became a city of 12,000, as a great wave of settlers filled the surrounding area. Radiating branch lines were built and the city became the commerical centre of an area of over 70,000 square miles. With the founding of The University of Saskatchewan in 1907, it became the leading educational centre of the province.

## Population

The city continued to grow rapidly, reaching 26,000 in 1921 and 43,000 in 1931. In 1941 it still had 43,000 but at the census of 1951, there were 53,000. People of British origin constitute 60% of the total, while those of Ukrainian, German, French and Netherlands origins are important among the remainder. About 58% were born in Saskatchewan, 19% in other parts of Canada, 11% in the British Isles, 7% in continental Europe and 4% in the U.S.A. The dominant religions represented in Saskatoon are: United Church 38%, Anglican 17%, Roman Catholic 15% and Presbyterian 16%. About 21,500 people are gainfully employed as follows: agriculture 2%, manufacturing 14%, construction 6%, transportation 10%, trade 25%, finance 4% and services 33%.

## City Site and Urban Landscape

Saskatoon is situated on both banks of the South Saskatchewan River and is linked together by several large bridges. A large concrete dam across the river has created a lake several miles in length adding greatly to the scenic and recreational resources of the city. Several large tree-shaded parks are located along the river

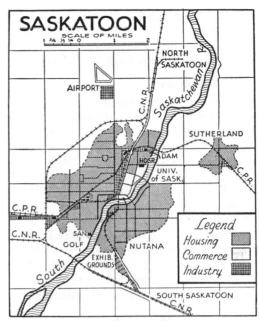

Figure 255. *Saskatoon.* The city occupies both banks of the South Saskatchewan River.

and there are also many beautiful tree-lined streets. Despite the fact that the river, flowing from southwest to northeast, forms a natural axis to the city, most of its streets are laid out on a strict astronomical grid with N-S and E-W directions.

The business district is located on the west bank, between the river and the railway yards, dominated by the Canadian National hotel set in spacious grounds by the river side. To the north, along the river, lie Central Park and the City Hospital while some distance to the south, and also near the river, is the Provincial Sanitarium. In the western part of the city, along the railways, one finds the industrial area containing large flour mills and packing plants. Many warehouses, also, attest the importance of the wholesale trade.

The eastern part of the city is largely residential, but here are located the University of Saskatchewan and the College of Agriculture with large experimental grounds. The buildings are substantial structures of native limestone set in a spacious campus. The exhibition grounds are on the southern edge of the city.

### Urban Functions

Saskatoon is the distributing and retail centre for central Saskatchewan, with a volume of sales not far behind that of Regina. It is the second manufacturing centre in the province; producing in 1954 a gross value of $70,000,000 (net value $22,000,000). Flour, cereal products and meats are important products.

Saskatoon is the seat of the provincial university, which has had an attendance of over 4,000 students during the post-war period. The city also has a normal school for teacher training, an excellent technical school and several collegiate institutes.

## Moose Jaw

Moose Jaw (30,000), third city of Saskatchewan, is located at the junction of Thunder Creek and Moose Jaw River, 47 miles west of Regina. It was first settled in 1882, became a town in 1884 and a city in 1903. The city is a divisional point for both the Canadian National Railway and the Canadian Pacific Railway and the focus of nine radiating lines. It is served by three provincial all-weather highways. It has also an excellent municipal air field and is the headquarters of Prairie Airways.

The industries of the city include flour mills, a large seed cleaning plant, storage elevators, stockyards, packing plant, oil refineries, creameries, a foundry and other smaller establishments. The total value of manufactured goods in 1954 was $46,000,000 with a net value of $12,000,000.

Moose Jaw secures its water supply from the South Saskatchewan River through a canal 70 miles in length in the valley of Thunder Creek, an old glacial meltwater spillway.

## Other Centres

### Weyburn

Weyburn (7,700) is located about 75 miles southeast of Regina on the Canadian Pacific Railway. It is the business centre for a good grain growing district with large elevators and a flour mill.

### Yorkton

Yorkton (8,300) is an important point in eastern Saskatchewan on the Canadian Pacific Railway line from Winnipeg to Saskatoon. It is 110 miles northeast of Regina to which it is connected by a Canadian National Railway linc. Its name commemorates the fact that its first settlers came from York County, Ontario.

### Melville

Melville (5,000) is a divisional point on the Canadian National Railway, 26 miles southwest of Yorkton.

### Estevan

Estevan (5,300) is located on the Soo line of the C.P.R. about 150 miles southeast of Moose Jaw, in the valley of the Souris River. It is the centre of a lignite coal field. An area of about 100 square

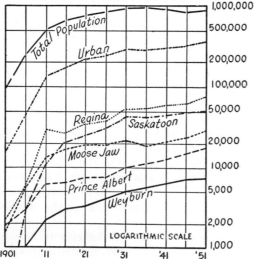

# SASKATCHEWAN CITY POPULATION

Figure 256. *Growth of Population in the cities of Saskatchewan.*

miles is underlain by coal seams covered by a relatively shallow overburden. Though at first worked by conventional underground methods, the coal is now obtained almost entirely by strip mining. Production in 1954 was almost 2,000,000 tons. Estevan coal is shipped to Moose Jaw, Regina, Brandon and Winnipeg. Estevan is the site of a large coal burning electric power plant, with lines to many parts of southeastern Saskatchewan.

The Assiniboine region is the most representative 'prairie' region in Canada. Mostly treeless plains of *chernozem* soil with few topographic breaks, it has become the primary area of extensive wheat growing in the country. Its agricultural population is, and will remain, more scanty and scattered than that of the adjoining mixed farming area. The cultural landscape is characterized by the huge rectangular wheat fields and by the beaded strings of railway villages, each with its cluster of grain elevators. This is the heart of Western Canada.

## III. The Dry Belt

Set apart chiefly by its semi-arid climate and sparse shortgrass vegetation, this region has also a rougher topography than the one previously discussed. Part of its boundary is along the Missouri Coteau and it contains the Cypress Hills and Wood Mountain giving it the characteristics of a rather maturely dissected plateau. Population is scanty and land use is not intensive. Ranching is common and while some irrigation is practised, there never can be enough to change the general characteristics of the region. A certain degree of industrial activity may result from the use of mineral deposits such as the pottery clays of Eastend, Claybank and Willows. Clay is shipped to Medicine Hat. There are also deposits of magnesium sulphate.

The Dry Belt has no population nucleus or regional centre, although Swift Current and Medicine Hat might be considered as rivals for this function. The latter city, however, is in a marginal position and might be considered to belong to the adjoining region.

## Swift Current

Swift Current (10,600) is on the main line of the Canadian Pacific Railway, 112 miles west of Moose Jaw and is the chief business centre for southwestern Saskatchewan. Nearby is a large experimental station operated by the Dominion of Canada Department of Agriculture for the study of the soil and crop problems of the semi-arid areas.

## Medicine Hat

Medicine Hat, (21,000) is Alberta's fourth city. It is a divisional point on the main line of the Canadian Pacific Railway and the junction point of the Crow's Nest branch. It lies 195 miles southeast of Calgary and 30 miles west of the Saskatchewan boundary. The settlement was founded in 1883 when the Canadian Pacific Railway reached the spot and began construction of a bridge across the South Saskatchewan River which is about 1,000 feet in width. The city is built on the south bank of the river on terraces within the valley. A plentiful supply of water from the river enables the city to have tree lined streets and parks in contrast to the treelessness of the neighbouring hills since Medicine Hat lies in the most arid part of the country. Natural gas from underlying formations provides cheap heat and power for domestic and industrial uses. In 1950, manufacturing employed over 1,000 people and produced goods worth $21,000,000 and a net value of $4,000,000. Flour milling, clay products and pottery are important. The largest greenhouses in Western Canada are located in Medicine Hat. *Redcliff* (2,000), seven miles west of Medicine Hat, on the north bank of the river, manufactures bricks, pottery and glass.

## IV. Southern Alberta or The Calgary Region

More complex, perhaps, than any other section of the Prairie Provinces, this region possesses a strong nucleus in the city of Calgary (200,000). It has a diversity of land forms composed of dissected plateau lands and old lake bottoms. Its climate is dry but the availability of irrigation water from the Rocky Mountains has encouraged a diversified agriculture to supplement the grazing economy. Coal, oil and gas form the basis of a growing industrial activity.

While Calgary is undoubtedly the centre of Southern Alberta, the city of Lethbridge (30,000) is the nucleus of an important southern subregion with important coal mines and irrigated agriculture.

## Calgary

Calgary, the Sunshine City of the Foot-hills, is situated on the Bow River, within sight of the Rocky Mountains. With a population of 200,450 (Calgary city 181,780), according to the 1956 census, metropolitan Calgary ranks as second city in Alberta and tenth in the whole of Canada.

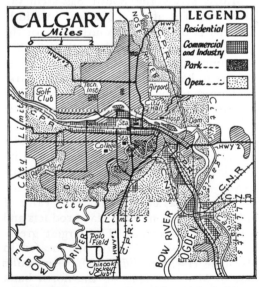

Figure 257. *Calgary.* From the original site at the junction of the Bow and Elbow rivers the city has tended to grow in a westerly direction.

### Historical Note

Calgary was founded as a Northwest Mounted Police post in 1875. It was at first called Fort Brisbois but in 1876 was renamed Fort Calgary after a place of that name on the Isle of Mull. Its early growth was slow; in 1881 it consisted of a Hudson Bay Store, one other store, the barracks of the Mounted Police and the house of the commanding officer. In 1883 the Canadian Pacific Railway reached Calgary and set up a boxcar as a station. A Dominion Land Office was opened at the same time. On November 17, 1884, the "town of Calgary" was incorporated, including an area of 1,600 acres and a population of 500 people. In 1887 the stockyards were established and Calgary became "cow town", the shipping centre of the foothill ranching country. In 1893 the "city of Calgary" received its charter. A further milestone in the growth of the city was the establishment of the Canadian Pacific Railway shops in 1898, and in 1904, the Canadian Pacific Railway irrigation district was set up to the east of the city. Calgary grew rapidly during the first decade of the twentieth century, expanding its area to more than 26,000 acres. The greatest boom came during 1911-13, after the discovery of oil in the Turner Valley. In spite of the collapse of the real estate boom, Calgary continued to grow rapidly until the depression of the 1930's. In recent years, however, its growth has been resumed.

### City Site and Urban Landscape

The site selected for the police post was a flat terrace at the juncture of the Bow and Elbow rivers. The railway station and new town were placed on the plain to the west of the Elbow River where the city centre is today. Calgary has spread over the whole valley and out of it in all directions. Including annexations in 1957, the area of the city is 70 square miles. The city centre contains some notable buildings such as the Palliser Hotel, the City Hall, Post Office and Canadian Pacific Railway station. The Courthouse is a short distance northwest, while the Canadian National Railway station is a few blocks south. Here also is the main retail and business district. Calgary has many new office buildings, erected to house the headquarters staffs of large oil companies and construction firms working throughout the province. Another landmark, somewhat to the north of the city centre, is the Memorial Auditorium, built by the Alberta government. A number of large bridges have been built over the Bow River. River front locations have been utilized for boulevards and parks. The famous Calgary Dinosaur Park and Zoo is located on St. Georges Island in the Bow River. Here life sized models of the extinct great reptiles of Alberta are displayed.

Though scattered, there are a number of fine residential districts in different parts of the city. The names of the various parts of the city, such as Mount Royal, Rideau, Rosedale and Sunnyside, were probably bestowed by former residents of Montreal, Ottawa and Toronto.

## Location

Calgary lies at the juncture of the Great Plains and the Rocky Mountain foothills, 840 miles west of Winnipeg and 640 miles east of Vancouver, by way of the Canadian Pacific Railway. It is about 150 miles north of the international boundary. Calgary is the creation of the railroad but it owes much to its mountain fed rivers. By damming the Elbow River a supply of pure water is obtained. The Bow River is harnessed to supply electric power, it serves to transport logs to the sawmills of the city, and within the city limits it is diverted into the canals of a great irrigation district. With the Bow River providing a good route through the mountains, Calgary can be said to be a "pass city". It is an ideal place from which to start a mountain vacation tour. Calgary is also well located with respect to mineral resources, being only 30 miles from the Turner Valley oil field and even less from the mines in Bow Valley.

## Transportation Facilities

Six railway lines radiate from the city of Calgary, tying in all parts of the province. Four hard surfaced highways also converge on the city. The municipal airport, just north of the city, has an area of one square mile and is used by transcontinental air lines. The street railway and bus service are municipally owned.

## Population

In 1901, Calgary had a population of 4,392 which in the next decade increased tenfold. Since then its growth has been slower but in 1946 it passed 100,000. About 44% are Alberta-born, 28% were born in other parts of Canada, 14% in the British Isles, 7% in Europe and 5% in U.S.A. British stock comprises 68% of the population, other important groups being French 3%, German 6% and Scandinavian 5%. The principal religious affiliations include United Church of Canada 35%, Anglicans 21%, Presbyterians 8%, Roman Catholics 13%, Baptists 5%, Lutherans 5%. In 1951, 56,000 or 43% of the population reported gainful employment with 19% in manufacturing, 11% in transportation, 23% in trade, 27% in various services and 8% in construction.

## Urban Functions

The city is becoming important as a manufacturing centre. Petroleum products, meat packing, milling, chemicals, metal products, railway shops and dairy products are important. Altogether there were in 1954, nearly 300 factories with about 8,500 workers employed and a total production of $143,000,000, with a net value of $52,-000,000. There is abundance of natural gas in Southern Alberta for use as industrial as well as domestic fuel. The city has large elevators and is an important centre of the grain trade. The Calgary Exhibition and Stampede, held every summer, is world famous and keeps alive Calgary's "cow town" traditions. Transportation and trade are dominant, however, and Calgary is

*Courtesy Exp. Farms Service*

Plate 87.   A sugar factory at Raymond, Alberta.

a rival of Edmonton in both the wholesale and retail fields.

## Lethbridge

Lethbridge (30,000) is the third most populous city in the province. It is located on the Oldman River about 110 miles west of Medicine Hat and 140 miles southeast of Calgary. It is served by the Crow's Nest line of the Canadian Pacific Railway. Lethbridge has an important airport where connection is made between Trans-Canada Air Lines and Western Air which provide a link with American air routes at Great Falls, Montana.

Lethbridge was built largely on coal which was mined from the river bank as early as 1872. Known at first as "Coal Banks", it received its present name in 1885 when first reached by a railway. It soon became the centre of an important ranching and grain growing area. Irrigation projects in the neighbourhood now bring water to over 250,000 acres which produce sugar beets, vegetables for canning and other important crops. In 1954, about 1,000 persons were employed in manufacturing, producing goods worth $15,000,000, and a net value of $7,500,000.

## Other Towns

*Drumheller* (2,600), on the Red Deer River, about 75 miles northeast of Calgary is an important coal mining town.

*Cardston* (2,600) and *Raymond* (2,400) are located in the irrigated areas south of Lethbridge. There is a sugar factory at Raymond, while Cardston is the site of a Mormon Temple.

*Taber* (3,700), a few miles east of Lethbridge, is the growing centre of an irrigated area. A large sugar refinery has recently been erected.

## V.  Central Alberta or the Edmonton Region

As a natural region, Central Alberta has been recognized for a long time. The environment has given rise to a fairly uniform but not monotonous parkland landscape over a wide area. The soil is black and fertile. Industrious settlers have made of this one of the best mixed farming regions in Western Canada, rivalling the Manitoba lowlands in the production of hogs and dairy products. This activity supports a relatively dense rural population. The region also has great mineral resources. The underlying Edmonton formation contains coal and more is available from the Kootenay rocks of the adjoining Foothills. The deeper seated Devonian rocks have proven to be one of the more important reservoirs of petroleum on the whole continent, thus giving the Edmonton region greater resources than those of Calgary.

With a total population of 251,000 in 1956, Metropolitan Edmonton is the undisputed centre of the region, in which there are no rival or even sub-regional capitals.

## Edmonton

Edmonton is the capital city of Alberta and well known as "the Gateway to the North". It is a thriving modern city with a population of 226,000 according to the census of 1956, thus attaining the rank of eighth city of the Dominion.

### Historical Note

The founding of Edmonton should probably be dated from 1808 when the Hudson's Bay Company and the North West fur traders of Montreal both built forts within the limits of the present city. Before that, however, both had maintained posts twenty miles down the river, built in 1794 and 1795. When the posts were merged in 1820, the Hudson Bay Company's name Fort Edmonton was retained, but the North West factor was left in charge.

The first land claims were staked in 1871, when the nearest established settlement was at Portage la Prairie, just 60 miles west of

*The Photographic Survey Corporation Limited*

Plate 88.   The central section of Edmonton, with the North Saskatchewan River in the foreground and the airport in the background.

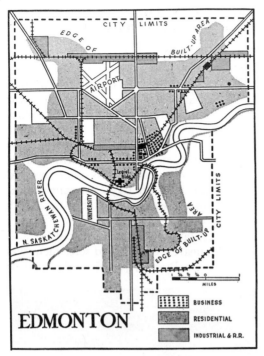

Figure 258. *Edmonton.* Originally two towns, Edmonton and Strathcona, the city was united in 1912 after the high-level bridge was built.

Winnipeg and three or four months distant by oxcart. In 1870 a telegraph line was built to Edmonton but the route of the Canadian Pacific went through Calgary. In 1891 the Canadian Pacific Railway built a branch line to Strathcona on the south bank of the river. There were thus for a time two cities which were amalgamated in 1912, the same year in which the high level bridge was built. The building of the Grand Trunk and Canadian Northern and later the Peace River and Athabaska railways made Edmonton an important railway centre.

When the Province of Alberta was created in 1905, Edmonton was chosen as the capital. A little later it was made the site of the University of Alberta.

### Location

The selection of Edmonton as a trading post was, perhaps, prompted by the fact that the North Saskatchewan River was the traditional boundary between the Crees and the Blackfeet. Its park belt environment is more pleasing than that of the semi-arid plains and, for the province as a whole, it is more centrally located than any other Alberta city. For the Canadian National Railways, it is a natural half way point, 793 miles west of Winnipeg, 771 miles east of Vancouver and 956 miles east of Prince Rupert. The strategic location of Edmonton was emphasized during World War II by the operation of the Northwest Staging Route and the building of the Alaska Highway, when it became not only the "gateway to the North" but the "Crossroads of the World".

### Transportation Facilities

In the early days, Edmonton was serviced by boats and canoes on the river or by the long ox-cart trail from the Red River. For a time the Hudson's Bay Company maintained a steamship service on the North Saskatchewan. Now, the city is served by eight radiating rail lines, by hard surfaced highways and by airlines. The large airport adjoining the city is one of the most important in Canada, being used not only by transcontinental lines but also maintaining connections with the far northwest.

### The City Site and Urban Landscape

The river, in its deeply eroded valley, cuts a great gash in the plains upon which the city is built. There are, also, many tributary ravines by which intermittent streams descend to the river. With a relief of nearly 200 feet, the river front and valley sides serve as park sites for the city.

Like other western cities, Edmonton sprawls over a large space, occupying over 27,000 acres. One reason for this was the presence of the Hudson's Bay Company Reserve which for many years remained empty. The chief industrial plants were built near the railway to the northeast while the railway shops were located to the northwest. In the central part of the city, overlooking the river, stand such buildings as the Alberta Legislature and the Provincial Office Buildings, the Federal Building, Macdonald Hotel, and the strikingly modern City Hall. Jasper Avenue is the axis of the central business district.

The University of Alberta occupies an excellent site on a high terrace within a great bend of the river to the southwest of the city centre. Near it is the Memorial Auditorium built by the Alberta government in 1955 to mark the fiftieth anniversary of the province.

## Population

Census figures show that Edmonton has grown from 4,176, in 1901, to 113,116 in 1946. By 1951, the population had increased to 159,000. This growth has been accomplished by the absorption of migrants from many lands and especially from other parts of Canada. In 1951, native Albertans numbered 53%, 22% were born in other parts of Canada, 11% in the British Isles and 10% in Europe. One-half of the people claim British descent; other groups include Ukrainian 11%, French 6%, German 7% and Polish 3%. The dominant religious groups are United Church of Canada 32%,

Anglicans 16%, Roman Catholics 18%, Presbyterians 7%, Baptists 4% and Lutherans 6%. In 1951, the labour force was 43% of the population. The gainfully employed were grouped as follows: mining and oil wells 3%, manufacturing 15%, construction 12%, transportation 10%, trade 22%, finance 4%, professions 10% and other services 21%.

## Urban Functions

Edmonton is an important trade centre and transportation node, a service centre for the booming petroleum industry, with a rapidly growing, diversified manufacturing industry. Amongst the chief industries of the Edmonton district are slaughtering and meat packing, dairy products, petroleum refining, chemicals and metal refining. Others are steel products, furniture, builders supplies, clothing, flour and feed and bakery products. More than 400 factories, employing 13,000 workers turned out goods worth $260,000,000 (net value $95,000,000) in 1954. Edmonton is blessed with cheap power, having a municipally owned electrical station operated by natural gas piped in from surrounding fields.

The provincial, civic and Dominion civil services employ about 6,000 persons, and another 5,000 are found in the various professions.

## Smaller Centres

*Red Deer* (12,500) is located at the point where the railway from Calgary to Edmonton crosses the Red Deer River. It is the centre of an important wheat growing and mixed farming area and has industrial dairy plants, machine shops and woodworking plants.

*Wetaskewin* (4,500) and *Camrose* (5,800) are local market centres south and southeast of Edmonton. Other towns in Central Alberta include *Lacombe* (2,700), *Ponoka* (3,400), *Stettler* (3,400), *Vegreville* (2,600), *Vermilion* (2,200), *Wainwright* (2,700) and *Lloydminster* (5,100).

Rising centres are found in the new oil fields of *Leduc* and *Redwater*. The latter grew from a station village of 160 persons

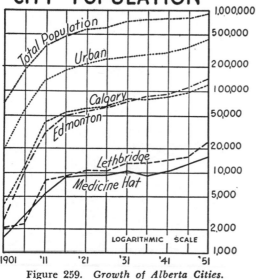

Figure 259. *Growth of Alberta Cities.*

to a town of 1,300, within two and a half years after the discovery well came in. Pipe lines connect the producing areas with Edmonton and with the Interprovincial pipe line to Lake Superior.

Although certainly occupying a marginal position at the time Edmonton was chosen as the provincial capital, the Central Alberta region is rapidly becoming the true geographic nucleus of the province.

## VI. The Rocky Mountain Region

The Rocky Mountains and the foothills may be taken as a region although it might be more accurate to say that they form the geographic boundary of the Prairie region. The width of the rough forested country west of Edmonton, however, demands regional recognition. There are a number of small urban centres but there is no popula-

tion nucleus nor can there ever be a true regional capital able to counteract the attractions of Calgary and Edmonton. Forestry, mining, and in the south, grazing, constitute the chief economic activities.

The recreational resources of the mountain resorts attract a considerable tourist trade. The region contains three large national parks: Waterton Lakes, Banff and Jasper. In all of them, superb mountain scenery is available. In each of them there is a small headquarters town, *Banff* (2,500) being the most populous. The Banff-Jasper Highway is Alberta's most scenic motor route.

The coal-mining towns of the region include *Blairmore* and *Coleman* in the Crow's Nest area, *Cochrane, Canamore* and *Bankhead* in the Bow Valley, and *Brazeau* and *Mountain Park* further north.

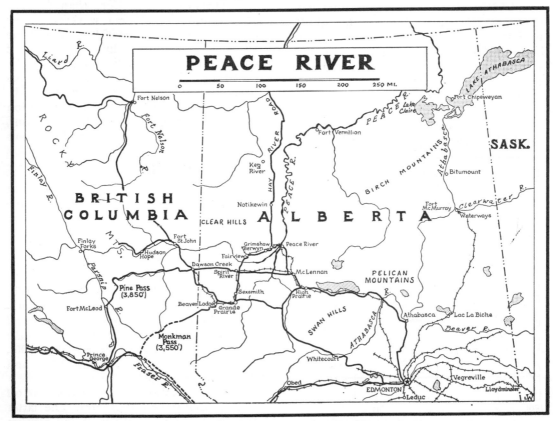

Figure 260. *The Peace River Region.*

An important part of the region is the Rocky Mountain Forest Reserve which, as well as being a timber supply, is a protection to the headwaters of the Saskatchewan and Athabaska river systems. These mountain streams are regarded as sources of potential hydro-electric power and water for irrigation, industrial and domestic uses.

# VII. Northwestern Alberta or the Peace River Region

The Peace River District, located in northwestern Alberta and adjoining parts of British Columbia, has for over a generation represented the fringe of agricultural settlement in Western Canada. It has recently been placed even more definitely upon the map as the gateway to the Alaska Highway.

In Alberta it includes the area between townships 69 and 96, from range 15 west of the fifth meridian to the B.C. boundary. Roughly, it is 165 miles long by 150 miles wide and contains approximately 25,000 square miles or 16,000,000 acres. It is bigger than the province of Nova Scotia and compares in size with the Clay Belt of Northern Ontario.

Although separated from Edmonton by over 150 miles of rough forest and muskeg country considered to be unsuitable for agricultural settlement, the physical conditions are similar to those of the parkland regions of Central Alberta. The northern extension of the Great Plains has a general elevation of about 2,000 feet above sea level, declining gradually toward the northeast. Above this stand some plateau-like remnants of an older erosion level, such as Saskatoon Mountain and the Burnt Hills, which are over 3,000 feet above sea level. Below the general level, the Peace River and its largest tributary, the Smoky, have cut valleys from 500 to 800 feet in depth.

Summer temperatures are but slightly below those of Edmonton although mid-winter is considerably colder. Precipitation figures, also, resemble those of Central Alberta, declining somewhat toward the north, and the same summer concentration of rainfall is found. Soils and vegetation also repeat the alternation of parkland and forest.

## Settlement

Alexander Mackenzie, in 1792, was the first white man to visit the Peace River. The fur traders and missionaries who followed experimented with the agricultural possibilities of the area. Settlers entered the area in 1879 but real settlement did not begin until the years 1906-11. In the latter year the census recorded a population of 1,200. The Edmonton, Dunvegan and British Columbia Railway reached Peace River Crossing in December, 1915, and Grande Prairie in July, 1916. Simultaneously settlers flocked in and by 1921 there were 18,000 in the area. Another "boom" period was experienced after 1926, pushing the population total to 40,000 in 1931. By 1941 there were about 48,000 people in the area but this had shrunk slightly to 45,000 by 1946. The 1951 census recorded 54,000.

## Towns

There are no large towns in the Peace River district. Urban population, however, is growing at the expense of the rural. *Grande Prairie* is the chief town, with a population of 1,645 in 1941 and 6,302 in 1956. It is the business headquarters of the region and has the finest hospital and high school in Northern Alberta. Its prosperity is, naturally, to be explained by the excellence of the surrounding agricultural area. *Peace River* (2,034), *High Prairie* (1,743) and *McLennan* (1,092) are next in size. Smaller centres include *Fairview* (1,260), *Grimshaw* (904), *Spirit River* (2,034), *Sexsmith* (345) and *Berwyn* (342).

## Transportation

Railway mileage reached its present status in 1931 but the system must be regarded as incomplete and unsatisfactory. The Peace River district has long desired a direct outlet to the ports of the Pacific coast, which can now be reached only by means

The Photographic Survey Corporation Limited
Plate 89. The Dufferin Bridge over the Peace River.

of the roundabout route through Edmonton. There are four possible routes, one or all of which may eventually come into use. The most southerly of these joins the Canadian National Railway at Obed about 160 miles west of Edmonton and would follow the valley of the Little Smoky river, eventually joining the Northern Alberta Railway at Aggie. A branch would also connect Grande Prairie. The second, and most direct, route is from Grande Prairie to Prince George via Monkman Pass. The third is from Dawson Creek via Pine Pass, and the fourth by way of the Peace River Pass, Finlay Forks and the Parsnip River valley. The extension of settlement northward almost certainly requires a railroad to Notikewin, Keg River and, eventually, to Fort Vermilion or, perhaps, to Hay River instead, paralleling the Hay River Highway.

The present highway system also funnels to Edmonton, an all season, all weather

road extending from the capital to Grimshaw just beyond Peace River. From this vicinity a highway leads north to Notikewin and Hay River while another leads southwest to Grande Prairie and thence northwest to Dawson Creek, and the Alaska Highway. A cut off leads from Grande Prairie eastward to High Prairie near the western end of Lesser Slave Lake. Another cross country route leads from Dawson Creek through Spirit River to Donnelly on the Edmonton Highway. A new direct highway route from Edmonton has been built by way of Whitecourt and Valleyview.

**Agricultural Progress**

The Peace River district has approximately 8,500 farmers who operate two and three quarter million acres of land, of which about 50% may be classed as arable or improved land. This means that, on the average, each farm occupies a half section. The progress of agricultural development may be understood from Table 17 which is taken from census returns for district 16 of Alberta. Census district 16 does not include quite all of the Peace River area but it does include most of the agricultural settlement. While there have been minor recessions in the growth of total population, numbers of farms and occupied land, the area of productive land has continued to expand. There has been no recent wave of settlement in this area but, on the contrary, as in other parts of the Prairie Provinces, there has been actual removal of farm population and consolidation of farm

| Table 17 | | | Thirty-five Years of Development in the Peace River District | | | | | |
|---|---|---|---|---|---|---|---|---|
| Date | Total Population | Number of Farms | Occupied Land Acres | Size of Farm | Improved Land Acres | % of Occupied Land | Crop Land Acres | % of Occupied Land |
| 1916 | 6,705 | 1488 | 371,505 | 250 | 75,804 | 20 | 54,463 | 16 |
| 1921 | 12,181 | 3578 | 879,945 | 245 | 243,570 | 28 | 170,589 | 19 |
| 1926 | 11,381 | 2796 | 857,154 | 300 | 308,232 | 36 | 222,840 | 26 |
| 1931 | 27,190 | 6977 | 1,804,418 | 258 | 674,179 | 37 | 491,390 | 22 |
| 1936 | 29,204 | 6522 | 1,864,056 | 284 | 778,972 | 42 | 539,542 | 29 |
| 1941 | 30,349 | 6395 | 2,066,907 | 324 | 951,416 | 46 | 610,589 | 30 |
| 1946 | 28,733 | 5764 | 2,045,916 | 360 | 1,028,851 | 50 | 708,683 | 35 |
| 1951 | 32,439 | 6074 | 2,388,637 | 393 | 1,303,978 | 54 | 960,887 | 40 |

holdings. Farms are becoming fewer and larger.

There are geographical contrasts. The earlier settlements around Sexsmith, Clairmont, Grande Prairie and Wembly are mainly on choice parkland soils, whereas the newer pioneer fringe is located on Grey Wooded soils. In the former areas wheat yields about 20 bushels and oats 37 bushels per acre; in the fringe areas the yields are 17 and 30 respectively.

In the older district, farms average nearly three quarters of a section in area and, although they carry on mixed farming, cash grain is their greatest source of income. Farm buildings are well constructed, community services such as roads, schools and churches are well developed and the general appearance of the community retains little of the pioneer landscape.

Farms in the newer districts average about 320 acres each, the buildings are mediocre in appearance and livestock is usually an important source of income.

While the older districts have certain natural and historical advantages, nevertheless, it is felt that the fringe areas will eventually become prosperous also. Modern power driven machinery is facilitating the process of land clearing, roads are being built, while high prices have stimulated both grain growing and livestock rearing. Rural population has declined but the individual farmer is better off on a larger farm.

**Future Possibilities**

Various estimates have been made of the possibilities for future settlement. Earlier reports indicated that between 8,000,000 and 9,000,00 acres in the Peace River might be considered fit for settlement. About 3,000,000 acres have already been occupied. A recent study indicates that about 20,000 quarter sections, or 3,200,000 acres are still available in the Peace River. In addition, the far north from Fort Vermilion to Hay River, contains approximately 15,000 quarter sections or 2,400,000 acres, making a to-

tal of 5,600,000 acres in northwestern Alberta. Subject to the influence of future agricultural markets and techniques, this might mean the establishment of 10,000 to 15,000 additional farmers and the tripling of the population of northwestern Alberta. However, present trends indicate that this is some distance in the future.

## VIII. Central Saskatchewan or the Prince Albert Region

A wide zone across the midsection of Saskatchewan is beginning to take on regional characteristics. The natural landscape originally included the complete transition from grassland in the south, through parkland to the northern forest. It was in no sense a natural unit. In the agricultural economy of the present it is a mixed farming region with a pioneer fringe along the north, beyond which is the forest. This boundary has been gradually advancing but will probably become fixed in the future. Parts of this zone are found beyond the borders of Saskatchewan in both Alberta and Manitoba but they are not well integrated parts of the human region. A regional capital at Prince Albert is beginning to exert its influence over Central Saskatchewan. Prince Albert owes some of its importance to the fact that it is a gateway to the north although its hinterland is not so rich as that of Edmonton. Subregional nuclei are also beginning to develop in this extensive zone, including North Battleford, Melfort and Nipawin.

### Prince Albert

Prince Albert (20,500) on the North Saskatchewan River, 80 miles north of Saskatoon, is the gateway to Northern Saskatchewan and, actually, the most centrally located city in the province. At the southern edge of the commercial forest belt it is a centre for woodworking industries. It is a distribution point and market for a large mixed farming area and a tourist mecca by reason of the highway to Prince Albert National Park and Lac la Ronge. Regular service to other points in Northern Saskatchewan is provided by the Saskatchewan Government Air Lines.

## North Battleford

North Battleford (9,000) is located on the north bank of the North Saskatchewan River, opposite the mouth of the Battle River. It is served by both Canadian National and Canadian Pacific railways, and by Canadian Pacific airlines. It is the commercial centre for a large area in west-central Saskatchewan and has a few small industries.

Battleford (1,500) is an older settlement lying on the south bank of the North Saskatchewan River. Fort Battleford National Park recalls the stirring events of the Northwest Rebellion.

## Other Towns

*Melfort* (3,300) is the centre for the Carrot River Valley, about 65 miles southeast of Prince Albert, and *Nipawin* (3,300) is an important frontier town on the Saskatchewan River about 90 miles east of Prince Albert.

## Northern Settlement

In Saskatchewan, the agricultural settlement of the "Pioneer Fringe" has penetrated about halfway through the commercial forest belt. This process was considerably hastened during the 1930's by the migration of farmers from the drought-stricken area in the south. From 1931 to 1941 the number of farms in the northern census districts increased by 20%, compared with a decrease of 4.5% in the rest of Saskatchewan.

Although the Grey Wooded Soil belt contains over 30,000,000 acres, only a small part of it is considered suitable for settlement. There can be no useful extension beyond this belt either, for the soils of the Shield are too infertile and the climate too hazardous. It is possible that there remains an area of three to five million acres of usable land consisting of first and second class Grey Wooded Soils. At most, this might allow for the establishment of 20,000 new farms, an increase of about one-sixth in the provincial total.

Studies of the area indicate that it is more difficult to develop than the land of the Peace River District. Much of it is found in the provincial forest reserves and, undoubtedly, will for a long time be devoted to the production of wood. The Saskatchewan Department of Natural Resources believes that undisposed of provincial land suitable for agricultural settlement is practically exhausted.

The same is true of Manitoba. Some agriculture is possible on alluvial land near The Pas. Mention is also sometimes made of a clay belt of 6,000,000 acres in Northern Manitoba but its future for agriculture is remote. All its physical conditions tend to make it much less desirable than the clay belt of Northern Ontario.

## IX. The North

This huge and formless region, nearly as large as all the rest, is uniform only in its lack of population. Politically divided amongst all three provinces, it is being provided with corridors of transportation and influence which run in a north-south direction. At the same time its natural divisions, based on geology, climate and vegetation, run from southeast to northwest. In time, therefore, several sub-regions may crystallize. Already the discovery of minerals, the growth of mining settlements, such as Flin Flon and Sherridon, and the building of roads and railways tend to give regional character to Northern Manitoba. Transportation is a major problem. Tractor trains are used in winter for freighting to out-of-the-way places. Air service is highly important. However, the canoe in summer and the dog-team in winter are still in active use.

## The Pas

The Pas (4,000), situated on the Saskatchewan River about 400 miles northwest of Winnipeg, is the gateway to the mining districts of Northern Manitoba, and is also the largest town on the Hudson Bay Railway. The name is a corruption of the Cree *opas*, meaning "narrows". Its history goes back to early fur-trading days but permanent settlement dates from about the year 1800. During the days of steamer navigation on the Saskatchewan it was an important settlement. The Pas was reached by the railway in 1908 and the town enjoyed prosperity during the construction of the Hudson Bay Railway in the years previous to World War I. There was a second "boon" when the branch line to Flin Flon was completed, and the population of The Pas reached 4,500 in 1929. Since that time the activity of the town has been rather stagnant. Its chief industry is the Pas Lumber Company which operates the largest sawmill in Manitoba. The logs are brought down the river from forests in the Province of Saskatchewan. There is also an important fish-packing industry at The Pas.

The Pas is the most important transportation node in Northern Manitoba. It is a divisional point on the Canadian National Railway and has highway and air service as well. Consequently it is the centre of both wholesale and retail trade in the region. Here too, are found many regional administrative offices as well as health, educational and religious institutions.

A small agricultural district is found on the alluvial lands of the Carrot River just to the west of The Pas.

## Flin Flon

Incorporated in 1946, Flin Flon (10,200) is Manitoba's newest city as well as its most important mining centre. It is located on the Saskatchewan border, 92 miles north of The Pas, with which it is connected by a branch of the C. N. Railway and by provincial highway. The ore body, which lies partly in both provinces, was discovered in 1914, but it required fifteen years to bring it into full production. Power

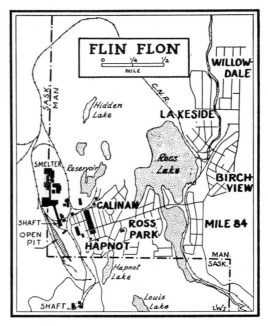

Figure 261. *Flin Flon*. The city is rather scattered, most of the subdivisions extending to the east of the mines, separated by lakes and swamps. Note the jog in the provincial boundary.

was obtained from Island Falls on the Churchill River, 60 miles to the north.

The urban landscape of Flin Flon is like that of other mining towns in the Canadian Shield. Dominated by the head frames of the mine shafts and the tall stacks of the metallurgical plants, the town is sprawled over bare, rocky hills. Water mains and sewers are laid on the surface, protected by wooden boxes and steam heated in winter. It is not a "company town" but, previous to its incorporation, was under direct supervision of the Manitoba government. However, the mining company has built and operated most of the public utilities and much of the housing as well. Less than half of the inhabitants live in single houses; flats and apartments are numerous. The civic government owns and controls all vacant land in the city.

Population has increased steadily, the census enumerated about 5,000 in 1936,

*National Film Board*
Plate 90. A street scene in Flin Flon, Manitoba. Note the insulated water mains on the surface of the rocky ground.

6,800 in 1941, 7,600 in 1946, and 9,900 in 1951.

The ore body is sufficient to last for many years and, while eventually it will be worked out, at present it supports one of the most thriving mining communities on the Canadian Shield.

## Churchill

Churchill, located at the mouth of the Churchill River, is the terminus of the Hudson Bay Railway which was completed to this point in 1929. The seaport with a 2,500,000 bushel elevator was built during the early 1930's. Prior to 1929 the fur trading settlement was located on the west bank of the river but the port was built on the east bank causing the whole settlement to migrate. In 1942 a large airfield was constructed, and in 1946 the Joint Services Arctic Testing and Experimental Station was established a few miles east of the town. Churchill thus has several functions: it is still a minor fur trading post and Indian settlement; it is the local headquarters of the R.C.M.P.; it is a defence centre and gateway to a large part of Arctic Canada; and it is a transshipment point for export grain. In 1951, 21 ships loaded a total of 7,500,000 bushels. There were about 3,000 residents in 1956.

## Other Settlements

Other settlements worthy of mention are *Lynn Lake* in Manitoba and *Uranium City* in Saskatchewan. Both are mining centres. Apart from minerals the chief resource of the region is its wild life which is being managed by its Indian inhabitants. For them the Hudson's Bay Posts are still the important settlements of the region.

Northeastern Alberta has a corridor of northern transportation along the Athabaska-Slave waterway. Associated with it there are a number of interesting settlements.

*McMurray,* at the confluence of the Clearwater and Athabaska rivers, is a long-established settlement and route junction. It is the site of a Hudson's Bay Post and a summer gathering place for the Indians of several thousand square miles. It has several churches, schools and a hospital. *Waterways,* on the Clearwater, three miles upstream from McMurray, is the terminus of the railway from Edmonton and the point at which goods and passengers are transferred to river shipping. In this general vicinity are found the famous Alberta deposits of "tar sands", a source of petro-

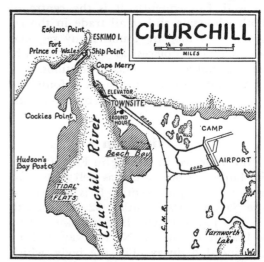

Figure 262. *Churchill.* A tidal harbour at the mouth of the Churchill River gives the Prairie Provinces their only port. It is important also as a military outpost.

*Courtesy Canadian National Railways*
Plate 91. The elevator at Churchill, Manitoba, the terminus of the Hudson Bay Railway. In 1951, some 7,500,000 bushels of grain were loaded for overseas markets.

leum which will, one day, be extremely important. The rocks of the area contain salt which is extracted by means of brine wells. A refinery produces both coarse and table grades.

In the delta region at the western end of Lake Athabaska, is located *Fort Chipewyan*. It has a strategic location, accessible from the lake and from the Peace, Athabaska and Slave river routes, hence its importance as a Hudson's Bay Post. The Slave is navigable for about 75 miles below Chipewyan to *Fitzgerald,* below which the river descends more than 100 feet in a series of rapids. Goods and passengers are portaged by road to *Fort Smith,* N.W.T., where they resume the river journey "down north". The Athabaska and Slave rivers form the eastern boundary of the Alberta section of Wood Buffalo Park, an area of several thousand square miles which has been set aside for the preservation of these huge animals.

## Regional Development

To say that regional differentiation is incomplete is another way of stating that regional development is still going on. It is true that the process of land settlement had all but ceased. Only in the narrow, northern, pioneer fringe is clearing in progress, mainly on farms already occupied for some years. Types of farming are being adopted which are more in harmony with the environment and in this way the Manitoba Lowland, Central Alberta and the Dry Belt become more fully differentiated.

The growth of cities, too, reflects regional influences and resources. In this case, the greatest change is occurring in Alberta where mineral resources provide the basis of urban industrialization. There is good reason to believe that Calgary and Edmonton, both, may double or triple their population in the next half century. They will, thus, become much stronger nuclei in their respective regions. The cities of Saskatchewan are also expanding, but at a much slower rate. The regions of Saskatchewan, therefore, will remain more strongly rural than those of the other two provinces. There are, however, chances for industrial development which should be carefully fostered. Chemicals and clay products are two important lines which are being encouraged. The history of the past twenty years has shown that it is unsound to rely completely upon a "wheat economy". The full development of the Prairie Provinces, as well as that of any other Canadian region, must depend upon the utilization of all resources.

## Selected References

Acton, B. K. and C. C. Spence. *A study of pioneer farming in the fringe areas of the Peace River, Alberta. 1942.* Canada Department of Agriculture. Publication 792. Ottawa. 1947.

Campbell, Marjorie Wilkins. *The Saskatchewan.* Rivers of America Series. New York. 1950

Dawson, C. A. *The Settlement of the Peace River Country.* The Macmillan Company of Canada Ltd. Toronto. 1934.

Harrington, Lyn. *North on the Hudson Bay Railway.* Canadian Geographical Journal XXXV, pp. 54-66. 1947.

Harrington, Lyn. *Tractor Trails in Manitoba.* Canadian Geographical Journal. XXXVIII, pp. 70-77. 1949.

Hooke, A. J. *Alberta, Nature's Treasure House.* Canadian Geographical Journal. XXXV, pp. 154-177. 1947.

Innis, H. A. *The Hudson Bay Railway.* Geographical Review. Vol. 20, pp. 1-30. 1930.

Kitto, F. H. *The Peace River Country.* Canada. Department of Interior. Ottawa. 1927.

Leppard, H. M. *The Settlement of the Peace River Country.* Geographical Review. Vol. 25, pp. 67-78. 1935.

Macfarlane, R. O. *Manitoba.* Canadian Geographical Journal. XXXV, pp. 124-152. 1947.

Mackie, V. J. *Manitoba—Province of Industry.* Canadian Geographical Journal. XXXXI, pp. 167-181. 1950.

*Regina 1947-1976. A thirty-year program for development.* Community Planning Committee. Regina. 1946.

Stead, Robert J. C. *Calgary—City of the Foothills.* Canadian Geographic Journal. XXVI, pp. 154-71. 1948.

Watt, A. B. *Edmonton.* Canadian Geographical Journal, XXXIII, pp. 242-51. 1946.

Williams, M. Y. *Churchill, Manitoba.* Canadian Geographical Journal. XXXIX, pp. 112-133. 1949.

*Winnipeg Master Plan Reports.* Prepared jointly by Metropolitan Planning Committee and Winnipeg Town Planning Commission, Winnipeg. 1948.

Wright, J. *Saskatchewan.* Canadian Geographical Journal. XXXIV, pp. 108-35. 1947.

# CHAPTER 19

# British Columbia, Physical Background

Bʀɪᴛɪsʜ Cᴏʟᴜᴍʙɪᴀ offers the most interesting study of geographical contrasts in Canada. A rough, mountainous terrain has caused a wide range of climate, vegetation and soil. Furthermore, it has greatly influenced the location and nature of agriculture and other primary industries and the distribution of population. In essence, topography is the basis of regional differentiation in the province.

British Columbia is the third largest province in Canada, with an area of 366,-255 square miles and a population of just over 1,400,000. The average density is about four persons per square mile but such a figure is meaningless. Seventy-five per cent of the people live in a few level sections within 90 miles of Vancouver, comprising less than 0.5% of the total area. Over 90% of the Province is too high, too steep or too rocky for farming or close settlement and, consequently, actual size is an economic disadvantage. It makes costs of administration high and, considering the rugged surface, has made building and maintenance of land communications difficult and expensive. To compensate somewhat, 30% of the total area is capable of sustaining commercial forests. They form the resource base of the forest industries which, collectively, lead all other primary industries in value of production. Similarly, size and topography do not deter the mining industry. The geological structure of the area favours the occurrence of a wide variety of minerals and thus size is an advantage. Lastly, size and, particularly, topography encourage the development of the tourist industry.

The Province faces westward to the Pacific Ocean and eastward to the heart of the continent. The coastal area has a maritime environment; the interior is continental. The former has been of great significance in the development of the leading city, Vancouver, which is located at a natural break-point between land and sea communications. Consequently, it is one of Canada's foremost trans-shipment centres. Lying on the great circle route to Asia, it is largely a Pacific port. However, the volume of Asiatic trade is small and, since the opening of the Panama Canal in 1920, Vancouver has turned eastward and has successfully competed in European trade. Nevertheless, it is, at present, marginal to the major trade routes of the world.

British Columbia is also remote from the principal centres of influence in Canada. It lies over 2,500 miles by rail from the densely populated sections of Eastern Canada. Many manufacturing industries, such as the textile, automobile, machine and furniture, have not located in British Columbia on a large scale. The Eastern Canadian market is too distant to be effectively entered by reason of high transportation costs; the local market is, as yet, too small to warrant the development of such industries. However, there are certain products such as lumber and salmon in which the province excels and which are required in other parts of Canada and the world. They can be marketed easily outside of the province. In the future, with the improvement of transportation facilities and an increase in the population of British Columbia, the limitations to the development of more diversified manufacturing will disappear, and the area will be woven more tightly into the web of the Canadian economy.

## Physiographic Regions

British Columbia includes two major physiographic divisions of North America, the Cordilleran and the Great Plains (see figure 263). The latter is found only in the northeastern corner and is referred to as the Tramontane. The Cordilleran occupies at least 90% of the province and is divided into three broad systems: the Western Mountain System, the Interior Uplands and the Eastern Mountain Sys-

tem. They all trend northwesterly from the American boundary, but differ geologically as well as topographically.

### The Western Mountain System

The chief structural elements of the Western Mountains are the great masses of intrusive rocks of Jurassic age. The system embraces three physiographic divisions, the Insular Mountains, the Coastal Trench and the Coast-Cascade Mountains. These features parallel one another in a basic southeast-northwest alignment.

*The Insular Mountains* include the mountainous portions of Vancouver Island and the Queen Charlotte Islands. They are bordered, on the west, by the Pacific Ocean and, on the east, by the Coastal Trench, and are separated by Queen Charlotte Sound.

The Vancouver Island Mountains rise

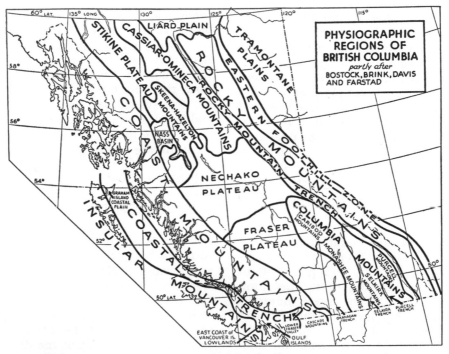

Figure 263. *Physiographic Regions of British Columbia.* Being a section of the Cordilleran Region of North America, the principal lineaments of British Columbia parallel one another along northwest-southeast axes. The broad central region, between the Rocky Mountains and the Coast Mountains, is further divisible into a number of smaller subdivisions.

steeply from the rocky, inhospitable Pacific coastline to a maximum elevation of 7,200 feet in the east-central part of the island, where the topography is exceedingly rugged. Towards the northwest and southeast, elevations diminish along the mountain axis to between 1,500 and 3,000 feet. These mountains have a rounded, subdued appearance and are separated by broad valleys, a few of which traverse the island from west to east. On the west, many deep, sheltered fiords penetrate the mountain mass, but a few narrow coastal plains have risen as platforms from the sea.

The mountains on the Queen Charlotte Islands are lower in elevation, but more rugged than those of Vancouver Island. They average 2,500 feet, while the highest peak stands at 3,945 feet, in the southern part of Graham Island. Most ranges are individual blocks, separated by deep, narrow valleys. The mountains drop precipitously on the Pacific side to an irregular, rocky coastline.

*The Coastal Trench* separates the Insular Mountains from the Coast-Cascade Mountains. Most of it is submerged beneath the sea. Two basins, Georgia and Hecate, and the Seymour Passage, are recognized as subdivisions.

The drowned portion of **Georgia Basin** includes Puget Sound, the Gulf of Georgia, the Strait of Georgia and part of the Strait of Juan de Fuca, and has a maximum depth of over 200 fathoms. The East Coast Lowland of Vancouver Island, the Gulf Islands and the Lower Fraser Valley are the principal emerged sections of the basin, and contain over 75% of the population of British Columbia.

The former district is composed of many small basins with elevations between 100 and 500 feet. Eastward extending, subdued spurs of the Vancouver Island Mountains, at about 1,000 feet, reach the east coast and separate the low lying areas. The lowland averages eight miles in width.

Many of the Gulf Islands arc monadnocks which existed as islands in the post-glacial sea. A few, such as Salt Spring Island, have elevations over 2,000 feet.

The Lower Fraser Valley extends inland on the eastern side of Georgia Basin. It is triangular in shape and less than 1,000 feet in elevation, except in its eastern section, where Sumas and Vedder Mountains just exceed 2,000 feet. To the north and south of the valley, the Coast and Cascade Mountains rise abruptly to elevations between 4,000 and 8,000 feet. Much of the area consists of recent delta, and is below 50 feet. An older, raised delta or terrace averages 200 feet. An upland, reaching a maximum elevation of 1,000 feet, forms the outer margin.

The submerged part of Hecate Basin comprises Queen Charlotte Strait, Hecate Strait, Milbanke Sound and part of Dixon Entrance. It is fairly shallow, being less than 100 fathoms. The most important emerged section is the northeastern low land of Graham Island, which has an area of 2,000 square miles. It is a fairly level plain, generally below 200 feet, and is interrupted by only a few residual volcanic hills. Sand dunes are conspicuous along the eastern coast.

Seymour Passage consists of hilly, rocky islands and peninsulas, interlaced with narrow, shallow inlets and straits, between Hecate and Georgia Basins. The Coastal Trench is, here, at its narrowest, and the topographic features of the Vancouver Island Mountains merge with those of the Coast Mountains.

*The Coast-Cascade Mountains* rise abruptly from the Coastal Trench, as a massive wall, broken only by the deep, canyon-like valleys. The area is divided by the Fraser River into two sections, the Cascade Mountains and the Coast Mountains.

The Cascade Mountains continue northward from the state of Washington into Southwestern British Columbia. There are three ranges, the Skagit, Hozomeen and Okanagan, from west to east, respectively. The latter is the highest, averaging 8,000

D. P. Kerr

Plate 92. The Fraser River gorge provides a corridor for two railways and a highway from the coast to the interior of British Columbia.

feet. It merges with the high, rounded slopes of the Fraser Plateau on the east. Westward, the elevations diminish slightly to an average of 6,000 feet in the Skagit Range. Relief is over 5,000 feet in many sections, especially on the western slopes, where rapid streams are cutting deep, steep-walled valleys to the Fraser River.

The Coast Range is, virtually, a solid wall of granite. It trends northwesterly from the Fraser River, for over 1,000 miles, into the southwestern corner of the Yukon. Elevations vary somewhat from southeast to northwest. Immediately north and west of the Fraser Valley, the mountains rise steeply to over 9,000 feet. In the vicinity of latitude 52°, the mountains rise to their greatest elevations, with many peaks above 10,000 feet. Mount Waddington, the highest in British Columbia, stands at 13,260 feet. Elevations diminish gradually towards the northwest until minima are found in the Skeena Saddle, a relatively low area

averaging about 4,000 feet. Through it, the Skeena River has cut its deep valley. To the northwest of Observatory Inlet, the mountains average 8,000 feet.

The Coast Mountains are irregular, rugged and deeply indented on their western side by fiords. They are interrupted by trench-like valleys and covered in many places, especially to the northwest, by permanent ice-fields. They appear from the air as a markedly dissected plateau, with numerous saw-toothed ridges and sharply serrated summits, extending to the horizon at a fairly common level. Some peaks, like Mount Waddington and its satellites, protrude above the general level. The mountains fall off abruptly, to the southwest, to the many rocky peninsulas and islands which form the margin of the Coastal Trench.

Of all the legacies of the Pleistocene the fiords are the most important. These deep, steep-sided, long, narrow arms of the sea penetrate the mountain mass as much as 80 miles. They are seldom less than one, and rarely more than three, miles in width.

The large rivers of the Coast Mountains, such as the Fraser, Dean, Skeena and Nass, are typically transverse to the trend. The Fraser, for example, flows from the Interior Uplands through the Coast Mountains and forms an important corridor for land communications.

## The Interior Uplands

The interior areas are, for the most part, underlain by volcanic rocks, but there are outcrops of metamorphics and sedimentaries. The topography is diversified. There is a well dissected plateau in the south, an area of somewhat subdued relief in the central portion, and, in the north, a variety of features including low mountains, deep basins and rugged tablelands. The region trends northwesterly from the American border to the Yukon, and separates the eastern and western mountain systems. It varies in width, reaching its greatest extent in the central sections. Five subdivisions are recognized: the Fraser Plateau, the Nechako Plateau, the Skeena-Hazelton Mountains, the Nass Basin and the Stikine Plateau.

*The Fraser Plateau* occupies the southern part of the Interior Uplands south of latitude 53°, where a poorly defined ridge, including in part the Telegraph Range, marks the boundary with the Nechako Plateau. It is well dissected and has a fairly great relief, especially in the south. A few river valleys are entrenched as much as 4,000 feet below the plateau level of 6,000 feet. Towards the northwest, the relief is more subdued in the Cariboo-Chilcotin district. The valleys are broader and the hills are lower and more rounded.

The Miocene lavas are responsible for most of the areas of slight relief. Glaciation has left its imprint in the form of till, terraces, morainic hills and dammed lakes. The Fraser is the principal drainage outlet. The Okanagan Trench, in the southern section, is the most densely populated district.

*The Nechako Plateau* is found in the central part of the Uplands. It has the most subdued relief in the British Columbia Cordillera. Only a very few rounded hills exceed 5,000 feet, and the major part of the area is a rolling upland at 2,500 feet. Large sections were flooded by post-glacial lakes and, consequently, thick lacustrine deposits account for fine-textured soils in those areas. The rivers flow in comparatively broad valleys which lie from 50 to 500 feet below the general level.

*The Skeena-Hazelton Mountains* may be considered as eastern outliers of the Coast Mountains. They are rugged, and the highest peaks are over 8,000 feet, but the average elevation is about 6,000 feet. Several ice fields and glaciers appear throughout the ranges, but they are not as large as those of the Coast Mountains. The Hazelton Mountains are situated south of the Nass Basin, and comprise the Nass and Bulkley Ranges. The Skeena Mountains cover a larger area and contain several ranges; the Babine, Groundhog and Eaglenest, being the most important.

*The Nass Basin* lies in the immediate lee of the Coast Mountains, south and west of the Skeena Mountains and north of the Hazelton Mountains. The major part of this intermountain depression is below 2,000 feet, but a few hills rise to 4,000 feet. The western section is drained by the Nass River; the eastern, by the Skeena and its tributary the Kispiox. The Bulkley graben, extending southeastward from Hazelton between the Bulkley and Babine ranges, has future agricultural significance and is included with the basin proper.

*The Stikine Plateau* is situated to the northwest of the Skeena Mountains, between the Cassiar and Coast Mountains. Its northwestern counterpart is the Yukon Plateau. In reality, it is composed of several plateaus, averaging 4,500 feet in elevation. These tablelands are separated by broad valleys, but the margins are often deeply cut by small streams. Most of the uplands are flat-topped and, consequently, have poor drainage in their central sections. Here and there, old volcanic peaks, up to 8,000 feet in elevation, rise above the plateau. The plateau is composed chiefly of lava, with an uneven cover of drift in most places. The Stikine, Taku and Teslin Rivers drain practically all of the area.

## The Eastern Mountain System

The Eastern Mountain System consists of three major mountain groups, the Cassiar-Omineca, the Columbia and the Rocky Mountains. They are separated by the Rocky Mountain Trench which broadens out into the Liard Plain in the extreme north of the province. The trend is northwesterly from the 49th parallel.

*The Columbia Mountains* are found in Southeastern British Columbia. They are broad in the south, comprising three principal ranges, the Monashee, Selkirk and Purcell, but narrow toward the northwest, in the Cariboo Mountains. The Monashee

Mountains rise somewhat above the Fraser Plateau, and are separated from the Selkirk Mountains by the deep Selkirk Trench, containing the Columbia River and the Arrow Lakes. In turn, the Selkirk and Purcell Mountains are divided by the Purcell Trench, part of which holds Kootenay Lake. The Rocky Mountain Trench forms the eastern border. The Columbia Mountains are very rugged, showing the effects of glaciation in the form of deep U-shaped valleys, cirques and moraines. The average elevation is about 7,000 feet, but several peaks exceed 10,000 feet in the Selkirk and Cariboo Ranges.

*The Cassiar-Omineca Mountains* represent a northwesterly continuation of the Columbia Mountains, being separated from them by the Nechako Plateau, which spreads northeastward to merge with the Rocky Mountain Trench. They lie between the Skeena Mountains and Stikine Plateau, on the southwest, and the Rocky Mountain Trench and Liard Plain, on the northeast, and fade out north of the British Columbia border. Several ranges, including the Finlay, Swannell, Stikine and Kechika, make up the mountain mass.

The eastern ranges, bordering the Rocky Mountain Trench, are the least rugged. They have smooth slopes, fairly even summits, and practically no glaciers. Westward, the most rugged topography is encountered in the Swannell and Stikine Ranges, carved out of the batholithic, granite core. Several peaks surpass 8,000 feet, but the relief is not as great as in many parts of British Columbia. The principal rivers flow in relatively broad valleys, which average 4,000 feet above sea level. Many small glaciers and ice fields occur throughout the area. Where the Cassiar-Omineca Mountains approach the Nechako and Stikine Plateaus, there are fairly broad transition zones.

*The Rocky Mountain Trench* is the most remarkable land form feature in British Columbia. This great valley lying between the Cassiar-Omineca-Columbia Mountains

and the Rockies, is continuous in a northwesterly direction, from the Flathead area of Montana to the Liard Plain, a distance of 1,000 miles. Its floor averages 2,500 feet above sea level, and it is from two to ten miles wide. Mountains rise steeply from the Trench, except in the central section, southeast of Finlay Forks, where it merges with the Nechako Plateau. Throughout most of the valley, till covers the bedrock to a considerable depth. Its local topography is fairly rough as a result of glacial activity, but extensive marshes are found in some areas.

*The Liard Plain* is a broad depression in Northern British Columbia just east of the Cassiar Mountains. It is drained by the Liard River and its tributaries, which have cut deeply into thick deposits of drift. Glacial features dominate the landscape and give it a rolling surface. The area has an average elevation of 2,500 feet, and only a few hills rise above 3,000 feet.

*The Rocky Mountains* form the eastern frontier of the Cordilleran Region. They make up a continuous range, trending northwesterly from the American border to the Liard Valley. In the southern part, their crest line is the continental divide and the British Columbia-Alberta boundary. Mountains in this section are very rugged with several peaks over 10,000 feet. Mount Robson, the highest in the Eastern Mountain System, rises to 12,972 feet. Large glaciers are conspicuous, the most extensive being in the Columbia Ice-field, between Banff and Jasper, and in the Reef Ice-field in Mount Robson Provincial Park. In the south, the Rockies average 50 miles in width. They are traversed by only a few passes, the three most noted being the Yellowhead (3,700 feet), the Kicking Horse (5,338 feet) and the Crowsnest (4,459 feet).

Towards the northwest, the Rockies narrow to 25 miles and become lower, averaging 5,000 feet in elevation. They are less rugged and have no glaciers. The Peace River traverses the mountains in a pass at only 2,000 feet while Pine Pass is just less than 3,000 feet. The continental divide lies west of the central Rockies.

To the northwest of the Peace River, the Rockies broaden to a maximum width of 75 miles and increase in elevation to places, a fairly bold east-facing escarpment. More gentle slopes obtain in the western areas. The compressive forces also produced a series of folds, which give the Rocky Mountains their characteristic parallel ranges.

National Film Board

Plate 93.  Mount Robson, British Columbia, is the highest peak in the Canadian Rockies, towering almost 13,000 feet above sea level.

an average of 9,000 feet. They are very rugged, but the glaciers are much smaller than in the southern sections.

The eastern foothill zone of the Rocky Mountains averages 25 miles in width and 4,500 feet in height. It slopes eastward to the Tramontane Plains. The landscape is characterized by smooth, rounded hills interspersed by a few sharp ridges, especially in the northern sections.

The Rockies were built by unusually strong compressive forces, originating to the west of the Rocky Mountain Trench. They developed a series of thrust faults which forced the mass of Precambrian, Paleozoic, and Mesozoic sediments eastward over a great fault plane to cover the soft Cretaceous shales of the Great Plains. Subsequent erosion has created, in most

## The Tramontane Plains

The Tramontane Plains occupy about 10% of British Columbia. They are situated in the northeastern corner of the province and are part of the Great Plains of North America. They differ markedly from the Cordillera in their subdued topography and horizontal structure. Most of the area is a rolling upland at 3,000 feet, sloping gradually to the east. Below the upland level the large basins of the Peace and Nelson Rivers average 2,000 feet in elevation. The surface is everywhere covered with glacial drift. The rivers have cut deeply into the drift and underlying rock, and are entrenched in some places as much as 600 feet below the basin level. Muskeg is common in the depressions.

## Landform Summary

To recapitulate briefly, all but the north-eastern corner of British Columbia falls within the broad Cordilleran physiographic province of North America. Consequently most land forms are rugged and mountainous. The topographic trend of the three principal subdivisions of the Cordillera, the Western Mountains, the Interior Uplands and the Eastern Mountains, is northwesterly from the 49th parallel.

## Physiographic History

The physiographic history of British Columbia is exceedingly complex and the following summary is quite generalized. Obviously, the area is one of geologic instability. At various times it has been severely affected by diastrophism and vulcanism of great magnitude and the result, as previously noted, has been a predominantly rugged, mountainous terrain.

Essentially, the physiographic story begins with the building of the Coast and Columbia Mountains (batholithic cores) in the late Jurassic. At this time, an ancient land mass, Cascadia, extended seaward from the Coast Mountains, and fairly level land was characteristic of the areas to the east of the present Rocky Mountain Trench. During the ensuing early Cretaceous epoch, no orogeny occurred and, consequently, the agents of degradation reduced the Coast and Columbia Mountains to small hills. The eroded materials were carried eastward and westward by large rivers to fill the Rocky Mountain geosyncline and the Cascadia lowland, respectively.

The Rocky Mountains were built, and other ranges uplifted, during the great Laramide Storm in the late Cretaceous and early Eocene epochs. Later, in the Miocene, all of Cascadia, except the crumpled sediments on Vancouver Island and the Queen Charlotte Islands, was downwarped beneath the sea. At the same time, large amounts of lava poured out over the interior districts.

British Columbia reached its greatest elevation (1,000 to 2,000 feet higher than now) during the regional uplift of the Pliocene. Plains, now submerged as the Continental Shelf, extended for approximately 50 miles west of Vancouver Island.

Partly as a result of this uplift, but mainly because of climatic change, the ice age or Pleistocene epoch followed. Heavy snow from Pacific storms fell on the highlands and, consequently, large mountain glaciers formed and merged as huge ice sheets. Well-marked glacial striae on several ridges, suggest that the ice had a maximum depth of 6,500 feet. There is evidence of at least two ice advances. This is illustrated in many places, but, especially, near the university campus in Vancouver, where two till layers are separated by interglacial sands.

The effects of glaciation are many. Drift of varying depth mantles much of the Province below 4,000 feet. Most of the mature soils of the area have been formed in this material. The conspicuous terraces of the interior and the fiords of the coast are outstanding legacies of the Pleistocene. Cirques, U-shaped valleys and hanging valleys, among many other features, enhance the natural scenery. In addition, glacio-fluvial deposits, scattered throughout the Province, have agricultural significance.

An uplift, averaging 600 feet, has taken place in the post-glacial period. Some vulcanism has occurred recently, and a few volcanic layers cover glacial till at points in the interior and in the Coast Range.

## Geological Materials

A great variety of geological materials is found in British Columbia. Rocks, ranging in age from Precambrian to Recent, have a complex distribution, principally because of the complicated structure of the area. Only broad generalizations are herewith set down.

Of great significance is the large number of intrusive rocks, which are most numerous to the west of the Rocky Mountain

Trench. Granitic bodies of Mesozoic Age are very common. They are most extensive in the Coast Range batholith. Large areas in the Columbia Mountains, especially near Nelson, and in the Cassiar-Omineca Mountains also, contain igneous bodies of batholithic proportions. Most metalliferous deposits are directly related to these huge intrusions and occur along their margins. Thus, copper, associated with Jurassic intrusives, is found along the edge of the Coast Mountains. Lead, zinc and silver ore bodies are genetically related to invasions of granodiorite in Carboniferous time.

As noted previously, vulcanism was widespread during the Miocene, particularly in the interior districts. Basaltic and andesitic lavas are the principal rocks. They cover a wide area in the Cariboo and Chilcotin, where they are, for the most part, several thousand feet thick.

Sedimentary and metamorphic rocks of many different ages are found throughout the province, but notably in the Rocky Mountains. A wide variety of rocks, including siliceous shales, blue-grey limestones, buff sandstones, and quartzites have been deeply eroded to form the majestic peaks of the Rocky Mountains. In other areas, relatively soft Cretaceous and Tertiary rocks underlie certain intermountain basins, such as Alberni on Vancouver Island. Virtually undisturbed sedimentaries of Cretaceous age comprise the bedrock of the Tramontane Plains. Coal measures are associated with this structure, and the underlying Devonian beds are suspected to contain petroleum.

During the Pleistocene, all of British Columbia was overridden by ice. Consequently, unconsolidated materials mantle the bedrock throughout most of the area. They vary noticeably in texture depending on whether they were laid down by the glacier, or resorted by water and wind. Post-glacial erosion has resulted in the formation of a thin veneer of sands, gravels, and clays in many low-lying areas.

In summary, many different rocks make up the structure of British Columbia. Three contrasting geological divisions obtain: the Coastal, Interior and Columbia systems; the Rocky Mountains; and the Tramontane Plains. The former is mainly characterized by batholithic intrusions and volcanic outpourings, but sedimentaries and metamorphics also appear. In the Rocky Mountains, the rocks are almost entirely of sedimentary origin, but have been intensively folded and faulted. Relatively undisturbed sedimentaries form the structure of the Tramontane Plains. Pleistocene materials, of glacial origin, cover most of the bedrock throughout the province.

## Climate

The climate of British Columbia is very diversified. The Pacific Coast is the most humid area in Canada; the interior, one of the driest. Sub-arctic conditions prevent all but the hardiest domesticated plants from maturing in the north; the growing season is warm and long enough for peaches and apricots in the southern valleys. To add to this regional diversity, there is marked local variation in climate. Because of the mountainous nature of the land, numerous micro-climates exist. In some areas, differences in climate are greater from the foot of a mountain slope to its peak, than at a low constant level, extending over several hundred miles. Depending on exposure to the sun and prevailing winds, two slopes of one mountain may exhibit very different climatic characteristics at comparable elevations.

### Climatic Controls

The North Pacific Ocean, the prevailing westerly flow of air, and the topography of British Columbia are major climatic controls. The former is a great storehouse of energy and moisture, especially in the winter, when it remains warm relative to the adjacent land areas. Consequently, mild, moist air moves onto the British Columbia coast from the ocean, in the normal eastward circulation. Low pressure systems (depressions) are a part of this flow, especially in the autumn, winter and early spring months, and heavy rains result. Furthermore, the air is forced aloft at the Insular and Coast Mountains, and this action augments the amount of rainfall considerably. The Pacific air is usually very unstable (will not subside to the earth easily after

North Pacific Ocean, as is the case in the summer, depressions are weak. They pass over Northern British Columbia, and little rain falls on the southern area. Small amounts of precipitation result from convectional activity in the warm season over the Interior Uplands and Eastern Cordillera.

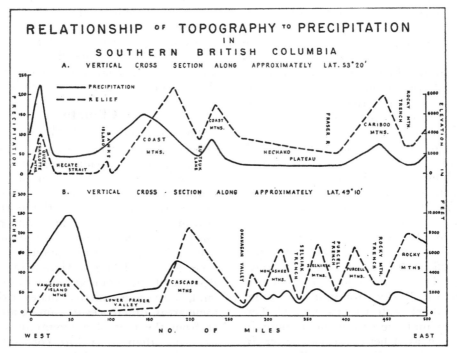

Figure 264. *Relationship of Relief and Precipitation.* Two cross sections of Southern British Columbia illustrate the manner in which successive mountain ranges extract the moisture from the Pacific Airmasses which cross over them. Each range has a wet western slope and a drier one on the east.

being pushed upwards) and, normally, crosses the Interior Uplands at intermediate levels. For this reason, and since the air has lost much moisture on the seaward slopes of the Coastal ranges, the entire interior area is relatively dry, lying in a great rain shadow of the coastal mountain wall. Slightly more rain falls along the western slopes of the Eastern Cordillera than on the Interior Uplands, but the amount diminishes progressively eastward (see figure 264).

When the pressure is high over the

Cold waves, of the type experienced frequently over continental Canada, seldom reach coastal British Columbia, since the area is dominated by westerly winds and protected by the high mountain barrier. Only when the Polar High becomes intense and moves into Southern British Columbia is this type of weather experienced over the southern coast. Northern British Columbia, to the east of the Coast Mountains, is subject to Arctic air during most of winter. The southern area, east of the Coast Mountains, is less frequently influenced.

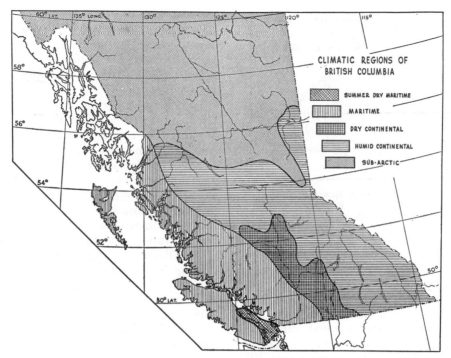

Figure 265. *Climatic Regions of British Columbia.* Northern British Columbia is classified as Subarctic because of its low temperature. The southern section of the province is divisible into parallel belts corresponding with land form and rainfall.

## Climatic Regions

Exclusive of the mountainous areas, five fairly well-marked climatic types can be recognized in British Columbia: the Summer-Dry Maritime, the Maritime, the Dry Continental, the Humid Continental and the Sub-arctic (see figure 265).

*The Summer-Dry Maritime type* is characteristic of Georgia Basin. The only part of the mainland, which may be included, is the extreme southwestern corner, within a radius of 15 miles of Boundary Bay. The area is sheltered from the main westerly flow of air by the Olympic and Vancouver Island Mountains. The former range is the American continuation of the Insular Mountains, and rises to over 7,000 feet.

The climate is cool and dry in summer, and humid and mild in winter. Annual

[1] Thornthwaite, C. W., *An Approach Toward a Rational Classification of Climate.* Geographical Review 38, pp. 55-94, 1948.

rainfall is less than 40 inches, and over 75% falls in the period from October to March, inclusive. A water deficiency[1] of between 5 and 10 inches prevails during the summer months. Precipitation is mainly in the form of rain and drizzle, with the average annual snowfall being about 15 inches.

The mean July temperature is 63° F.; the January mean is 38° F. Average annual temperature range is less than 25° F. (see figure 266.) Temperature extremes are rare, because cold or heat waves, common in interior British Columbia, seldom visit the area. The all-time low temperature record for the area is −2° F. Victoria receives over 2,200 hours of bright sunshine annually, being surpassed, in Canada, only in southern Alberta and Saskatchewan. Sunshine varies considerably in the area, however, depending on location.

*The Maritime or Marine West Coast*

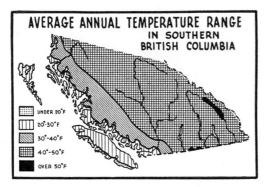

Figure 266. *Average Annual Range of Temper-ature in British Columbia*. Range of temperature is largely controlled by nearness to the coast and by elevation.

type prevails over the remainder of the coast. It is characterized by mild, exceedingly wet winters; cool, moderately wet, foggy summers; high relative humidities throughout the year; and, a small annual range of temperature. Annual precipitation, practically all rain or drizzle, except on the mountain slopes, averages over 100 inches (see figure 267). One station, Henderson Lake, recorded an average of 262 inches over a five year period. Most of the rain falls in autumn and winter, but, normally, there is no deficiency of moisture in summer.

Except in sheltered valleys, the average July temperature is under 60° F. The average January temperaure is above freezing. Temperature extremes rarely occur. Sea fog and low stratus clouds are common in the summer, in exposed areas. Radiation fog frequently forms in the low-lying districts, during the autumn and early winter. Hours of bright sunshine vary from 1,832 at Vancouver to only 1,053 at Prince Rupert.

The Insular, Coast and Cascade Mountains receive an enormous amount of snow during the winter. It is wet and heavy, and accumulates rapidly. Farrow[1] reports an accumulation of 48 inches in a 24 hour period in the Coast Mountains. In some

years, over 30 feet of snow has piled up by March, on the protected slopes of the Coast Mountains. Normally, snow accumulation in the Coast Mountains in spring is over 10 times that in the Eastern Cordillera.

*The Dry Continental* type of climate occupies most of the Fraser Plateau. The entire area is in the rain shadow of the Coast-Cascade Mountains, and has less than 20 inches of precipitation annually. The southern Okanagan and middle Thompson valleys are the driest sections, having less than 10 inches annually.

The summer is hot and sunny, with the average July temperature varying from 74° F. at Oliver, to 63° F. at Quesnel. Extremely high temperatures are frequently recorded. Lytton reported 115° F. in July, 1941. Average temperatures in January at Oliver and Quesnel are 26° F. and 13° F., respectively, values from 10 to 20 degrees lower than coastal ones, but from 15 to 25 degrees higher than at comparable latitudes in Saskatchewan. Sub-zero temperatures are common every winter, and −66° F. has been recorded once at Williams Lake. Most stations receive over 2,000 hours of bright sunshine annually.

*The Humid Continental* type of climate prevails throughout the remainder of southern British Columbia, in the Nechako Plateau, and in the valleys and along the lower slopes of the Eastern Cordillera. Annual precipitation exceeds 20 inches, except in a few sheltered pockets. More rain falls in the Nechako district than in any other part of the Interior Uplands, because the Coast Mountains are at their lowest elevation in the Skeena Saddle, and Pacific air moving eastward holds more moisture than it does further south. The average annual precipitation at Prince George is 20 inches.

Average July temperatures vary from 66° F., in the southern Kootenay valleys, to just less than 60° F., in the Nechako district. Average January temperatures are much lower (12° F.) in the Nechako, than in the Kootenay valleys (23° F.). Tem-

[1] Farrow, R. C., *Forecasting Run-Off from Snow Surveys,* Geographical Journal 100, pp. 206-222. 1942

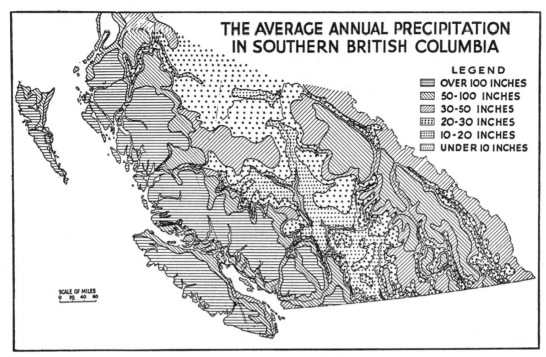

Figure 267. *Average Annual Precipitation*. West coast location and mountain barriers cause a belt of heavy precipitation along the coast while the interior gets much less moisture. The West Coast is the wettest part of Canada.

perature extremes are common throughout the area. Frost occasionally strikes in the Nechako area during the summer months.

The *Subarctic* type is found in the northern half of British Columbia, except in the Peace River area of the Tramontane Plains. The latter district has a climate which is transitional from the Subarctic to the steppe climate of the Southern Prairies. The Subarctic climate is characterized by long cold winters, short cool summers, and fairly low precipitation (less than 16 inches). The annual mean temperature is just under 32° F. The July average temperature is about 58° F., the January, —4° F.

Precipitation is fairly evenly distributed throughout the year, but most stations show a summer maximum and spring minimum. Toward the west, a secondary winter maximum becomes prominent. Between 40% and 45% of the annual precipitation is snow.

## Natural Vegetation

The natural vegetation of British Columbia is extremely varied including a very large number of species and contrasting associations. Trees, principally conifers, predominate, but they are by no means uniform in size or distribution. The lofty evergreens of the coast may be contrasted with the stunted firs and pines of the northern interior. Bunch grasses and drought-resistant bushes have significant distributions in the southern, interior valleys, and reflect the dryness of those districts. Furthermore, approximately one-third of the province is alpine, consisting of bare rock, permanent ice and a few patches of meadow and scrub.

### Vegetation Regions

Five vegetation regions are recognized in British Columbia: the Coast Forest, the Fraser Plateau Forest and Grassland, the

Nechako Forest, the Columbia Forest and the Northern Forest (see figure 268). Apart from the regional differentiation, vertical zonation of plant life occurs within each region, and is of great significance.

The Coast Forest is the densest and most luxuriant in Canada. It is a part of the great coniferous forest belt of the North Pacific Slope, extending from northern California to southern Alaska. Deciduous trees have a limited distribution, but are increasing, as they tend to form part of the second growth in logged areas.

Dominant species along the Coast are western red cedar (Thuja plicata) and western hemlock (Tsuga heterophylla). They thrive in the most humid areas, where they attain an average height of 150 feet and a diameter of between 2 and 5 feet. Douglas fir (Pseudotsuga taxifolia) is, typically, a larger tree, averaging 200 feet in height and 5 feet in diameter. Specimens as high as 250 feet, with a diameter of

9 feet, have been found on Vancouver Island. Being intolerant of shade, it grows best in southern Vancouver Island and the southern mainland coast, where dryness in summer limits the full development of the cedar-hemlock canopy. Sitka spruce (Picea sitchensis), the other important species, has its greatest distribution on the Queen Charlotte Islands, where it reaches an average height of 125 feet and a diameter of 4 feet.

The tree-line varies in the Coast Forest, but is reached at about 5,000 feet in the south and 4,000 feet in the north. It is as low as 1,700 feet in several places in the Queen Charlotte Islands. Mountain hemlock (Tsuga Mertensiana) and alpine fir (Abies lasiocarpa) are found near the upward limit of timber. Two interesting species usually linked with Mediterranean environments, Garry oak (Quercus Garryana) and madrona (Arbutus Menziesii), grow only in the southern coastal trench.

The Fraser Plateau Forest and Grass-

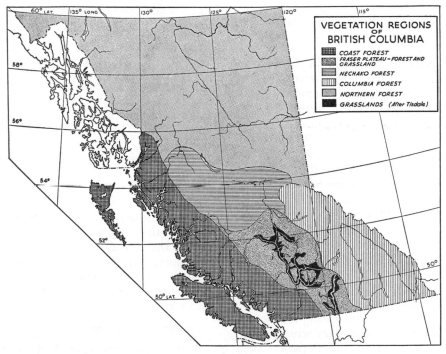

Figure 268. *Vegetation Regions of British Columbia.* Vegetation regions delimited on the basis of tree species and habits of growth correspond very closely with the climatic regions, outlined on the basis of temperature and rainfall.

D. P. Kerr

Plate 94.  Open pine woodland, characteristic of the forest-grassland transition in the interior of British Columbia.

*land* region coincides with the dry continental climatic zone. It includes the southern half of the Montane forest where the principal species are ponderosa pine (*Pinus ponderosa*), lodgepole pine (*Pinus contorta*) and Douglas fir. It also comprises large areas of grassland especially in the southern Okanagan, middle Thompson, Nicola, Middle Fraser and lower Chilcotin valleys.

The forest is characteristically open and park-like. Grassy patches alternate with tree groves. Ponderosa pine (western yellow pine) is found in the driest areas for tree growth, particularly where the annual precipitation averages from 12 to 15 inches. Its greatest distribution is at elevations between 1,500 feet and 3,000 feet, south of latitude 51°. It favours well-drained, south-facing slopes and, normally, attains a height of 80 feet and a diameter of 30 inches. Douglas fir is prevalent at higher altitudes in the south, and at diminishing elevations in the Cariboo and Chilcotin districts. Since the climate is much drier, it is smaller than on the coast, normally attaining a height of 100 feet and a diameter of 3 feet. Lodgepole pine covers a large part of the area, averaging 80 feet in height and 20 inches in diameter. It has an extraordinary abil-

ity to reproduce after fire, and to grow on thin, stony soils. Engelmann spruce (*Picea Engelmanni*) and alpine fir dominate the forest cover between 4,000 feet and the timber-line, which averages 6,000 feet. Aspen (*Populus tremuloides*) becomes increasingly important in the northern parts of the region.

The forest is replaced by a natural grassland where the precipitation is generally less than 12 inches annually. In the Okanagan Valley, south of Penticton, and in the middle Thompson Valley, between Kamloops and Spences Bridge, the annual precipitation is less than 10 inches, and xerophytes, such as sagebrush (*Artemisia tridentata*), cactus (*Opuntia fragilis*) and antelope bush (*Purshia tridentata*) are common. Bluebunch wheatgrass (*Agropyron spicatum*) is the most important grass. In the slightly more humid areas, grasses dominate, including introduced downy brome (*Bromus tectorum*), rough fescue (*Festuca scabrella*) and Columbia speargrass (*Stipa Columbiana*). In the south, on well-exposed south-facing slopes, the grassland environment extends up to 4,000 feet; in the Cariboo and Chilcotin sections, it is mainly below 3,000 feet. The structure of the grassland formation has changed greatly in the last century, because of over-grazing and the introduction of exotic spe-cies. The conspicuous spread of sagebrush is one of the major alterations.

*The Nechako Forest* includes the north-ern half of the Montane forest and coin-cides, to a large extent, with the Nechako Plateau. In this area, in comparison with the Fraser region, the annual precipitation is higher and more effective because of lower summer temperatures. Consequently, the forest is more dense and grassy open-ings occur only in the most sheltered loca-tions. Engelmann spruce has a wide distri-bution. It averages 125 feet in height and 2 feet in diameter. Alpine fir is important on the higher slopes; aspen dominates the southern part of the region; lodgepole pine is scattered throughout. Grassy patches have formed on south-facing slopes, especially in the Bulkley Valley, where the precipi-tation is less than 15 inches annually.

*The Columbia Forest* is found in the Eastern Cordillera south of latitude 54°. It is extremely heterogeneous, containing many species, several of which show affini-ties with the Coast, Nechako, and Fraser Forests. The forest is mainly an associa-tion of western red cedar and western hem-lock with ponderosa pine, Douglas fir, grand fir (*Abies grandis*) and western white pine (*Pinus monticola*) important in the south, Engelmann spruce and alpine fir in the north and on higher slopes. Lodgepole pine has a broken distribution throughout the region. As in other parts of Southern British Columbia, black cottonwood (*Pop-ulus trichocarpa*) frequently reaches a considerable size in the alluvial bottom-lands. In general, the cedars and hemlocks are smaller than on the coast and the forest is less luxuriant. Both the Coast and Colum-bia forests have a dense undergrowth, con-sisting of tall ferns and thick bushes. The Montane forest has, in general, little under-growth.

*The Northern Forest.* Approximately 75% of Northern British Columbia is for-ested; about 25% of the land is composed of alpine meadows, grassy openings, bare rock or permanent ice. At least half of the forest consists of scrub trees, and even the largest specimens average only 100 feet in height and 20 inches in diameter. Extensive areas of poorly drained muskeg country are evident.

The chief species throughout the area is white spruce (*Picea canadensis*). In the south, where the area merges with the Nechako forest, Engelmann spruce is significant. Toward the northeast, in the Tramontane Plains, white birch (*Betula papyrifera*), balsam fir (*Abies balsamea*) and jack pine (*Pinus Banksiana*), all mem-bers of the central Boreal forest, are en-countered. In the extreme west, in the Sti-kine, Nass, and other valleys, coast forest species, principally cedar and hemlock, have come into the district. Aspen and lodge-pole pine have wide distributions through-out the area. Black spruce (*Picea mariana*) and alpine fir are also important.

Natural grasslands occur in the Peace River area, where they are outliers of the Prairie Grassland Formation. Grassy open-ings are found also in the intermountain sections, throughout the northern Cordil-lera. It is difficult to explain their origin, but, in all probablity, most of them have developed because of repeated fires.

## Summary

In conclusion, the diversified vegetation cover of British Columbia reflects the di-versified physiography and climate. Coastal forests are the most luxuriant in Canada; natural grasslands of the Interior have a wide distribution. A large portion of the province has no plant cover but consists of bare rock or ice.

## Soils

The soils of British Columbia are the most varied in Canada. They range from heavily leached, very acid Podzols of the coastal districts, where the climate is ex-tremely humid, to more alkaline Brown Soils of the arid southern Okanagan Valley. Practically all soils have been formed on glacial material.

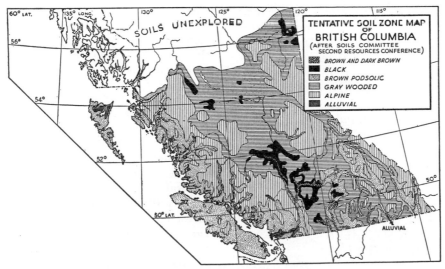

Figure 269. *Generalized Soil Zones of British Columbia.* The wet coastal regions have podzolic soils, the dry interior has dark surface pedocals, while the forested north has Gray-Wooded soils like those of Northern Alberta.

## Soil Zones

The following discussion of soil zones may give an impression of uniformity of soil patterns throughout British Columbia, which does not in fact exist. On the contrary, the area contains important alluvial and intra-zonal soils, within certain zones, as well as large sections of bare rock, particularly along steep slopes and near mountain tops. Furthermore, only a few areas have been surveyed in detail, and much of the province, especially in the north, is undescribed. Six soil zones are recognized: the Brown, Dark Brown and Black formed under a grass cover, the Brown Podzolic and Gray Wooded formed under forest, and, the Alpine zone (see figure 269).

*Brown, Dark Brown and Black Soils* are found principally in the southern interior valleys, where the annual precipitation is generally less than 15 inches. The three zones reflect different degrees of aridity: the Brown receives less than 10 inches of precipitation annually; the Dark Brown, 10 to 12 inches; and the Black, 12 to 15 inches. Only slight downward movement of minerals takes place in the soils and the Brown and Dark Brown, in particular, are fairly high in bases, such as calcium. They show neutral to slightly alkaline reactions, except in the most humid areas where some leaching has occurred, and the soils, classified as Degraded Blacks, are faintly acidic. The sub-surface layers are alkaline in reaction, and lime has accumulated at various depths. The Black Soils are rich in organic matter but it diminishes considerably in the Brown Soils. Most of these soils give excellent yields of fruits and vegetables when irrigated.

The map shows the general distribution of the soil zones: Brown in the southern Okanagan and middle Thompson valleys; Dark Brown, in the middle Okanagan and parts of the Thompson and Fraser Valleys; Black, around Vernon in the Okanagan, parts of the Thompson and Nicola Valleys and, particularly, in the middle Fraser Valley through the Cariboo and Chilcotin districts. Degraded Black Soils occur in the Peace River area and in the eastern Nechako district. The map does not indicate the marked vertical zonation of soil zones. (See figure 270). Spilsbury and Tisdale (1944) illustrate this phe-

nomenon on the Tranquille Range near
Kamloops. Brown Soils are found between
1,100 feet and 2,300 feet; Dark Brown,
between 2,300 and 2,800 feet; and Black,
from 2,800 to 3,200 feet. Above 3,200 feet
Podzols dominate. In the Okanagan, according to Kelley and Spilsbury (1949),
Black Soils may be found up to 4,500 feet
on south-facing slopes.

*Brown Podzolic Soils* have formed under
a forest cover. They are found principally
in the coastal districts, from sea level to

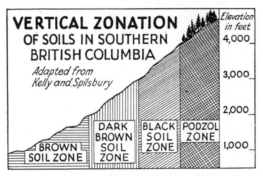

Figure 270. *Vertical Zonation of Soils in the
Interior of British Columbia.* Where the mountains are high enough the soils may range from
semi-desert Brown Soils, through Mountain
Podzols to Alpine Tundra beyond the tree line.

the timber line, and, sporadically, in the
Eastern Cordillera, south of latitude 53°.
On the coast the climate is very wet, cool
in summer and relatively mild in winter;
in the Eastern Cordillera, it is less humid,
with slightly warmer summers and colder
winters.

The coastal soils are brown to reddish
brown in color, strongly leached, low in
basic elements and very acid. In the southern coastal trench, mid-summer drought
arrests the downward movement of water
and brings about dehydration and chemical precipitation in the form of iron con-
cretions or small pellets, which are found
in the sub-surface layers. In the Lower
Fraser Valley, recent alluvial soils are the
most important. They are usually very fertile, but are associated with flat areas

where drainage and flooding are problems.
Peat and muck soils also occur in the
Lower Fraser Valley and, particularly, on
the Graham Island Plain in the Queen
Charlotte Islands.

In the Columbia and Rocky Mountain
regions, Brown Podzolic Soils are less severely leached, less acid and richer in basic
elements than on the coast. On the drier
margins, where this zone makes contact
with the Black Soil zone, iron pellets and
a lime accumulation layer occur in the
sub-soil.

*Gray Wooded Soils* have formed under a
forest cover, where the precipitation averages 20 inches annually. They are best developed in the Tramontane Plains and the
Nechako district. They occur also on the
Fraser Plateau, at elevations generally
above 4,000 feet on south-facing slopes,
and above 2,500 feet on north-facing slopes.
It is thought that they cover a large acreage in Northern British Columbia, especially in the well-drained areas. All in all,
they cover an extremely large area.

Gray Wooded Soils have a rather poor
structure and are not naturally very fertile. The majority are acid and moderately
leached. When the soil has formed under
a deciduous forest cover it is less acid than
under a coniferous one. A pronounced gray
layer appears about two inches under the
surface. It averages six inches in depth,
and is almost entirely lacking in basic elements.

*Alpine or Tundra Soils* are found above
the timber line, throughout British Columbia. In the highland areas, chemical weathering is reduced to a minimum, and
organic matter decomposes slowly. The
regolith is thin and, consequently, the few
mature soils are also thin. Leaching is of
less significance than further downslope,
since high winds and intense insolation
make precipitation less effective. Red and
yellow heaths, false heathers and blueberry
bushes are common plants. Grasses also
grow in the interior districts. Much of the
area is bare rock or permanent ice.

## Summary

To recapitulate briefly, many different soils are found in British Columbia, reflecting the diversified physiography, climate and vegetation. Brown Podzolic Soils have formed under a coniferous forest in the most humid areas; Brown Soils, under a grassy cover in the arid interior valleys. Alluvial soils in the Lower Fraser Valley, and in the Kootenay Valley near Creston, are the most intensively cultivated. Brown, Dark Brown and Black Soils usually give good yields of fruits and vegetables when irrigated. Brown Podzolic and Gray Wooded Soils are, in general, not good agricultural soils.

## Selected References

Bostock, H. S. *Physiography of the Canadian Cordillera.* Geological Survey of Canada, Memoir 247. Ottawa. 1948.

Brink, V. C., and L. Farstad. *The Physiography of the Agricultural Areas of British Columbia.* Scientific Agriculture 29, pp. 273-301. 1949.

Connor, A. J. *Climate of Canada.* Handbuch der Klimatologie, Band II, Teil J, pp. 332-424. 1938.

Davis, N. F. G. *Relief Features of Southern British Columbia.* In O. W. Freeman and H. H. Martin, *The Pacific Northwest,* pp. 97-103. John Wiley & Sons, New York. 1942.

Geological Survey of Canada. *Geology and Economic Minerals of Canada.* Economic Geological Series 1. Ottawa. 1947.

Halliday, W. E. D. *A Forest Classification for Canada.* Dominion Forest Service Bulletin 89. Ottawa. 1937.

Kelley, C. C., and L. Farstad. *Soil Survey of the Prince George Area.* B. C. Soil Survey Report No. 2. Canada Dept. of Agriculture. Ottawa. 1946.

Kelly, C. C., and R. H. Spilsbury. *Soil Survey of the Lower Fraser Valley.* Publication 650, Canada Dept. of Agriculture. Ottawa. 1939.

Kelley, C. C., and R. H. Spilsbury. *Soil Survey of the Okanagan and Similkameen Valleys.* B. C. Soil Survey Report No. 3. Canada Dept. of Agriculture. Ottawa. 1949.

Kelley, C. C. *The Nature of Soil Parent Materials in Southern British Columbia.* Scientific Agriculture 20, pp. 301-307. 1940.

Kirk, D. W. *Moisture Regions in the East Kootenacy Lowlands of British Columbia.* Scientific Agriculture 31, pp. 15-24. 1951.

Mulholland, F. D. *Forest Resources of British Columbia.* British Columbia Forest Service, Dept. of Lands and Forests. Victoria. 1937.

Peacock, M. A. *Fiord-land of British Columbia.* Bulletin of the Geological Society of America 46, pp. 633-696. 1935.

Rowles, C. A. *Soils of British Columbia.* Transactions of the Second Resources Conference. pp. 7-34. Victoria. 1949.

Spilsbury, R. H., and E. W. Tisdale. *Soil Plant Relationships and Vertical Zonation in the Southern Interior of B. C.* Scientific Agriculture 24, pp. 395-436. 1944.

Taylor, Griffith. *British Columbia: A Study in Topographic Control.* Geographical Review. 32, pp. 372-402. 1942.

Tisdale, E. W. *The Grasslands of the Southern Interior of British Columbia.* Ecology 28, pp. 346-82. 1947.

Whitford, H. N., and R. D. Craig. *Forests of British Columbia.* Commission of Conservation, Canada. Ottawa. 1918.

Williams, M. Y. *The Canadian Rockies.* Transactions of the Royal Society of Canada 41, section 4, pp. 73-85. 1947.

Williams, M. Y. *British Columbia During the Pleistocene.* British Columbia Academy of Sciences, Second Scientific Conference. University of British Columbia. 1948.

The reader is also referred to the many excellent memoirs on the geology of various areas in British Columbia, by the members of the Geological Survey of Canada.

# CHAPTER 20

# Economic Geography of British Columbia

## The Historical Factor

THE northwestern coastline of North America was among the last in the world to be charted accurately. Vague impressions of the huge area were sketched by early Spanish explorers in the sixteenth and seventeenth centuries, but it was not until the latter half of the eighteenth century, that an accurate survey was achieved. It was carried out by Captain George Vancouver in 1793, when four powers, Russia, Great Britain, Spain and United States were rivals for the control of British Columbia. Their interest was partially that of imperialistic glory, but mainly for control of the rich fur trade. None of the powers, not even the British, who finally won out, was interested in colonization. British Columbia was discovered, from the east, by exploring fur traders of the Hudson's Bay and North West Companies, including Alexander McKenzie, in 1793, and Simon Fraser, in 1805. Fur trading posts, the first semi-permanent white settlements, were subsequently established.

Settlement, before the coming of the fur traders, was only partially sedentary. Fairly permanent Indian villages had been established along the coast, but not in the interior, where a nomadic type of life prevailed. Throughout the entire area, salmon was the basic food, supplemented by starchy roots (camas) and berries in the whole region, and by game in the interior. Agriculture had not been introduced into the area before the coming of the Whites, and the Indians, who were hunters and fishers, made only minor imprints on the landscape.

The discovery of gold, in 1858, challenged the control of the fur trade and changed the economic structure of the area. Population increased, roads and trails were built in the interior, and agriculture developed. The Hudson's Bay Company lost authority over the area and it became a Crown Colony.

Placer mining, the dominant type for the first few years, declined after 1863, because of partial exhaustion of accessible gravels and high transportation costs in the export of gold. The number of miners decreased, and population growth was retarded. In the meantime, lumbering developed on the coast, and an export trade was established as early as 1863. Salmon fishing was started in the sixties, but fish were sold on local markets only. A small amount of land had been cleared for farming around the fur trading posts in the first half of the 19th century. But, agriculture, as an industry, did not take root until 1860, when miners' demands for food caused the opening of parts of the Lower Fraser Valley, the East Coast Lowland of Vancouver Island and the northern Okanagan Valley for mixed farming, and the grasslands of the interior valleys for cattle ranching.

The two colonies, Vancouver Island and the Mainland, were united in 1866 and joined Canada in 1871. The latter contract was dependent upon the building of a transcontinental railroad within 10 years, the completion of which, in 1886, accelerated the growth of the province. Mining, lumbering and fishing increased greatly in output and value, because of improved transportation and the introduction of new techniques. Agriculture advanced more slowly.

The most important mining developments were centered in the Kootenay district. Rich mines were opened around Rossland, Ainsworth and Slocan. Copper, lead and zinc became as significant as gold and silver. Smelters were built and mining was firmly established in the economic geography of southeastern British Columbia.

The forest resources of coastal British Columbia also brought wealth to the province. Hand logging in the 19th century gradually gave way to widespread cutting in the 20th century, and the forests were penetrated beyond the coastline. Logging railroads were constructed, especially on Vancouver Island, but coastal inlets, fiords and channels served as the chief transportation outlets of the Mainland. The number of saw mills increased greatly, particularly in the rapidly growing city of Vancouver, which became the main lumber port of Canada.

Fishing advanced in importance also. Canning and rapid transportation solved marketing problems. The industry was valued at $8,000,000 in 1901 and $14,000,000 in 1914.

The most significant changes in agriculture were the expansion of the fluid milk industry in the Lower Fraser Valley and the planting of a few commercial orchards in the Okanagan Valley in 1892, followed, in a few years, by the installation of irrigation systems. Cattle ranching increased throughout the interior, but overgrazing had become a serious problem at the turn of the century.

The coming of the railroad made Vancouver a great port. Its advantage as a transshipment point between the Orient and Eastern Canada was realized, and

steamship connections were established in 1891. The opening of the Panama Canal made it a world port after World War I, competing in the Atlantic as well as the Pacific trade. Grain from Alberta was shipped to Europe via Vancouver after 1921. Furthermore, it was chosen as the western terminus of a second transcontinental line, which later became a part of the Canadian National Railway System. At present, fully 50% of the population of British Columbia lives within the environs of Greater Vancouver.

To summarize, the fur trade gave way to mining as the dominant economy in 1858. Agriculture, lumbering and fishing were stimulated by the gold rush. The completion of the Canadian Pacific Railway, coinciding wth the introduction of improved techniques in the mining, lumbering and fishing industries, caused a rapid development of the southern part of the province and an increase in population from 49,459, in 1881, to 98,173, in 1891, and 392,480,

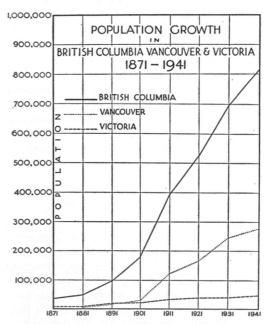

Figure 271. *Growth of Population in British Columbia.* In 70 years the population of the province has grown twenty-fold. The cities of Vancouver and Victoria continue to gain in comparison with the rest.

in 1911 (see figure 271). At present, lumbering is the leading primary industry; mining, agriculture and fishing are next in importance. Manufacturing and the tourist industry are also significant sources of wealth.

## Forestry

Forestry is the most important industry in British Columbia. In 1952, the annual cut was almost five billion board feet, the total value of the forest industries was $496,506,550, and over 55,000 people were employed in extraction and fabrication. Approximately 50% of the population depends, directly or indirectly, on the forest resources.

### Timber Trees

As noted before, climatic influences have favoured the growth of a wide variety of trees. The most important commercial species are Douglas fir, western hemlock, western red cedar, Sitka and Engelmann spruce and western yellow pine (ponderosa pine). The greatest stands are on the coast, where penetrating fiords allow fairly easy exploitation.

Douglas fir comprises approximately 40% of the annual harvest. It is in great demand, being a tough, strong, durable wood. Douglas fir is one of the best structural timbers, and is used in the construction of buildings and bridges. It is also used for interior finishing and for furniture manufacturing.

Western red cedar accounts for about 15% of the annual cut. Like Douglas fir, it is very durable, but it is softer. It has a wide variety of uses, the most important being in the manufacture of shingles and ships. It resists weathering and resultant decay extremely well.

Western hemlock, represents approximately 19% of the annual cut. It is a fine-grained wood, non-resinous but lighter and not so sturdy as the afore-mentioned species. Its uses include various types of construction, ship building, and pulp and paper.

Sitka spruce is a light but strong wood, soft and easily worked. It is important in the pulp industry but has a variety of uses, including exterior and interior finishing, furniture and aeroplane manufacture.

Engelmann spruce, western white pine and western yellow pine are less important commercial species. The former is a light wood used in pulp manufacturing, interior finishing and boxes. Western white pine has a limited distribution in the extreme south of the province. It is soft and easily worked, and is used in sash and door stock. Western yellow pine is light in weight and is used principally in the manufacture of boxes.

### Logging

The Coast Forest provides, on the average, 68% of the annual cut, 62% coming from the southwestern corner of the province including Vancouver Island and the Lower Mainland coast, and only 6% from the northern coast. The interior sections account for 32%, with the Columbia Forest producing 12%, and the Fraser and Nechako forests 6% and 14% respectively.

Logging on the coast is characterized by the use of heavy machinery and clear cutting. Briefly, a company will enter an area and cut all the mature trees. Logs are brought to a yard by various means, usually by a donkey engine hauling them along a sky line, or by caterpillar tractors towing them over improvised roads. In any event, the smaller trees are almost entirely destroyed by these methods and natural reforestation is set back. Furthermore, slash remains on the ground, presenting a potential fire hazard. From the yard, logs are hauled by truck or rail to tide-water where they are dumped. In some instances, the yard may be at the water's edge and then the logs are rolled directly into the water. They are arranged in rafts or booms and towed by tug to a mill. The coastal waterways, protected by mountains, are usually very calm and provide ideal conditions for towing logs from the forest to the mill. On occasion, mainly during the winter, gales will churn the water and temporarily delay the movement of log booms. The fiords, channels and inlets remain ice-free during the winter and shipping is possible all year.

Logging is, for the most part, a year round activity on the coast. The threat and occurrence of forest fires interrupt operations temporarily, almost every summer, but the location and length of forest closure varies greatly from year to year. Normally, it is possible to log throughout the winter because of light snowfall and moderate temperatures. Very seldom is the temperature too low or the snow too deep to permit operations.

Selective logging and hand logging are more common in the interior than on the coast, but are not as widely practised as in Eastern Canada. Operations are much smaller in the interior than on the coast. Horses are used extensively, but are being replaced by trucks and tractors. Logging is, generally speaking, a year round activity but is restricted in the spring and summer because of forest fire hazards. During the winter, a snow layer of two feet will hamper logging; three feet will stop it. Transportation of logs to the mill is delayed in spring when roads are soggy and muddy. Sleighs are used in winter.

## Processing

The largest saw mills are found on the coast and the greatest concentration is in the city of Vancouver. Large saw mills are centralized, principally because they represent a substantial capital investment, and cannot be dismantled and moved easily to follow logging operations. Furthermore, marketing of sawn lumber is easier from a central point where rail and ship facilities are available. Finally, labour supply is more reliable in a town or city. Saw milling accounts for over 50% of the net value of all forest industries.

Following saw milling, the pulp and paper industry is most important. Its value of production is over $90,000,000 per year, 28% of the gross value of all forest indus-

tries in British Columbia. Pulp mills are located at Port Alice, Port Alberni and Nanaimo on Vancouver Island, and at Port Mellon and Woodfibre on Howe Sound. Two large pulp and paper mills

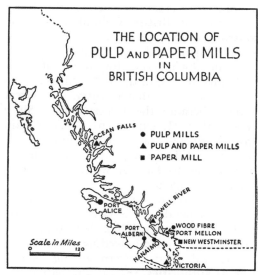

Figure 272. *Pulp and Paper Mills in British Columbia.* The pulp and paper mills of British Columbia are all located in the coastal region. This is the heavy forest belt and also the area with most plentiful water power resources.

are found at Powell River and Ocean Falls, both company towns (See figure 272). Victoria has a small pulp and paper mill, and New Westminster, a small paper making establishment. Over 500,000 tons of paper are manufactured in British Columbia annually, of which almost 80% is newsprint. Hemlock and spruce are the chief trees used in the manufacture of wood pulp. Most mills are located near the source of supply. Power is an important consideration and mills are situated to take advantage of cheap hydro-electric energy.

A cellulose plant, constructed at a cost of $27,000,000 is located at Port Edward, a few miles from Prince Rupert. Other forest industries in British Columbia are veneers and plywood (8% by value), sashes and doors (5%) and boxes, poles, piles and props (less than 3%).

## Economic Relations

Forest products, principally lumber and paper, are exported to many different areas but, at present, United States is the best customer. Trade conditions change because of factors over which the forest industries of British Columbia have no control. For example, in the 1920's, United States, Japan and the Prairie Provinces were the best markets. Imposition of tariffs by United States, in the 1930's, directed exports away from that country, and Great Britain became the largest buyer. Since World War II, exports to Great Britain have declined because of the dollar shortage. The stiffest competition, British Columbia has to face in world markets, is from Scandinavia.

The economic prosperity of British Columbia depends, to a large measure, on its forest resources. That these stands are being cut at a rate exceeding replacement, has caused great concern among governmental authorities. Several alternatives are open. Reduction of the cut would solve the problem, but at the same time, British Columbia would lose important markets and her economy would suffer. Greater exploitation of interior forests would be costly, but would tend to prolong the life of the coastal forests. Selective cutting, rather than clear cutting, would be much less wasteful, but would be more expensive. According to a recent Royal Commission report, fire protection must be greatly improved and artificial reforestation must be greatly expanded. Improved techniques will reduce waste in processing logs and bring greater wealth to the area. The important point, however, is that at the present rate of cutting, resources such as Douglas fir will not last much longer than 20 years. All commercial species could be exhausted within a century. However, it is cheering to note the government's concern and to know that programs are being initiated by the government and by industry to safeguard the forest resources.

To recapitulate, forestry is the most important industry in British Columbia. The coastal area has the most luxuriant forest and the largest logging and lumbering operations. The pulp and paper industry is growing in importance. Forestry depends on the export market and therefore suffers from the trade policies of other nations. Conservation of forest resources is an acute problem.

## Mining

Mining is the second ranking primary industry in British Columbia. Value of production in 1951 was $168,293,273, and average value from 1942 to 1951 was $104,970,000. However, the prosperity of the industry is extremely sensitive to world economic conditions. Prices for certain precious metals have fluctuated from a low of 40 cents to a high of $100 per ounce; for base metals from 3 cents to $2 a pound. Witness the decline in value of gold production (lode and placer) from over $23,000,000, in 1940, to $7,000,000, in 1945, and the increase in value of lead production from $17,000,000, in 1945, to over $40,000,000, in 1947. It is difficult to assess the industry accurately with reference to any one year or any one decade, because conditions change so rapidly. Nevertheless, because of the diversity of mineral resources, depression in one phase of the industry is usually counterbalanced by prosperity in another.

### Nature and Distribution of Mineral Deposits

Metalliferous deposits are varied and widespread through British Columbia. Non-metallic minerals, including coal and gypsum are also found in the province.

Associations of minerals, such as lead-zinc-silver and gold-copper, the two most common, are directly related to the huge granitoid intrusions of late Mesozoic and early Tertiary times. Consequently, most metal mines and prospects are located along the margins of the Coast and Columbia Mountains and not in the Rocky

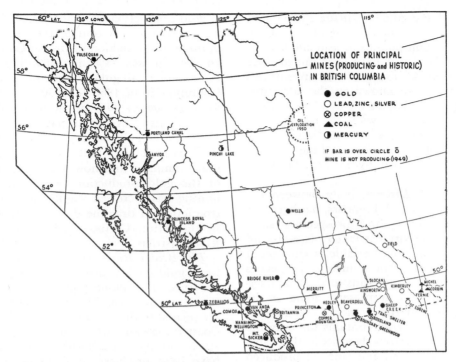

Figure 273. *Principal Mines in British Columbia.* The most important mines are in the southern interior part of the province.

Mountains. (See figure 273). Undoubtedly, in the future, valuable deposits will be uncovered in the vicinity of the Cassiar, Omineca, Skeena and other smaller batholiths.

Certain metals, principally gold, are found in stream placers. Mechanical and chemical weathering may frequently release minerals from rocks. They may then be transported by running water until, because of their great weight, they are dropped and collect in sand and gravel to form a placer. Placer gravels in British Columbia range in age from Tertiary to Recent. Such deposits formed the basis of placer mining during the early gold rushes through Western Canada. The only equipment needed by the miner was a pick and pan or sluice-box. Obviously, these accessible deposits were soon depleted. Lode mining, depending on heavy equipment, is now predominant in the industry.

Most coal measures in British Columbia are of Upper or Lower Cretaceous age. They are found principally on the east coast of Vancouver Island and along the flanks of the Rocky Mountains in southeastern British Columbia.

## Lead and Zinc

In recent years, the extraction of lead and zinc has been the most important aspect of the mining industry in British Columbia. The province produces nearly all the lead in Canada, and about half the zinc. Value of production in 1950 was $84,000,000, or about 61% of the total value of all minerals produced in British Columbia. Most lead and zinc mines are found in southeastern British Columbia between the Selkirk and Rocky Mountain Trenches.

*Sullivan,* located along the eastern flanks of the Purcell Mountains near the town of Kimberley, is the largest lead and zinc mine in Canada and one of the largest in the world. It produces on the average over 90%

of the lead and zinc in Canada and 11% of the lead and 8% of the zinc of the world. Over 9.5 billion pounds of lead and 6.5 billion pounds of zinc have been mined since its inception. Although the resources of this great mine were known in the late nineteenth century, large scale development did not begin until 1923 when the introduction of the flotation process made possible the separation of complex ores. All the ore from Sullivan is shipped by rail to Trail for smelting.

*The Slocan District,* lying between the Selkirk and Purcell Trenches, has been the centre of mining and prospecting since 1891. Most activity has taken place around the town of Sandon. Variable production of lead and zinc, from numerous properties around Slocan and Ainsworth, characterizes the industry at present. Some of the mines are Lucky Jim, Standard and Yale.

*The Field District* contains the only important metalliferous deposits in the Canadian Rockies. Lead and zinc are produced at the Monarch and Kicking Horse mines, located on the steep north slope of Mount Stephen, and the south slope of Mount Field, respectively.

## Gold

At the outset and for many years thereafter, gold mining was the most important branch of the industry. Lately, its significance has diminished. In 1950, the value

*National Film Board*
Plate 95. Hydraulic mining in the Barkerville district in the interior of British Columbia.

of gold production was only $11,000,000, or less than eight per cent of the total value of mineral production in British Columbia. In 1940, it was 33%, in 1860, 98%. The total value of all gold production in British Columbia from 1860 to 1950, was almost $470,000,000, or 20% of the total value of all minerals recovered in that period. Until 1893, placer gold booms characterized the industry, but after that date, lode mining took command and now accounts for 90% of the gold production. Recently, placer mining has increased slightly with the introduction of dragline dredging, especially in the Atlin, Cariboo and Lower Fraser River districts.

*The Bridge River Area* contains the Bralorne gold mine which is the largest in the province. The Pioneer properties are also found in this area. The gold-bearing veins are related to the Mesozoic intrusions of the Coast Range and are located along its eastern flanks. Almost 2,000,000 ounces of gold have been produced at these mines since 1929. A road leads from Shalath, on the Pacific Great Eastern Railway, to the mines.

*The Barkerville Gold Belt,* located along the western margins of the Cariboo Mountains, was the centre of the first gold rush in 1858. No lode mining began until 1934 but, since then, over 500,000 ounces of gold have been recovered. Most activity is centered at Wells. Quesnel, to the west, serves the adjacent mining community.

*The Hedley District,* located along the edge of the Cascade Mountains in the southern interior, has been important for gold mining since 1903. The Hedley Nickel Plate Mine was at one time the largest producer in Canada. After closing down in 1931, the mine was subsequently revived in 1935, and, along with the Hedley Mascot mine, produced almost 500,000 ounces of gold from 1935 to 1945.

*The Sheep Creek* gold mining area is situated between Nelson and the American border in southeastern British Columbia. Many small companies have mined gold in this area since 1899. The Sheep Creek property has been the biggest producer, accounting for over 700,000 ounces of gold since its inception in 1899.

*The Rossland Area* was very notable in gold production up to 1930. Only small operations are apparent now. From 1894 to 1930, the Rossland mine produced 2,868,227 ounces of gold.

*The Tulsequah Mine,* located on the Taku River in northwestern British Columbia, is relatively new. Closed during the war, it is now very active.

*Other gold mines* include Zeballos, on Vancouver Island, where production has gone on intermittently since 1938. A few mines have produced gold, from time to time, in the Atlin district. Other mines, such as the Surf and Pugsley, on Princess Royal Island, have been important. Gold is also recovered at many other copper, lead, zinc and silver mines.

## Copper

Over 2,000,000 tons of copper have been mined in British Columbia since the early part of the century. Huge amounts of low grade ore were produced in the Greenwood area from 1900 to 1919. Smelters were located at Grand Forks and Greenwood. All operations were suspended in 1919. The Granby company also focussed its attention on Anyox in the Portland Canal area as early as 1912. Copper mines in this district diminished in significance after 1935.

At present, most of the copper in British Columbia is mined at Britannia. Value of production in 1950 from all mines was over $9,800,000.

*Britannia,* on Howe Sound, is the leading mine. Operations began in 1905. Over 6,000 tons of ore are mined daily and about 20,000 tons of copper are recovered annually. It is shipped to Tacoma, Washington, for smelting.

*The Copper Mountain Mine* is located near Princeton, British Columbia. It was discovered in 1892, and operated periodically until 1957 when it was closed. Approximately 5,000 tons of ore were mined daily, and about 20,000 tons of copper were extracted annually. Granduc and Bethlehem have large deposits of copper.

## Coal

Coal accounts for approximately 7% of the value of production of the mining industry annually. On the average, just over 1,300,000 long tons are mined each year—a decline from the peak year in 1910 when over 3,000,000 long tons were extracted. Coal mining began as early as 1836, from the beach at Suquash on the northeastern coast of Vancouver Island. After 1850, the Nanaimo-Wellington field was opened and, in 1888, the Comox field. Both areas are located on the east coast of Vancouver Island. Production in the Crow's Nest district, principally at Fernie, Corbin and Michel, began in 1898. The Nanaimo-Wellington field continues to diminish in importance, but the other two fields remain significant.

Coal reserves are not being used to their maximum capacity. Severe competition from petroleum and hydro-electric power, combined with the loss of certain markets, has retarded the expansion of the industry. Although some areas have been almost exhausted, large reserves remain, principally in the East Kootenay area.

## Other Minerals

*Silver* is produced at many mines, but only one, the Highland Bell Mine in the Beaverdell district, depends on it entirely. The total value of all silver production in British Columbia, in 1950, was just over $6,890,000. Over 320,000,000 ounces, at a value of $190,000,000, were produced in the province from 1890 to 1950.

*Mercury* was discovered in 1938, near Pinchi Lake, north of Fort St. James in the Nechako Plateau. A mine was subsequently opened in 1940. Another mine, the Bralorne Takla, located 90 miles north of Pinchi Lake, began operations in 1943. Production was suspended at both mines in 1944, because of the lack of markets rather than exhaustion of ores.

*Iron ore* was not mined in British Columbia until recently in spite of the existence of large reserves on Texada Island, located about 50 miles northwest of Vancouver. The development of these deposits was retarded, principally because the Vancouver market is not large enough to support an iron and steel industry, and the magnetite ores are not highly prized for the fabrication of pig iron. Most of the iron ore extracted from these deposits is shipped to Japan.

*Gypsum* is mined at Falkland, located 45 miles southeast of Kamloops. In 1953, 6,500 tons on the average, were shipped out monthly.

*Sodium and magnesium salts* are derived, on a very small scale, from a few of the small saline lakes in the interior of British Columbia. Most activity has been centered in the Clinton, Chilcotin and Ashcroft areas.

*Building and monumental stone* is quarried in the Coast and Columbia Mountains. The principal rock is granodiorite of the batholithic intrusions. *Sandstone* is quarried near Nanaimo and *marble* has been produced to the north of Kootenay Lake at Marblehead. All of these operations are on a limited scale.

## The Trail Smelter

The Consolidated Mining and Smelting Company operates the largest smelter in Canada, and one of the largest non-ferrous smelters in the world, at Trail. Chemical plants are also located here. Besides lead, zinc, copper and silver, many by-products are recovered including cadmium, bismuth, antimony and tungsten. Sulphur, another by-product, is combined with phosphates, nitrogen and hydrogen in the production of commercial fertilizers.

Most of the installations have been built on a narrow terrace on the western bank of the Columbia River. Several hydro-electric plants on the Kootenay River supply the smelter and associated plants with power. Recent expansion has given the zinc refinery a capacity output of over 450 tons of electrolytic zinc per day. Normally, over 600 tons of lead are refined daily. About 7,000 men are employed in the various operations.

## Summary

In summary, mining is one of the principal sources of wealth in British Columbia. Minerals are varied. The Sullivan mine is exceptionally large, but others, such as Bralorne and Britannia, are also important. Lead and zinc are the leaders but gold, copper, silver and coal are significant. Iron ore and good coking coal are found within a short distance of Vancouver and an iron and steel industry should eventually emerge in that area.

## Fishing

Fishing is less important than other primary industries in value of production but, nevertheless, contributes substantially to the wealth of the province. Total annual marketed value of fish and fish products has been over $65,000,000, in the last few years. British Columbia accounts for approximately 37%, by value, of the Canadian catch, and is the leading province.

The industry has a long history. The economy of the coastal Indians was based principally on the salmon. Fish formed a large part of the diet of the early fur traders. The Hudson's Bay Company entered the fish trade and exported salted salmon to Asia as early as 1835. The gold rush created a domestic market for fish. The first commercial salmon cannery was established in 1870, near New Westminster, and the first cold storage plant, in 1887.

### Fishing Grounds

The environmental relationships of the North Pacific fisheries are not fully understood. Little is known of off-shore pastures and only slightly more of the coastal waters. No truly warm current reaches the British Columbia coast. Contrary to former opinion, the so-called Japanese current (Kuroshio extension) reverses its flow in mid-Pacific, at least 3,000 miles to the southwest of the coast [1]. The north branch of the Aleutian current, part of a counter-clockwise gyral in the Gulf of Alaska, influences the British Columbia coast, mainly in the cool season. Although it carries sub-arctic water, it is slightly warmer than the ocean surface along the coast because its flow is from the southwest. The current is insignificant in comparison with its counterpart in the North Atlantic Ocean. Cold water from sub-surface layers upwells along the coast of British Columbia in summer.

The continental shelf is extremely narrow, and the bed of the ocean falls abruptly to great depths, immediately to the west of the off-shore islands. No extensive banks, similar to those off Newfoundland or northwestern Europe, exist. The great transverse rivers, such as the Fraser, Skeena and Nass, which cut through the Coast Mountains to the sea, offer vast fresh water spawning grounds for salmon.

The environment of the North Pacific fishing grounds is very diverse, as indicated by the great variety of marine life. It ranges from tuna in southern waters to cod in the far north; from the quasi-stationary shell fish of the coastal waters to migratory salmon; from the submarine inhabitants such as the halibut to the sub-surface dwellers such as the herring.

## Salmon

The salmon fishery is the most important, and usually contributes from 60% to 70% of the total value. On the average, 1,500,000 cwt. are caught and landed, of which over two-thirds are canned.

The sockeye or red salmon averages seven pounds. It is the most valuable species but production has diminished because of over-fishing. Most of these fish are canned. The humpback or pink salmon weighs, on the average, four pounds. Most of these fish, also, are canned, but they are not so highly prized as the sockeye because of their less appealing colour. The coho averages nine

pounds and receives a lower price than sockeye at canneries, because of its pale-coloured flesh. The chum is also light-coloured and weighs about nine pounds. In the last few years approximately one-third of this species has been marketed fresh or frozen. The spring salmon is the largest, weighing over 20 pounds. Many of these are "mild-cured," but a large portion are sold fresh.

Salmon fishing is essentially a seasonal industry. The run begins in late spring, when mature fish, after feeding from two to six years in the ocean, return to the fresh water streams for spawning, and continues until October. Fishermen concentrate near river mouths where the fish converge on their way up-stream. Canneries are located near fishing grounds, because the fish are perishable and must be processed as soon as possible after leaving the water. Almost complete mechanization and rapid output characterize the modern cannery. The finished product is shipped to Vancouver for distribution.

The salmon fishing industry is faced with many problems. Salmon stock has been greatly depleted because of intensive fishing, and no increase in production is possible at present. In fact, further restrictions may have to be imposed to reduce the catch. Furthermore, interference with fresh water breeding grounds by the building of dams, diversion of water for agriculture and industrial use, and alteration of run-off conditions through logging, has caused some impoverishment of the stock. Finally, approximately 70% of the salmon pack is normally exported and is consequently influenced by world trade conditions.

## Halibut

Halibut is the second most important fish resource in British Columbia. Unlike the salmon, it remains in the ocean during its entire life, and is caught from sturdy trawlers, usually over 50 miles off shore. The fishing season is limited by law to the period from the beginning of April to the end of October. Halibut varies greatly in size

[1] Sverdrup, H. U., *Oceanography for Meteorologists*, Prentice-Hall, New York, pp. 196-205, 1942.

but the average weight is about 70 pounds. The fish are packed in crushed ice at sea, and rushed to either Prince Rupert or Vancouver for marketing. From these points, rapid rail service makes possible distribution of fresh halibut on the Eastern Canadian and American markets. Some of the fish are frozen and sold during the winter.

Commercial halibut fishing in the North Pacific Ocean dates from 1888. With declining Atlantic production and improved marketing facilities, the industry expanded very quickly, until exhaustion of the species was threatened. As a result, the International Fisheries Commission, consisting of two Canadians and two Americans, was established in 1924 to regulate the size of the catch. Because of the excellent work of this board during the last 25 years, the halibut fishery has been made secure for the future.

## Other Fish

Many other fish are caught off shore. The herring catch has averaged over 2,000,000 cwt. annually. Many herring are reduced to oil and meal, for which there is a good market; others are canned. Tuna (albacore) fishing has increased greatly in the last few years. Most of the catch, which was 19,656 cwt. in 1948, is frozen and exported for canning. Other species including sole, cod and flounder are also caught off shore. The catch varies with the ability of British Columbia fishermen to compete with Americans in international waters.

The shell-fish industry contributes less than two per cent to the annual value of the fisheries. Clam and crab fisheries are most valuable, but production is erratic from year to year. Experts believe that the oyster and shrimp fisheries could be greatly expanded and made very productive.

To conclude, the maritime position of British Columbia has resulted in the development of commercial fishing on a large scale. The industry is confined to the coast, there being no commercial fishing on the inland lakes. Salmon fisheries dominate but halibut is also important.

## Agriculture

In normal years, the value of agricultural production is exceeded by that of both forestry and mining. Unlike the central provinces, British Columbia is not an important agricultural area. Topography, climate and soils impose significant limitations on the location, nature and possible expansion of agriculture. Markets, rail rates and the attitude toward the land on the part of various cultural groups are also noteworthy. Whereas topography primarily controls the location of agriculture in the province, climate determines the types of crops that may be cultivated. Dairying, fruit and vegetable growing, poultry raising and cattle ranching characterize the industry.

Just over 1,000,000 acres, or less than 0.5% of the total land area, are cultivated. Another three million acres are classified as unimproved land, and are used mainly for cattle and sheep grazing. The Southern Coastal Trench and the Okanagan Valley are the most important agricultural regions; farming and ranching are scattered throughout the rest of the area (see figure 274) .

## Agricultural Regions

*The Southern Coastal Trench*, including the Lower Fraser Valley, the East Coast Lowland of Vancouver Island, and the Gulf Islands, contains about 35% of the land under cultivation in the province. In the Lower Fraser Valley, post-glacial deltas and old lake bottoms with their level topography and fine-grained, fertile soils, offer the best farming land. Two large areas exhibit these characteristics: the *western* part of the Lower Fraser Valley, including Lulu Island, the Ladner district, Langley Prairie and Pitt Valley; the *eastern* part comprising the Sumas Prairie, Agassiz and Harrison districts. Much of this land is below 10 feet in elevation, and has to be dyked against spring flooding. Furthermore, many areas are poorly drained and expensive pumps and drainage canals must be main-

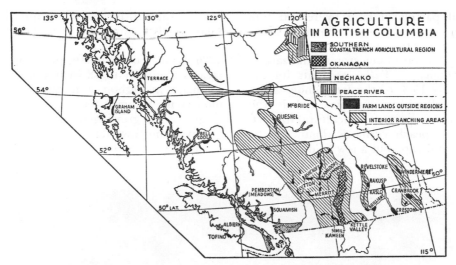

**Figure 274.** *Agriculture in British Columbia.* Agricultural districts in British Columbia are scattered and very small in comparison with the total area. The dry interior has a rather large area of grazing land.

tained. Such areas are intensively utilized, especially for vegetable growing and dairying. Higher parts of the valley, particularly those over 200 feet, have excessively leached, infertile soils which, in many places, are quite stony. Mixed farming has developed in a few sections; large portions remain heavily forested.

Along the southeastern coast of Vancouver Island, and in the Gulf Islands, the area of good farming land is much smaller than in the Lower Fraser Valley. The soil in the Saanich Peninsula is moderately fertile, and intensive berry farming, bulb growing and dairying are carried on, in the topographically suitable sections. Alluvial soils occur in the Duncan area and specialized farming has resulted. Scattered tracts of good soil and smooth topography are also found around Parksville and Comox.

The climate of the Southern Coastal Trench is characterized by rainy, mild winters and dry, cool summers. It may seem anomalous that in Saanich Peninsula, about 75 miles from the open ocean, irrigation is necessary during the summer to insure profitable yields. Moisture deficiency is not so pronounced, throughout the rest of the area. The climate favours dairying, poultry

raising, small fruits and vegetable growing. Pastures are green throughout the year, except in unusually cold winters and very dry summers. Egg production remains fairly constant the year round as temperature extremes are lacking. Strawberries, peas, lettuce, and potatoes enjoy a cool, moist start and are intolerant of extremely hot weather. Consequently, they grow well in this region. The cultivation of hops and grapes also reflects the climatic environment.

In addition, economic factors encourage agricultural specialization. Three urban areas, Vancouver, New Westminster, and Victoria, contain about 750,000 people, constituting a large market for whole milk and cream, eggs, poultry, meats, vegetables and fruits. The manufacture of butter and cheese is not important, but some milk is canned.

One of the most pressing problems in the region at present is the impingement of urban functions on rural areas. The rural-urban fringe has widened, resulting in prices for some land becoming too high for agricultural use. Agricultural production has thereby been reduced in these sections. Moreover, subdivision of farms has been accelerated because of the growing demand for small parcels of land by retired folk from central and eastern Canada. Some units are either too small to be profitable or suffer the dangers of one crop specialization.

*The Okanagan Valley* accounts for approximately 15% of the land under cultivation in British Columbia, and is the second most important agricultural district. Apple and peach orchards dominate the cultural landscape but a few fields of grain,

has less than 10 inches of precipitation annually, a hot summer (July average temperature 74° F.) and a long growing season (226 days). To the north, precipitation increases gradually to 12 inches at Kelowna, 15 inches at Vernon, and 19 inches at Salmon Arm. Summer temperatures and the length of the growing season decrease progressively northward. A few miles north of Vernon, a mixed forest replaces the natural

*Courtesy Exp. Farms Service*

Plate 96.   The benchlands along the shores of Lake Okanagan. Jerseys on irrigated pasture in the foreground and irrigated orchards in the background illustrate the importance of agriculture in this valley.

cattle ranches, vegetable plots and dairy farms are also visible.

The valley extends northward for over 130 miles from the American border to Shuswap Lake. It averages two miles in width south of Kelowna but broadens out to include significant tributary valleys in the north. Steep walls rise to over 4,000 feet to the east and west of the depression. Most of the valley bottom is occupied by lakes bordered by extensive terraces.

The extreme southern part of the valley

grassland of the southern sections. Brown, Dark Brown and Black Soils are found in the southern and central districts; Brown Podzolic Soils, in the north. It is impossible to farm in the south without the aid of irrigation, but mixed farming is common in the north without it.

Raising of orchard fruits is the most important aspect of agriculture in the valley. About 2,200,000 fruit trees are under cultivation, of which over half are apple, 15% pear, 13% peach and 10% plum trees.

Over 90% of all the fruit trees are irrigated. Melted snow from the neighbouring hills provides water for irrigation. It is released from storage reservoirs during the spring and summer, and runs down through flumes. A few attempts have been made to pump water from the lakes which offer an unlimited supply.

Climatic conditions favour horticulture. Long spells of sub-zero weather rarely affect the area and tender stone fruits, such as the peach, can survive [1]. The long, dry, hot growing season promotes the development of brightly coloured, highly flavoured fruits. The relative humidity is low and the growth of parasitic fungi is reduced. Higher humidity, north of Kelowna, encourages the spread of apple scab and careful spraying is necessary. Late spring frosts are a hazard to the orchards but the terraces are less seriously influenced than the valley bottoms, where cold air from the hills collects on clear, calm nights. Apple orchards are scattered through the valley, but peach and apricot trees are concentrated on the Brown Soils of the terraces, close to the southern end of Lake Okanagan, where very low temperatures (below $-15°$ F.) are unlikely.

Tree fruit production has increased steadily since 1920 and especially, during the last decade. The apple crop has risen from 67,000,000 pounds in 1920 to over 325,000,000 pounds in 1950. The industry is very sensitive to world trade conditions. Reliable markets in British Columbia, the Prairies and, lately, in eastern Canada do not absorb the entire crop, and overseas exports must be maintained to support the producers. With increased canning and better marketing to reach an even larger segment of the Canadian population, the surplus could be absorbed.

Recently, a larger output of dairy products, small fruits and vegetables has resulted in a more diversified economy. Melons, tomatoes, and other vegetables for an early market are grown in the Oliver district where the spring is warm and dry, the soil is mainly a friable loamy sand, and irrigation water is available. Onions, strawberries and potatoes are also important throughout the entire valley. Dairy farming has increased in response to a growing market. In the Salmon Arm district, a more humid climate encourages the raising of dairy cattle. Butter is exported and it is expected that, as the city of Vancouver continues to grow, the district will become a part of its milkshed. Dry wheat farming has a limited distribution on the Black Soils in the vicinity of Vernon.

*The Fraser Plateau*, exclusive of the Okanagan Valley, is a large area in which cattle and sheep ranching dominate. A few irrigated plots are scattered throughout the area, on which is grown feed for livestock and some fruits and vegetables. Cultivated land totals about 140,000 acres. Diversified topography, dry climate, pedocalic soils, grassy valleys and a park forest on the slopes, characterize the landscape between the Coast and Columbia Mountains and from the American border to latitude $53°$.

The development of a livestock industry followed the gold rush of 1858, when cattle and horses were introduced from the Oregon country. The grassland areas were used exclusively until the turn of the century, when serious depletion forced the ranchers to invade the forest areas. At present, transhumance is successfully practised in many sections. Livestock are driven to alpine pastures in early summer, where they graze until late August. Following summer feeding, a large part of the herd is "rounded-up" and marketed. The remainder range in the valleys during winter. If the cover of snow is thick, the animals must be fed on hay.

The animal population is relatively small. Normally, 250,000 beef cattle (4% of the total number in Canada) and 75,000 sheep range throughout interior British Columbia including the Kootenay country. Many of the ranches are very large—in fact,

---

[1] The winter of 1949-50 was an exception. The temperature dropped to $-16°$ F. at Penticton. Thousands of trees were severely damaged.

the historic Gang ranch, located southwest of Williams Lake in the Chilcotin district, covers 750,000 acres. Practically all ranches, large or small, have irrigated fields from which they derive winter feed.

Scattered irrigated farms are found in the Thompson Valley between Lytton and Chase. Tomatoes and potatoes are grown near Ashcroft; apple orchards are found to the east of Kamloops. Some mixed farming has developed in the Merritt and Princeton basins and in a few other sections, such as the North Thompson Valley.

*The Nechako District* has a few scattered agricultural communities, principally along the Canadian National rail line from Smithers to Prince George. Approximately 90,000 acres are under cultivation. Estimates indicate that about 1,500,000 acres are potentially arable, making it one of the largest areas in British Columbia with a topography suitable for farming.

The area has a subdued relief, with only a few sharp ridges breaking the general roll of the land. Stone-free, clay soils are found in post-glacial lake bottoms and even the till often contains few stones. These are forested soils, consequently they are somewhat acid, strongly leached and rather poor in structure. Careful management is required to maintain productivity.

Low temperatures and too much moisture are climatic hazards. No crop failures have ever been attributed to drought, but heavy rains in September have periodically interfered with harvest. The Prince George area has recently had six unsuccessful harvests due to heavy autumn rainfall. Severe summer frosts strike occasionally, and cause damage. Furthermore, extremely low temperatures in winter restrict hardy orchard fruits and if the snow cover is light, even winter wheat.

Because of the climatic environment, hay and root crops are the most successful. Over half the cultivated land is in hay. Dairying is important in the Prince George and Telkwa districts, where creameries have been built. Timothy and alsike seeds are the chief cash crops in the entire area. Having

a high value per unit weight, they can stand expensive shipping costs to distant markets. Oats and wheat are moderately successful on the Degraded Black Soils in the Vanderhoof, Burns Lake, François Lake and Smithers' districts. Normally, small surpluses are shipped out. Turnips, cabbages, potatoes, peas and other vegetables are grown for local consumption. Factors which will retard development are: a short growing season (80 days) allied with danger of summer frosts, heavy autumn rains and distance from markets. If the population increases, dairying will form an important source of income.

*The Kootenay Valleys* have approximately 130,000 acres under cultivation. The chief districts are in the Kettle Valley, Anarchist Plateau, the Selkirk Trench, Slocan area, the Purcell Trench near Creston and Kaslo, and the southern Rocky Mountain Trench near Cranbrook and Windermere.

Parts of the region are irrigated, and used for the production of tree fruits. Cherry orchards are significant on the terraces of the Purcell Trench near Creston and Kaslo, and apples are grown in the Kettle Valley near Grand Forks. Wheat farming is specialized on the alluvial lowlands of the Kootenay River Valley between Kootenay Lake and the American border. Yields average over 60 bushels to the acre. The lowland is vulnerable to periodic flooding. In 1948, almost all the farmlands were submerged until late July. Dry farming with emphasis on wheat is attempted on the shallow Black Soils of the Anarchist Plateau just east of the Okanagan Trench, and on the calcareous soils near Cranbrook in the Rocky Mountain Trench. Mixed farming, featuring dairying, is common around small cities and towns. Throughout the Kootenays, grazing of cattle and sheep is important on the fringes of the cultivated pockets. Crops from many farms are used mainly to supplement natural forage and provide feed for the range animals.

*The Coastal District,* exclusive of the Southern Coastal Trench, has approximately 20,000 acres under cultivation. Farming communities are widely scattered and are associated with narrow, discontinuous coastal plains or platforms, recent deltas at the heads of fiords, and small intermountain basins. The extraordinarily humid climate limits the variety of plants to pasture grasses, root crops and small fruits. Although summer is free of frost, it is cool and cloudy. Sub-zero temperatures are rarely experienced in winter.

Subsistence farming is common in most of these communities. About 1,500 acres are under cultivation in the northeastern lowlands of Graham Island. Since the environment is very similar to that of Northwestern Europe, a prosperous dairy industry could develop if accessible markets were found and if the dense forest and muskeg soil could be cleared and drained cheaply. Small agricultural settlements appear in the vicinity of Terrace, in the Bella Coola delta at the head of Burke Channel, in the Squamish delta at the head of Howe Sound, and in Pemberton Meadows at the head of Lillooet Lake. Each settlement has fairly fertile soils but is subject to periodic flooding and is inaccessible to markets. The Tofino and Alberni districts on Vancouver Island have a few scattered farms.

*The Peace River Block* within British Columbia contains approximately 200,000 acres of cultivated land. The agricultural area to the east and southeast in Alberta is much larger. The region is a part of the Tramontane Plains. It has a continental climate, with a short but warm growing season that is not so greatly endangered by unseasonable frosts as the Nechako region. Gray-Wooded Soils dominate, but Degraded Black Soils have a fairly wide distribution.

Settlement in the British Columbia portion began after World War I. The rail line was completed to Dawson Creek in 1930 and by 1951, the population in the area had reached 13,000. Mixed farming, with emphasis on wheat, oats and the rais-

ing of hogs and cattle, characterizes the district. Small seeds are grown successfully and constitute an important cash crop. It has been suggested that excellent agricultural lands are still available[1]. Physically, the Peace River Block is promising but, economically, it remains marginal to most markets.

Except for a few gardens around the villages, airports and fur trading posts, no agricultural development has taken place in Northern British Columbia. Pockets of arable land exist in the Finlay, Parsnip, Fort Nelson and Kechika River Valleys. Full assessment of the physical qualities of this large, empty area awaits further investigation.

## Summary

In summary, British Columbia has a diversified agriculture. Specialized fruit cultivation is found in the Okanagan Valley; dairying, in the Lower Fraser Valley; wheat farming, in the southern Purcell Trench. In contrast, subsistence farming is typical in the isolated arable pockets along the coast and in the Kootenays. Cattle and sheep ranching are significant on the natural grasslands in the interior. Location of farmland is greatly influenced by topography. All in all, not more than 4% of the total area will ever be cultivated. Climate and the lack of markets restrict expansion at present in the topographically suitable districts.

## Hydro-Electric Power

British Columbia stands next to Quebec and Ontario in hydro-electric power developments, but is second to Quebec in undeveloped water power resources. The installed hydro-electric turbine capacity, at the end of 1955, was 2,369,915 horsepower, the undeveloped potential, approximately 21,000,000 horsepower. Over 60% of the energy generated is sold in large blocks to industries which process basic raw materials. The Trail smelter, the aluminum smelter at Kitimat, and the pulp and

[1] *Canada's New Northwest,* North Pacific Planning Project, Section on Agriculture, pp. 43-48, Ottawa, 1947.

paper mills on the coast, absorb practically all of this power. Approximately
40% of the energy is distributed by central
electric stations, such as the British Columbia Electric Company, to domestic users,
public utilities and industries.

A combination of topographic and climatic factors accounts for the large water power potential in the area. The many streams
which drain the area carry a tremendous
volume of water annually, and tumble over
rough terrain offering many sites for power development. On the other hand, these
rivers normally have a great variation in
flow. In many places catchment basins are
small and steep and runoff is extremely
rapid. If water is to be harnessed in such
areas, large storage reservoirs have to be
built to insure an even flow throughout the
year. However, many favourable power sites
cannot be developed at present, because of
remoteness from centres of population or
because the topography between them and
the market is extremely rugged making the
costs of transmission exorbitant.

Southwestern British Columbia, including the Lower Mainland Coast and Vancouver Island, has hydro-electric plants
capable of generating 965,000 horsepower
or almost 40% of the British Columbia total. Much of the energy is distributed by

central electric stations to the larger centres of Vancouver and Victoria. The British
Columbia Electric Company plants at Stave
Lake, Buntzen Lake, Ruskin and Bridge
River supply the bulk of the power needed
in the Lower Fraser Valley (see figure 275).
Sites on the Campbell and Jordan Rivers
furnish power for Vancouver Island. Almost 100,000 horsepower is generated on
the Lois and Powell Rivers for the pulp and
paper industry at Powell River. It is estimated that undeveloped sites in the region
could produce another 3,000,000 horsepower with 1,300,000 available at the Moran
site on the Fraser River.

Southeastern British Columbia, or the
Kootenay district, has several plants supplying 650,000 horsepower, or almost 27%
of the British Columbia total. In contrast
to southwestern British Columbia, over
90% of the power is sold in large blocks to
mining industries. The remainder goes
chiefly to the towns and cities of the area.
The largest plant, located at Waneta on
the Pend Oreille River, has a capacity of
240,000 horsepower. Other important developments are found at Upper Bonning-
ton, Brilliant, Corra Linn and South Slocan
on the Kootenay River. In the area, about
800,000 horsepower remain to be developed.

Hydro-electric plants along the northern

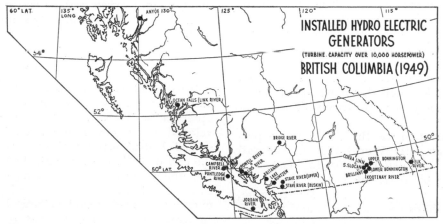

Figure 275. *Hydro-electric Stations in British Columbia.* Most of the developed power
sites are in the southern part of the province. but there is much undeveloped power
in the north.

coast generate almost 650,000 horsepower which is used in smelting, mining and pulp and paper industries. The largest development at Kemano produces 560,000 horsepower for the aluminum smelter at Kitimat. It is estimated that 2,200,000 horsepower remain to be exploited. Another large project is the Lois River (50,000 horsepower) near Powell River.

The Okanagan Valley and adjacent areas are served by several sites having a total installed turbine capacity of 48,050 H.P. In the entire Fraser Plateau, several sites capable of generating over 500,000 horsepower remain to be harnessed. One of the largest is that at Soda Creek on the Fraser River (310,000 horsepower).

It has been suggested that approximately 7,000,000 horsepower could be generated in Northern British Columbia. The largest undeveloped sites are located on the Yukon-Taku Rivers (4,900,000 horsepower). Others are found on the Peace, Quesnel, Bulkley, Nass and Skeena Rivers.[1]

## Manufacturing

Manufacturing in British Columbia depends on the timber, fish, agricultural and water power resources. This is borne out by the fact that saw-milling, pulp and paper, fish curing and packing, and fruit and vegetable preparations are leading industries. Factories which combine several partially fabricated materials in the production of automobiles, furniture or textiles, are, for the most part, not found in British Columbia. British Columbia lies over 2,500 miles to the west of the major Canadian market in southern Ontario and Quebec. Western manufacturers cannot compete in that market, except in products peculiar to the west, because of transportation costs. The limited Pacific market has retarded the establishment of duplicate plants such as soap, shoe or tobacco factories. Most consumer's goods except perishable products such as

[1]The first stage of the Nechako-Kitimat project of the Aluminum Company of Canada has been completed. 560,000 horsepower have been installed.

## Table 18     Leading Manufacturing Industries in British Columbia 1951*

| INDUSTRIES | No. of Establishments | No. of Employees | Salaries and Wages $000,000 | Average Annual Wage $ | Cost of Materials $000,000 | Net Value of Products $000,000 | Gross Value of Products $000,000 | % of Canadian Total |
|---|---|---|---|---|---|---|---|---|
| 1. Sawmills | 1,564 | 29,462 | 81.8 | 2,780 | 176.7 | 167.0 | 347.1 | 58.5 |
| 2. Pulp and Paper | 11 | 5,778 | 21.9 | 3,800 | 44.9 | 90.8 | 141.5 | 11.4 |
| 3. Fish processing | 63 | 4,168 | 11.3 | 2,720 | 51.6 | 31.5 | 84.1 | 51.6 |
| 4. Slaughtering and Meat Packing | 11 | 1,370 | 4.3 | 3,140 | 52.8 | 6.0 | 59.1 | 6.6 |
| 5. Veneers and Plywoods | 12 | 3,416 | 9.8 | 2,860 | 18.1 | 24.8 | 43.2 | 59.5 |
| 6 Petroleum Products | 6 | 579 | 2.1 | 3,640 | 28.5 | 12.3 | 41.9 | 7.0 |
| 7. Sash, Door and Planing Mills | 166 | 2,770 | 7.2 | 2,600 | 27.1 | 13.8 | 41.3 | 23.1 |
| 8. Misc. Food Preparations | 47 | 782 | 1.6 | 2,050 | 30.2 | 6.3 | 36.6 | 14.1 |
| 9. Fertilizers | 6 | 1,280 | 4.6 | 3,580 | 9.9 | 20.8 | 30.8 | 40.0 |
| 10. Fruit and Vegetable Preparations | 71 | 2,355 | 4.2 | 1,780 | 16.0 | 8.7 | 24.9 | 12.4 |
| Ten Industries | 1,957 | 51,960 | 148.8 | 2,870 | 453.8 | 382.0 | 850.5 | 5.2 |
| All Industries | 3,897 | 93,647 | 262.6 | 2,800 | 789.8 | 592.5 | 1,404.9 | 8.0 |
| Leading Industries as % of All Industries | 50.2 | 55.5 | 51.6 | 102.5 | 57.5 | 64.5 | 60.5 | |

*Non-ferrous metal smelting and refining is a leading industry but statistics are not available.     Data from D.B.S. 1953

bread and milk, are shipped in from Eastern Canada. Iron and steel, the basis of our
present industrial structure, are not processed in British Columbia and this has
retarded the development of secondary
machinery industries. Sugar and petroleum
refineries, typical of industries using overseas raw materials, are located in the port
cities.

Greater Vancouver is the leading manufacturing centre in the province, for several
reasons. It is in the heart of the most active lumbering and fishing area. Saw milling is normally the most important industry. Furthermore, the metropolitan district
contains approximately half the population of the province and manufacturing
concerns have located here to supply this
large market. It is the principal transshipment centre on the Pacific Coast of Canada
and at such a break point between land
and sea transportation, manufacturing invariably develops. Slaughtering and meat
packing, food processing, printing and publishing and sheet metal production are the
most important industries apart from saw
milling. Ship building and aircraft manufacturing, paramount during World War
II, have diminished somewhat in significance.

The manufacture of wood products,
paint and the processing of fish are locally
important in Victoria. In addition, the
city boasts of one of the largest dry docks
in the world, making ship repairing a significant activity. Fruit and vegetable canning
is the only important industrial enterprise
in the Okanagan cities. Pulp and paper
mills are discussed in a previous section on
forest industries. The Trail Smelter is referred to in the section on mining. A very
large aluminum plant has been built on
the northern coast near Kitimat to take advantage of cheap power.

## Transportation

The task of building rail lines and highways in British Columbia was difficult. The
topographic trend in the area is northwest-
southeast and the basic communications
pattern is east-west. Gaps piercing the various mountain ranges became important
arteries. For example, the Fraser Corridor
which traverses the Coast Mountains to
Vancouver is used by two transcontinental
railways and the Trans-Canada Highway
and has great strategic significance. Air
lines, obviously, are less influenced by topography, except indirectly from turbu-
lence, squalls and lack of emergency landing fields due to rough terrain. Coastwise
shipping conforms with topography entirely, in that vessels use the drowned Coastal
Trench, a remarkable inside water passage
from Vancouver to Prince Rupert and
through to Skagway, Alaska.

## Railways

Five railways, the Canadian Pacific, the
Canadian National, the Pacific Great Eastern, the Great Northern and the Northern
Alberta serve Southern British Columbia
(see figure 276). Almost 4,000 miles of
single track have been laid. No railroads
have been built in the northern sections of
the province.

The main line of the *Canadian Pacific
Railway* enters British Columbia from the
east at Kicking Horse Pass (5,337 feet) in
the Canadian Rockies. It then swings
northwest along the Rocky Mountain
Trench from Golden (2,583 feet), to
Beavermouth (2,433 feet), then follows the
Purcell Trench (drained by the Beaver River) southward. Leaving the latter, the line
turns to the west to cross the Selkirk Mountains, climbing to a maximum elevation at
Glacier (3,778 feet). The traverse of the
Selkirks has been facilitated by the construction of a remarkable tunnel under
Rogers Pass. The narrow, tortuous Illecil-
lewaet River Valley is followed as far as
Revelstoke (1,494 feet) where the Selkirk or
Columbia Trench is crossed. An indefinite
valley drained by several rivers, of which
the Eagle is the most important, serves
as a corridor through the Monashee Mountains. The railway then follows the shore

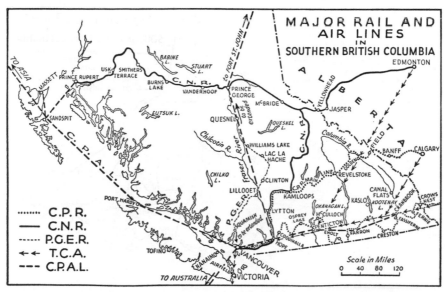

Figure 276. *Railways and Airlines of British Columbia.* Railways must follow very crooked routes through the mountains; airplanes fly straight courses over them.

line of Shuswap Lake and the South Thompson Valley to Kamloops (1,159 feet). There is a gradual descent along the Thompson-Fraser Corridor to Vancouver. In many places, the valley is extremely narrow and steep sided, and tunnels, bridges and cuttings have been necessary.

The *Canadian National Railway* has much easier routes to its coastal termini, Vancouver and Prince Rupert. It crosses the Canadian Rockies through Yellowhead Pass (3,717 feet). It then follows the Fraser River to the Rocky Mountain Trench where it divides: one branch follows the Trench toward the northwest and the other enters the North Thompson Corridor to the south. The latter, after leaving Kamloops, parallels the Canadian Pacific Railway to Vancouver. The northern line follows the Rocky Mountain Trench and enters the Nechako Basin to the west. From Prince George (1,869 feet) it passes along the Nechako, Bulkley, and Skeena Valleys through the Coast Mountains with a relatively easy grade to Prince Rupert.

In the extreme southern part of the province, a secondary Canadian Pacific Railway line, including the *Kettle Valley Railway,* and the *Crowsnest Railway,* roughly parallels the American border from Lethbridge to Vancouver. It enters British Columbia through the Crowsnest Pass (4,450 feet) and ascends and descends every major topographical obstacle in the southern part of the province. Undoubtedly it is one of the most scenic rail routes in the world.

Several branch lines of the two main railways serve the southern interior valleys and the eastern lowlands of Vancouver Island. One independent railway, the *Pacific Great Eastern,* traverses the Coast Mountains and Fraser Plateau from North Vancouver on Burrard Inlet to Prince George. It is being extended to Fort St. John. The *Great Northern Railway* has spur lines entering Southern British Columbia, particularly to Vancouver, Hedley and Nelson. The *Northern Alberta Railway* serves the peace River Block and its northern terminus is Dawson Creek.

### Highways

British Columbia has over 21,000 miles of roadway, of which one-third are classi-

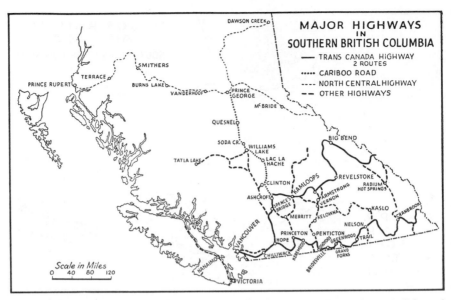

Figure 277. *Major Highways in Southern British Columbia.* The highway builders of British Columbia have performed a stupendous task in linking up the southern part of the province. More good roads, however, are needed.

fied as trunk and main highways. The *Southern Trans-Canada Highway* (see figure 277) follows the Lower Fraser Valley eastward from Vancouver to Hope where it enters the Sumallo and Similkameen Valleys to cross the Cascades and pass through Princeton, Hedley and Keremeos. From the latter point the road crosses the Western Okanagan Highland and descends into the Okanagan Valley at Osoyoos. To the east, it climbs several ranges of the Monashee

D. P. Kerr

Plate 97. The ferry across the Columbia River at Castlegar, British Columbia.

Mountains before reaching Trail and proceeding to Nelson. The motorist must cross Kootenay Lake by ferry to Balfour and then follow the Purcell Trench to Creston. The road has an easy grade through the Purcell Mountains to Cranbrook. It crosses the Rockies via Fernie and the Crowsnest Pass.

The *South-central Trans-Canada Highway* parallels the main line of the Canadian Pacific Railway across British Columbia, except through the Selkirk Mountains. To avoid the high cost of cutting through these ranges, it has used the Selkirk and Rocky Mountain Trenches from Revelstoke to Golden. This portion is known as the Big Bend Highway.

The *North-central Highway* is as yet incomplete. It parallels the Canadian National Railway from Prince Rupert to Prince George via the Skeena-Bulkley-Nechako Corridor. From Prince George one branch goes north along the Crooked River Valley, cutting east to the Pine River Valley through Pine Pass to Dawson Creek. The other route will follow the Rocky

Mountain Trench through McBride and across Yellowhead Pass to Jasper.

*The Cariboo Road,* which traverses the Interior Uplands from Ashcroft to Prince George, is the oldest highway. It was constructed in the 1860's to afford access to the Cariboo gold fields. Other important highways in Southern British Columbia run from Victoria to Campbell River on Vancouver Island; from the American border to Salmon Arm through the Okanagan Valley and from the American border to Golden, along the Rocky Mountain Trench.

*The Alaska Highway* (see figure 278)

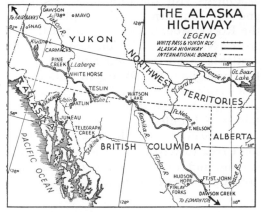

Figure 278. *The Alaska Highway.* The route of the Alaska Highway crosses Northern British Columbia, opening up a vast wilderness area.

runs from Dawson Creek, British Columbia, to Fairbanks, Alaska—a distance of 1,523 miles. Construction began in March 1942 and was completed in November of the same year. It was built as a military highway by the United States, at a cost of $140,000,000, to link airfields and to supply Alaska in the event that the Japanese Navy blockaded the coast. Maintenance and control of the Canadian section of the highway was turned over to the Canadian government on April 1st, 1946. At present, it has a gravelled, all-weather surface and is open the year round.

The road runs northwesterly from Dawson Creek to Fort Nelson on the Tramontane Plains. A few outliers of the Rockies

as high as 4,000 feet, have to be crossed. It turns directly west from Fort Nelson and begins a long climb through the Rocky Mountains. North of Muncho Lake it follows the Liard River Valley, descending into the Liard Plain. Then, following the Rancheria River Valley through the Cassiar Mountains, it traverses the undulating Teslin Plateau to Whitehorse. From this point to the Alaska boundary the highway follows the Takhini and Shakwak Valleys.

### Air Lines

An extensive network of air lines is found in the province. Trans-Canada Air Lines follow a trans-provincial route. Its western terminus is Victoria and eastward flights land at Vancouver and proceed to either Lethbridge, Calgary or Edmonton without stop. Canadian Pacific Air Lines has a main route from Vancouver to Whitehorse via Prince George. Another flight runs between Vancouver and Calgary via Penticton. It recently inaugurated a service between Vancouver and Asia, via the Aleutian Islands and between Vancouver and Australia, via the Hawaiian Islands. Independent companies have scheduled flights to Tofino and other points on the west coast of Vancouver Island and to the Queen Charlotte Islands and the northern coast.

### Shipping

Three main shipping lines serve coastal localities: the Canadian Pacific, the Canadian National and the Union. Tugs and small craft also use the coastal waters. The Vancouver-Victoria route has the heaviest traffic. North-bound shipping follows the Strait of Georgia, Johnstone Strait, Queen Charlotte Sound and Hecate Strait from Vancouver to Prince Rupert. In recent years, volume of shipping along the North Coast has declined. Nearly all passengers move by air. New ferry services have been established between Vancouver and Nanaimo because of the great increase in automobile traffic.

## Tourism

The tourist industry in British Columbia yields an annual revenue of approximately $90,000,000. Over 2,500 people are permanently employed and many thousands more are engaged in tourism during the summer. British Columbia has a greater variety of scenery and more natural advantages for the tourist than any other part of Canada. However it is remote from the large centres of population in eastern America and, furthermore, it faces severe competition from neighboring states to the south which enjoy a similar landscape.

The coastal area combines maritime and mountainous features in unrivalled scenery. Tourists can view the entire panorama from steamships plying the many sheltered passages. No resorts have been built in the middle and northern coastal areas.

On the southern coast, the Vancouver and Victoria areas have natural and cultural attractions. The latter has many characteristics of a small English city and innumerable Americans visit it on that account. Summer trade outranks that of winter, when only a few Canadians from the Prairies and the East come to take advantage of the normally mild climate. Many accommodations including luxury hotels, ski lodges and cabins, are scattered through the Southern Coastal Trench.

The Rocky Mountains attract many tourists each year. The oldest and best known resorts are located at Banff, Lake Louise and Jasper, on the Alberta side of the border. At present, motorists outnumber those coming by train and, consequently, camping grounds, cabins, and lodges have been built near the main highways, not only in Alberta, but also in British Columbia. Fewer tourists visit the Columbia Mountains and the southern Interior Uplands than the Rocky Mountains or Southern Coastal areas. Nevertheless, accommodations are available in all the towns and, in particular, throughout the Okanagan Valley.

Recently, the Alaska Highway has opened Northern British Columbia for the tourist. Scheduled buses, with night stopovers, operate along the road from Dawson Creek to Whitehorse and on to Alaska. Cabins and other accommodations have been built for the motorist.

## Selected References

Angus, H. F., F. W. Howay, and W. N. Sage. *British Columbia and United States: the North Pacific Slope from Fur Trade to Aviation.* 1943.

Carrothers, W. A., *The British Columbia Fisheries.* University of Toronto Press. Toronto. 1941.

Carrothers, W. A., *Forest Industries of British Columbia,* in A.R.M. Lower, *The North American Assault on the Canadian Forest,* pp. 227-344. Macmillan Company of Canada. Toronto. 1938.

Currie, A. W., *Economic Geography of Canada,* (Chapter V, The Cordilleran Region). Macmillan Company of Canada. Toronto. 1947.

Freeman, O. W., and H. H. Martin. *The Pacific Northwest.* John Wiley and Sons, New York. 1942.

This book contains several sections on the physical and economic geography of British Columbia, written by the late Dr. Gordon Davis, who was this author's first instructor in geography.

Geological Survey of Canada. *Geology and Economic Minerals of Canada.* Economic Geology, Series No. 1. Ottawa. 1947.

Hudson, S. C., et al, *Types of Farming in Canada.* Dept. of Agriculture, Publication 825, Farmer's Bulletin 157. Ottawa. 1949.

Innis, H. A. *Settlement and the Mining Frontier,* in *Canadian Frontiers of Settlement* (chapters on the Kootenay region, pp. 270-320). Macmillan Company of Canada. Toronto. 1936.

Jones, S. B. *Recreation Regions of the Canadian Rocky Mountains.* Bulletin of the Geographic Society of Philadelphia. July, 1936.

Mulholland, F. D. *Forest Resources of British Columbia.* British Columbia Dept. of Lands and Forests. Victoria. 1937.

Ormsby, M. A. *The History of Agriculture in British Columbia,* Scientific Agriculture 20, September, 1939.

Taylor, Griffith. *Canada, An Advanced Text* Methuen, London. 1947.

*Transactions of the Second Resources Conference.* Dept. of Lands and Forests. Victoria. 1949.

This memoir contains excellent articles on the agricultural, mining, fishing and forest industries of British Columbia. Other articles include soils, water power and energy, recreation and wildlife.

The reader is also referred to the bulletins on soils, listed at the end of Chapter 19. They contain information on agriculture in the areas which have been surveyed.

# CHAPTER 21

# Regions and Cities of British Columbia

WITHIN the last century, an exceedingly diversified landscape has emerged in British Columbia. The intensively cultivated, irrigated plots of the Okanagan contrast strongly with the large cattle ranches of the Cariboo; the densely populated Lower Fraser Valley stands out against the rest of the province which, with few exceptions, is sparsely settled; the industrial city of Trail has a personality distinct from that of the many frontier towns like Prince George and Dawson Creek.

Regional differentiation has been established. Each geographic region has characteristics, both natural and cultural, which set it apart from neighboring areas, but the basic and controlling influence in British Columbia is that of topography. Figure 279 depicts seven regions: The Southern Coastal Trench, the Coast Region, the Fra-

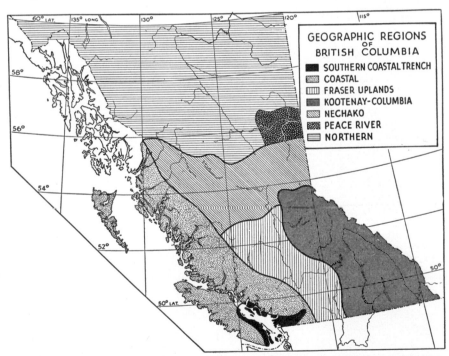

Figure 279. *Geographic Regions of British Columbia.* The southern part of British Columbia contains six more or less recognizable regions in which human-use patterns have become fairly well adjusted. The north is differentiated by its lack of human population.

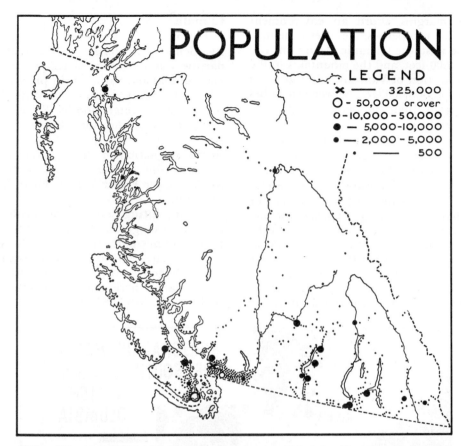

Figure 280.  *Population Distribution of Southern British Columbia.* The greatest concentration of population is in the southern part of the coastal trench. Other smaller concentrations are found in the interior valleys.

ser Uplands, the Kootenay-Columbia Region, the Nechako Plateau, the Peace River Area, and, Northern British Columbia. They are described in the following sections.

## 1. The Southern Coastal Trench

Although it is the smallest, the Southern Coastal Trench is the most important geographic region in British Columbia. It consists of two somewhat separate sections; the Lower Fraser Valley, and the lowlands of the east coast of Vancouver Island and the Gulf Islands. Two large cities, Vancouver and Victoria, dominate these areas, but each contains a number of smaller

urban municipalities as well. Approximately 75% of the people of the province (see figure 280) live in this region which, also, contains 35% of the cultivated land, many of the manufacturing industries, and practically all of the wholesale trading establishments. Furthermore, it is the location of the leading political, educational and cultural institutions of the province.

### Structure

Structurally, the region is part of the Puget Sound Lowland, an intermountain basin, virtually enclosed by mountain ranges, extending from Tacoma, in the State of Washington, to Powell River. The central, and greater portion, has been drowned, but the margins afford an environment suitable for prosperous, close settlement.

To the west, the Olympic Mountains rise to over 5,000 feet, and the mountains in the southern section of Vancouver Island reach an elevation of 3,000 feet. Between them lies the Strait of Juan de Fuca, a water-gate which permits direct access from the Pacific to the cities of Tacoma, Seattle, Vancouver and Victoria (see figure 281).

On the east, the Coast and Cascade Mountains ascend abruptly to elevations of 6,000 feet, while, between them, the Fraser River occupies a deep, narrow and scenic canyon. This corridor is followed by all important land communication systems, linking Vancouver with the interior of the province and with all eastern centres. Without it, Vancouver would have been just another isolated little coastal town.

## Climate

The region possesses strong climatic unity, being characterized throughout by a narrow seasonal range of temperature and marked seasonal variation in precipitation.

Cloudy, rainy weather prevails during the fall and winter months. From time to time, the intensification of either the Pacific or the Interior anticyclone will result in the stagnation of the air over the lowlands causing nocturnal fogs, particularly in the Lower Fraser Valley. There is little snowfall.

In the spring, rainfall diminishes and temperatures gradually rise. Many plants grow intermittently throughout the winter but, by late February, all vegetation is normally active. Spring flowers and shrubs bloom earlier here, than in any other place in Canada. July and August are dry, and

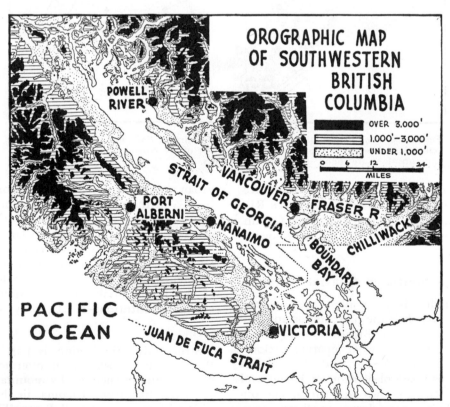

Figure 281. *Orography of Southwestern British Columbia.* This map outlines the relief of this area and emphasizes the small area of land favourable for human habitation.

irrigation is needed, particularly in the Victoria area. These mild and cloudless months have great appeal to the tourist.

Total rainfall, however, varies greatly over the region. Victoria is the driest city with 27 inches annually; Vancouver receives 60 inches; North Vancouver, 80 inches; while the lower mountain slopes get 120 inches per annum (see figure 282).

### Vegetation

The climate encourages the growth of a luxuriant vegetation. Most of the original forest has been removed, but the Douglas firs and western red cedars in Stanley Park give evidence of its former grandeur. In the driest areas, around Victoria, a more open forest prevails, in which such trees as madrona and Garry oak indicate a similarity to some Mediterranean environments.

## Vancouver

Vancouver is the leading city of the region. It has a population of 345,000, making it not only the largest city in British Columbia, but third in all of Canada. The metropolitan district embraces 670,000 people.

### Site Factors

Burrard Inlet, a remarkably deep fiord, provides an ice-free harbour which is the city's major asset (see figure 283). The city is situated on a rolling upland between it and the flat delta of the Fraser River, to the south. North of the inlet rise the rugged peaks of the Coast Range, providing a very scenic background. Few cities in the world can equal its superb natural setting.

Although its climate is broadly classified as maritime, Vancouver has many microclimates. For example, average annual rainfall varies from 40 inches at the Airport (5 feet), located on the Fraser delta, to 140 inches at Seymour Falls (700 feet), 10 miles to the north on the slopes of the Coast Mountains. Dense radiation fogs which form most frequently during the autumn and early winter are confined almost entirely to low lying areas below 200 feet. Upland districts, such as Shaughnessy Heights, Point Grey and Burnaby Heights, rarely have fog. Gales often blow in the open straits to the west of the city, but the harbour area is well protected from gusts and squally weather.

### Historical Factors

Vancouver is a young city. Hastings Saw Mill, built in 1865, was the first permanent settlement on Burrard Inlet. Apart from the saw mill a few small settlements fringed the Inlet, collectively known at various times as "Granville," "Gastown," "Liverpool," "Hastings," etc. Incorporation oc-

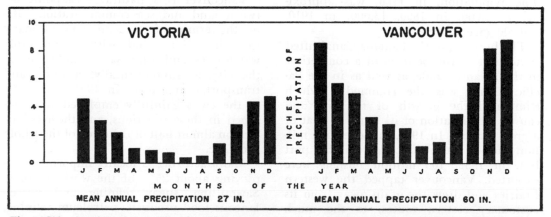

Figure 282. *Precipitation at Victoria and Vancouver.* Both in the coastal trench, both have definite summer minima, but Victoria is directly in the lee of the Vancouver Island Mountains while Vancouver lies to windward of the Coast Range and gets much more rain, especially in winter.

Plate 98.   The Lions, spectacular mountain peaks in the Coast Range, north of Vancouver.

curred in 1886 and Vancouver was chosen as the name of the new town in memory of the first British explorer to visit the area. New Westminster and Victoria had been booming frontier towns for about 25 years but their supremacy was soon lost to the new city. The completion of the Canadian Pacific Railway initiated a rapid growth. The population, in 1886, was approximately 1,000; in 1890, 13,000; in 1910, 100,000 (See figure 271).

The building of the Panama Canal lifted Vancouver to the position of a competitor in the Atlantic trade, as well as in the Pacific. Grain was the commodity which stimulated the growth of the city and caused the elevation of its status to that of a great seaport. In 1921, just over one million bushels were shipped from this port but, in 1932, 105 million bushels were exported. Vancouver tapped the western Prairies and drew the grain away from its customary eastern routes, to the much cheaper western route to Europe via the Panama Canal. Nine large grain elevators

on Burrard Inlet reflect the importance of this commodity in the economy of the port. The population increased from 163,000 in 1921 to 246,000 by 1931. Lumber and fish products remained significant exports throughout its history.

### Functions

Vancouver is a natural breakpoint between land and sea communications. Being the terminus for two railways and many steamship lines, and with innumerable warehouses and wholesale establishments, the city is, fundamentally, a trade and transportation centre. In 1951, over 31% of the city's gainfully employed were engaged in these functions, and the city carried on almost half of the trade of the whole province.

Manufacturing is locally important, employing about 25% of the working force. Sawmilling, sugar refining and miscellaneous food products, petroleum refining, fish processing, metal work and machinery, printing and publishing were leading industries in 1954. Under wartime conditions shipbuilding was of major importance. In 1954, there were 1,300 manufacturing establishments, employing 34,400 workers, producing goods with a gross value of $487,000,000 and a net value of about $208,000,000.

The educational function of Vancouver is represented by the University of British Columbia, which is situated in the extreme western part of the city, overlooking the sea. Founded in 1915, it has a student body of about 7,000, having grown very rapidly since 1946.

## Urban Landscapes

The most important section of the city is the port area adjoining Burrard Inlet. Intermingled with large docks, elevators and storage plants are many industries. Another industrial zone is found in the False Creek Lowland where industry is diversified. The commercial core, including retail and wholesale districts, is situated on a rise of land between False Creek and Burrard Inlet. The Chinese Quarter, second in size to San Francisco's in North America, is a colourful section on the eastern edge of the commercial zone.

The residential city has spread from its first settlement along Burrard Inlet, southward until it covers most of the upland area between the harbour and the Fraser River. Shaughnessy Heights, Drummond Drive,

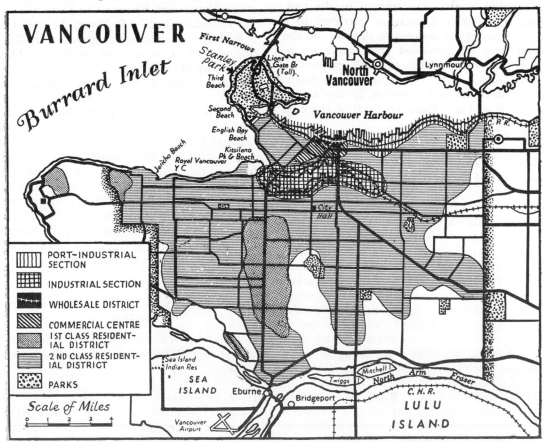

Figure 283. *Functional Plan of Vancouver.* Beginning on the south shore of the harbour where the downtown section is still located, the city has grown completely over the peninsula between Burrard Inlet and the Fraser River. Important suburbs are found also on the north shore of the harbour.

and the University Heights are first class districts. Shaughnessy, set aside by the Canadian Pacific Railway Company for residential purposes, is the most extensive and modern area. The other two have unparalleled views of the Inlet and the Coast Mountains. The "West End", adjacent to Stanley Park, is a separate district of old, large, houses built a half century ago. Many are now used as boarding houses or apartments.

Second class residential districts such as Dunbar, Kitsilano, Kerrisdale, Point Grey, Fairview and South Vancouver, have neat, well-kept and well-spaced houses. Flower gardens decorate all homes from the largest mansion to the most humble dwelling. Crowded houses, so common in the east, are rarely seen. Slums are restricted to a few areas in the downtown district and the east end. A diversified area, made up of scattered farms, Chinese truck gardens, a few houses, golf courses and some industrial development, appears in the southeastern and southwestern parts of the city.

## Suburban Areas

Several smaller communities, whose life is very closely tied in with Vancouver, are situated to the north, east and south of the city proper. *North Vancouver* is an industrial and residential suburb on the north shore of Burrard Inlet, at the foot of the towering Coast Mountains. Shipbuilding and saw milling are the main manufacturing industries. North Vancouver City has a population of 20,000, while the adjacent municipality has over 27,000. *West Vancouver* is spread out along Burrard Inlet to the west of North Vancouver and its population is over 20,000. It is a residential suburb with many beautiful houses, including those in British Pacific Properties—a well-developed subdivision on the south-facing slope of Hollyburn Mountain. *Burnaby* is a large municipality located just east of Vancouver. It is a residential suburb which has not as yet been incorporated into the city. Its population is about 85,000. *Port Moody* is a small community situated at the head

of Burrard Inlet, about 12 miles east of Vancouver, with a population of 2,800. It was selected as the terminus of the Canadian Pacific Railway in 1884, but was later abandoned in favour of Vancouver. The town has a few saw mills, and oil refineries are found at Ioco across the Inlet.

## New Westminster

New Westminster is an important seaport, located on the Fraser River, about 12 miles southeast of Vancouver. Formerly the capital of the Mainland of British Columbia, it relinquished the position after the coalition in 1866, when Victoria became the capital of the entire Province. Its growth has been slow but steady since 1886, when Vancouver became the terminus of the Canadian Pacific Railway. At present, it is chiefly a manufacturing and a trading centre, with a population of 32,000. The processing of lumber and fish products are the main manufacturing enterprises. In 1950 the city had 100 factories which employed 6,300 workers and produced goods with a gross value of $92,790,000, and a net value of $41,000,000.

The city has been built on the north bank of the Fraser River. The commercial core is on the first terrace about 50 feet above the river. Residential sections penetrate northward to over 200 feet. New Westminster has extended along the Kingsway and Grandview highways, leading to Vancouver, until the two cities are virtually one.

## Other Towns Of The Lower Fraser Valley

There are numerous small trading centres, scattered throughout the Lower Fraser Valley.

*Chilliwack* (7,500) is the largest town. It is located on the Canadian National Railway, 60 miles east of Vancouver. It is the chief centre for the Sumas Prairie district and for the extreme east of the valley. *Mission* (3,000) has an intermediate location, about 40 miles east of Vancouver.

*Port Coquitlam* (5,000), *Abbotsford, Langley Praire* and *Ladner* are less important local centres. *Steveston,* on the southwest corner of Lulu Island, is a fishing village and the site of a small naval establishment.

## Powell River

Powell River is an important paper mill town, located on the east shore of the Strait of Georgia, 85 miles northwest of Vancouver. It is built on a hillside between Powell Lake and the Strait, from which the main street ascends abruptly. Powell Lake is situated 200 feet above sea level and supplies fresh water to the mill. Its outlet has been dammed for the generation of hydro-electric power. The urban area, comprising the company town and three residential suburbs, *Westview, Cranberry Lake* and *Wildwood,* has a population of 10,000. No highway or railway connects the town with Vancouver and communication is by sea and air only.

## Victoria

Victoria, the capital of British Columbia, is the second largest city in the Southern Coastal Trench Region. It is situated at the southeastern extremity of Vancouver Island, 80 miles southwest of Vancouver.

The older part of the city lies along the edge of a sheltered cove; recent residential expansion has followed the low and rocky coastline. Local topography is diversified with many hills, small lakes, strips of level land and, most significantly, two deep harbours. Victoria Harbour, within the old part of the city, is the centre of port activities and Esquimalt Bay, to the west of the city, has a naval yard equipped with one of the largest dry docks in the world.

Because Victoria had a deep, ice-free harbour, a good fresh water supply, and potential agricultural land that was easy to clear, it was chosen for a Hudson's Bay Company fur trading post in 1843. Fort Victoria remained a small town until 1858, when gold was discovered in the Cariboo. Since it was the only accessible, settled port, miners made the town their headquarters and, consequently, the population began to grow (See figure 271). Victoria remained the principal commercial town of the province until 1886; from that time it grew steadily, but could not match the rapid pace of Vancouver. In 1956 the population of the city was 54,600.

### Functions

Victoria is a port, but is more important as a political and tourist centre, and as a

*Courtesy British Columbia Travel Bureau*

Plate 99.   The Inner Harbour of Victoria, seen from the top of the Parliament Building.

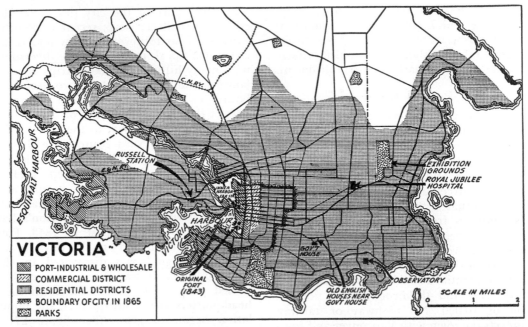

Figure 284. *Functional Plan of Victoria*. Beginning as a small settlement on the east shore of Victoria Harbour in 1843, the city has spread across both adjoining peninsulas.

city of retired people. The metropolitan district, including Esquimalt and Oak Bay, has a population of about 126,000. It is a trading headquarters for that part of Vancouver Island south of Nanaimo. Agricultural, forestry, mining and fishing products from this area are shipped to Victoria. Fruit, fish, logs and wood pulp are the main exports. Manufacturing is relatively unimportant. In 1954, there were 200 establishments, employing 4,900 persons, producing a gross value of $58,000,000 and a net value of $31,000,000.

### Urban Landscapes

The commercial core of Victoria is located in the old Fort district and its margins (see figure 284). A small wholesale and industrial district is found to the immediate north, along the upper stretches of the harbour; the docks to the south, in the central harbour section; the parliament buildings to the southeast, overlooking the harbour. The remainder of the city is made up of residential districts, parks and mili-

tary establishments. Houses or apartments are not crowded, even in the poorest areas. The finest houses are situated in Uplands, an exclusive residential section overlooking the Gulf of Georgia. Other large homes are found mainly along the shoreline, where a magnificent view is unimpaired. Old English manors are situated in the Government House district. Beacon Hill is a splendid park near the downtown area. Small farms, found chiefly to the north, supply the city with dairy and vegetable products.

Although English culture has made an imprint on the landscape in the form of carefully managed gardens, narrow, winding streets, fine speciality shops and unmistakable house-types, Victoria is essentially a modern Canadian city which moves at a slightly slower pace than the average North American metropolis.

### Nanaimo

Nanaimo is a small port on the east coast of Vancouver Island, 40 miles due west of Vancouver and 60 miles due north-west of Victoria. It was founded as a coal mining village in 1854. Later, it became the first terminus of the Esquimalt and Nanaimo Railway, and an important regional centre for the surrounding agricultural district. The commercial part of the city is located on a narrow terrace behind the bay. Saw mills, and ship building yards are located in the harbour area. A large pulp and paper mill has recently begun to operate. Residential districts extend westward from the industrial zone. The population, in 1956 was approximately 12,700.

## Other Towns on the East Coast of Vancouver Island

*Courtenay, Comox* and *Cumberland* lie in close proximity, forming a ring of settlement around Comox Bay, 140 miles, by rail, northwest of Victoria. They have a combined population of about 6,000. Coal, mining, agriculture, trade and tourism are the important activities of the area. Between Nanaimo and Cumberland, *Qualicum Beach* is a famous resort. *Ladysmith* (2,100), *Chemainus* and *Duncan* (3,200) are the chief centres along the Esquimalt and Nanaimo Railway. *Sidney* (1,400) is a fishing centre on the Saanich Peninsula and has direct car ferry service to Steveston across the strait.

## Regional Relations

Viewing the whole North American scene, most geographers disregard the political boundary which bisects this basin. The landscapes, the economic problems and the people, are similar, on both sides of the border. The relations of each segment as the Pacific outlet of its own country also bear considerable resemblance. Vancouver is Canada's western gateway, through which passes a very active trade.

In contrast with this intense activity, there is, in all the towns and cities of the Coastal Trench, a large contingent of retired folk from the Prairie Provinces, Eastern Canada, and even from the British

Isles, who find, in this mild climate, an ideal place to spend their declining years.

## II. The Coastal Region

The Coastal Region comprises the rest of Vancouver Island, the Queen Charlotte Islands and the seaward slopes of the Coast Mountains. Only three per cent of the population of British Columbia is scattered throughout this large area. Most people live in Prince Rupert and Port Alberni, with the remainder residing in pulp and paper towns, fishing villages, logging camps and mining communities.

### Physical Factors

Along most of the coast, the mountains descend steeply to the sea. With the exception of the Graham Island Plain, in the northeastern corner of the Queen Charlotte Islands, little land is available for agricultural use. Heavy precipitation falls on the area during most of the year. A slight rainfall minimum occurs in early summer, but there is seldom any water deficiency. Snow accumulates very rapidly in winter, along the middle and upper slopes, but very little falls in the low-lying areas. On the average, temperatures near the water remain above freezing in the cool season, and, consequently, some plants grow during most of the winter. A luxuriant coniferous forest has emerged in response to this climatic environment. It mantles the seaward inclines of the Coastal Mountains upwards to 4,500 feet.

### Economic Factors

Forest industries dominate the economic geography of the region. Most trees are cut in the southern districts, but, of late, more activity is taking place in northern areas. Fishing and mining industries are locally important, while agriculture is virtually non-existent.

### Prince Rupert

Prince Rupert is the largest town in the region. Its site, as a terminal port for the railway from Prince George, was chosen on Kaien Island, near the mouth of the Skeena River. In 1906, a city plan was designed to accommodate a population of 50,-000. Many expected the port to rival Vancouver, since it was situated closer to Asia, on the Great Circle Route. It did not grow according to expectations, stagnating with a population of about 7,000 for many years but, because of prosperous economic conditions in the last decade, its population has risen to 10,500. Fish processing is the chief industry but a new celanese plant, located at Port Edward, will undoubtedly influence the growth of Prince Rupert. In 1950, there were 25 manufacturing establishments with a net value of production of $3,000,000 and a total employment of 560.

## Port Alberni and Alberni

Port Alberni and Alberni, with a combined population of 14,500, are twin towns located at the head of Alberni Canal, a continuation of Barkley Sound, on the west coast of Vancouver Island. They form a regional centre for extensive forest industries. Large saw mills and wood working plants are located in the towns. The net value of manufacturing was over $20,000,-000, in 1954, and over 2,500 men were employed.

## Ocean Falls

Ocean Falls is situated at the head of Cousins Inlet, which is an extension of Dean Channel, along the northern coast, approximately 350 miles northwest of Vancouver. A large pulp and paper mill supports a population of about 2,200. This company town has good services, including schools, churches and a hotel.

## Coastal Villages

The coastal region contains several small villages. Indians live in many of them and, in addition, have a few villages of their own. Since fishing is the main function of most villages, and water vessels and seaplanes are the only forms of transportation, they are situated at or near tide-water.

On the west coast of Vancouver Island, *Tofino, Clayoquot, Kyuquot* and *Quatsino* are tiny villages, each with a population under 400. The gold mine at *Zeballos* normally supports a few hundred people. *Port Alice* has a population of several hundred, many of whom work in the pulp mill.

On the northeastern coast of Vancouver Island, *Campbell River, Alert Bay* and *Port Hardy* are supply centres for logging camps and fishing vessels. A large airport has been built near the latter point.

Along the middle coast, *Rivers Inlet, Bella Bella,* and *Bella Coola* are very small settlements. A new town has been built at *Kitimat* to house the employees of the large aluminum plant. Population has quickly risen to over 10,000.

On the northern coast, the mining industry supports *Premier* and *Stewart.* Along the Skeena Valley, *Terrace* (1,500), is a small community located 90 miles east of Prince Rupert on the Canadian National Railway.

*Massett, Queen Charlotte City* and *Port Clements,* are very small settlements located on Graham Island in the Queen Charlotte group. Fishing and forestry are the principal industries. *Skidegate* is an old village of the Haida Indians. Airports have been built at *Sandspit* and near Massett.

## III. The Fraser Uplands

The Fraser Upland Region is situated between the Coast-Cascade Mountains, on the west, and the Columbia Mountains, on the east, and extends northwestward from the American border to latitude 53°. In reality, it forms the northern segment of the grazing and irrigated crops region of North America, a major geographic region linked by rough topography and a dry climate.

### Physical Factors

Most of the region is a rolling upland, ranging from 3,000 to 6,000 feet above sea level. Deep, narrow valleys, incised as much as 4,000 feet below the upland surface, contain the transportation routes and most of the population, numbering approximately 140,000.

Lying in the direct lee of the Western Mountains, the entire area has a semi-arid climate. The valleys receive less than 15 inches of precipitation annually and, on the whole, irrigation is necessary for any agricultural activity. Here, the natural vegetation is grass, and in the most arid areas where the rainfall is less than 10 inches annually, it consists of drought-resistant bushes such as sagebrush. Slightly higher precipitation (20 inches) is normally recorded in the uplands and, consequently, a forest cover replaces the grasslands of the valleys.

## Contrasting Landscapes

The contrasts in landscape between the coast and the interior are sharp. In a traverse of the Fraser and Thompson River Valleys, the route of the transcontinental railways and the trans-Canada highway from Vancouver to Salmon Arm, the traveller passes from the damp meadowlands of the Lower Fraser Valley, through the dense Coast Forest near Yale, to the forest-grassland transition at Lytton. Eastward, one passes through the grasslands near Ashcroft and a sagebrush cover just east of that point. Irrigated orchards appear east of Kamloops, while the cool, damp forest along the western slopes of the Columbia Mountains near Salmon Arm, indicates the abrupt termination of the dry belt.

## Okanagan Valley

The Okanagan is the most important valley in the region (See figure 285). Most of the terraces which flank the valley sides are intensively utilized for fruit growing. In summer, these vivid green patches stand out clearly against the brown, unirrigated grazing lands. Lakes occupy much of the valley bottom, but vegetables and small fruits are cultivated in a few low-lying sections. Behind the valley in the highlands, numerous small lakes serve as reservoirs

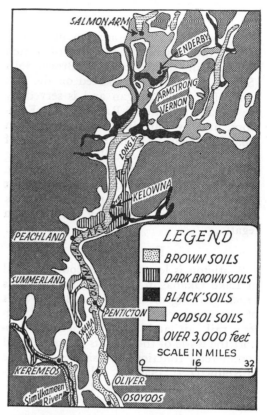

Figure 285. *The Okanagan District*. The long trench-like depression in the plateau, which contains Okanagan Lake, is the chief area of settlement in the Fraser Plateau. It is semi-arid in the south, but water for irrigation is obtainable from the surrounding highlands.

to supply the farms with irrigation water by a simple gravity process.

The population of this prosperous valley has been increasing steadily since 1892, when only 400 people lived in the area. At the present time the population is 75,000, of which more than half is urban. Settlement is by no means uniform throughout the trench, but is concentrated in several rural-urban communities. The size of each urban centre depends directly upon the extent and prosperity of its rural hinterland. Such places as Kelowna, Penticton and Vernon are to be considered among the exceptionally attractive and pleasant small cities of Canada.

## Kelowna

Kelowna, with a population of 10,000, is the chief distributing centre of a rich fruit growing district on Dark Brown Soils (See figure 285). It is located on the east bank of Lake Okanagan and is served by the Canadian National Railway from Kamloops, and by Canadian Pacific barges on Lake Okanagan to Penticton. A number of industries, such as saw milling, box making and fruit canning, are found in the city. Net value of production, in 1954, was about $2,800,000. A thriving tourist industry is highlighted each August by the Kelowna regatta.

## Penticton

Penticton is located at the southern end of Lake Okanagan. It serves a prosperous peach growing district on the Brown Soils of the southern Okanagan Valley. Excellent rail, air and highway facilities support the trade of the city. Its industrial and commercial functions are similar to those of Kelowna. In 1954, net value of manufacturing was $2,000,000 and in 1956, the population numbered almost 12,000.

## Vernon

Vernon (9,000) is an important trade city in the heart of the Black Soils area, near the northern end of Lake Okanagan. Diversified farming characterizes the environs of Vernon, but apple growing dominates. Canneries, creameries and other small industries, which are complementary to the agriculture of the area, have located in the city. Net value of production, in 1954, was about $2,000,000. The tourist industry is greatly encouraged by an active bureau. The Canadian National Railway serves the city.

### Small Towns in the Okanagan Valley

Oliver (1,000) and Osoyoos (900) are the main towns in the extreme southern section of the valley. Vegetables and small fruits are raised under irrigation on Brown Soils, where the growing season is very long and the summer is the hottest and driest in Canada. To the south, in the state of Washington, a similar landscape obtains.

Summerland (4,000) is located just northwest of Penticton. It is a small distributing centre and contains a large government experimental farm.

Armstrong (1,200), Enderby (1,000) and Salmon Arm (1,400) are trade and transportation centres in the more humid northern quarter of the Valley. Mixed farming has developed on the Podzolic Soils of the area.

## Other Districts

The other valleys in the Fraser Upland region contain scattered settlements. A few irrigated orchards dot the landscape in the South Thompson Valley, but, in the main, most of the land throughout the region is used for cattle ranching.

## Kamloops

Kamloops is the most important city outside of the Okanagan Valley. It is located at the confluence of the North and South Thompson Rivers and is a focal point of routes. Both the Canadian Pacific Railway and the Canadian National Railway use the city as a divisional point. Kamloops is the distribution centre for a wide area. Founded as a Hudson's Bay post in 1812, it was incorporated as a city in 1893 and, in 1956, it had a population of 13,500. Only 400 people were engaged in manufacturing in 1954 and the net value of production was only $2,000,000. A large sanatorium is located a few miles from the city at Tranquille.

### Other Towns

Toward the west in the Thompson Valley, Ashcroft, Spences Bridge and Lytton are small trading centres, each with a population under 1,000. Keremeos (500) in the Similkameen Valley, Merrit (1,800) in the Nicola Valley, and Lillooet (1,000) in the Fraser Valley, are the only other towns of any significance in the southern part of the region.

The Cariboo and Chilcotin districts have many large cattle ranches. The Pacific Great Eastern Railway traverses the area and serves such small communities as *Clinton* (500) and *Williams Lake* (1,800). Many cattle are shipped from the latter town each fall. *Quesnel* (2,500) is also located on the railway and supplies gold mining and lumbering camps.

## IV. The Kootenay-Columbia Region

The Kootenay-Columbia Region comprises the southeastern angle of British Columbia, with an area of about 40,000 square miles. The topography is mountainous, since the area includes the Rocky Moun-

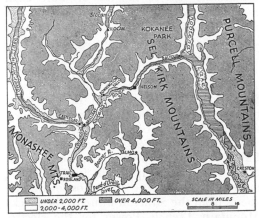

Figure 286. *The Kootenay District.* The Purcell and Selkirk trenches are also areas of settlement; not quite so arid as the Okanagan, nevertheless, they have a number of irrigated areas also. The lakes were formerly very important for transportation.

tain, Purcell, Selkirk and Monashee ranges, with their intervening trenches and transverse valleys (See figure 286). Transportation routes and practically all settlements are confined to these narrow lowlands. Because of the greater elevation of the mountain masses, the climate, on the whole, is more humid than that of the Fraser Uplands. Forests cover the mountain slopes to elevations of over 6,000 feet. Some of the

[1] Kirk, D. W. *Moisture Regions in the East Kootenay Lowlands of British Columbia.* Scientific Agriculture 31, pp. 15-24, 1951.

valleys, however, are relatively dry, and irrigation is necessary for successful farming. Kirk[1] has pointed out the correlation of elevation, moisture supply and vegetation in the Rocky Mountain Trench.

The region contains about eight percent of the population of the province. Mining is the most important industry. From Wells in the Cariboo Mountains, southeastward to Kimberley in the Purcell Mountains, through to Fernie in the Rocky Mountain area, mining dominates the scene. The early settlements were all mining camps, many of them have practically become "ghost towns", although a few, with larger resources, have become the small cities of the present day.

Lumbering is important locally, and the tourist trade continues to increase. Some farming is carried on in the valleys, while the lower slopes of the mountains are used, as well as the valleys, for the grazing of cattle and sheep.

There are few Canadian landscapes with more variety, or with such unique and well-differentiated geographic personality. The "sea of mountains", topped by ice fields and snow capped peaks, the great longitudinal trenches with their rivers and lakes, the scattered farming settlements, power plants, mines and small cities combine to form one of the most scenic regions in North America, if not in the whole world.

### The Doukhobors

The numerous Doukhobor settlements of the Kootenay, Columbia and Kettle valleys are a peculiar feature of the cultural landscape. These Russian-speaking people came, first, to the Canadian prairies in the 1890's. A little later, a number of them moved to the interior valleys of British Columbia, believing that the isolation would help them to preserve, intact, their religious tenets and their peculiar communal way of living. All real estate is owned, and all outside business is done, by the community, through its leaders. Canadian ideas have been rather slow to penetrate the community, even though school attendance is compulsory.

One sect, "the Sons of Freedom", has caused a great deal of trouble, burning homes, schools and other public buildings, and staging nude parades in the nearby settlements. Their actions are repudiated by the community, which is unable to exercise any control over them.

There are, also, many independent Doukhobors. Although still holding similar religious beliefs, they have left the community to follow a more Canadian way of life as independent farmers, or as industrial workers in the nearby towns.

D. P. Kerr

Plate 100. A typical pair of Doukhobor houses near Brilliant, British Columbia.

Doukhobor settlements are conspicuous by reason of their house type. The houses resemble the large, square, plain, two-storey wooden farmhouses common in Eastern Ontario. They stand in pairs, while behind them is a large quadrangle, enclosed by one-storey sheds, which also contain living quarters. Each of these "villages" usually has a population of about forty persons, constituting a multiple-family group. Each village is presided over by a headman, who is responsible to the community headquarters.

The community headquarters, located at Brilliant, overlooks the junction of the Kootenay and Columbia Rivers. Here, in addition to residences, halls and offices, a large packing and canning plant was built by the community. The tomb of Peter

Verigin, former leader of the colony, sits on the hillside above.

Although they have attempted to carry on somewhat the same type of irrigated farming as other settlers in these valleys, their agricultural techniques have been rather primitive, and the full development of their lands has been retarded. The presence of this unassimilated group is, also, to be regarded as a distinct problem in the social organization of the region.

## Trail

*Trail* (11,500) is the largest city in the region. It is located in the Selkirk Trench, a few miles north of the American border. Mountains rise to heights of more than 5,000 feet in the immediate vicinity of the city, which is built upon a series of Pleistocene terraces, bordering the Columbia River.

The town is dominated by the huge smelter of the Consolidated Mining and Smelting Company. Behind it, also on a higher terrace, is the fertilizer plant, operated by the same company. The first smelter was built in 1895 to treat local ores. Later, as local supplies became exhausted, other ones were shipped in from outlying mines. At the present time, most of the ore comes from the Sullivan mine in the Rocky Mountain Trench. Power for the electrolytic refining process is supplied from plants on the Kootenay and Pend d'Oreille rivers. Trail is a rather smoky, unattractive city, but *Rossland* (4,600), formerly a noted mining camp, is a pleasant residential suburb, located in the uplands, a few miles to the west.

## Nelson

*Nelson* (7,300) is the second largest city in the region. It is picturesquely located on the West Arm of Kootenay Lake, about 50 miles northeast of Trail. Mountains, over 5,000 feet in elevation, virtually rim the settlement; while, a few miles to the north, Mount Kokanee (9,400 feet) dominates the rugged grandeur of Kokanee Glacier Park. An older settlement than

Trail, Nelson is the leading commercial centre and the seat of justice for the district. Nucleus of an early mining district, it was, for a time, the site of a smelter. During its history, Nelson has seen the rise and fall of many mining ventures, but has always maintained its position as a financial and trading centre. Lumbering and fruit growing are the industries of the surrounding valleys. Nelson is served by the Canadian Pacific and Great Northern railways. For a long time, Nelson was the terminus of steamship services on Kootenay Lake. There are a number of small manufacturing plants, the gross value of whose products in 1954, was $6,300,000, with a net value of $3,300,000.

## Other Centres

*Grand Forks* (2,000) is a small railway and trading centre in the Kettle Valley, about 40 miles west of Trail. Formerly the site of a large copper smelter, it is now a service and distribution point for the surrounding agricultural district.

*Creston* (1,900) is the leading town in the Purcell Trench. Located to the south of Kootenay Lake, near the delta of the Kootenay River, it serves the rich wheat-growing area of dyked, alluvial land, as well as the thriving fruit and mixed farms of the terraces and valley slopes.

*Kaslo* (700), on the northeast shore of Kootenay Lake, is the centre of a small fruit-growing and mining district. *New Denver* (800), *Slocan* (400), and *Silverton* are small mining villages. A pulp and paper mill is being built at *Castlegar* (1,700).

*Revelstoke* has a population of 3,500 and is located on the Columbia River. It is a divisional point on the main line of the Canadian Pacific Railway and the southwestern terminus of the Big Bend Highway. Some farming is practised to the south in a lowland which runs north from Upper Arrow Lake. Mountainous scenery in the Revelstoke area is outstanding. Many peaks over 8,000 feet high may be seen from the town.

Several significant towns are located in the Rocky Mountain Trench. *Cranbrook* (4,500), is an important lumber centre in the western edge of the trench, in its southern section. It is served by the Canadian Pacific Railway. Some farming and ranching take place near the town. Value of manufactured products in 1954 was just under $2,500,000. *Kimberley* is a mining town located on the eastern flank of the Purcell Range, some 25 miles northwest of Cranbrook. Sullivan, one of the largest lead mines in the world, is the main industry in the city. Recently, a new fertilizer plant has been built. The combined population of Kimberley and a few smaller settlements around the mine is approximately 6,000.

Further north in the trench, *Invermere* (Windermere), with a population of about 500, is a small tourist centre. *Golden* (800) is located on the Canadian Pacific Railway at the western end of Kicking Horse Pass.

In the Rocky Mountains proper, *Fernie* (2,800), is the largest town. It is a coal mining centre located on the Elk River. The Canadian Pacific Railway (Crowsnest Branch) passes through the town. *Field* (700), is located on the Canadian Pacific Railway in the heart of the Rocky Mountains. It is a divisional point, with much railroad equipment, such as snow ploughs and spare engines, kept in reserve. It is situated as a western gate to the most picturesque part of the Rocky Mountains. Many resorts including Emerald Lake, Yoho and Wapta Lake are located nearby.

## V. The Nechako Region

The Nechako Region is situated to the northwest of the Fraser Uplands and directly east of the Coast Mountains. It is lower in elevation and more subdued topographically than the Fraser Uplands. A rolling to hilly surface averages 2,500 feet in elevation, and most rivers flow in fairly broad valleys about 500 feet below the general level. A few mountains rise to 5,000 feet.

*D. P. Kerr*

Plate 101. A pioneer homestead in Central British Columbia.

The entire region is forested, a reflection of the humid continental climate. Rainfall is heavier and temperatures are lower than in the Fraser Uplands to the south. Most soils in the region are acidic and low in plant nutrients.

The region is sparsely settled, containing only three per cent of the population of British Columbia. The main elements of the economic geography of the area are lumbering and pioneer farming, near the Canadian National Railway route. Occasional summer frosts, heavy autumn rains, infertile soils and distance from markets impose limitations to agricultural expansion.

## Urban Centres

*Prince George*, located at the confluence of the Fraser and Nechako Rivers, is the most important town in the region. It is a divisional point for the Canadian National Railway and a distributing centre for surrounding farms and lumber camps.

Founded as a Hudson's Bay post in 1807, it was incorporated as a city in 1915. It has grown rapidly after the completion of the Pacific Great Eastern Railway. Population in 1931 was 2,479; in 1941, 1,989. In 1956, the population was found to be 10,500. Manufacturing enterprises employed 1,400 people in 1954 and had a net value of production of over $7,000,000. Wood processing industries are the most important.

*McBride* (600), *Vanderhoof* (1,000), *Smithers* (2,000), *Burns Lake* (1,000), and *Hazelton* (300), are small settlements along the railway.

## VI. The Peace River

The Peace River area in British Columbia is physically and economically a part of the Canadian Prairie Region. It lies to the east of the Rocky Mountains, on the Great Plains, adjoining the province of Alberta.

The rolling plains average 2,500 feet in elevation, but a few hills, which increase in number toward the west and north, rise to 3,500 feet. The rivers of the area flow in fairly narrow valleys, which are entrenched as much as 500 feet below the level of the plain. Many of the bottom lands and terraces in the valleys have alluvial soils and, consequently, have been appropriated for agricultural use. On the wide interfluves, patches of Shallow Black Soils obtain, and they are the most highly prized for grain growing.

The climate is humid continental. There is, normally, a moderate summer rainfall, but long droughts occasionally occur. The chance of frost during the growing season is not so great as in the Nechako Basin but nevertheless, serious summer frosts should be expected in one year out of five. The early fall season is much drier than in the Nechako region and harvesting is usually successful. The winter season is long and cold. Several sharp outbursts of intensely cold polar air drop temperatures to −30° F. every winter.

Mixed farming characterizes the economic geography of the area. Grain growing and hog raising are normally the most important aspects but, of late, the cultivation of clover seeds has increased greatly. Natural gas and petroleum resources are being developed in the area. A pipeline has been built to supply the southern Coast and the Interior with Peace River gas.

**Urban Centres**

*Dawson Creek* is a small regional centre with a population of approximately 7,500. It was named after Dr. George M. Dawson, the eminent Canadian geologist who first surveyed this area in the 1880's. Dawson Creek serves the surrounding farming communities, but has a wider function as the southern terminus of the Alaska Highway and the northern terminus of the Northern Alberta Railway. Recently, its position as a transportation focus has been expanded by the completion of a road to Prince George through Pine Pass. The town is also served by Canadian Pacific Airlines.

*Fort St. John,* located 50 miles north of Dawson Creek on the Alaska Highway, has a population of about 2,000. It is a small supply centre. A large airport on the Northwest Staging Route is located here. Farming ends about 17 miles north of Fort St. John at Rose Prairie. *Hudson Hope,* toward the west, is a tiny mining and supply centre. *Pouce Coupe* is a village of 500.

## VII. Northern British Columbia

Northern British Columbia is a vast area containing fewer than 3,000 people. In fact, most of the region is devoid of any settlement whatsoever.

Surface configuration throughout the region is extremely varied. Mountains predominate, but dissected plateaus, narrow river valleys and some plains, are also important features. Little land is available for agricultural settlement. The Nelson Basin and the Kechika and Finlay River Valleys are the only large areas topographically suitable for farming.

The climate imposes limitations on agriculture. The growing season is short and frequently interrupted by summer frosts. Rainfall is light and irrigation would be necessary. The winter season is very long and cold in eastern areas but is slightly more moderate in western districts. Trees in the area are scrubby and have little or no commercial value.

The Alaska Highway runs diagonally across the region from Dawson Creek to Teslin in the Yukon. A few tourist camps have been built, but volume of traffic is light. Other settlements throughout the area are defense establishments, fur trading posts, mining camps and Indian villages. The chief types of transportation in areas away from the highway are the canoe in summer, the sleigh in winter and the aeroplane the year round. Population will remain sparse in the region unless the mining industry is greatly expanded.

## Selected References

Adams, John Q. *Prince Rupert, British Columbia.* Economic Geography, 14 pp. 167-83. 1938.

Anderson, W. J. *A Study of Land Settlement in the Prince George-Smithers Area, British Columbia.* Canada Department of Agriculture. Publication 794. 1947.

Gough, John. *British Columbia.* Canadian Geographical Journal. XXXV, pp. 2-35. 1947.

Raup, H. F. *Towns and Cities of the Northwest.* (Chapter 256, pp. 477-519. The Pacific Northwest,* edited by O. W. Freeman and H. H. Martin). John Wiley & Sons. New York. 1942.

Sheffield, P. H. *The Trail Metallurgical Plant.* Canadian Geographical Journal III, pp. 177-97. 1931.

Taylor, G. *British Columbia, A Study in Topographic Control.* Geographical Review, Vol. 32, pp. 372-402. 1942.

Weir, T. R. *New Westminster, B. C.* Canadian Geographical Journal XXXVI, pp. 22-38. 1948.

# CHAPTER 22

# The Canadian Northland

CANADA has two Northlands—the Arctic in the central and eastern regions and the Northwest. (See figure 287) The regions differ in many respects. The northern tree-line separates the subarctic, forested Northwest from the tundra of the Arctic. The Canadian Northwest includes Yukon Territory and the Mackenzie Valley, except for the Arctic coast. The rest of the Northland is the Arctic. Much of the confusion in understanding Northern Canada comes from attempts to reconcile opposing facts and conditions for the area as a whole. The two Northlands differ in climate, topography, vegetation, peoples, and resources. Because of differences in physical geography, the problems met in the development of each region are also different. An exact knowl-

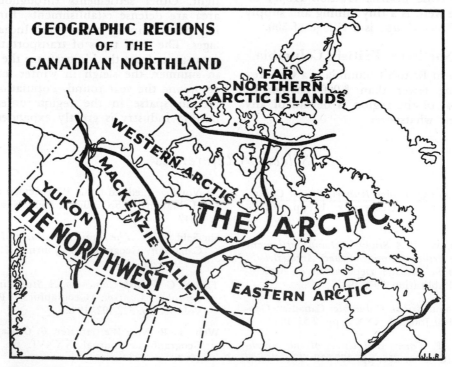

Figure 287. *The Canadian Northland.* There are two northlands — the Northwest and the Arctic. The boundary between them is approximately the northern limit of tree growth.

480

edge of the geographical character of *each* region will help to clarify the misunderstandings arising from fact, fable, and half-truths concerning the Canadian Northland.

The contrasts between the two Northlands are numerous. Climatically, the whole of Northern Canada is cold in winter. The Northwest, however, has recorded the lowest temperatures known in North America. The Arctic, on the other hand, although not experiencing such extreme cold, is continuously cold throughout its longer winter. Summers in the Northwest are mild, and, occasionally, may become actually hot. In the Arctic there is no summer, according to climatic definition, and "summer" days are cool. Topographically, the Northwest is chiefly a region of mountains and linear valleys. The Arctic has a variety of topographic features ranging from ice-capped mountains which are the highest in Eastern North America, to extensive, lake covered, tundra plains. The vegetation line between the forested, subarctic Northwest and the treeless tundra of the Arctic is the natural basis of division between the two areas.

Peoples, resources and stage of development also differ between the Northwest and the Arctic. The Northwest is inhabited by some 5,000 Indians, and by more than 15,000 resident whites, whose numbers are increasing annually. The Arctic is occupied by 8,500 migratory Eskimos, and about 1,000 transitory white residents, scattered around the coasts in tiny post settlements. The extent of natural resources is better known in the Northwest and they have greater possibilities of development than the few resources of the Arctic. The former region already supplies Canada with gold, oil, pitchblende, lead, silver, furs and fish. The Arctic has only one utilized resource—the white fox.

The Northland is being developed in the Northwest; transportation facilities are being improved; settlements are growing. A few changes came to the Arctic during the war years, but the inhospitable environment is such that development is naturally retarded. It is not likely that the Arctic region can attain the stage of prosperity known in the Northwest.

## Northwestern Canada

Northwestern Canada, by political boundaries, includes Yukon Territory and much of Mackenzie District, Northwest Territories. As a geographic region it extends farther south and includes the region tributary to the Alaska Highway in northern British Columbia, and the sparsely-inhabited region north and northeast of the Peace River country of Northern Alberta. In Mackenzie District only the Mackenzie River Valley is within the region since northeastern Mackenzie District is in the Arctic zone.

## Physiographic Divisions

Northwestern Canada contains the northern extensions of two major physiographic regions of North America, and touches on the edge of a third. (See figure 288). The Cordillera extends northward from British Columbia and continues into Alaska. It includes all of Yukon Territory. The Mackenzie Valley is the narrow northward extension of the Great Plains region. It is bounded on the west by the Mackenzie Ranges of the Cordillera, and, on the east, by the Canadian Shield. The northwestern edge of the Canadian Shield is included within this geographic region since it is forested, subarctic, and linked economically with the Mackenzie Valley.

### Yukon Plateau

In Yukon Territory the main topographic feature is the basin-like area of the dissected Yukon Plateau. This interior plateau has an average elevation of 2,000 to 3,000 feet, and is rimmed to the southwest, east and north by mountains. The plateau continues northwesterly into Alaska. It is composed of crystalline rock, chiefly old metamorphosed strata of Precambrian and Paleozoic ages. There are, also, younger in-

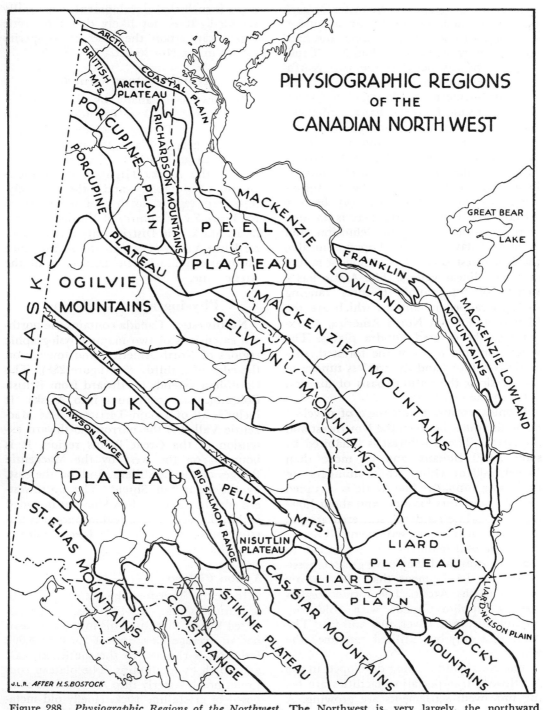

Figure 288. *Physiographic Regions of the Northwest*. The Northwest is, very largely, the northward continuation of the Cordilleran region of mountain ranges, trenches and plateaus.

trusives and some Tertiary lavas and sediments. A broad trough in the southeast is
occupied by folded Mesozoic strata.

The surface of the plateau is one of rolling uplands, with a uniform level over
broad areas, separated by deeply entrenched
valleys. A few local mountain ranges rise
above the plateau level, sometimes reaching altitudes of 7,000 feet. Owing to the
lack of precipitation in this interior basin,
the west-central part of the Yukon was
never glaciated. The major rivers meander
across broad-bottomed valleys and are entrenched 1,000 to 2,000 feet below the upper plateau surface. The main tributaries
form a branching network all leading towards the major river, the Yukon. The
branches, in turn, are connected with large
tributary valleys, formerly glacially cut
near the mountains, but which are now occupied by small misfit streams. A major
transverse valley cuts across the plateau
from the southeast to the west-central part.
It is occupied by the Pelly, Stewart, Klondike and Yukon Rivers. To the south, the
Yukon Plateau merges with the Stikine Plateau and the Cassiar Mountains of Northern British Columbia.

## Coast and St. Elias Mountains

Southwestward, the rugged barrier of the
Coast and St. Elias Ranges separates the
Yukon Plateau from the Pacific Ocean and
the Alaskan Panhandle. The Coast Mountains are the northern continuation of similar ranges in British Columbia, and termin-
ate in Yukon Territory near Kusawa Lake.
They are formed chiefly of granitic intrusions, with roof pendants of old metamorphic rocks. Altitudes average about 7,000
feet.

West of the Coast Mountains, the mighty
St. Elias Range rises in ice-capped grandeur
to peaks which are the highest in Canada.
Many peaks exceed 13,000 feet and Mount
Logan, 19,850 feet, is the second highest
peak in North America. The front ranges
of the St. Elias Mountains rise abruptly
above the Yukon Plateau to altitudes of
about 7,000 feet. They are composed of

Paleozoic and Mesozoic strata. They are
separated from the main ranges, which lie
to the southwest, by a linear plateau composed of Tertiary sediments and capped by
volcanic rocks.

The great peaks of the St. Elias Range are
reported to be of granitic rocks, but geological information is scanty. Large permanent ice-fields discharge twisting glaciers
down to the scenic Pacific Coast and also
northward into a few valleys. The ranges
are cut by the deep, little-known, canyon of
Alsek River. This river heads in the northeast slopes of the St. Elias ranges and empties directly into the Pacific Ocean. It has
maintained its course while the mountains
were being uplifted.

## Selwyn and Ogilvie Mountains

The eastern and northern rims of the Yukon Plateau are bounded by the Selwyn
and Ogilvie Mountains, respectively. The
former are composed of thousands of feet
of folded and faulted sediments of various
ages. Granitic intrusive rocks form some of
the mountains in the Selwyn range east of
Frances Lake. Sharp peaks in this range
average from 7,000 to 8,000 feet above sea
level. The Selwyn Mountains hold the position relative to the Mackenzie Mountains
to the east, that the Selkirk Range holds to
the Rocky Mountains of British Columbia.
The more rounded peaks of the Ogilvie
Mountains are a continuation of the Selwyn
Range to the northwest.

## Porcupine Basin

North of the Ogilvie Range the scrubby
forests of the Porcupine Basin cover a smaller plateau. This flat to gently rolling basin
drains westward via the Porcupine River,
which empties into the Yukon River in
Alaska. The flat-lying strata underlying the
level expanse are believed to be chiefly
Mesozoic in age. Another little-known,
swampy plateau lies north of the Selwyn
Range at the headwaters of Peel River, and
is a sub-feature of the Porcupine Basin.

Porcupine Basin is separated from Mackenzie River to the east and the Arctic

Ocean to the north by the Richardson and British Mountains, respectively. These rugged ranges average around 5,000 feet, and are composed of upfolded Paleozoic and Mesozoic strata. Northward there is a narrow Arctic Plateau and Plain which is tundra covered, and extends to the ice-filled Arctic Ocean.

## Liard Basin

Yukon's third basin lies in the southeast, in the headwaters of Liard River, and extends southward into British Columbia. This narrow, well-forested valley is bounded by the rounded Cassiar Mountains on the west and the dissected Liard Plateau on the east.

## Mackenzie Mountains

*The Mackenzie Ranges* are a sharp-peaked barrier between Yukon Territory and Mackenzie District. These jagged ridges

of barren, sedimentary rock are similar in structure to the Rocky Mountains to the south. They are separated from the Rockies by a plateau and plain along Liard River. The range is composed of several little-known mountain chains which extend in an arc to the east of the Yukon boundary, and northward to Peel River. The Peel Plateau on both sides of the latter river separates the Mackenzie ranges from the Richardson Mountains to the north.

The Mackenzie ranges have a north-south alignment, and are crowned by peaks of about 8,000 feet altitude. The rock is of Paleozoic age, ranging from Cambrian to Carboniferous, with numerous faults and folds. During Pleistocene times the Mackenzie mountains were occupied by part of the Cordilleran ice-sheet. The broken, rugged character of these ranges, off the main lines of north-south travel, has made them

*R.C.A.F. Photograph*

Plate 102. The jagged peaks and ridges of the Mackenzie Mountains, east of the Yukon boundary, North of June Lake. This region was unexplored prior to 1942.

difficult to explore and they remain virtually uninhabited.

*The Franklin Mountains* are a front range of the Mackenzie Mountains, lying on the east side of the Mackenzie River. This rounded, mature range has barren crests of about 4,000 feet altitude. Great Bear River, which joins the Mackenzie River from the east, divides the Franklin mountains into two sections. The mountains are formed chiefly of Silurian strata, but among others, Cambrian rocks are also represented.

## Mackenzie Lowland

The Mackenzie Lowland is the forested northern continuation of the Great Plains physiographic region. The Lowland is about 450 miles wide at the southern border of the Northwest Territories. It narrows a short distance to the north, being pinched between the eastward bulge of the Mackenzie Mountains and the northwest trend of the Canadian Shield. The plain is separated into two sections by the Franklin Mountains. The Mackenzie River occupies the narrower western part of the lowland.

The flat-lying rocks of the Mackenzie Valley are chiefly Paleozoic in age. Ordovician and Silurian rocks, overlapping the Canadian Shield, form the base along the eastern edge. Devonian rocks lie beneath the muskegs and lakes of most of the southern Mackenzie Valley. Cretaceous strata occupy a large area south of Great Bear Lake and appear again over much of the northern part of the valley. Smaller sections of Cretaceous rocks outcrop west of the central part of Mackenzie River, and along the western shore of Great Bear Lake.

The Mackenzie Lowland is not level throughout, although some sections are extremely flat. West of Slave River the lowland slopes upward to the low, rolling Caribou Hills. These hills, and others, extend westward along the Territorial boundary to beyond Hay River. The northern edge of the hills is a sharp escarpment over which rivers tumble in spectacular waterfalls. Between the escarpment and Great Slave Lake and Mackenzie River the lowland is very flat, and covered with scrub forest, muskegs and lakes. A poorly-drained lowland extends northward from Great Slave Lake to Great Bear Lake. The flat-topped, dissected plateau of Horn Mountains rises about 1,000 feet above the plain north of Mackenzie River, between Fort Providence and Fort Simpson.

The lowland narrows to widths of 20 to 50 miles between the Franklin and Mackenzie mountains. Much of it is covered with hundreds of feet of unconsolidated glacial material into which the broad Mackenzie River has cut to flow between steep gravel banks. North of Norman Wells the lowland again broadens out into a flat, poorly-drained plain, broken occasionally by low limestone escarpments. Large areas are swampy, with many small lakes and few large ones. Most streams have entrenched meanders.

## Mackenzie Delta

The Mackenzie River crosses the Arctic Coastal Plain by means of an amazing network of shallow branching channels. The main channels of the Mackenzie and Peel Rivers may be followed through the delta in twisting, meandering courses, but from the air they are hard to distinguish from the numerous intertwining tributary channels. Between the channels are innumerable shallow lakes and cut-offs of all sizes and shapes. So much water covers the surface that from the air the delta looks like strips of land separating bodies of water. The delta is slowly building northward, where shallow water and sand bars are found 10 to 20 miles from the island-studded river mouth.

## Climate, Vegetation and Soils

Northwestern Canada has a subarctic climate, forests in the valleys, and productive soils on the lowlands. The mountain tops and upper slopes, which make up a notable percentage of the area, are barren, treeless and have an Arctic climate. There are great variations in climate from year to year in the Northwest, depending upon the source of the dominant air masses. In some winters, cold air from the Arctic Ocean spreads southward over the Yukon Plateau, or follows a southward route up the Mackenzie Valley. Under this polar influence temperatures are very low throughout the whole area. In other years warm air from the North Pacific Ocean may cross Southern Yukon and occasionally reach the Mac-

kenzie Valley. These winters are mild. Both types of air masses enter the region during the winter, and the characteristics of a particular winter depend upon which air mass is more frequent and dominant.

## Temperature

In Yukon Territory, average mean monthly January temperatures range from zero degrees F. at Carcross, in Southern Yu-

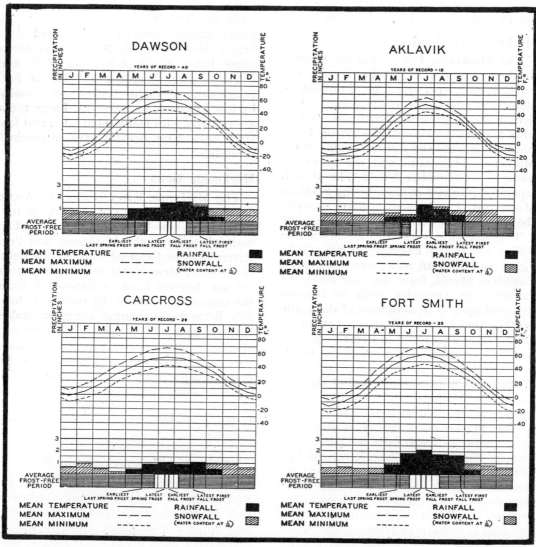

Figure 289. *The Climate of the Northwest.* The climatic diagrams for Dawson City, Y.T., Carcross, Y.T., Aklavik, N.W.T., and Fort Smith, N.W.T., illustrate climatic conditions at widely spaced points within the region. (Courtesy Canadian Geographical Journal).

kon, to −13° F. at Mayo, in Central Yukon, to −21° F. at Dawson, in west-Central Yukon. In the Mackenzie Valley, where there is more uniformity of topography and consistency in the source of air masses, January averages are about −15° F. in the south and −23° F. in the north.

Temperatures may become quite severe anywhere in the Northwest, when Arctic air masses stagnate over the region for some time. Readings of −50° F. are typical of most stations at sometime during the winter. The record low temperature in North America, −81° F., was observed at Snag, Western Yukon, in February, 1947. Previous to that time the record low of −79° F. had been noted at Fort Good Hope, in the Mackenzie Valley.

Northwestern Canada, unlike the Arctic, may have mild summers. Whereas both regions are cold in winter, the Northwest has from one to three months in summer when average monthly temperatures are between 50° and 60° F. Mean daily maximum temperatures are characteristically from 65° to 75° in the afternoon and drop to 40° or 50° in the short nights. Maxima of about 85° are usually recorded at some time during each summer, at most stations. The hottest temperature ever recorded in the Yukon was 95° F. at Dawson. Each station in the Mackenzie Valley, except Aklavik, has recorded above 90° at some time in its history, and 103° F. in July at Fort Smith is the extreme record.

## Frost-free Period

The average length of the frost-free period is one measure of future agricultural possibilities in a region. In Northwestern Canada the average is somewhat misleading because of the great range between earliest and latest recorded first autumn frosts. Valleys in west-central Yukon have an average frost-free period of about 75 days. First autumn frosts may strike there as early as the end of July or as late as mid-September, depending upon whether Arctic or Pacific air masses are dominant in that year. South-ern Yukon, with higher elevations, has an average frost-free period of only 45 days.

In the Mackenzie Valley, the frost-free period ranges from 45 days at Fort Norman to 92 days at Fort Resolution. The southern settlements around Great Slave Lake have the longest growing season and less irregularity in time of occurrence of autumn frosts. The last spring frost occurs around mid-June in the southern Mackenzie Valley, which is about the same time as that recorded in the better-known agricultural area of Fort Vermilion in Northern Alberta.

## Precipitation

Precipitation is light in the Northwest, ranging from nine to thirteen inches. There is little possible source of moisture since central Yukon is surrounded by high mountains, and the Mackenzie Valley is the path of cold air which contains little moisture. From 35 to 50 per cent of the total precipitation falls as *rain* during the four summer months. This small amount, assisted by melting of the top layers of permanently frozen subsoil, is sufficient for agriculture in most years. Southern Yukon, in the lee of the barrier of the St. Elias Mountains, and sandy areas along the banks of the Mackenzie River, sometimes experience drought conditions.

*Snowfall*, although not heavy, accumulates on the ground throughout the winter. It blankets the low areas, which are impassable in summer, to sufficient depth for dog-team and snowshoe travel in winter. The average annual snowfall of 40 to 60 inches which is recorded in the valleys of the Northwest is similar to that of Winnipeg, and about half that of the central St. Lawrence Valley of Eastern Canada.

## Forests

Northwestern Canada is forested in the valleys. Much of the timber is small, however, and is not considered to be of economic importance. Commercial stands are found in the Liard Valley of southeastern Yukon and southwestern Mackenzie District, and on the delta of Slave River. Forests belong to the Northern or Boreal Forest Region, in which the most important timber species is white spruce. This tree grows best on fertile river-bottom soils. Black spruce does not generally reach usable size in this region; it is characteristic of muskegs, or poorly-drained areas. In Yukon Territory, alpine fir is sub-dominant in the eastern and central valleys, whereas lodgepole pine is characteristic of the drier western sections.

Along the Alaska Highway in Southern Yukon commercial stands are found as high as 3,500 feet up the valley slopes. Timberline is about 1,000 feet higher. In the valleys of southwestern Yukon vegetation has a park-like appearance. Tree-cover is not complete, and grass growth is quite ample for a small grazing industry. The Yukon River Valley has a complete forest cover on the lower terraces and flood-plains, but not of sufficient size for export lumber. Local areas, especially around Dawson, have already been well cut over for fuelwood for homes and river steamers. The wood was also used to thaw gravels during the early placer-mining period.

The Mackenzie Valley is forested to within about 50 miles of the Arctic Ocean. Trees grow well near the river banks, but tree-cover is not complete over the whole lowland. Poor drainage away from the rivers has resulted in numerous lakes, swamps and muskegs, with forest growth only in favourable sites. The lack of drainage is caused by the permanently frozen sub-soil, which thaws to a depth of only a few feet during the summer. Since the water cannot drain away it lies on the surface, forming innumerable shallow lakes.

Spruce is the characteristic tree of the Mackenzie Valley. Jack pine is found on the sandy or gravel ridges. Aspen poplar and birch, when seen along the river banks, are often indicative of better soils. Willow and alder grow on many of the river flats and islands.

## Tundra

The northern limit of trees is the line which separates Northwestern Canada from the Arctic region. Although not as definite as it appears on the map, the transition zone between forest and tundra is quite noticeable from the air. Flying northward, one notices that the trees become smaller, more bent in the wind, and farther apart. Soon the rocky hilltops are bare. A short distance to the northward trees disappear from the slopes, and grow only in alluvial deposits near river banks or delta mouths. One is then in the tundra region. Small trees or shrubs sometimes grow along the well-drained slopes of eskers. Hardy black spruce or dwarf willows may grow on some of the sheltered lowlands beyond the tree-line but they only serve to emphasize the lack of forest in the vicinity.

## Soils

The characteristics of the soils of the Canadian Northwest are not yet well known. Leahey, in 1947, reported the presence of three soil zones in the Mackenzie Valley.

Most southerly of these is the Grey-Wooded Soil Zone which extends as far north as Fort Simpson (61°52′N.) where, on an abandoned alluvial terrace under a mature stand of white poplar, there is a soil development very like that of the Peace River district. There is no permafrost at this site.

At Fort Norman (64°54′N.), under a mixed forest of spruce, birch, alder, and willow on a level terrace, the surface soil is slightly acid, but apart from some yellowish brown mottling shows little evidence of soil development. Permafrost was encountered at 39 inches (August 20, 1945). Fort Norman is considered to be in the Subarctic soil zone.

Aklavik (68°26′N.) is in the Arctic zone. Permafrost is found at shallow depths. The surface has a pattern of polygons, 3 to 5 feet across, separated by narrow channels filled with organic soil. Under a shallow organic layer the top 4 inches of soil is slightly acid but the greyish brown subsoil is almost unweathered.

In the Yukon Valley, also, there is a marked difference between the areas which have and have not permafrost. The Yukon Valley is a rainshadow area with 5 to 7 inches of rain during the growing period. In the well-drained uplands, free from permafrost, the soils vary from dark brown types under grass to reddish brown forested soils with little evidence of podzolization. Soils in the permafrost area are usually poorly drained and have a thick covering of peat and muck.

Intrazonal peats and mucks are found in great abundance in all zones. The azonal soils of the alluvial valley floors differ little from one zone to another.

## Population Growth and Settlement Pattern

Both whites and Indians are few and scattered in the Canadian Northwest. Mackenzie Valley settlements are old. The first trading posts were established in the later part of the 18th century. By the middle of the 19th century, most of the present-day

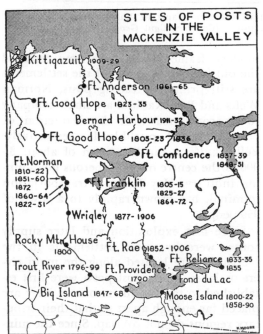

Figure 290. *Former Fur Trading Posts in the MacKenzie Valley.*

settlements were in existence as tiny fur-trading posts. They were strung out along the Mackenzie River, and supplied by canoe brigades which came down the Athabaska and Slave Rivers after portaging from the Churchill or North Saskatchewan Rivers. During the first half of the 19th century explorer-traders had penetrated through the mountains to the headwaters of the Pelly and Porcupine Rivers in the Yukon. By the middle of the century there were four posts in the Yukon and eight in the Mackenzie Valley.

Opposition from hostile Indians forced the abandonment of the Yukon posts, but the Mackenzie Valley settlements grew. In 1858 missionaries entered the latter region and soon had small mission churches built at most of the trading posts. Their coming gave an air of permanence to the posts in the fur-exploited region. Until the end of the 19th century however, these hardy missionaries and traders remained the only permanent white residents among some 5,000 Indians.

Prospectors began to move into the Yukon during the last two decades of the 19th century. There were several hundred miners in the area, and at least four alluvial gold locations were worked prior to the famous Klondike strike in 1896. The "boom" that came to the Yukon then is well-known. In 1898 the area was created a separate Territory, and within a few years had some measure of responsible government. In 1900 Dawson City and area had 30,000 inhabitants. Within eight years of the strike more than 100 million dollars in gold had been obtained from the Klondike placer deposits. A narrow-gauge railroad had been built from Skagway, Alaska, to the head of navigation at Whitehorse, Yukon, and river-steamers operated on the main rivers in the Territory.

The population of the Yukon gradually declined in this century as the more accessible gold was exhausted. By 1920 the region had about 5,000 inhabitants, including Indians, and remained stabilized at that

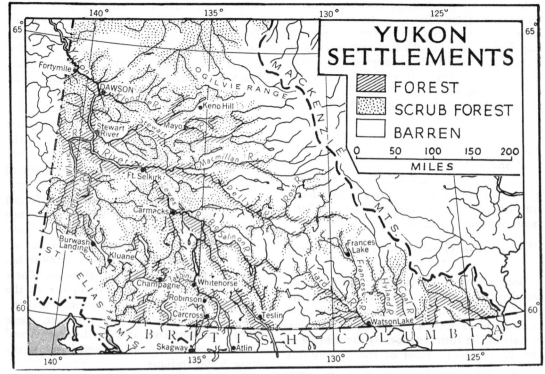

**Figure 291.** *Settlements of the Southern Yukon.* Most of the inhabitants of Yukon Territory live in the mining settlements of the southern part of the territory. (*Courtesy Can. Geog. Journal*)

figure until World War II. There was another "boom" during the war years when the airfields of the Northwest Staging Route, and the connecting Alaska Military Highway, were built. The town of Whitehorse reached a peak population of about 15,000 owing to its cross-roads position on road, rail and river transportation. Like the Dawson of 40 years before, the population of Whitehorse decreased at the end of the war, but the town, aided by its strategic position, still contains over half of the white population of the Yukon.

In the Mackenzie Valley, population growth has been steady, but never spectacular. Early in the present century the Royal Canadian Mounted Police extended their authority northward and placed detachments at many of the post settlements, thus adding a few more permanent buildings to the tiny cluster of log houses. Although

modern frame homes have now replaced the old log cabins, many of the settlements are still primarily trading posts. Norman Wells and Port Radium are small company towns concerned with the extraction of petroleum and pitchblende, respectively. Yellowknife, a bustling town of about 3,-000 is the centre of a prosperous gold-mining industry. Hay River, a transportation terminal, has grown rapidly to a town of 950 people.

Since first exploration and later supply routes were by water, settlements in the Northwest are located along the main rivers or lakes. Since most posts were first established to tap the fur resources, they are placed far enough apart so that their tributary regions do not overlap. Since the mining towns are located in poor fur areas, where no posts existed, they have increased the scattered nature of settlement rather than increasing the number of functions of the earlier settlements.

## Mining

Within this century mining has been the major industry of the Yukon, but only in 1938 did it exceed the fur trade in value in Mackenzie District. Gold is the mainstay of the Yukon mining industry. Over 200 million dollars worth of gold had been taken from the Yukon by the end of 1946, and over half of it came from the fabulous Klondike placers during the first decade after discovery. By 1907, the value of gold production had dropped to about three million dollars for the year, and production has never exceeded that annual amount. Consolidation of interests, the use of modern hydraulic equipment and dredges, and the discovery of a gold-bearing underground gravel channel, have helped to maintain production for over 50 years. Recent discoveries in other nearby streams, and also in Southern Yukon, indicate that the historic Yukon will be producing gold for many years to come.

Lode mining has also been carried on in the Yukon. A silver-lead ore found at Mayo proved to be exceedingly rich in silver. Mining commenced in 1913 and the mines have produced almost continuously since that time. In recent years the value of silver and lead from the Mayo area has each been greater than that of gold. Zinc is increasing in importance.

Copper was discovered near Whitehorse in 1897 by prospectors on the trail to the Klondike. Production was intermittent between 1900 and 1920, although relatively important during World War I. The deposits are spotty in character and are presently not considered economical to mine.

Coal of Mesozoic age was mined at Carmacks from 1900 to 1938, and production started again in 1948. About 150,000 tons were mined during the first period, and used almost entirely for local fuel needs. Coal has also been mined from other small

*National Film Board*
Plate 103.   A gold dredge in the Klondike Valley, Yukon.

properties in the Yukon. Although not of high grade, Yukon coal is useful in an area where transportation costs are high, and winters are cold.

Other minerals have been found in Yukon Territory, but high costs for supplies, equipment, and transport of ore have usually prevented development. Known occurrences include tungsten, antimony and tin. Despite over a half-century of mining, the Yukon has not been fully prospected. Increased accessibility since World War II has encouraged the search for minerals, and raised high the hopes for "another Klondike".

### Norman Wells

In the Mackenzie Valley prospectors staked claims while on their way to the Klondike at the turn of the century, but no mining development took place until 1920. In that year petroleum was encountered by pioneer drillers at Norman Wells, on the Mackenzie River. There was little demand for the product until a mine was opened at Port Radium after 1930. The discovery of gold at Yellowknife, on Great Slave Lake, increased the demand for oil, but two wells supplied the needs of the whole Mackenzie Valley until 1939. A small refinery was constructed in 1940.

In 1942 Norman Wells oil was needed along the Alaska Highway; the wartime

"Canol Project" was the result. It involved an extensive drilling program which produced 60 wells, a four-inch pipeline, and an accompanying road across the almost inaccessible Mackenzie Mountains, as well as a refinery at Whitehorse, Yukon. The work was undertaken by the United States government following an agreement with Canadian authorities. The Norman Wells field produced almost two million barrels of oil during the duration of the Project (1942-45). The field has an area of 4,000 acres, partially under the Mackenzie River, with a recoverable reserve of 35 million barrels. After the abandonment of the pipeline, production has been confined to a few weeks of the summer to supply Mackenzie Valley industries and homes.

## Port Radium

Pitchblende was discovered on the east side of Great Bear Lake in 1930. Despite difficulties of extracting the radium, and transportation problems of shipping supplies about 1,600 miles by water from the head of rail at Waterways, in Alberta, a mill was in operation by 1933. A refinery was constructed at Port Hope, Ontario. The mine soon made Canada one of the world's leading producers of radium, and greatly reduced the price of this rare product. Production ceased during 1940 to 1942 and when it started again they were seeking from the pitchblende the former by-product, uranium. The dropping of the atom bombs on Japan in 1945, illustrated the importance of the tiny settlement of Port Radium in the future peace of the world.

## Yellowknife

The gold-mining town of Yellowknife arose from the barren rocky shores of Great Slave Lake in 1935. The first gold brick was poured in 1938 and within four years there were six producing gold mines in the area. The value of their production totalled almost four million dollars in 1942. The richest gold was found in sheer zones along the West Bay fault, on the west side of Yellowknife Bay. Other deposits, some of too low grade for the high cost of northern transportation, have been found in quartz veins in the rocky Canadian Shield to the east and north of Yellowknife. Indications are that the area is well-mineralized, but the limiting factors are production costs and the problem of shipping in supplies and equipment.

Numerous other minerals have been found in the Mackenzie Valley and adjoining edge of the Canadian Shield, but none has proved rich enough for development. Coal, salt, and gypsum deposits outcrop at several places throughout the Mackenzie Lowland. Lead-zinc mineralization of considerable extent has been found south of Great Slave Lake. The nearby Canadian

*J. Lewis Robinson*

Plate 104.　Port Radium on the rocky shore of Great Bear Lake.

Shield has yielded small quantities of tungsten, molybdenite, tin, tantalum, beryllium, lead, zinc and copper.

## Agriculture

Despite northern latitude, crops have been raised successfully for many decades in the valleys of the Canadian Northwest. The long duration of summer daylight, in addition to mild temperatures, encourages crop and garden growth. At the turn of the century the terraces and lower slopes of the Yukon River around Dawson were cleared. Local agriculture supplied much of the food for the mining population. Agriculture gradually declined in importance in the Yukon as population decreased. Contributory factors were the disappearance of work horses which consumed grain, and the easier methods of importing food from low-cost agricultural regions farther south. In 1951, there were only four farms (larger than three acres) in all of Yukon and Northwest Territorities. They had 80 acres of improved land. The main crop was cultivated hay.

Since mining is the chief primary occupation in the Yukon, and population is small, agriculture can scarcely hope to be more than a subsidiary industry. There is more land available for settlement, however, particularly for subsistence farms. Preliminary surveys indicate that there are about 200,000 acres of potential agricultural land in the territory. The largest single block is 100,000 acres in the Takhini-Dezadeash Valley, west of Whitehorse. Most of the soils are lacustrine clays, which are similar in appearance to dark brown prairie soils. Clearing will not be difficult since this region is semi-arid, but precipitation may be too scanty. Another 60,000 acres of possible agricultural land is scattered along the silt-covered flats and lower terraces of the Yukon River, particularly north of Stewart River.

The Mackenzie Valley also had more land under crops at the beginning of the century than at present. At that time traders and missionaries were encouraged to raise their own food because of the high cost and length of time of transporting it from outside. Most of the cleared land was on the well-drained river terraces near the present settlements. An agricultural survey made in 1943 indicated that the whole Lowland of some 125,000 square miles had only ten farms and 150 gardens, with a cultivated area of about 300 acres.

Most of the Mackenzie Valley lowland is unsuited to agriculture. Much of it is poorly-drained, covered with swamps and muskegs, and underlaid with permanently frozen sub-soil close to the surface. The "Upland" soils (back from the main rivers) resemble the Grey Wooded type found in the northern Prairie Provinces. Their texture is quite sandy, and they are usually low in organic material. No accurate estimates have been made of the area of potential agricultural land, but it is doubtful if it exceeds 100,000 acres. Probably the largest single block of farm land lies in southwestern Mackenzie District, along the well-forested lower terraces of Liard River, but distant from present settlements. Other potential acreages are reported along the Hay River Valley and west of Slave River near Fort Smith. The lower terraces which have had infrequent flooding have varying depths of loamy to clay soils over sands and gravels. The organic matter content of the upper 6-12 inches is usually good. Summer drought will be the major problem in utilizing these scattered soil areas. Unfortunately, near the only large town of Yellowknife agriculture land in the Canadian Shield is scattered in small pockets. It is possible that the Mackenzie Valley may some day support a larger agricultural population as total numbers for the whole area increase but it is doubtful if large-scale settlement will come before more accessible regions farther south are occupied.

## Fur Trade

Fur-bearing animals have long been a major resource of the Northwest. They were the reason for exploration, and later fur-trading posts were the nuclei for settlements. Because of the small native population in the Yukon, less than 2,000 Indians, that area has never been as important in the fur trade as the Mackenzie Valley. Muskrats make up about 75 per cent of the annual fur catch of the Yukon. Other fur-bearers of importance are beaver, mink, marten, weasel, lynx, and foxes. The Yukon has an excellent natural environment for fur-bearers including forest protection, lakes and rivers, and cold winters. Govern-

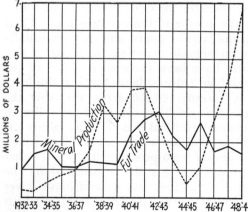

## VALUE OF FUR TRADE and MINERAL PRODUCTION in the NORTHWEST TERRITORIES

Figure 292. *Furs and Minerals.* Furs and minerals constitute the chief commercial products of the region.

ment regulations are in force to protect this resource and maintain it for the use of resident whites and Indians.

The Mackenzie Valley is one of the last large regions of Canada where the fur trade remains a major industry. Until 1920 it was the only industry of this vast northland. Its value has ranged from one to three million dollars a year, amounting to 10 to 15 per cent of the value of the total Canadian catch. Although white trappers are more numerous than they are in the Yukon, they constitute a minority of the trappers, and catch only about 20 per cent of the annual total. Much of the Valley is set aside in Native Preserves so that the means of live-

lihood of the Indian population can be maintained.

Trapping begins in November after there is enough snow on the ground for travelling by dog-team and sledge. Indian camps are usually located on tributary streams or well-known trails in the woods, and consist of a group of families. The men visit their respective trap-lines periodically while the women and children remain in the central camp. Winter homes are log cabins or tents banked with boughs. Occasional trips are made to the nearest settlement to trade furs for food and supplies. Wild game, chiefly moose, caribou or deer, supplies most of the winter's food. The amount of additional "store" food depends upon the success of trapping. Most families have a second cabin in the main settlements where they stay during the summer months, living almost entirely on fish.

The chief fur-bearer in the Mackenzie Valley both in value and numbers caught is muskrat. The 300,000 trapped or shot annually, chiefly in the lake-covered Mackenzie River delta, constitute about one-seventh of the total Canadian catch. The annual catches of the other fur-bearers vary from year to year depending upon the particular cycle of abundance of each animal and the trapping regulations currently in force. Fur-bearers are the same kind as those trapped in Yukon Territory and in other parts of Northern Canada. In order of decreasing importance they are: beaver, mink, marten, lynx, coloured foxes, and ermine.

### Forestry

Although the Northwest is forested in the valleys and well-drained areas, there is very little commercial use of the timber. Several small portable mills scattered throughout the region near the main settlements cut lumber for local needs. Prior to World War II about 1½ million board feet of lumber and 20,000 cords of fuel wood were cut and used annually in the region

*J. Lewis Robinson*

Plate 105.   (Upper)   The Mission buildings at Fort Resolution, N.W.T.
(Lower)   Indian cabins at Fort McPherson, N.W.T.

without any appreciable effect upon the total forest reserve.

In recent years the annual cut in the Yukon and North West Territories together has been between 4,000 M and 8,000 M board feet, with a value of about $500,-000. Most of the cutting in the Yukon Territory is done along the Alaska Highway and in the vicinity of Mayo. Local depletion is already apparent in some areas along the Yukon River where the river steamers have been cutting fuel wood for half a century.

A few large sawmills (by northern standards) operate in the forests of the Slave River delta, and smaller mills are located along the Mackenzie Highway south of Hay River. Most of their cut is transported across Great Slave Lake to the growing town of Yellowknife, which is located in the poorly-forested Canadian Shield. Numerous forest fires during the war years cut into the forest reserve of the Northwest and resulted in the Federal Government forming a Forest Fire Protection Service for the region.

## Fishing

Commercial fishing was begun in Great Slave Lake in 1945. Previous to that time the fish of northwestern lakes and rivers had been used wholly for local food, chiefly by the Indians, and for dog feed by anyone who had to travel in winter.

In Yukon Territory there is a local fishery in the Yukon River near Dawson, catching king and dog salmon. Indians use the ingenious fish wheel, and market their catch in Dawson. The Alsek River, which empties into the Pacific Ocean, does not have salmon in its headwaters, as do most other Pacific Coast rivers, probably because of some obstacle near the Alaska Border. Tatsenshini River, which empties into the Alsek not far from the sea, however, does have all of the five common species of salmon. The summer fishery at its headwaters is the main support of the few Indians of southwestern Yukon.

The lakes of Yukon also contain ample fish for local residents and tourist fishermen. The chief catches are lake trout and whitefish. Grayling and Dolly Varden trout are the most common game fish, but rainbow trout are also found in southwestern Yukon.

In Mackenzie District careful fishery surveys were made of Great Slave and Great Bear Lakes to determine the number and reproduction rates of fish before commercial fishing was permitted. As a result, a limited catch of lake trout and whitefish was permitted from Great Slave Lake, but Great Bear Lake was found lacking in sufficient quantity of commercial fish. The fish from Great Slave Lake are filletted and frozen on large barges operating on the lake and shipped southwards in refrigerated barges or trucks to the head of rail in Alberta.

The Mackenzie River has sufficient fish for local use, particularly near the outlet of Great Slave Lake and towards the river delta. Important "fisheries" are held every fall at all settlements to catch enough fish for winter dog-feed. The chief catches are several species of whitefish. One of the species is the distinctive "coney", or inconnu, so named by the explorer, Alexander Mackenzie, because the fish was not known in other parts of Canada.

# Transportation

The key to development of the natural resources of the Northwest is transportation. Inaccessibility, and a small local population, have prevented the resources of the Northwest from having much impact upon Canadian economy. Canadians have been occupied in building up the southern part

of their country and only recently have turned their attention northward.

## Water Routes

*Water transportation* was the original means of bringing supplies and trade goods into the region and carrying out furs. Water still transports the bulk of the freight during the four-month open season. The first steamer navigated up the Yukon River to Fort Selkirk in 1871 and the first boat began operations on Mackenzie River in 1887. Modes of river transportation have remained little changed since those days. Flat-bottomed, stern-wheeled steamers pushed from one to five barges ahead of them carrying the annual freight for the river settlements. During World War II small diesel-powered motor vessels were introduced into the Mackenzie River system to push new and larger steel barges. A small fleet of these efficient tugs, operated by the government-owned Northern Transportation Company, now carries most of the freight of that area.

The Yukon River is navigable for 1,777 miles from Whitehorse to its mouth in Bering Sea. River boats begin operations after mid-May, when break-up comes, and shuttle back and forth between Whitehorse and Dawson until freeze-up in mid-October. Other boats ply the Stewart River bringing out ore concentrates from Mayo. The broad-bottomed valleys of the Yukon have excellent waterways which serve most of the inhabited area. The rivers heading in the glaciers of southwestern Yukon reach a peak in July and August and remain navigable for shallow-draft boats throughout the summer. Those rivers draining from southeastern Yukon and the Mackenzie Ranges flood early in the spring when snows melt, and often have low water in the autumn.

The Mackenzie River system has only one break in navigation in the 1,700 miles from the head of rail at Waterways, Alberta, to the Arctic Ocean. There are 16 miles of rapids in Slave River, terminating at Fort Smith on the southern boundary of the Northwest Territories. There are, therefore, two groups of steamers and motor tugs operating south and north of these rapids. Supplies are carried down the Athabaska River, across the shallow western end of Lake Athabaska, to Slave River. Seasonal fluctuations in water levels may cause depths to decrease to less than two feet in the Athabaska River delta in fall. Vessels and barges must therefore be of shallow draft and lightly loaded in the fall. At Fort Fitzgerald, Alberta, goods are transhipped on trucks and trailers over the portage roads to the head of northern water transportation at Fort Smith. The remainder of the route along Slave River, Great Slave Lake, and Mackenzie River, is 1,400 miles of broad, navigable waterway, hindered only by occasional shallows. The busy route across Great Slave Lake to Yellowknife has no serious hazards except for wind storms.

The transportation season on the Athabaska River begins in mid-May, but opens later in the Northwest Territories. Although the Mackenzie River ice breaks up around mid-May north of its junction with Liard River, Great Slave Lake often has ice in it until the middle of June. Great Bear Lake is usually not open for navigation until mid-July. Although small boats come down the Liard River early in the season from supply points on the Alaska Highway, the big steamers and many tugs do not begin operations on Mackenzie River until Great Slave Lake is ice-free. Two trips are usually made downstream to Aklavik or Port Brabant (Tuktoyaktuk) before freeze-up in late September, whereas Yellowknife may be served by water until late October.

Freight for the Western Arctic is transferred at the Mackenzie River delta to coastal schooners. One of the major problems of costs and equipment in the Mackenzie Valley is that the amount of freight shipped downstream is many times the volume which is moved southward.

## Land Routes

Sufficient freight is carried in a summer to keep most of the Mackenzie Valley settlements in supplies for the remainder of the year. The town of Yellowknife, however, needs additional supplies during the winter. Prior to World War II a rough road was cut through the forest and over the frozen muskeg from Grimshaw, near the Peace River in Northern Alberta, to the Hay River Valley. Tractors pulled large sleds slowly over this winter road to Hay River settlement, and then in early January crossed the ice of Great Slave Lake to Yellowknife. The trail to Hay River was made into an all season road suitable for trucks in 1947, but winter travel to Yellowknife must still wait until the large lake is frozen over.

The Alaska Highway is the only permanent road in Yukon Territory. Built as a military necessity during 1942, it stretches for 1,523 miles from Dawson Creek, B.C. to Fairbanks, Alaska. Its route opened up previously untouched parts of northeastern British Columbia and Southern Yukon. The purpose of the road was to connect the series of airports previously constructed by the Canadian Government along the Northwest Staging Route between Edmonton and Alaska. The Alaska Highway has improved the accessibility of the scenic southwestern and southeastern areas which were most difficult to reach by water transportation.

Yukon Territory has the only rail line in the Northwest. This narrow gauge railroad extends 100 miles from tidewater at Skagway, Alaska, to the head of river navigation at Whitehorse, Yukon.

## Air Routes

*Air transport* is the modern method of opening up the Northwest. "Bush-flying" was a well-developed art in the region long before World War II gave an impetus to flying. The first plane entered the Northwest Territories in 1921. By 1929 there was air-mail service as far north as Aklavik. About the same time prospectors began to use small float-equipped planes which could land anywhere in the lake-dotted region.

Trappers also saved many weeks of hard canoe labour by flying into their remote trapping grounds.

War-time emergencies encouraged a new phase of aerial activity in the Northwest. Large cargo planes needed permanent landing strips, as well as emergency fields, at frequent intervals along the major routes. As a result most settlements have air strips which may be used by wheeled planes throughout the year. The large airports along the air way from Edmonton through Southern Yukon are better equipped than the smaller, dirt-surfaced fields from Edmonton north to Fort Smith and Norman Wells. A modern field was constructed by the Federal Government at Yellowknife in order to give that isolated settlement daily communication with Edmonton.

### Summary

The Northwest is a vast region occupying about ten per cent of the area of Canada. Although divided into two sub-regions—the Yukon and Mackenzie Valley—there are similarities within each which give the whole geographic unity. Both the Yukon valleys and Mackenzie Valley have similar types of topography, drainage, climate, vegetation, and population distribution. They also face similar problems in the development of natural resources. The whole region is just beginning to open up. As Canadians turn their eyes northward it is the Northwest which holds promise of greater things to come.

## The Canadian Arctic

The Canadian Arctic comprises the mainland of Canada, north of the tree-line, and the many Arctic Islands between it and the North Pole. The Arctic mainland includes the narrow strip of Yukon coastal plain, the outer edge of the Mackenzie river delta, the rolling tundra north of Great Bear Lake, the rocky Canadian Shield northeast of Great Slave Lake, and it broadens eastward to take in most of the treeless Keewatin District. The geographic region extends beyond the political boundaries of the Northwest Territories to include the large Arctic area of northwestern Quebec between Richmond Gulf and Ungava Bay. The numerous Arctic Islands may be divided into two major groups. The southern tier is close to the mainland and inhabited. The northern group, north of the wide channels between M'Clure Strait and Lancaster Sound, is not so well-known and has no inhabitants, except policemen and weather observers.

The Arctic area of Canada may be divided into three sub-regions. (See figure 287). The Western Arctic is so-called because it has been serviced chiefly from the west; that is from the Mackenzie Valley or occasionally from around the coast of Alaska. It includes the Arctic mainland, west of Boothia Peninsula, and the islands of the southern group, west of Somerset Island. The Eastern Arctic includes the treeless mainland, west and east of Hudson Bay, and the Arctic Islands north of the Bay, notably the huge expanse of Baffin Island. This region is supplied from the east—either from Churchill, or from along the coast of Labrador. There is very little intercourse between these two sub-regions. The problems of development in the one Arctic region need not necessarily be those of the other. The third sub-region comprises the Far Northern Arctic Islands. Until recently, only the coasts of many of these islands have been seen by a few white men. Their ice-girt shores make them almost inaccessible by ship.

## Physiography

Since the Arctic region occupies about one million square miles, there is space for a variety of topographic features. The area has the highest mountains in Eastern North America, and some of the most extensive plains. Large areas are covered with spongy tundra vegetation, whereas other sections consist of barren rock, either in solid ridges or in disintegrated rock plains.

Most of the Arctic mainland is underlain by the ancient, worn-down Precambrian rocks of the Canadian Shield. This rough plateau usually has little relief, but there is rugged, broken topography near the coast of Northern Quebec; around Wager Bay, in Keewatin District; and near Bathurst Inlet, in northeastern Mackenzie District. Gently rolling hills of glacial drift, interspersed with innumerable, small, oval lakes characterize large areas. West of Hudson Bay and south of Queen Maud Gulf broad depositional plains, covered with lakes, muskegs, and swamps, lie between the bare, rock-controlled topography east of Great Bear and Slave lakes and the coasts. Other lowlands, usually marked by raised beach-lines and other features of emergent coastal plains, may be identified in figure 293.

Precambrian rocks are also found on the islands. They form the rugged base of southern and eastern Baffin Island, eastern Devon Island and south and east-central Ellesmere Island. These rocks have been

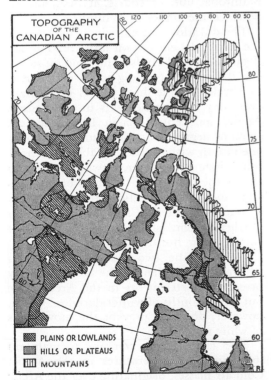

Figure 293. *Topography of the Canadian Arctic.*

TOPOGRAPHY
OF THE
CANADIAN ARCTIC

PLAINS OR LOWLANDS
HILLS OR PLATEAUS
MOUNTAINS

tilted up on the east coast of Baffin Island, and sculptured by ice tongues, extending from permanent ice-caps in the interior. Alpine peaks of 9,000 feet have been reported, and the general altitude of the range is from 5,000 to 7,000 feet. Numerous scenic fiords cut far into the rugged interior. The south and east coasts of Devon Island are similarly glaciated, and discharge picturesque glaciers down broad twisting valleys, from the large, permanent, inland ice-cap.

Ellesmere Island is also steep and rugged on the east coast, but slopes down to tundra-covered lowlands along the central-west coast. It has several large ice-caps in the little-known interior. The northern section of the island is a mountain complex with numerous linear ranges paralleling the north coast. Many of these sedimentary peaks have a reddish colour, but their geoology has not been studied. Altitudes of 10,000 feet are reported, similar in appearance to the sharp-crested Mackenzie Mountains of the Northwest. The interior of Axel Heiberg Island is also mountainous and partially ice-capped.

Plateaus of Paleozoic sedimentary rocks extend through the central Arctic Islands, and form the base of some of the northwestern islands. The coasts of northwestern Baffin Island, Somerset Island, northern Prince of Wales Island, western Devon Island, western Melville Island and northern Banks Island rise sheer for 500 to 800 feet, in cliffs of horizontally stratified rock. The perpendicular walls are broken frequently by canyons and long steep-sided inlets. The barren plateau surfaces are generally flat, except where gashed by ravines and are usually covered with a loose mantle of angular, disintegrated rock.

Some of the islands in the western section of the northern group have low coasts which rise in gentle, tundra-covered slopes to bare, rough, rocky hills and ridges. The interior uplands have been greatly dissected by numerous streams, in well-developed dendritic patterns. Large lakes are notably absent in most of the far northern Arctic

Islands. In winter the low coasts of these islands are difficult to distinguish from the snow-covered sea-ice. The north-central Arctic Islands show a great deal of structural control in their topography. Bathurst Island, north-central Melville Island, and the Ringnes Islands have outstanding structural domes, with surrounding concentric ridges. Other features are characteristic of eroded synclines.

Lowlands of glacial or marine deposition form the central region of the southern group of islands. They comprise all of King William Island, the west coast of Boothia Peninsula, southern Prince of Wales Island, and eastern Victoria Island. The emergent coasts are low and shelving, rising in parallel ridges marking ancient beach-lines. Isolated hills of 300 to 600 feet are outstanding topographic features in this region. The lowlands, like those on the mainland, are covered with countless shallow lakes of irregular shape, and have scanty vegetation.

Parts of Banks Island and western Victoria Island have rough topography which is the result of bedrock control. Western Victoria Island is underlain by Precambrian rock and is similar in appearance to the "ridge and valley topography" along the Coppermine River on the mainland. These ridges extend northeastward from Minto Inlet to Wynniat and Hadley bays. Elevations range from 1,000 to 1,500 feet. The imposing southern tip of Banks Island rises 1,000 feet directly from the water, with higher elevations inland. The west coast and parts of the central interior are low and well-covered with tundra vegetation.

## Climate

### Temperature

Meteorological stations in the Arctic region have no monthly average temperatures above 50° F. Their winter mean temperatures are the lowest monthly averages recorded in Canada, but they do not have the extreme minimum temperatures, characteristic of the Northwestern region and the northern prairies. Winters are con-

tinuously cold, seldom being influenced by warm air masses from either the North Pacific or North Atlantic. Afternoon temperatures, in the short "summer", frequently exceed 60° F. and, in places, surpass 70° F., but the monthly average remains below 50° F.

All Northern Canada is cold in winter, but the Arctic region has the lowest monthly averages. Most of the Arctic stations have average January temperatures of –20° F., or lower. The coldest settlements, at Cambridge Bay, Pond Inlet, and Chesterfield average –27° F. for that month. The record minima at these stations ranges from –60° to –63° F. Southeastern Baffin Island, which is influenced by open water and occasional warm air masses sweeping back from the North Atlantic, is not as cold as the rest of the Arctic. January temperatures in that section average about –5° F. This is about the same average as that of Winnipeg, Manitoba, but, of course, it does not experience the thaws of Winnipeg.

The duration of total winter darkness in the Arctic depends upon latitude. The settlements around Hudson Bay and on southern Baffin Island, being south of the Arctic Circle, have a short period of daylight every day. The settlements in the western Arctic, and central Baffin Island, located about 69 degrees North latitude, have about one month without the sun above the horizon. There is, however, a twilight glow on the southern horizon, the light of the stars and moon, and reflections from the snow. The most northerly Canadian Eskimos, on northern Baffin Island, restrict, but do not curtail, their hunting and trapping activities during the two months of darkness which they experience. The most northerly present-day settlements in the Arctic have but three months of winter darkness, which, however, does not prevent the movements of white residents.

Two chief factors combine to maintain low summer temperatures in the Arctic. Cold air masses, originating over the Arctic Ocean, shift their routes eastward in sum-

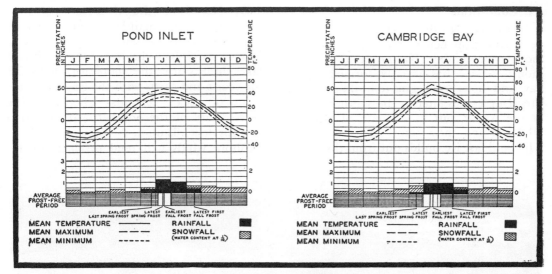

Figure 294. *Arctic Climates.* The characteristics of the true Arctic climate are low temperature and relatively low precipitation. (Courtesy of the Canadian Geographical Journal).

mer, crossing the Arctic Islands and northern mainland towards Hudson Strait. This dominance of cold air, combined with cold Arctic waters offshore prevents summer temperatures from rising as high as those in the Northwest. Although the duration of summer daylight is equally as long in the Southern Arctic as in the subarctic Mackenzie or Yukon Valleys, the period of maximum insolation comes in late June and early July when the heat of the sun's rays is spent in melting the snow and ice cover rather than warming the tundra and rock.

Most of the inhabited Arctic region has July average temperatures ranging from 45° to 50°F. Lower summer temperatures are recorded in the far northern Arctic Islands, and at the marine-influenced station at the entrance to Hudson Strait. During the short "summer" period of July and August daily temperatures may be pleasantly cool, reaching into the 60's. Numerous flowers bloom in colourful display across the snow-free tundra and in sheltered valleys, and myriads of mosquitoes swarm over the low, wet coasts.

*The frost-free period* is short, and, combined with the lack of developed soil, dis-

courages the possibility of agriculture. The longest period without frosts, about 65 days, is recorded on the mainland west of Hudson Bay, where the lowland warms up and is influenced by occasional prairie air. Most of the Southern Arctic stations average 40 to 50 days without frosts. Northern Baffin Island has frosts occurring in every month.

**Precipitation**

*Precipitation* is low in the Arctic, as it is in the Northwest. Most of the region receives less than ten inches of precipitation annually. Greater amounts are recorded on southeastern Baffin Island, the mountainous east coast of Baffin Island, and around the shores of Hudson Bay. Almost half of the precipitation falls as rain during the three or four warmest months. Arctic snow is fine and granular, and is difficult to measure because of continuous drifting. By November it has accumulated on the ground and sea-ice in sufficient depths for snow-house building. Although the lowlands become completely snow-covered, rocky ridges may remain bare throughout the winter.

## Ice Conditions

In the Far Northern Arctic Islands temperatures drop below freezing throughout most of September. By the middle of the month sea-ice has usually formed across bays and inlets and begins to build outward. Freeze-up comes later in the southern parts of the Arctic, but by the end of October all lakes and most coasts are ice-covered. The land-fast ice builds out from the coasts

By late June the river-ice begins to break-up on the mainland, and the land-fast shore ice is loosened along the coasts. During early July the ice in the mainland lakes breaks up; the shore ice moves off the coasts and drifts with the general movement of ocean currents. Thereafter the accessibility of the Southern Arctic coasts to ships depends upon the prevailing winds. Offshore winds will tend to clear the ice

J. Lewis Robinson

Plate 106.   The treeless tundra of the Canadian Arctic. (Upper) Along the Coppermine River. (Lower) Near Cambridge Bay.

a distance of five to seven miles, and by late winter attains a thickness of five to seven feet. Many of the straits and central Hudson Bay freeze over, but the central ice may be separated from the land-fast ice by a strip of open water. Hudson Strait, for example, is packed with heavy floes moving back and forth with tides, currents and winds, whereas northern Baffin Bay and eastern Lancaster Sound have open water throughout the winter.

away, whereas onshore winds will pack the loose ice into harbours. In the Southern Arctic most of the floes are melted or broken up by early August.

In the Far Northern Arctic Islands break-up does not come until August. Most coasts remain ice-bound throughout the summer since new floes move in from the Arctic Ocean as fast as the old ice drifts away. Accessibility depends greatly on a favourable period of offshore winds. In some years the few large lakes in the Northern Arctic Islands do not lose their ice throughout the year.

## Ocean Currents and Ice Conditions

The physical geography of the Arctic must include ocean currents, a factor not present in the interiors of other Canadian regions. Currents have a profound effect upon present settlement and possibilities of development. Water from the basin of the Arctic Ocean moves between the Canadian Arctic Islands, from the north and west towards Davis and Hudson Straits and the coast of Labrador. There are three main channels through the Islands. The narrow straits and basins between Greenland and Ellesmere Island are frozen over most of the year. They are a route for Arctic water and, in late August and early September, also carry ice-floes southward from the revolving mass in the Arctic Ocean. This movement continues southward off eastern Baffin Island and Labrador. The wide channels of M'Clure Strait, Viscount Melville Sound, and Barrow Strait are frozen during the long winter, and when they break up a little in early August, they carry heavy pack-ice eastward to Lancaster Sound and Baffin Bay. The sea-ice joining the far northwestern islands probably never breaks up in "summer", and this area might, therefore, be considered as one large "land" mass. The third route of ocean currents follows the shallow seas off the mainland coast. Amundsen Gulf has varying amounts of sea-ice in summer, depending on the prevalence of northwest winds. Coronation and Queen Maud Gulfs are usually ice-free in August and September. M'Clintock Channel is filled with heavy polar ice from Viscount Melville Sound throughout the year. Water and ice from the western Arctic enter the eastern Arctic through narrow Bellot Strait. Committee Bay and the southern Gulf of Boothia have southward-drifting ice all summer. Some of the ice continues eastward, through narrow Hecla and Fury Strait to enter ice-filled Foxe Basin. These currents carry the ice southward into the counter-clockwise movement in Hudson Bay.

The cold Arctic waters, moving through the archipelago, reach far into the interior of the continent. Arctic conditions are thus extended as far south as latitude 57°, almost 700 miles *south* of the Arctic Circle. These waters remain cold throughout the year, thus decreasing the temperature of the nearby land masses. The short ice-free period of the southern parts is, therefore, quite cool. One of the fundamental differences in settlement history, between western Greenland and nearby eastern Baffin Island, lies in the influence of warm and cold ocean currents. Southwestern Greenland is washed by a relatively warm branch of the North Atlantic Drift, whereas Baffin Island is surrounded by cold Arctic water.

The direction of movement of ocean currents in the Arctic has a further geographic significance. During early summer, the land-fast ice breaks away from the coasts and is carried along with the currents, towards the east and south. In the Eastern Arctic, this movement is directly into the shipping routes and delays the opening of navigation for several weeks. In some years, some places in the Far Northern Arctic Islands may remain inaccessible throughout the season because of drifting ice.

## Natural Resources

The known resources of the Arctic are limited and the developed resources are few. The region lacks soil and suitable climate for agriculture. There can be no forestry in a treeless zone. Mineral possibilities have been only superficially investigated, and none of economic importance has been found. The only resource of the area is the wildlife population on the land and in the sea. These animals, notably the caribou and seal, have supplied the native Eskimo with food and clothing for centuries. The fur of the white fox, is the only important export. Its pelt is the native's chief means of obtaining something from his environment to be exchanged for white man's tools, equipment and food.

Prospecting for minerals has been carried on sporadically on the Arctic mainland, but winter conditions and inaccessibility have hindered any intensive work on the Islands. The copper of the Coppermine River has been known since the days of Samuel Hearne's overland explorations in 1770-1772. It has been utilized for tools by both Eskimos and Indians for centuries. Each of several intensive investigations by large companies has ended with the decision that the ore is not of high enough quality to overcome the high costs of transportation and development.

In Keewatin District, gold mineralization has been reported in the Canadian Shield near Padlei, but no development has taken place. A nickel ore body, found at Rankin Inlet during a spectacular flurry of prospecting in 1928-29, did not prove large enough to mine. Southern Baffin Island has yielded low-grade deposits of mica, graphite and garnet. Near Pond Inlet, northern Baffin Island, lignite coal has been mined since 1924, and transported to the settlement to be used as fuel for the residences. Small amounts of coal are also mined in the Western Arctic at Darnley Bay, and used by the mission at Paulatuk.

The only exploited resource of the Arctic is the white fox. This fur-bearer has been trapped for traders since early in the century, and was occasionally purchased by whalers of the last century. Most Eskimos, particularly those in the Western Arctic, now depend greatly upon their white fox catches to keep them in supplies and ammunition. The white fox has a usual four-year cycle of abundance (but the cycle may be three or five years) which has introduced a factor of instability into the lives of the Eskimos. Since the fox pelt might be classed as a luxury article the trade is at the mercy of whims in the market in southern cities. Prices received by Eskimos thus fluctuate widely. Largest catches come from the Western Arctic but this is probably due to more intensive trapping rather than more foxes. Keewatin District has recorded high catches in years of plentiful foxes, owing partially to the few efficient white trappers, who used to live in the southern part of the District. Blue foxes, a colour phase (one or two percent) in a white fox litter, are traded at most posts. Red foxes are extending their range into the southern edge of the Arctic, and are being trapped more frequently.

## Transportation and Settlements

Since resources are limited and population is small, transportation is not elaborate in the Arctic. The tiny post settlements are nearly all located on the coast, about 100 to 200 miles apart, in order to be serviced by water. The residents at the posts represent one or more of the following organizations: Hudson's Bay Company, Royal Canadian Mounted Police, Department of Transport Radio and Meteorological operators, Roman Catholic or Anglican missionaries, Government doctors. The population of a post may range from two to about twenty-five. The total resident white population in the Canadian Arctic is about 300 persons, with individuals usually staying only two to five years at a time.

Most incoming supplies and outgoing furs are carried by water during the short summer season. In the Western Arctic small coastal schooners receive supplies for transshipment from Mackenzie River steamers at Port Brabant (Tuktuk). In early August the schooners work their way eastward, staying close to shore in shallow water, in order to avoid the Polar pack-ice in Beaufort Sea and Amundsen Gulf. Their season lasts for about one and one-half months. They seldom proceed east of Cambridge Bay.

In the Eastern Arctic schooners operate from the two rail terminals at Churchill, Manitoba, and Moosonee, Ontario. They serve posts along the west and east coasts of Hudson Bay, respectively. At one time the Hudson's Bay Company's famous old icebreaker, "Nascopie", also serviced the posts in Hudson Bay, and was the only large vessel to visit the far northern posts. Its loss on a reef off southwestern Baffin Island in 1947 necessitated replacing the historic vessel with new vessels, including a Government-owned ice-breaker to patrol the most northerly regions.

Air transport is the only means, except for dog sledge, of reaching the Arctic in winter. Planes equipped with skis, or with wheels, can land nearly anywhere in the region on the smooth ice of harbours or large lakes, or at the few permanent air bases. In summer float-planes are used, chiefly for inspection trips, rapid transfer of personnel, or scientific investigations. The times and places of landing depend upon local ice conditions.

## Eskimo Population

The chief inhabitants of the Canadian Arctic are some 8,500 Eskimos. They are scattered in small groups of families over the Arctic mainland and coasts, and along the coasts of the Southern Arctic Islands. They are migratory hunters and trappers. Although fundamentally of the same cultural group, and speaking a similar language, there are local differences within the large area of the Arctic.

The Western Arctic has almost 2,000 Eskimos. Those at the western end of this subregion have been most influenced by contact with white civilization. Many of them differ very little in clothing and equipment from prosperous white trappers. This worldly Eskimo group, however, is not typical of the remainder of the Canadian Eskimos. A few hundred Eskimos in the Central Arctic, on the other hand, from King William Island to Boothia Peninsula and Pelly Bay and southward to Back River, are the most primitive in Canada. Many of them were still in a Stone Age civilization when white men began coming into the region after 1920. Some of these Eskimos, living solely on fish and wander-

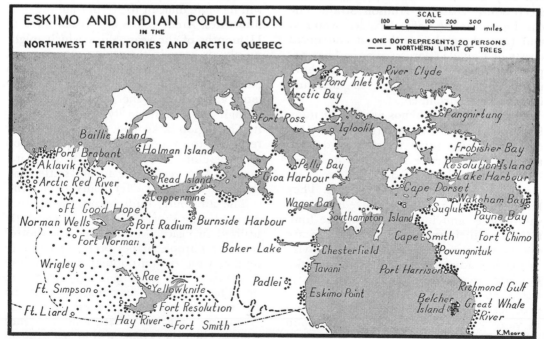

Figure 295. *Eskimo and Indian Populations.* For the most part, the Eskimo people live north of the tree line while the Indians are found south of it. In Arctic Quebec only the Eskimo population is indicated.

ing herds of caribou in the interior of the Arctic mainland, have seldom seen whites, and still live much as their ancestors did. Other Eskimos of the Western Arctic are coastal dwellers, living on seal meat throughout the winter and fish in the summer.

The Eastern Arctic Eskimos are in a transitional stage. They have been less modified by white civilization than the Eskimos of the Mackenzie River delta, but have advanced beyond the primitive stage of the central mainland people. The Eastern Arctic Eskimos occupy three main regions, each of which has about 2,000 scattered inhabitants. About half of those in Keewatin District are inland caribou hunters. The remainder are coastal hunters living along the west shores of Hudson Bay. Hair-seals, walrus, white whales and fish are their chief game. A poorer group of Eskimos inhabit Northern Quebec, hunting and trapping along the eastern shores of Hudson Bay and near inlets cutting into the steep south coast of Hudson Strait. The third group is the Baffin Islanders who seal and trap along the south, east and north coasts of Canada's largest island. They appear to have less troubles, and to have made a happy adjustment to their unfavourable environment.

The Canadian Eskimos are few in number and scattered over a large territory because the game upon which they depend for food is also scarce and migratory. They have inhabited this poorly-endowed environment for over a thousand years. They have adapted themselves, by means of snow-houses and fur clothing, to the limitations of their surroundings. Changes are taking place, however, since white civilization has advanced into the Arctic. Eskimos are becoming specialized trappers rather than hunters; but they are trapping a product which fluctuates in numbers and in value. They are depending more upon imported food and equipment instead of living off the country. Since this change is taking place rapidly, within the space of

a few decades, there are growing pains and problems for the Eskimo culture.

## Strategic Position

Canada's Arctic region lies on the direct global route between Central North America and Western Europe and Eastern Asia. Planes flying the shortest route from Chicago to Berlin would pass over Baffin Island. A direct flight from Toronto to Tokyo would pass over Yukon Territory. Canada's Arctic region borders on the basin of the Arctic Ocean, which is shared by the United States (Alaska), the Soviet Union, Norway, and Denmark (Greenland). Another small world, little-known, and until the "Air Age", little-realized, lies in these regions rimming the central Arctic basin. Instead of the forgotten "top of the world", a map on a polar projection illustrates that the Arctic could become the centre of the Northern Hemisphere.

A study of the Arctic environment, however, indicates that this strategic position will be more difficult to attain than the map illustrates. Arctic coasts are frozen for 9 to 11 months of the year. Ships which might supply air bases in the region cannot reach them throughout the year. There are from one to four months of darkness over the land areas during the winter, which although not preventing flying, does hamper it. The region lacks food, forests, and other resources to support a resident population and therefore all supplies have to be imported. As a region for future settlement, the Arctic does not offer many attractions.

The air route, built across the Eastern Arctic during World War II, has been little utilized in peace. Although it is a shorter route to Europe, planes prefer to fly more southerly routes over populated areas where way-freight and passengers may be picked up. The "Air Age" may indicate that the Arctic occupies a strategic position, but environment suggests that long distance routes, when they come, will be *over* the region rather than greatly helping to develop it. The discouraging natural environment has yet to yield resources which would make the extensive use of planes economical. The increasing use of planes for service and inspection, however, does give the Arctic year-round accessibility never before available, and will greatly assist in the gradual accumulation of scientific information about this partially-known region.

## Selected References

Baird, P. D. and J. L. Robinson. *A brief History of Exploration and Research in the Canadian Eastern Arctic.* Canadian Geographical Journal. XXX, pp. 136-54. 1945.

Bostock, H. S. *Physiography of the Canadian Cordillera, North of Latitude 55°.* Geological Survey Memoir 247. Canada Department of Mines and Resources. Ottawa. 1948.

Camsell, Charles. *The New North.* Canadian Geographical Journal. XXXIII, pp. 264-77. 1946.

Canada. Department of Trade and Commerce. *Physical Geography of the Canadian Eastern Arctic.* Canada Year Book, pp. 12-19. 1945.

Canada. Department of Mines and Resources. *The Northwest Territories. Administration, Resources, Development.* Northwest Territories and Yukon Services, Ottawa. 1948.

Canada. North Pacific Planning Project. *Canada's New Northwest.* King's Printer. Ottawa. 1948.

Canada. Department of Trade and Commerce. *Physical Geography of the Canadian Western Arctic.* Canada Year Book, pp. 9-18. 1948-49.

Canada. Department of Resources and Development. *Yukon Territory Iistory, Administration, Resources and Development.* Ottawa. 1950.

Canada. Department of Mines and Technical Surveys. Geographical Branch. *An Introduction to the Canadian Arctic.* Canadian Geography Information Series No. 2. Ottawa. 1951.

Clarke, C. H. D. *A Biological Investigation of the Thelon Game Sanctuary.* National Museum of Canada. Bulletin No. 96. Ottawa. 1940.

Dawson, C. A. (ed.) *The New North West.* University of Toronto Press. 1947.

Keenleyside, H. *Recent Developments in the Canadian North.* Canadian Geographical Journal. XXXIX, pp. 156-76. 1949.

Leahey, A. *Characteristics of Soils Adjacent to the Mackenzie River in the Northwest Territories of Canada.* Soil Science Soc. of Amer. Proc. vol. 12, pp. 458-461. 1947.

Lloyd, Trevor. *The Mackenzie Waterways: A Northern Supply Route.* Geographical Review XXXIII, pp. 415-34. 1943.

Lord, C. S. *Mineral Industry of the Northwest Territories.* Geological Survey. Canada Department of Mines and Technical Surveys. 1951.

Polunin, N. *Botany of the Canadian Eastern Arctic.* National Museum Bulletin. 104. Part 3. Department of Mines and Resources. Ottawa. 1948.

Robinson, J. L. *Mineral Resources and Mining Activity in the Canadian Eastern Arctic.* Canadian Geographic Journal. XXIX, pp. 55-75. 1944.

Robinson, J. L. *Eskimo Population in the Canadian Eastern Arctic.* Canadian Geographical Journal. XXIX, pp. 128-42. 1944.

Robinson, J. L. *Land Use Possibilities in Mackenzie District. N.W.T.* Canadian Geographical Journal. XXXI, pp. 30-47. 1945.

Robinson, J. L. *Agriculture and Forests of Yukon Territory.* Canadian Geographical Journal XXXI, pp. 55-72. 1945.

Robinson, J. L. *Water Transportation in the Canadian Northwest.* Canadian Geographical Journal. XXXI, pp. 236-56. 1945.

Robinson, J. L. *Weather and Climate of the Northwest Territories.* Canadian Geographical Journal. XXXII, pp. 124-41. 1946.

Taylor, Griffith. *Arctic Survey No. 3. A Mackenzie Domesday* 1944. Canadian Journal of Economics and Political Science, 11. pp. 189-233. 1945.

Taylor, Griffith. *Arctic Survey No. 4 A Yukon Domesday* 1944. Canadian Journal of Economics and Political Science, 11. pp. 432-66. 1945.

Wright, J. G. *Economic Wildlife of Canada's Eastern Arctic—Caribou.* Canadian Geographical Journal. XXIX, pp. 184-195. 1944.

Numerous excellent articles have been published in *The Beaver*, Hudson's Bay House, Winnipeg, Man., and in *Arctic*, Arctic Institute of North America, Montreal, P. Q.

# CHAPTER 23

# Canadian Production

THE economic geography of each major region of Canada has been discussed and it remains for us to glance briefly at a series of pictures of the development of the whole country. By adding together the market values of all goods and services, from whatever source, made available in a year, a comprehensive index of Canadian economic activity is built up, which is known as the "Gross National Product." The "National Accounts" for 1951 reported its value as more than $21,000,000,000, almost two and one-half times what it was in 1941, and three and one-half times as great as in the pre-depression year of 1929. Even when allowance is made for the inflation of the Canadian dollar, this is an increase of 45% over the total for 1941 and more than 100% over that of 1929.

By deducting indirect taxes less subsidies, depreciation allowances and similar business costs, a figure is obtained which represents "Net National Income." Over the years its behaviour is in fairly close accord with that of "Gross National Product." In 1951, the Bureau of Statistics reported its value to be slightly more than $17,000,000,-000.

**Commodity Production**

The commodity-producing industries include agriculture, forestry, fishing, trapping, mining, electric power, manufacturing and construction. The combined value of their out-put in 1951 was approximately $13,000,000,000. Glancing over the record in Figure 296, it is seen that this is more than six times as great as the value of pro-

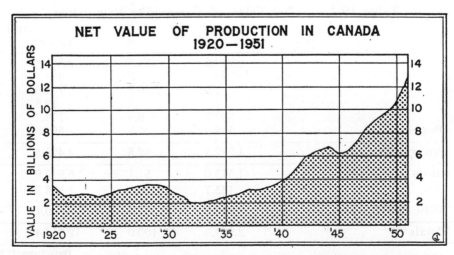

Figure 296.   Annual Net Values of Commodity Production, 1920-51. (Data from D.B.S.)

duction in the depression years of 1933 and 1934, and over four times as great as that of 1939.

Table 19 is based upon the estimates for 1939 and 1951 and shows the changes which have affected the shares to be credited to each group of productive industries. The share of the primary industries has fallen from 43% to 34% while that of the secondary industries has risen from 57% to 66%. For over a century Canada has been known as a producer of primary raw materials, but in recent decades the secondary industries have been developed to a point where they provide two-thirds of the new wealth. As time goes on, the preponderance of the secondary industries is likely to increase.

On a regional basis, production values are very unevenly divided; Ontario contributes approximately 41%, Quebec about 26%, British Columbia 10%, the Prairie Provinces about 18% and the Atlantic Provinces about 5% of the total net value of commodity production.

## Agriculture

Canada is a large country, but the area which is suitable for agriculture is surpis-ingly small. In every province save one, and it the smallest, the non-agricultural land is greater than the present and potential farm land. The area of land occupied by farms has not increased in the last decade. According to the census of 1951 the total farm area was 174,000,000 acres of which 97,000,000 acres were classified as improved land, while slightly more than 62,000,000 acres were under crop. The current value of farm captial was estimated to be $9,471,000,000, land and buildings being valued at $5,527,000,000 or 59%; implements and machinery were worth $1,933,000,000 or 20%, while farm livestock was valued at $2,010,000,000 or 21%. The total cash income of Canadian farmers in 1950 was estimated to be about $2,221,000,000 while the net income amounted to about $1,453,000,000. About 32.5% of the cash income was derived from the sale of field crops, 40.5% from sales of livestock, 19.3% from dairy products and eggs, with the remainder coming from many minor sources. There were approximately 623,000 farms in Canada, a 15% decrease since the census of 1941. The average Canadian farm in 1951, therefore, appeared to consist of 290 acres of land, with a captial value of $15,200 and a cash income of about $3,600. It must be re-

| Table 19 | Net Value of Commodity Production | | | |
|---|---|---|---|---|
| | 1939 | | 1951 | |
| | $000,000 | % | $000,000 | % |
| Agriculture | 710.5 | 23.7 | 2,685.4 | 20.8 |
| Forestry | 94.6 | 3.2 | 484.3 | 3.7 |
| Fisheries | 21.9 | 0.7 | 102.0 | 0.8 |
| Trapping | 7.9 | 0.3 | 19.8 | 0.1 |
| Mining | 297.7 | 9.9 | 770.2 | 6.0 |
| Electric Power | 149.9 | 5.0 | 363.6 | 2.8 |
| Totals, Primary Production | 1,282.5 | 42.8 | 4,425.3 | 34.2 |
| Manufactures | 1,513.0 | 51.1 | 6,940.9 | 53.7 |
| Construction | 183.7 | 6.1 | 1,568.2 | 12.1 |
| Totals, Secondary Production | 1,714.8 | 57.2 | 8,509.1 | 65.8 |
| Grand Totals | 2,997.3 | 100.0 | 12,934.4 | 100.0 |

Data from D.B.S. 1953.

## Table 20                Farm Land and Livestock—1951.

| | Farms 000 | Farm Area 000 Acres | Farm Crops 000 Acres | Farm Animals | | | | |
|---|---|---|---|---|---|---|---|---|
| | | | | Horses 000 | Cattle 000 | Sheep 000 | Swine 000 | Poultry 000 |
| Newfoundland | 3.6 | 85 | 20 | 3 | 8 | 18 | 2 | 76 |
| Prince Edward Island | 10.1 | 1,095 | 428 | 21 | 98 | 34 | 72 | 1,030 |
| Nova Scotia | 23.5 | 3,174 | 477 | 26 | 166 | 95 | 48 | 1,670 |
| New Brunswick | 26.4 | 3,470 | 712 | 31 | 162 | 55 | 78 | 1,283 |
| Quebec | 134.3 | 16,786 | 5,790 | 233 | 1,641 | 316 | 1,108 | 10,584 |
| Ontario | 149.9 | 20,880 | 8,645 | 261 | 2,466 | 360 | 1,755 | 24,766 |
| Manitoba | 52.4 | 17,730 | 7,335 | 131 | 671 | 65 | 338 | 8,890 |
| Saskatchewan | 112.0 | 61,663 | 23,705 | 304 | 1,275 | 136 | 533 | 9,074 |
| Alberta | 84.3 | 44,460 | 14,428 | 261 | 1,563 | 331 | 931 | 8,872 |
| British Columbia | 26.4 | 4,702 | 672 | 36 | 321 | 68 | 50 | 3,741 |
| Canada | 623.0 | 174,045 | 62,212 | 1,307 | 8,371 | 1,478 | 4,915 | 69,986 |

Census of Canada 1951.

membered, however, that there are many part-time and non-commercial small farms included in this average. On the other hand, more than 21,000 farmers in Canada reported sales of over $10,000.

There are great differences in agricultural capacity and development of the various provinces. This is demonstrated in Table 20, in which the statistics of the number and area of farms, crops and various types of livestock are recorded. It is very evident that the Prairie Provinces excel in field crop farming, while the eastern provinces are more concerned with mixed farming, in which the raising of livestock is often the more important consideration. The agriculture of the Atlantic Provinces, however, ranks far behind that of the Central Provinces, while Newfoundland, in particular, can hardly be said to have a really commercial agriculture. In Newfoundland also, there is a good deal of gardening and livestock activity not connected with commercial farming.

The regional differences are even more striking when placed on a financial basis as is done in Table 21, which is in part taken from the 1951 census and in part

## Table 21          Financial Status of Agriculture*

| Province | Farm Population 000 | Engaged in Agriculture 000 | Farm Values $000,000 | Cash Income $000,000 | Net Income $000,000 | Net Income Per Farm $ | Net Income Per Capita $ |
|---|---|---|---|---|---|---|---|
| Newfoundland | 20 | 4 | 20 | 3 | 2 | 565 | 100 |
| Prince Edward Island | 47 | 13 | 87 | 22 | 13 | 1,280 | 270 |
| Nova Scotia | 115 | 23 | 152 | 39 | 24 | 1,000 | 210 |
| New Brunswick | 150 | 27 | 158 | 47 | 33 | 1,270 | 222 |
| Quebec | 793 | 195 | 1,399 | 361 | 252 | 1,870 | 318 |
| Ontario | 703 | 201 | 2,548 | 678 | 460 | 3,060 | 655 |
| Manitoba | 219 | 74 | 917 | 195 | 126 | 2,410 | 580 |
| Saskatchewan | 400 | 148 | 1,992 | 408 | 265 | 2,270 | 662 |
| Alberta | 345 | 115 | 1,790 | 368 | 236 | 2,800 | 685 |
| British Columbia | 120 | 28 | 408 | 100 | 42 | 1,580 | 350 |
| Canada | 2,912 | 828 | 9,471 | 2,221 | 1,453 | 2,340 | 500 |

*Data from Census of Agriculture, 1951; and Canada Year Book, 1952-53.

from the production estimates for the year 1950 extracted from the 1952-3 edition of the Canada Year Book. Ontario and the Prairie Provinces have definitely the most remunerative agricultural activities. The below-average per capita incomes in the other provinces are, in part, due to the subsistence and part-time agricultural development in many areas. While there has been virtually no change in the total occupied land in Canada in recent years, there has been considerable abandonment in older sub-marginal areas, which has been compensated by new farms in pioneer areas.

For its size, the population of Canada is supported by the broadest agricultural base of any country in the world, each person having the produce of 6.5 acres of improved land to draw upon. It has been estimated that 2.5 acres of crop will provide sufficient food at an acceptable standard, so that, on this basis alone, Canada might expect to feed about 25,000,000 people without any expansion of the agricultural area. It would, of course, require considerable intensification of effort and adjustment of production programs.

What are the possibilities for agricultural expansion? The Canada Year Book gives the area of potential agricultural land as 548,000 square miles or 350,000,000 acres, just double the present area of occupied land and almost four times that of the improved land. This estimate appears to be grossly over-optimistic, and is completely out of line with the estimates of officials in the various departments of agriculture, from which Table 22 is largely derived.

In this estimate, no attention is paid to agricultural possibilities in Newfoundland or the Northwest Territories where, admittedly, small areas of potentially arable land exist.

There is room, apparently, for some increase in the agricultural industry. Discounting the present area of improved land by about 5% for areas which should be retired from cultivation because of erosion or exhaustion, there is left about 87,000,000 acres of good land in use. Comparing this with the potentially arable land shows approximately 45,000,000 of potentially arable land still unused. Part of this unused land lies within the occupied area, but it has been estimated that there are about 27,000,000 acres of "unused, reasonably accessible land which is regarded as physically suitable for agricultural settle-

## Table 22   Estimate of Arable Land in Canada

| Soil Zone | Total Area ac. | Potential Arable Land ac. |
|---|---|---|
| Brown Soil Zone | 32,500,000 | 8,000,000 |
| Dark Brown Soil Zone | 35,000,000 | 21,000,000 |
| Black Soil Zone | 42,000,000 | 30,000,000 |
| Grey Wooded Soil Zone | 150,000,000 | 25,000,000 |
| High Lime Soil Zone | 20,000,000 | 500,000 |
| Cordilleran Zone | 230,000,000 | 4,750,000 |
| Pacific Coast Zone | 4,000,000 | 750,000 |
| Grey Brown Podzolic Soil Zone | 25,000,000 | 15,000,000 |
| Eastern Podzol Soil Zone | 50,000,000 | 10,000,000 |
| Precambrian Shield* | 692,000,000 | 17,000,000 |
| Totals (Nine Provinces) | 1,280,500,000 | 132,000,000 |

*Includes Hudson Bay Lowland.

ment". [1] For the most part this land does not occur in large uniform areas and, in order to include it, an almost equal area of non-arable natural pasture or woodland will need to be occupied. Thus, Canada might some day expect to have a total of 225,000,000 acres occupied as farm land, of which 132,000,000 acres would be arable and 86,000,000 acres in crop each year. Under sufficient pressure this figure could probably be raised to 100,000,000 acres. If 2.5 acres would still provide food for one person, this area would feed 40,000,000 people. There would, also, be the live stock output of many millions of acres of natural pasture lands to supplement the yields of food crops.

There are many types of farming in Canada, including extensive grain growing, dairying, various sorts of mixed crop and livestock economies, and numerous specialties, such as truck gardening, canning crops, and fruit growing. Livestock ranching flourishes in the rough foothills of Alberta and the interior of British Columbia; while, even in some parts of Eastern Canada, livestock grazing is the major industry.

Agriculture has undergone great changes in recent years. While there are areas where small scale unmechanized, subsistence or part-time agriculture is carried on with little improvement in methods, commercial agriculture has been evolving. Combines have revolutionized grain harvesting in the Prairie Provinces, while rural electrification has made possible the use of all sorts of mechanical devices on the dairy and mixed farms of the east. The result has been the enlargement of the scope of the individual enterprise. Farms are becoming larger and less numerous; production is rising, but farm population is decreasing. As the population of Canada rises, there will be greater attention given to the demands of the domestic

*Courtesy Exp. Farms Service*
Plate 107. Self propelled combines save labour on many Canadian Farms.

market and less effort directed to the production of bulk goods for export. The physical volume of the production of many commodities will increase, but the fraction of the national wealth derived from agriculture will continue to shrink in comparison with that derived from secondary industries.

Farm population in 1951 stood at about 2,912,000, having lost almost ten per cent in the past two decades. This decrease is greater in some regions than others, but it should not continue indefinitely. The increased demands for food, which will come from the expanding total population, will result in the increase of specialized types of farming. The increase in farm workers thus employed will compensate for the decrease due to mechanization in the large scale agricultural areas. Agriculture will continue to be an important basic industry, but the farm population will always be a relatively small minority.

## Forestry

The forest area of Canada is more than 1,300,000 square miles, of which 450,000 may be classed as productive and accessible, and another 400,000 as a productive,

[1]Hurd, W.B. *Post-war agricultural possibilities in Canada.* Journal of Farm Economics 27, pp. 388-404. 1945.

but at present unaccessible, reserve. The total stand of accessible merchantable timber is estimated to be about 200,000,000 000 cubic feet. Trees large enough for saw-logs contain 250,000,000,000 board feet of lumber and there are 1,700,000,000 cords of pulpwood, fuel wood, posts and mining timber. The annual depletion in recent years has been about 3,500,000,000 cubic feet of which about 75% was used and 25% wasted by fire, insects or disease. This is roughly 1.75% of the total, a rate which is somewhat in excess of the annual growth of accessible forests. Depletion is probably more severe in the saw-timber than in the pulpwood reserves.

## UTILIZATION OF TIMBER 1925-'47

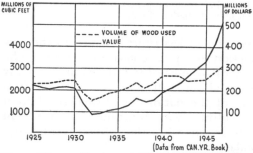

Figure 297. *Utilization of Timber, 1925-47.* (Data from D.B.S.)

One-eighth of Canada's net production in 1951 was derived from forest products. This, however, is the result of both primary and secondary industries. Woods operations, alone, accounted for a total of $600,000,000 and provided about 3% of the total employment, with more than 200,000 men in the woods at the winter peak. About 8,000 sawmills were in operation, employing 62,000 men and turning out $590,000,000 of saw mill products, including 7,000,000 M f.b.m. of lumber. Almost one-half the lumber was exported.

The pulp and paper industry includes three classes of mills; 34 which make pulp only, 26 which make paper only, and 66 combined pulp and paper mills, a total of 126 establishments.

Employing more than 57,000 men and paying $213,000,000 in salaries and wages, the mills produced 9,315,000 tons of pulp worth $728,000,000. About 12,000,000 cords of pulpwood were used. About one-quarter of the pulp was exported, the remainder being converted into 7,225,000 tons of paper, worth $824,000,000. Newsprint production was 5,560,000 tons of which over 90% was exported.

Forestry and the industries directly connected with it employ approximately 300,000 men and support, directly, a population of three-quarters of a million Canadians. Much of Canada is bound to remain in forest and national planning must envisage a considerable increase in the employment offered by wood producing and wood using industries. The emphasis in the past has been entirely upon wood using, while nature has been left the job of producing, unaided, the required supplies. The current estimates indicate that it is time that forestry should also be considered a type of crop husbandry, as well as a harvesting operation. Such a program would have a marked effect upon the distribution of population in the forested area by the creation of permanent forest villages, instead of the temporary loggers' and pulp-cutters' shanties which have characterized the human occupance of the forest for a century and a half. The forest should be regarded as a permanent asset, capable of providing a living for 1,000,000 Canadians.

### Fisheries

Fishing is Canada's oldest industry, predating any permanent settlement. The waters off the coasts comprise some of the most important fishing grounds in the world. With the accession of Newfoundland, Canada now has the most valuable fisheries in the world. Nevertheless, it is a minor industry, since it brings in less than 1.0% of the national income. The industry is, however, of great importance to the coastal communities, providing full time or seasonal employment for 90,000 persons. About 70,000 of these are engaged in catching fish, and 20,000 are employed in processing plants. The total value of fish and fish productes marketed in 1951 amounted to about $200,000,000, of which British Columbia produced 42%, the Maritime Provinces 31% and Newfoundland 14%. Since the fishery statistics of Newfoundland, prior to union, were not taken on the same basis as those of the other provinces, all comparisons must be regarded as approximations only. The trends for the thirty-year period 1918-48 are shown in figure 298. In spite of considerable fluctuation, both the total weight of all fish caught and total value have shown an upward trend in the three decades.

The salmon fisheries have for a good many years been the most valuable, followed by cod, herring, lobsters, sardines and halibut.

Nearly all the salmon and halibut and a large proportion of the herring are taken in British Columbia waters thus making that province the leader in the industry. Nova Scotia, in second place, relies almost equally on cod and lobsters, with haddock in third place. Newfoundland, which may in the future occupy second place among the provinces, relies on cod for more than half the total. In New Brunswick, the leaders are sardines,

lobsters and herring, with cod in fourth place. Quebec, the province which ranks last in sea fisheries, relies on cod, herring and lobsters. Ontario and Manitoba both have valuable inland fisheries which, in some years, surpass in value the output of Quebec. White fish, herring, pickerel and lake trout are the most important fish taken from the inland lakes. The inland fisheries take about 900,000 cwt, of fish per year, with a value of about $21,000,000 in 1951.

The fisherman uses a great deal of expensive equipment. The value of the trawlers, draggers, schooners, boats, nets traps and other gear used in sea fishing was estimated at about $69,000,000 in 1950. The inland fishermen had $11,500,000 invested in tugs, boats, nets and other equipment. The capital investment of the fishermen of Newfoundland was over $12,000,000 according to the census of 1945.

Very closely connected with fishing itself, is the fish processing industry. It is carried on in about 600 widely scattered canneries, freezing and reduction plants and fish curing establishments. Some 250 canneries operate in Canada. Of these 125, located in the Maritime Provinces, are concerned wholly or mainly with lobsters, while 30 in British Columbia are concerned wholly or mainly with salmon. Clams, scallops, pilchards, herring and sardines are also canned in large numbers. Fish curing plants also number about 250, and are most numerous in Nova Scotia and Quebec. In 1947, there were 95 freezing and reduction plants, more than half of which were located in Nova Scotia and British Columbia.

The statistics in Table 23 show certain definite trends. The number of canneries. particularly of lobster canneries, has greatly decreased although the total catch has risen slightly. There has been concentration of the work in larger canneries, and a great increase in the fresh lobster trade. Fish curing establishments have increased, except in British Columbia. A marked increase is

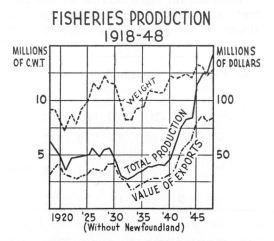

Figure 298. *Fisheries Production, 1918-48.* (Data from D.B.S.)

shown, also, in the number of freezing and reduction plants in all provinces, which is an indication of the growing importance of the fresh fish market. Newfoundland, also is beginning to share in the fresh frozen fish trade.

In 1937, the fish processing plants employed 14,000 people and paid $4,000,000 in salaries and wages: in 1947, 18,600 persons were paid $16,600,000. This shows some improvement, but the work is still very largely part time and seasonal and the workers in fish processing as a group are compelled to accept a lower standard of living than any other large group of industrial workers in Canada.

Fish catching and processing has, in the past, been the mainstay of a scattered and isolated coastal population, using traditional and antiquated methods of production and marketing and, therefore, compelled to accept a low standard of living. They produced a cheap article for the overseas market, the dried fish being sold chiefly in the Mediterranean, West Indian and Latin American markets. The depression and World War II effectively closed much of this market. In 1937, the United States took 48½ per cent of the fish exports; the United Kingdom, 23%; Australia and New Zealand, 8%; France about 3%; British West Indies, 3½%; Latin America, 2½% and South Africa, 2%. Since the war, the share exported to the United States has risen to 68% in 1948, while the share taken by the United Kingdom has fallen to 2%.

Canadians are not large eaters of fish, the annual consumption being about 12 pounds per head of all fish products. This is only about one-eighth of the amount available from domestic production, thus, fully seven-eighths of all the fish caught by Canadian fishermen must find an export market. Compared with meats, fish protein is much cheaper and, with increasing population, it would seem reasonable to expect Canadians to eat more fish. This in turn would lead to a still greater proportion of the catch being marketed fresh or frozen, with a consequently higher return to the fisherman. Along with the mechanization now in progress, the change in market demand may bring about a geographical redistribution of the industry and the people dependent upon it. The isolated shore hamlets will be abandoned in favour of a few more centralized fishing ports.

## Trapping and the Fur Trade

The fur trade is a minor source of Canadian wealth today but, in age and historical importance, it ranks along with the fisheries. From earliest times the Basque and Breton fishermen traded for furs as a sideline. With the building of Tadoussac in 1599, the fur trade became an independent and exclusive enterprise. Quebec, Montreal and Three Rivers were founded

| Table 23 | | Fish Processing Plants in Canada * | | | | | | | | | | |
|---|---|---|---|---|---|---|---|---|---|---|---|---|
| | P.E.I. | | N.S. | | N.B. | | Que. | | B.C. | | Can. | |
| | 1937 | 1947 | 1937 | 1947 | 1937 | 1947 | 1937 | 1947 | 1937 | 1947 | 1937 | 1947 |
| Canneries | 78 | 63 | 84 | 47 | 92 | 80 | 87 | 20 | 41 | 39 | 382 | 249 |
| Fish curing establishments | 8 | 2 | 69 | 110 | 26 | 59 | 44 | 72 | 31 | 7 | 178 | 250 |
| Fresh fish freezing and reduction plants | 0 | 3 | 8 | 34 | 7 | 14 | 9 | 20 | 13 | 24 | 37 | 95 |
| Totals | 86 | 68 | 161 | 191 | 125 | 153 | 140 | 112 | 85 | 70 | 597 | 594 |

*Data from Canada Year Books.

as fur trading posts. The French traders took in enormous quantities of pelts, and the beaver skin, for decades, was the recognized unit of Canadian currency.

English interest in the fur trade brought about the establishment of the Hudson's Bay Company in 1670 and, from then on, the French traders of the St. Lawrence encountered strong competition to the north. After the English victory, the rivalry continued with the Montreal traders, or the North West Company, taking the place of the French. Eventually, the rivals merged their interests in 1821. As was the case with the French forts, the sites of former Hudson's Bay Posts have given rise to a number of important Canadian cities.

The fur trade has seen great changes. Settlement has pushed the trapper from many once productive areas. The improvements in transportation of the past century have caused furs to take new routes to market. The first revolutionary influence was that of the railroad, but now, even the most isolated posts is "close in" for the air-borne traveller. Competition is keener than ever, and governments have had to take steps to conserve the wild life resources which are the only means of livelihood of the aboriginal population.

Fur trapping is a major industry in an area of over 1,500,000 square miles of Canadian wilderness. Because prices and demand for furs react violently under the influence of world economic conditions, it is difficult at times to prevent over-trapping of valuable species. The enforcement of closed seasons and other trapping regulations have been beneficial, although rather hard to carry out. In this way, the beaver has been brought back from the verge of extinction in recent years. The development of marshlands as, for example, in the Saskatchewan delta, has resulted in a great increase in the muskrat population. All provinces and territories now have trapping licenses. In some provinces trap-lines are registered, others register trapping areas. The individual trapper is, in this way, given an incentive to protect and conserve his stock of fur-bearing animals.

Not all furs, however, come from the wilderness: about one-tenth of the total number of pelts and about one-third of the total value have come from fur farms in recent years. Modern fur farming was started at Tignish, Prince Edward Island, in the 1880's. Foxes were the first fur bearers to be kept in captivity, but now many others, including mink, raccoon, skunk, martin, fisher and rabbit, are also raised. Scientific breeding has stabilized the fur farming business and made it possible to specialize on the new colour phases which bring the highest market prices. In

Figure 299. *Fur Production, 1921-48.* (Data from D.B.S.)

1947, there were over 6,000 fur farms, capitalized at over $26,000,000. They produced and sold over 750,000 pelts, valued at $11,700,000, about 37% of the total value of all furs produced in that year. Fur farms are found in all provinces, but are most numerous in Ontario, Quebec, Alberta and Manitoba.

In recent years the average number of pelts marketed in Canada has been about 7,000,000. Mink, muskrat, beaver, fox, squirrel and ermine are the most important. Both total numbers and total values are shown in figure 299. Except for 1942, when several extra millions of rabbits and squirrels were taken, the numbers show very little variation. Values have fluctuated more widely, ranging from $10,000,000 in 1933 to $43,000,000 in 1946. This has a serious effect on the trapper in the north who has no other source of income. It also results in a rather great year-to-year variation in the number of fur farms.

In 1950 fur manufacturing was carried on in 609 establishments, employing over 6,000 persons and producing goods valued at $61,900,000. Fur dressing and dyeing was carried on in 22 establishments employing about 1,400. More than 13,600,000 pelts were treated, adding to their value by $6,500,000.

Montreal is the leading fur processing centre in Canada. It is, also, the leading fur market but sales are also held in Winnipeg, Regina, Edmonton and Vancouver. The United States and the United Kingdom are the best customers for Canadian furs. In recent years the annual value of this export trade has ranged from $23,000,000 to $30,000,000. On the other hand the average annual value of the furs imported into Canada has been about $22,000,000. Canada's exports, of course, consist of those furs produced in greatest abundance such as mink, beaver, muskrat and fox, while Persian lamb, certain types of muskrat, rabbit and squirrel, opposum and raccoon are imported.

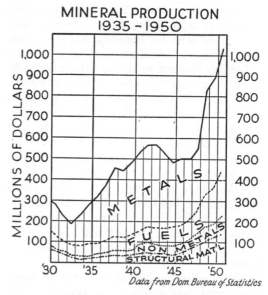

Figure 301. *Mineral Production, 1930-1950.* (Data from D.B.S.) During this period metals have been the leading group.

## Mineral Industries

Minerals are produced from both domestic and imported ores. The industry has grown very rapidly in recent decades, and though it suffered a slight recession at the end of World War II, it has made a quick recovery. The gross production of minerals from domestic sources has more than doubled in value since 1945, when it was $499,000,000. It reached $645,000,000 in 1947 and was estimated to be $1,245,000,000 for 1951 (Figure 300). The addition of the gross primary processing of imported minerals brought the total to over $1,000,000,000 in 1947. Although much of the increase in value is due to the advance in prices, there have also been large gains in the physical volume of production.

The minerals of Canada may be divided into four great groups: (a) metals, (b) mineral fuels, (c) non-metallic industrial minerals, (d) clay and other structural materials. Figure 301 gives the proportionate values of each of these groups in the annual productions from 1930 to 1950. Met-

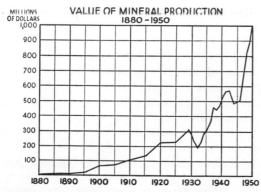

Figure 300. *Mineral Production, 1880-1950.* (Data from D.B.S.)

als account for about 60% of the production.

## Metals

The chief metals produced in Canada are gold, copper, nickel, zinc, lead, platinum, silver and iron; but there are, also, many minor ones, including antimony, bismuth, cadmium, calcium, chromium, magnesium, manganese, molybdenum, radium, selenium, tellurium, tin, titanium, uranium and tungsten. Some of the latter are produced only as ores or concentrates and exported for refining. In addition to the ores produced in Canada, some ores, notably those of aluminum and iron, have been imported into Canada in large amounts for the production of metals. The Canadian production of metals is very important, not only in the internal economy of the country, but in world trade, for Canada ranks high in the production of a number of important metals.

## Gold

Gold is mined in Nova Scotia, Quebec, Ontario, Manitoba, Saskatchewan, Alberta, British Columbia, Yukon and the Northwest Territories. The leaders, however, are Ontario, Quebec and British Columbia. The principal producing districts are Porcupine, Kirkland Lake, Larder Lake, Thunder Bay and Patricia in Ontario; Rouyn and Malartic in Quebec; Rice Lake, God's Lake and Flin Flon in Manitoba; Bridge River and Hedley in British Columbia; and Yellowknife in the Northwest Territories. About 85% of the production comes from gold-bearing quartz; about 12%, from mines in which gold is found with ores of copper, nickel, zinc, etc.; and about 3%, from alluvial deposits.

| Table 24 | Canada's Rank in World Metal Production — 1949 * | | | |
|---|---|---|---|---|
| | First | Second | Third | Fourth |
| Aluminum** | U.S. | Canada | France | Norway |
| (Thousands of short tons) | 603 | 367 | 59.7 | 39.4 |
| Cadmium | U.S. | Canada | Australia | U.K. |
| (Thousands of lbs.) | 8,024 | 845 | 469 | 222 |
| Copper | U.S. | Chile | Rhodesia | Canada |
| (Thousands of short tons) | 762 | 409 | 290 | 259 |
| Gold | S. Africa | Canada | U.S. | Australia |
| (Thousands of fine oz.) | 11,700 | 4,104 | 2,000 | 890 |
| Lead | U.S. | Mexico | Australia | Canada |
| (Thousands of short tons) | 404 | 257 | 224 | 160 |
| Nickel | Canada | New Caledonia | U.S. | —— |
| (Thousands of short tons) | 128 | 3 | 0.8 | —— |
| Platinum | Canada | S. Africa | Colombia | U.S. |
| (Thousands of fine oz.) | 151.3 | 94.1 | 19.7 | 19.0 |
| Silver | Mexico | U.S. | Canada | Peru |
| (Millions of fine oz.) | 49.4 | 34.4 | 17.3 | 10.6 |
| Zinc | U.S. | Canada | Mexico | Australia |
| (Thousands of short tons) | 584 | 290 | 211 | 169 |

*Excluding the U.S.S.R. which does not report production. It may rank second in nickel and third in gold and platinum and have important standing in other metals as well.
**All Canadian aluminum is processed from imported ores. (*Northern Miner. 1950*)

## GOLD PRODUCTION·1911-1950

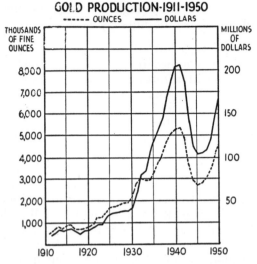

Figure 302. *Production of Gold in Canada, 1911-50.* (Data from D.B.S.) The production of gold, both by weight and value, reached a peak in 1941, with a sharp reduction during the latter part of World War II.

Gold production rose steadily to a peak of 5,345,000 ounces in 1941, but slumped off rapidly when manpower was more urgently needed in the production of war materials. Since the war, it has begun to climb back again, allowing Canada to maintain her place as the second ranking gold producer in the world. (See figure 302)

## COPPER PRODUCTION
### 1911 – 1950

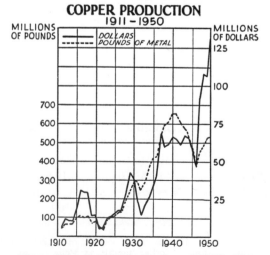

Figure 303. *Copper Production, 1911-50.* (Data from D.B.S.)

## Copper

Copper is a very active element, being found in many different compounds along with sulphur, iron, antimony and arsenic in deep seated igneous rocks, or as carbonates and oxides in secondary formations. Native or metallic copper is also found occasionally. In Canada, the ores of copper are usually found along with those of other metals. About one-half of Canada's copper comes from the Sudbury district, where it is mined along with nickel ores. The International Nickel Company of Canada, at Copper Cliff, produces both converter copper and the refined metal. Falconbridge Nickel Mines, at Falconbridge, produces nickel-copper matte which is exported to Norway for refining. Western Quebec produces about 20% of Canada's copper. It is smelted at Noranda and sent to the Canadian Copper Refinery, at Montreal East, for refining. About the same amount is produced in Northern Manitoba; blister copper from the smelter at Flin Flon being also sent to Montreal for refining. Most of the remainder of the copper output comes from the Britannia and Granby mines in British Columbia, and is exported to the United States for refining. The output of refined copper in 1951 was 270,000 tons, (See figure 303) of which about half was used in Canada and one-half exported, mainly to the United Kingdom and the United States.

## Nickel

About 90% of the world's supply of nickel, exclusive of the production of the U.S.S.R., comes from the nickel-copper ores of the Sudbury area. There are two producers: International, with its smelters at Copper Cliff and Coniston, and its refinery at Port Colborne; and Falconbridge, with its mine and smelter a few miles northeast of Sudbury, and its refinery in Norway. A small amount of nickel is recovered from the silver-cobalt-nickel-arsenic ores of the Cobalt district, while nickel bearing ores are also being developed at Lynn Lake and Moak Lake in Northern Manitoba.

Nickel is an extremely useful metal. As an alloy in steel, it imparts great strength and toughness. During World War I, the demand for armour plate just about doubled the Canadian output. In the interwar years, many other markets were developed. Among others, monel metal, an alloy of copper, nickel and iron, is extremely useful. It is a white substance, stronger than steel, yet it can be annealed and rolled like copper. It does not rust nor corrode and is used on stoves, kitchen and shop furnishings. During World War II, nickel production rose to 288,000,000 lbs. in one year, over three times the amount produced in the peak year of World War I. (See figure 304)

## NICKEL PRODUCTION
### 1911 – 1950

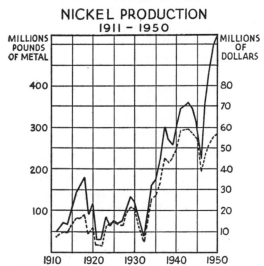

Figure 304. *Nickel Production, 1911-50.* (Data from D.B.S.)

## Lead

Lead is produced mainly in British Columbia from the lead-zinc ores of the Sullivan Mine, refined at the Trail Smelter of the Consolidated Mining and Smelting Company. In 1948, Canada produced 160,000 tons (Figure 305), about 3% of which came from Quebec and Yukon. In the same year, Canada used over 62,000 tons of refined lead; of which 20,000 tons

## LEAD PRODUCTION
### 1911 – 1950

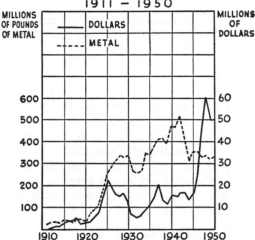

Figure 305. *Lead Production, 1911-50.* (Data from D.B.S.)

were used in storage batteries; 15,000 tons, for babbit metal and solder, 12,000 tons, for covering wires and cables; 10,000 tons, for pigments; and 5,000 tons, for other purposes. Exports totalled over 103,000 tons.

## Zinc

The Sullivan Mine in British Columbia is, also, the largest producer of zinc. Other mines in B.C. produce small amounts. The province produced 60% of the Canadian

## ZINC PRODUCTION
### 1911–50

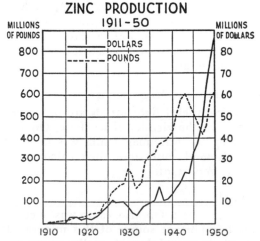

Figure 306. *Zinc Production, 1911-50.* (Data from D.B.S.)

total of 330,000 tons in 1951. The remainder is produced by Manitoba and Saskatchewan (Flin Flon smelter 22%) and Western Quebec (20%). About three-fourths of the zinc is exported.

## Silver

Silver is obtained as a by-product of most gold and base-metal mines. For many years, Cobalt, in Ontario, supplied most of the silver output, but it is not very important now. British Columbia now leads, with about 40% of the total. In recent years, the total has varied between 12,000,-000 and 24,000,000 fine ounces worth from $5,000,000 to $22,000,000 per year.

## The Platinum Group

Platinum, palladium, rhodium, ruthenium, osmium and iridium occur in the nickel-copper ores at Sudbury, and are recovered in the tank residues from the nickel refinery at Port Colborne, whence they are sent to the refinery at Acton, England. This source has made Canada the leading producer in recent years. The annual value varies from $10,000,000 to $25,000,000.

## Radium and Uranium

Canada is one of the chief producers of radio-active minerals. The earliest important find was at Port Radium, N.W.T. Large producers are now to be found in the Beaverlodge area of Saskatchewan, and near Blind River and Bancroft in the Province of Ontario.

## Calcium and Magnesium

These useful light metals are being produced in the vicinity of Renfrew, Ontario. During the war, magnesium was in greatest demand, but since then calcium has been important.

## Cobalt

The Cobalt, Ontario, camp was once the most important source of this mineral. It is still produced, but in smaller quantities. The refining is done at Deloro, Ontario.

## Iron

The use of iron and steel is one of the chief supporting techniques of modern civilization but, up to the present, Canada has experienced a shortage of domestic raw materials. Bog iron ore was early discovered near Three Rivers, Quebec, and the first processing plant was erected about 1730. In the 19th century, iron ore was produced at Bathurst, N.B., Torbrook and Londonderry, N.S. A complete iron works was for years in operation at Londonderry. In 1895, the Wabana mines on Bell Island, Newfoundland, were opened and, a few years later, the Sydney iron and steel works were established and have, ever since, taken about half the yearly production of Wabana ore. Along the southern margin of the Canadian Shield in Ontario, a number of small mines were found; and the Marmora furnaces began to operate in 1820, but have long been discontinued. Recently, geophysical prospecting has indicated that the district contains important bodies of ore. In Northern Ontario, the Moose Mountain, Magpie and, particularly, the Old Helen Mine produced several million tons of ore between 1900 and 1923. The steel plants at Sault Ste. Marie and Hamilton, from 1895 on, relied mainly, and after 1923 entirely, upon ores imported from American mines. From 1923 to 1939, Canada produced no iron ore.

Steep Rock, 135 miles west of Port Arthur, and the new Helen Mine in the Michipicoten area, both began production in 1939, and have raised nearly all the ore produced in Ontario since that date. In 1951, Canadian production was about 4,-700,000 tons, of which 1,500,000 were from Steep Rock, 1,400,000 from the Helen Mine and 1,800,000 from Wabana. This was almost equivalent to the amount used in Canadian furnaces. Except at Sydney, where Wabana ore is used, most of the ore used in the Canadian iron and steel industry is imported, in order to get a proper mixture, while the larger part of the Ontario ore is exported. About 50% of the Wabana ore also is exported, going to Europe. Steel production has varied from a low of 380,-000 tons, in 1932, to over 3,500,000 tons in the year 1951. A considerable part of the steel used in Canada is imported from the United States. The newest development is in the centre of the Labrador peninsula, astride the Labrador-Quebec boundary. Here, on the Lake Plateau, a vast iron-bearing rock formation, similar to that of the Mesabi Range in Minnesota, has been known to geologists since 1885; although the first ore body was not found until 1929. Since 1947, diamond drilling has proven the presence of a 90 mile zone containing more than 400,000,000 tons of high grade ore which may be shipped direct from open pits. More than 200,000,000 tons lies within a two-mile radius of Knob Lake.

In order to haul the ore, 360 miles of railway have been constructed from Knob Lake to Seven Islands on the Gulf of St. Lawrence. Leaving Seven Islands, it ascends the valleys of the Moisie, Nipisis and Wacouna rivers for 100 miles, before reaching the height of land at 1,900 feet. The remaining 260 miles were built on the nearly level plateau surface. New hydro-electric power plants have been built at both ends of the line.

The railway, port, power development, townsites and mining equipment require an initial capital expenditure of $225,-000,000. Construction was very largely completed in 1955, and, from 1956 on, it is planned to ship 10,000,000 tons of ore per year. The great market for this ore is in the interior of the continent, providing a powerful argument for the completion of the St. Lawrence seaway to permit the operation of large ore carriers. Further north along the Ungava Trough other important iron discoveries have also been made. It is expected that this ore will be shipped through new ports to be built on Ungava Bay.

An important new mine, also, will soon be in operation at Marmora in Southern Ontario.

## Aluminum

No aluminum ore is mined in Canada, but an abundance of hydro-electric energy has enabled the development of a smelting and refining industry which is second only to that of the United States. During World War II, production was greatly expanded, reaching a peak of 991 million pounds in 1943. (See figure 307) Over 80% of the aluminum is exported as bars, blocks, etc., largely to the United States and the United Kingdom. The industry

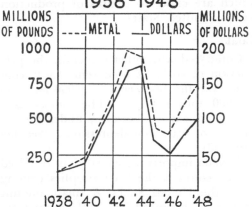

Figure 307. *Aluminum Production, 1938-48.* (Data from D.B.S.)

was largely centred in the Province of Quebec, but new plants have been erected at Kitimat in British Columbia.

## Fuels

The fuel situation in Canada is anomalous, for, in spite of great reserves of both coal and petroleum, the output has never been enough to fill the domestic requirement. This is an accident of location. Coal is found in the Maritime Provinces and in Western Canada; oil is found in the West, particularly in Alberta, but the greatest demands for both are in the

### Table 25          Coal Reserves in Canada

| Province | Probable Reserves (000 tons) | Possible Additional Reserves (000 tons) | Total Reserves (000 tons) |
|---|---|---|---|
| Nova Scotia | 1,967,024 | 1,147,382 | 3,114,406 |
| New Brunswick | 89,814 | 11,566 | 101,380 |
| Ontario | 100,000 | 50,000 | 150,000 |
| Manitoba | 33,000 | 67,200 | 100,800 |
| Saskatchewan | 13,126,880 | 11,004,000 | 24,130,880 |
| Alberta | 34,437,740 | 13,436,560 | 47,874,300 |
| British Columbia | 11,795,480 | 7,034,556 | 18,830,036 |
| Yukon | 434,560 | 1,449,840 | 1,884,400 |
| Northwest Territories | 140,000 | 2,489,760 | 2,629,760 |
| Canada | 62,125,098 | 36,690,864 | 98,815,962 |

Great Lakes and St. Lawrence Lowland, which are closer to centres of production in the United States.

## Coal

Compared with other minerals, the production of coal has been remarkably constant, varying between 11,000,000 and 19,000,000 tons per year. The values have fluctuated widely, however, under the influence of wars and depressions. (See figure 308).

Canada imports more coal than is mined in the country, the chief supplies coming from the United States. A small amount of coal is exported. In 1951 imports totalled 27,000,000 tons, while exports were only 435,000 tons. The total consumption for that year was over 44,000,000 tons.

Nova Scotia (6.4 million tons) and Alberta (7.8 million tons) were the chief producers, while Ontario is the chief importer of coal. The coal mined in Nova Scotia, New Brunswick, British Columbia and Yukon is classed as bituminous, that of Alberta is bituminous and sub-bituminous, while Saskatchewan produces lignite only. The coal supply of Canada for the year 1951 is summarized in Table 26.

## Petroleum

The petroleum supply of Canada is even more unequally distributed than its coal supply. Apart from a small amount produced in Ontario, and a very small amount in New Brunswick, all the oil is obtained in Western Canada, east of the mountains. Alberta has been important since the discovery of Turner Valley in 1914. Its output eventually reached a peak of

### Table 26          Canadian Coal Supply—1951

| Grade | Canadian Coal | | Imported Coal tons | Available for Consumption tons |
|---|---|---|---|---|
| | Produced tons | Exported tons | | |
| Anthracite | ----------- | ---------- | 3,892,000 | 3,892,000 |
| Bituminous | 13,363,000 | 304,000 | 22,459,000 | 35,519,000 |
| Sub-bituminous | 3,000,000 | ---------- | ---------- | 3,000,000 |
| Lignite | 2,223,000 | 1,000 | ---------- | 2,222,000 |
| All Grades | 18,586,000 | 305,000 | 26,351,000 | 44,633,000 |

Canada Year Book

## COAL PRODUCTION
### 1911 - 1949

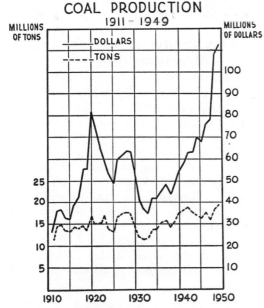

Figure 308. *Coal Production, 1911-49.* (Data from D.B.S.) Production of coal has shown a moderate increase in physical volume due mainly to greater development of mines in Alberta. Values have fluctuated widely.

10,000,000 barrels in 1942 and began to decline. In 1947, the Leduc field near Edmonton was discovered and, since that, several other fields have also been found.

## PETROLEUM PRODUCTION
### 1911-49

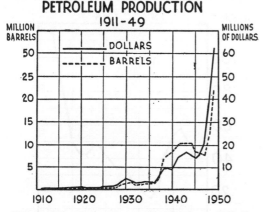

Figure 309. *Petroleum Production, 1911-49.* (Data from D.B.S.) New fields in Alberta have been responsible for the recent rapid increase in production which is going a long way toward making C a n a d a self-sufficient in petroleum products.

By 1952, the proven reserves were over one and a half billion barrels, enough for ten years' requirements. Because of the distance to consuming markets, a pipeline was built to the head of Lake Superior and later extended to Sarnia, Ontario. A second line was built to Vancouver. In Ontario, pipelines have been laid from both Sarnia and Montreal to Toronto and Hamilton. Refineries have been enlarged and new ones built in several Canadian cities. Total oil production was over 60,000,000 barrels (worth $143,000,000) but the refineries used 137,000,000 barrels in 1952, the balance being imported. Further discoveries are being made every year, not only in Alberta but in Saskatchewan and Manitoba as well.

Alberta also possesses a large reserve of petroleum in the Athabasca tar sands, which will be valuable in the future.

Natural gas is produced in New Brunswick near Moncton, in southwestern Ontario and in Alberta. The production in 1952 was about 87,000,000 cu. ft. valued at $9,300,000.

## Non-Metallic, Industrial Minerals

The important non-metallic, industrial minerals, produced in Canada, are asbestos, gypsum and salt, but there are numerous other items, including feldspar, fluorspar, graphite, iron oxide, magnesitic dolomite, mica, nepheline syenite, sulphur, silica, sodium sulphate, soapstone and talc. In 1952, the production of these commodities was valued at over $124,000,000.

### Asbestos

Asbestos has long been mined in the Eastern Townships of Quebec. From a value of $24,700 in 1880, production has risen to $88,823,000 in 1952. (See figure 310). This is the world's largest source of asbestos, most of which finds a market in the United States. Another Canadian mine was opened in 1949, at Matheson, Ontario.

Asbestos is also being mined in British Columbia.

## ASBESTOS PRODUCTION
### 1911-49

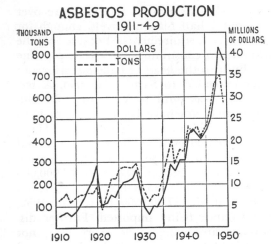

Figure 310. *Asbestos Production 1911-49.* (Data from D.B.S.) Canada is the largest producer of asbestos in the world.

### Gypsum

Gypsum is known to occur in nearly every province except, perhaps, Saskatchewan and Prince Edward Island. Although produced in quantity in New Brunswick, Ontario, Manitoba and British Columbia, about 85% of the Canadian output is obtained in Nova Scotia. Crude gypsum is exported by sea to the United States, where it is processed for builders' supplies. Production reached a peak of 3,593,000 tons in 1952, with a value of $6,073,000.

### Salt

Salt is obtained in Nova Scotia, Ontario, Manitoba and Alberta. In all four provinces it is recovered by evaporation of brine pumped from deep wells. At Malagash in Nova Scotia, it is mined as rock salt. Peak production in 1952 was 992,000 tons worth $7,500,000.

### Fluorspar and Nepheline Syenite

Fluorspar, obtained chiefly from St. Lawrence on the Burin Peninsula of Newfoundland is used as a flux in steel making and aluminum reduction.

The only source of nepheline syenite in the western hemisphere is at Blue Mountain near Lakefield, Ontario. It is used in glass manufacture and as a glaze in ceramics.

## Clay Products and Other Structural Materials

Structural materials form a very important group of mineral products valued at more than $164,000,000 in the year 1952 (See figure 311), or about one-eighth of the total mineral production. The importance of construction in the post-war economy is, of course, the basis of this activity. Besides brick and tile, this group includes Portland cement, lime, sand, gravel and stone. More than two-thirds of the total production is centred in Quebec and Ontario, because of the rapid growth of the cities and the extensive highway construction programs of those provinces.

## Employment in the Mineral Industry

During the years 1950-52 the mineral industries of Canada have given employment to an average of 125,000 men each year. Three fifths of these worked in metal-

## VALUE OF CLAY PRODUCTS and OTHER STRUCTURAL MATERIALS
### 1926-1949

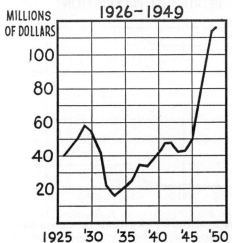

Figure 311. *Value of Clay Products and other Structural Materials, 1926-49.* (Data from D.B.S.)

lic mines and smelters. In 1951, these men earned an average of $3,300 each. The second group in importance are those producing fuels, about 28,000 in number. In 1951, the average wage for this group was a little over $2,800 each. The workers in non-metallic mines and plants in 1951 numbered 10,600, half of them in asbestos. Their average wage was $2,900. Clay products and structural minerals employed 14,700, paying an average wage of $2,700.

Through its payroll the mineral industry supports a population of almost 500,000 people, or 3% of the total. It is the mainstay of several towns and cities ranging from 5,000 to 50,000 in population. Mining has contributed much to the development of Canada, but it is a wasting asset since, eventually, even the best mine or oil well must become exhausted. For a long time to come, however, mining may be expected to support even more people than it does at present. The expansion of the first half of the 20th century has been phenomenal, but it has not yet reached its peak.

## Power

Water power is Canada's most important single natural resource. Although the

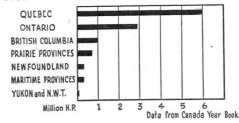

Figure 313. *Distribution of Developed Water Power in the Regions of Canada, 1948.* (Data from D.B.S.) Quebec has about half the total power, Ontario about one quarter of the total.

market value of power is only about 1.5% of the annual gross production of the country, it, alone, makes possible the exploitation of the mineral and forest resources and the vast development of secondary industry in the towns and cities. The invention of long distance transmission of electricity provided the key to the industrial development of Canada. Among the countries of the world, Canada is outclassed by only the U.S.S.R. in total water-power potential, and in total installed capacity by the United States, alone.

The total potential power at ordinary minimum flow is estimated to be 32,000,000 h.p., while the total possible installation permitted by present recorded resources at ordinary six months flow is 52,000,000 h.p. (See figure 312). Turbine installations in 1950 stood at about 12,000,000 h.p., with many new power plants in the process of construction. It is a great achievement, but less than half of the easily available minimum flow has yet been put to work.

In large measure, the distribution of available water power in Canada compensates for the unequal distribution of coal resources, fully 50% of the available energy being located in Ontario and Quebec, which constitute the critical fuel region.

The regional distribution of developed power is shown in Figure 313. Quebec has half of the turbine installations, while a further 25% of the total developed power is found in Ontario. These two prov-

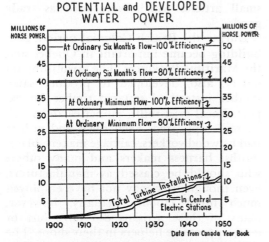

Figure 312. *Potential Water Power in Canada, and Growth of Power Installations, 1900-50.* As yet, only half of the available minimum flow has been developed. (Data from D.B.S.)

inces are, also, the ones in which further construction is going forward most rapidly.

More than 91% of the total power is developed in central electric stations. In 1900, the corresponding percentage was 33.5, thus showing the tremendous growth made possible by long distance transmission of electricity. In 1948, central hydro-electric stations produced 97% of all the electric current put on the market.

More than two-thirds of the other installations are found in pulp and paper mills. In addition, this industry purchases about 33% of all power sold by the central stations for industrial use. Domestic or residential requirement for electric power amounts to only one-tenth of the total production of the central stations.

With a total turbine installation of about 14,000,000 horse power in 1951, there was an output of almost 50,000,000,000 Kilowatt hours and a total revenue of $324,000,-000. In 665 plants nearly 33,000 persons earned $89,000,000. This is not great in comparison with the total employment for Canada, but if any one enterprise should be given special mention, this one should be regarded as the key to Canadian development.

Only a small amount of power is provided in other ways. In the coal producing areas of the Maritimes and the Prairie Provinces, central electric stations are powered by coal-burning steam plants. The use of imported coal in standby or supplementary central electric stations is also a feature of the Ontario power system. Many manufacturing plants, especially sawmills, use steam power and there are also some which use internal combustion engines.

## Manufacturing

The recent development of manufacturing in Canada has been most spectacular. Although she has a small population in comparison with many other countries, yet not more than 5 or 6 surpass her in volume of manufacturing. It is natural that there should be a variety of large enterprises concerned with the processing of natural products of the country, and this has led to a great industrial development; but, in addition, there has been an enormous growth of secondary manufacturing which has given Canada self-sufficiency in a great many lines of consumers' goods.

### Early History

Manufacturing is almost as old as settlement. The first agriculture in Canada was the growing of a crop of grain at Port Royal in 1605, the grinding of that grain was a manufacturing process. Even before this, undoubtedly, articles of clothing had been made from local furs and wooden tools had been carved from local wood. Manufacturing began with the settlement of Quebec in 1608 also. The colonial policy of France did not favour the manufacture of any article which could be imported from France, but the uncertainties of transportation forced the colonists to make many things for themselves. The census of 1681 enumerates a large number of tailors, shoemakers, masons, carpenters, gunsmiths and makers of edged tools. The raising of sheep and flax led to the household industries of spinning and weaving. Hudson's Bay factories, from 1670 on, made many small articles which were used as trade goods.

During the British Colonial period, ship building became important in Quebec and the Maritime Provinces. The sawmilling industry, also, developed to produce sawn lumber instead of squared timber for export. Local grist mills, tanneries and woolen mills appeared. Each town and village had its woodworkers, carriage makers, blacksmiths, harness makers and many others who should be classed as manufacturers, even though they may not have employed much hired labour. Actually, however, many of these artisans did have one or more apprentice helpers in their shops. The geographic pattern of industry was then quite different from the present. The village manufacturers, and many of the villages themselves, have vanished and most of the manufacturing has been concentrated in towns and cities.

Even after Confederation, however, manufacturing grew slowly. The gross value in 1870 was about $222,000,000; in 1900, it was $481,000,000. The great growth in population, and the establishment of important milling, steel, and pulp and paper industries, caused the gross value to rise to nearly $1,200,000,000 in 1910. With the impact of World War I, not only were ships, munitions and other war supplies produced in quantity; but many lines, formerly imported from Europe, were begun by enterprising Canadian manufacturers. By 1920, the gross value had tripled, reaching $3,700,000,000, and there were 592,000 persons employed in manufacturing.

## Recent Development

The annual census of manufacturers, begun in 1917, gives a pretty clear picture of the progress of the industry in the past three decades. Figure 314 shows, in graphic form, both gross and net values from 1917 to 1948. Gross value reached an all-time peak of $11,800,000,000 in the latter year. Inflation and depressions, however, tend to accentuate the variations of the curve, so a physical index has been added to the figure. This is in part plotted from figures published by the Bureau of Statistics and in part approximated by the use of factors derived from annual price indices. According to it, physical volume reached a peak in 1943 under the stress of war-time demands. In that year, also, the number employed in manufacturing reached an all-time peak of 1,241,000. During the next three years, there was some recession, but manufacturing is again on the increase. In brief, the three decades since World War I have seen employment doubled, while the physical output of goods has trebled, and the dollar value increased fourfold.

## Leading Industries

In Table 27 are given the principal statistics of the 30 leading industries of Canada in the year 1951. Each of them had a gross value of production exceeding $160,000,000 and, together, they accounted for 64.7% of the total production. The other statistics in the table are fairly comparable. The outstanding position of four processing industries is notable. Pulp and paper, slaughtering and meat packing, non-ferrous metal smelting and refining and sawmilling account for 20% of all manufactured goods and emphasize the forest, agricultural and mineral resources of the country as well as the manufacturing industries. It is interesting also to compare the changes in rank of the leading industries as shown in Table 28. The non-ferrous metal industry is a comparative newcomer and was not even to be found in the 40 leading industries in 1922. Its place was taken by flour and feed. Since its development in the 1930's, however, it has nearly always been in the top three.

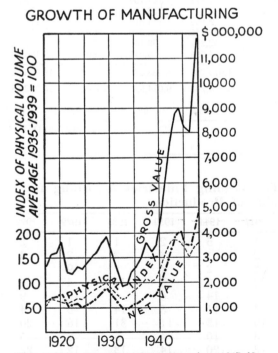

Figure 314. *Growth of Manufacturing, 1917-48.* (Data from D.B.S.) In a period of thirty years the actual physical volume of manufactured goods has increased more than three-fold.

## Table 27          Thirty Leading Industries of Canada in 1951.

| Industry | Estab-lishments | Employ-ees | Salaries and Wages $000 | Cost of Materials $000 | Net Value of Products $000 | Gross Value of Products $000 |
|---|---|---|---|---|---|---|
| 1. Pulp and paper | 126 | 57,291 | 213,170 | 483,014 | 679,258 | 1,237,897 |
| 2. Slaughtering and meat packing | 155 | 20,914 | 62,109 | 767,367 | 120,489 | 892,091 |
| 3. Non-ferrous metals | 17 | 22,814 | 75,475 | 553,659 | 262,973 | 861,316 |
| 4. Motor vehicles | 19 | 30,479 | 101,343 | 469,114 | 271,114 | 742,896 |
| 5. Petroleum products | 52 | 10,611 | 37,079 | 438,467 | 135,903 | 598,941 |
| 6. Sawmills | 7,934 | 62,415 | 132,059 | 313,175 | 271,866 | 591,552 |
| 7. Primary iron and steel | 57 | 33,393 | 108,562 | 223,012 | 209,472 | 464,587 |
| 8. Butter and cheese | 1,690 | 20,900 | 46,782 | 284,603 | 82,416 | 373,746 |
| 9. Rubber goods | 67 | 23,054 | 64,358 | 146,952 | 161,185 | 311,678 |
| 10. Railway rolling stock | 37 | 33,410 | 94,029 | 175,965 | 119,895 | 300,627 |
| 11. Flour mills | 108 | 4,864 | 13,597 | 242,132 | 37,078 | 280,867 |
| 12. Cotton yarn and cloth | 54 | 27,632 | 58,735 | 172,443 | 97,158 | 273,651 |
| 13. Motor vehicle parts | 161 | 21,197 | 65,283 | 142,841 | 117,021 | 263,133 |
| 14. Miscellaneous foods | 328 | 9,194 | 20,965 | 192,186 | 65,325 | 260,431 |
| 15. Bread and bakery products | 2,607 | 32,252 | 67,116 | 121,377 | 116,352 | 245,288 |
| 16. Men's factory clothing | 577 | 32,732 | 62,316 | 131,612 | 106,308 | 238,661 |
| 17. Heavy electrical machinery | 50 | 25,296 | 75,599 | 96,604 | 123,141 | 221,569 |
| 18. Electrical apparatus and supplies | 141 | 21,257 | 60,690 | 100,025 | 119,120 | 221,082 |
| 19. Industrial machinery | 300 | 22,326 | 67,287 | 79,106 | 120,611 | 201,990 |
| 20. Fruit and vegetable preparations | 459 | 16,401 | 30,108 | 116,053 | 82,000 | 200,779 |
| 21. Women's factory clothing | 912 | 28,688 | 56,764 | 102,136 | 95,098 | 197,751 |
| 22. Sheet metal products | 277 | 17,437 | 49,037 | 108,335 | 86,629 | 197,114 |
| 23. Printing and publishing | 801 | 27,300 | 76,242 | 56,976 | 137,863 | 196,718 |
| 24. Furniture | 1,430 | 27,274 | 61,429 | 90,324 | 98,474 | 190,907 |
| 25. Brass and copper products | 153 | 10,077 | 29,318 | 121,704 | 56,176 | 179,998 |
| 26. Sash, door and planing mills | 1,698 | 19,357 | 40,461 | 109,506 | 66,936 | 178,765 |
| 27. Feeds, stock and poultry | 648 | 5,505 | 12,180 | 144,617 | 27,953 | 174,510 |
| 28. Paper boxes and bags | 187 | 13,384 | 32,235 | 102,219 | 68,940 | 172,230 |
| 29. Agricultural implements | 81 | 17,236 | 52,217 | 96,469 | 72,719 | 171,172 |
| 30. Synthetic textiles and silk | 46 | 17,997 | 44,694 | 66,041 | 96,477 | 166,550 |
| TOTAL, 30 INDUSTRIES | 21,082 | 712,687 | 1,911,237 | 6,188,034 | 4,105,950 | 10,608,497 |
| TOTAL, ALL INDUSTRIES | 37,021 | 1,258,375 | 3,276,281 | 9,074,526 | 6,940,947 | 16,392,187 |
| Leading Industries as per cent of all Industries | 57.0 | 57.0 | 58.4 | 68.2 | 59.3 | 64.7 |

Data from D. B. S.

## Table 28          Changes in Rank of Ten Leading Industries According to Gross Value of Production

| | 1951 | 1949 | 1947 | 1944 | 1939 | 1933 | 1929 | 1922 |
|---|---|---|---|---|---|---|---|---|
| Pulp and paper | 1 | 1 | 1 | 5 | 2 | 1 | 1 | 2 |
| Slaughtering and meat packing | 2 | 2 | 2 | 1 | 3 | 3 | 2 | 3 |
| Non-ferrous metals | 3 | 3 | 3 | 2 | 1 | 2 | 9 | -- |
| Motor vehicles | 4 | 4 | 6 | 7 | 5 | 11 | 4 | 6 |
| Petroleum products | 5 | 5 | 9 | 14 | 6 | 6 | 10 | 9 |
| Sawmills | 6 | 6 | 4 | 11 | 8 | 14 | 5 | 4 |
| Primary Iron and Steel | 7 | 8 | 10 | 13 | 11 | 31 | 16 | 20 |
| Butter and Cheese | 8 | 7 | 8 | 10 | 4 | 5 | 6 | 5 |
| Rubber goods | 9 | 15 | 12 | 20 | 14 | 13 | 12 | 22 |
| Railway rolling stock | 10 | 9 | 16 | 7 | 16 | 23 | 7 | 24 |

Data from D.B.S.

## MANUFACTURING INDUSTRIES RANKED IN ORDER OF
## NET VALUE OF PRODUCTION IN 1947

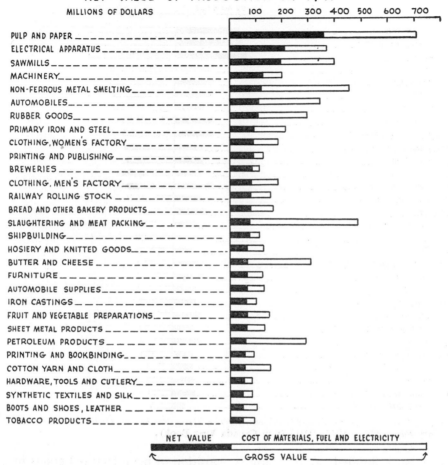

Figure 315. *Leading Manufacturing Industries, in order of Net Value of Production in 1947*. (Canada Year Book) Net value is obtained by subtracting the cost of materials, fuel and electricity from the figure for gross value.

Sawmills, fourth in 1922, were fourth again in 1947, having slipped badly during the depression. During the war the needs of the armed forces and the bacon contracts with Britain placed meat packing in the first rank, its closest rivals being the nickel, copper and aluminum output of the non-ferrous metal industries and miscellaneous chemicals (explosives) and aircraft, neither of which rank as peace-time industries.

Gross value of production is, however, a somewhat misleading criterion. Net value,

that is the value added by industry, is actually more important. Figure 315 shows the 30 leading industries on the basis of net value, arranged in descending order. Pulp and paper, sawmills and non-ferrous metals remain near the top, but meat packing is a long way down the list since the cost of producing the raw materials (meat animals) is beyond the cost of manufacture. On the other hand, if the raw material be considered to be grass and grains, then the most important processes of manufacture

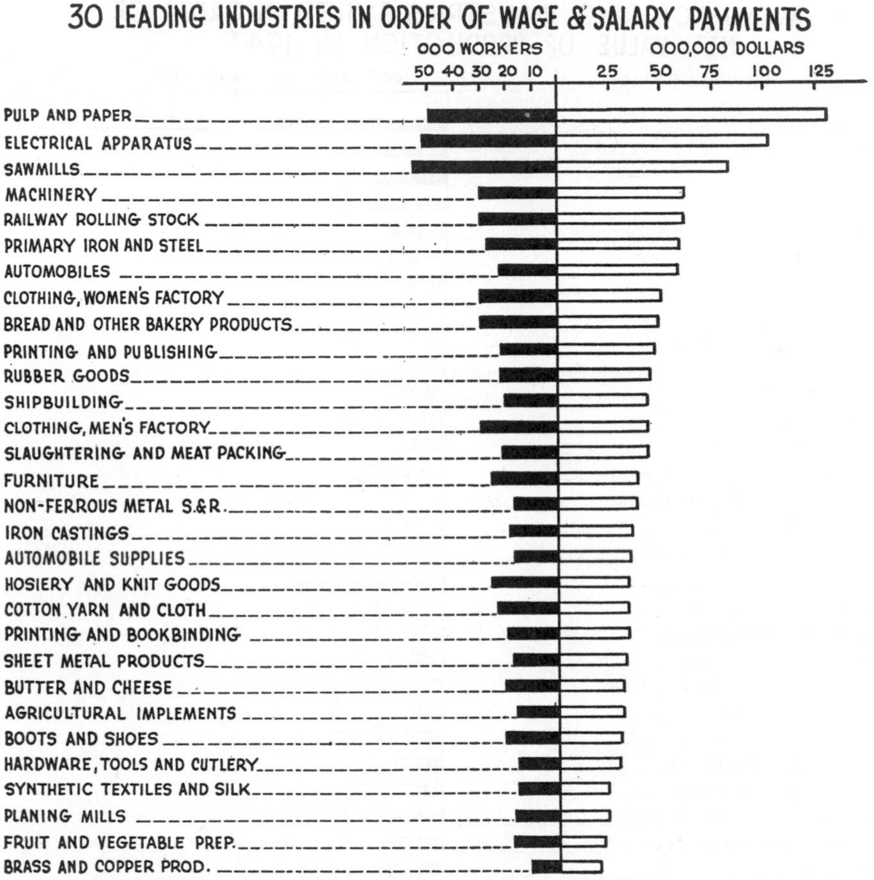

## 30 LEADING INDUSTRIES IN ORDER OF WAGE & SALARY PAYMENTS

| | 000 WORKERS | 000,000 DOLLARS |
|---|---|---|
| | 50 40 30 20 10 | 25    50    75    100    125 |

PULP AND PAPER

ELECTRICAL APPARATUS

SAWMILLS

MACHINERY

RAILWAY ROLLING STOCK

PRIMARY IRON AND STEEL

AUTOMOBILES

CLOTHING, WOMEN'S FACTORY

BREAD AND OTHER BAKERY PRODUCTS

PRINTING AND PUBLISHING

RUBBER GOODS

SHIPBUILDING

CLOTHING, MEN'S FACTORY

SLAUGHTERING AND MEAT PACKING

FURNITURE

NON-FERROUS METAL S.& R.

IRON CASTINGS

AUTOMOBILE SUPPLIES

HOSIERY AND KNIT GOODS

COTTON YARN AND CLOTH

PRINTING AND BOOKBINDING

SHEET METAL PRODUCTS

BUTTER AND CHEESE

AGRICULTURAL IMPLEMENTS

BOOTS AND SHOES

HARDWARE, TOOLS AND CUTLERY

SYNTHETIC TEXTILES AND SILK

PLANING MILLS

FRUIT AND VEGETABLE PREP.

BRASS AND COPPER PROD.

Figure 316. *Thirty Leading Manufacturing Industries Ranked in Order of Wage and Salary Payments in 1947.* (Data from **Canada Year Book**).

have already been finished on the farm. Petroleum refining is another industry which operates on a relatively high priced raw material. There are other products such as machinery, beer, iron castings and hardware, in which the finished article is many times as valuable as the raw material. Another measure of industry is its ability to absorb and pay for labour. (See Figure 316). Pulp and paper heads this list also, followed by electrical apparatus sawmills and machinery in the same order as under net value of production.

The spending power of Canadian workmen is highly important, for they are their own best customers. This is indicated in Figure 317 which shows the origin and dis-

position of manufactured goods in Canada for the years 1935-47. In each year, of course, the imports and domestic manufactures equal the exports and apparent consumption. The exports are always just a little more than the imports, indicating that domestic manufacture is more than the consumption. The diagram also shows the growing capacity of Canada to make use of manufactures. In 1947, this amounted to more than $800 per capita.

### Regional Distribution

Manufacturing is concentrated, largely, in Ontario and Quebec, which produce nearly 80% of the gross value and 82% of the net. The principal statistics of regional

# ORIGIN AND DISPOSITION OF MANUFACTURED GOODS

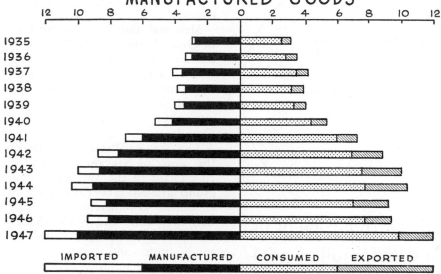

Figure 317. *Origin and Disposition of Manufactured Goods in Canada, 1935-47.* (Data from D.B.S.) The apparent value of manufactured goods, on the market in Canada in 1947, was about $12,000,000,000. Imports accounted for one-sixth. Canadian consumers took five-sixths of the total and one-sixth was exported.

employment and production, for the year 1951, are shown in Table 29. Figure 318 also shows the regional distribution of net production as of 1947.

Manufacturing, however, is far more centralised than even these figures suggest, for within these regions, there are urban groups which, existing very largely upon the proceeds of manufacturing, have come to contain the larger part of the industry. Table 30 contains the principal statistics for the eight most important of these groups, each of which, in 1951, produced more than $150,000,000 net value. Six of these are the

## Table 29

### Regional Distribution of Manufacturing Activity in Canada in 1951.

| Region | Number of Establishments | Number of Employees | Salaries and Wages $000 | Cost of Materials $000 | Net Value of Production $000 | Gross Value of Production $000 |
|---|---|---|---|---|---|---|
| Newfoundland | 822 | 9,622 | 12,681 | 43,117 | 53,690 | 100,643 |
| Maritime Provinces | 2,695 | 56,752 | 119,982 | 365,652 | 245,128 | 633,316 |
| Quebec | 11,861 | 417,183 | 1,005,602 | 2,696,639 | 2,083,934 | 4,916,157 |
| Ontario | 13,025 | 599,433 | 1,669,387 | 4,334,394 | 3,569,400 | 8,074,731 |
| Prairie Provinces | 4,603 | 81,586 | 195,597 | 843,786 | 395,587 | 1,260,440 |
| British Columbia | 3,897 | 93,647 | 262,626 | 789,840 | 592,449 | 1,404,880 |
| N.W.T. and Yukon | 18 | 152 | 406 | 1,097 | 758 | 2,019 |
| Totals | 37,021 | 1,258,375 | 3,266,281 | 9,074,526 | 6,940,946 | 16,392,187 |

Data from D.B.S. 1953.

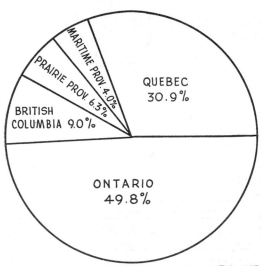

# REGIONAL DISTRIBUTION OF NET VALUE OF MANUFACTURING – 1947

Figure 318. *Regional Distribution of Manufacturing Activity, Measured by Net Value, 1947.* (Data from D.B.S.) Because of its great development of secondary industry and the manufacture of completed consumers goods, Ontario produced half of the value added by manufacturing processes.

greater cities of Montreal, Toronto, Hamilton, Windsor, Winnipeg and Vancouver while the other two are clusters of smaller cities and towns in rather restricted geographic areas. As can be seen from Table 30, these eight districts contain about half of all the manufacturing activity in the country.

Montreal and Toronto are both centres of great diversity with Montreal having a tendency to specialize in clothing trades, chemicals, railway rolling stock, aircraft and petroleum products. Hamilton is noted for its iron and steel while Windsor is the greatest centre of the automobile industry in Canada.

The Niagara-Welland area depends upon the power of Niagara Falls and the localizing factor of the Welland canal. In this group are Niagara Falls, Fort Erie, Port Colborne, Humberstone, Welland, Thorold, Merritton and St. Catharines. Here we find shipbuilding, machine work of all kinds, pulp and paper, chemicals and smelting and refining of metals, a highly diversified area. In the Grand River area the largest cities are Brantford, Kitchener, Waterloo, Galt and Guelph. Here agricultural and other machinery, textiles, leather goods and rubber goods are the leaders.

Winnipeg as the "gateway of the West" naturally has a large share in the milling and meat packing industries, while its position in the transportation system leads to the building and repair of rolling stock.

### Table 30      The Great Manufacturing Areas in 1951.

| Industrial Area | Number of Factories | Number of Employees | Salaries and Wages $000 | Cost of Materials $000 | Net Value of Products $000 | Gross Value of Products $000 |
|---|---|---|---|---|---|---|
| Greater Montreal | 4,600 | 222,000 | 511,890 | 1,311,850 | 987,550 | 2,350,000 |
| Greater Toronto | 4,650 | 208,500 | 516,675 | 1,285,000 | 1,125,000 | 2,430,000 |
| Greater Hamilton | 640 | 57,500 | 150,715 | 321,930 | 302,985 | 648,045 |
| Greater Windsor | 295 | 35,200 | 106,380 | 348,200 | 274,125 | 627,330 |
| Niagara-Welland | 490 | 36,000 | 101,435 | 289,815 | 224,905 | 533,160 |
| Grand River | 915 | 53,500 | 122,845 | 253,685 | 238,575 | 499,570 |
| Greater Winnipeg | 950 | 34,800 | 76,450 | 250,500 | 151,000 | 407,000 |
| Greater Vancouver | 1,460 | 44,000 | 109,500 | 316,000 | 234,000 | 550,000 |
| Total, 8 Areas | 14,000 | 691,500 | 1,695,890 | 4,376,980 | 3,538,140 | 8,045,105 |
| Per cent of Total for Canada | 37.8 | 55.0 | 51.8 | 48.2 | 51.0 | 49.0 |

Adapted from D.B.S.

Vancouver has shipyards and sawmills and a host of small processing activities which tend to locate in port cities.

Other smaller concentrations of industry might be pointed out including the Saint John, Halifax and Sydney harbour areas: the Saguenay, the St. Maurice and the Ottawa River areas; and single cities such as Sault Ste. Marie with its steel industry, Peterborough, London, Calgary and Edmonton.

Many factors have combined to centralize the manufacturing industries of Canada, not only within the central regions, but within very restricted urban areas. Transportation and power were probably among the most powerful of these. Such concentration is no longer necessary and the strongest efforts should be made to set up new manufacturing centres. Alberta with its great wealth of oil, coal and natural gas should expect to develop industries based on them, as well as further growth of those it already has. The established centres will continue to expand under the momentum of their present activity, but it will probably require concerted planning effort and perhaps even subsidization to develop others. The present circulatory troubles of Montreal and Toronto and the beginning of similar trouble in Hamilton, Vancouver and other cities seem to point clearly to some advantages to be gained by decentralization. The success of detached cities such as Sherbrooke, Peterborough and Oshawa might well be emulated by many others.

The wisdom of decentralization of industry is becoming apparent even in peacetime, but it is even more important from the viewpoint of possible war-time defence.

The manufacturing industry of Canada is now its most vital activity, by all statistical criteria. A study of the tables and curves of development through two world wars brings out its role in national defence. If this resource is, itself, left in its present vulnerable condition, the defence of the whole country will suffer.

## Custom and Repair

Including automobile repairs, cleaning, pressing, laundry, watch repairing and

*The Photographic Survey Corporation Limited*

Plate 108. The British-American Oil Refinery at Clarkson, Ontario. With a lakeside location almost midway between the important market areas of Toronto and Hamilton, it is a good example of the modern tendency in industrial location.

many minor industries, *custom and repair* constitute a separate group in the economic statistics of Canada. A good deal of it could be classed as manufacture from the nature of the work done. Being but a small part of the secondary industry (3% in 1947), and fairly uniformly distributed, there is not much of geographic significance to be discussed. Such services, of course, are to be found chiefly in the larger centres of population.

## Construction

Construction holds more than a passing interest for the students of geography in any area. Much of human geography is concerned with the description of cities, houses, factories, canals, docks, bridges, railways, highways, dams and other structures. The construction industry is the medium by which civilization leaves its impress upon the landscape. It is also a pretty fair economic barometer of the country as a whole, or of any one of its parts. The economics of construction is not necessarily very different from that of manufacturing; indeed, the industry may consist pretty largely of further fabrication of manufactured goods, but the geographical relations are much more definite. The end products of manufacture, whether they be durable or non-durable goods, are movable and, indeed, they are usually moved to some more or less distant scene of use or consumption. The plant and the workers remain as they were. Whether they produce much or little in a year may have considerable effect upon their economic welfare, but little effect upon their geographic ensemble. On the other hand it is the product of construction which remains a permanent feature of the landscape while the machinery, tools, camps and the workers themselves move on to new undertakings. It is a startling contrast to compare the bustling town of several thousand people, who today are completing a gigantic dam and power-house, with the village of a hundred in-

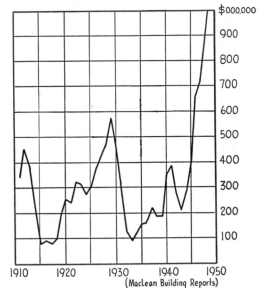

VALUE OF CONSTRUCTION CONTRACTS

(MacLean Building Reports)

Figure 319. *Value of Construction Contracts, 1911-49.* The values are credited to the year in which the contract was let, even though the work may be done through several years.

habitants who will next year take over the operation and maintenance.

The costs of construction are capital investments and the product is real capital, yet it is difficult to get accurate statistics. An annual census of construction has been conducted since 1935, but it is not all inclusive. Building done by farmers and other individuals, and much of that done by railways and public institutions, goes unrecorded. The total annual value of building permits for 204 larger municipalities is recorded, but there are 4,000 municipalities in Canada. Another good check on the progress of construction is the value of contracts awarded. They are credited to the year in which they were let, but, of course, the work of large contracts may extend through several years. Since such a series exists from 1911 on, it is presented in Figure 319 as it portrays rather vividly the cyclic nature of construction activity. Figure 320 gives the annual estimates of the Dominion Bureau of Statistics from 1935 to 1948 for value of con-

## VALUE OF CONSTRUCTION WORK PERFORMED 1935-48

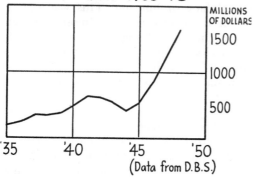

Figure 320. *Gross Value of Construction Work Performed 1935-48*. These figures are estimates for work actually completed.

struction work actually performed in those years. This reached a total of $2,728,000,-000 in 1950.

Net value of construction means total value, less cost of materials and power. A series of official figures, from 1919 on, for net values is shown in Figure 321. Along with this, is shown a physical volume curve based on the 1926 dollar. The index of construction costs reached 200 in 1948, the same year in which the physical volume of work surpassed the peak set in 1930. This would seem to be still well below the volume of building needed by a great-

## NET VALUE OF CONSTRUCTION 1919-1948

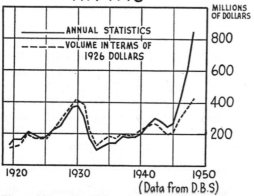

Figure 321. *Net Value of Construction, 1919-48.* The peaks, in terms of actual work done, occurred in 1929 and 1948.

ly increased population, even though the former peak may have been over ambitious.

The regional distribution of construction values for the year 1947 is given in Figure 322. They have much the same

## VALUE OF CONSTRUCTION BY REGIONS – 1947

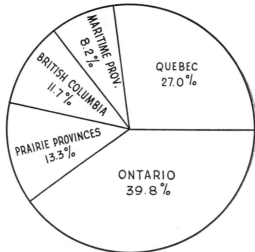

Figure 322. *Regional Distribution of Construction, 1947.* (Data from D.B.S.)

## TYPES OF CONSTRUCTION 1947

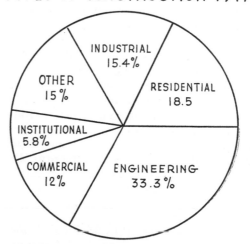

Figure 323. *Relative Values of Types of Construction, 1947.* (Data from D.B.S.)

## CONSTRUCTION CONTRACTS
### BY TYPES OF CONSTRUCTION

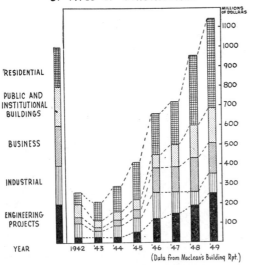

Figure 324. *Values of Construction Contracts by Types of Construction, 1942-49.* Post war construction has gone in heavily for housing and large engineering projects.

relation to one another as in the other post-war years. In proportion to population, Ontario and British Columbia were doing more building than the other regions of Canada, while the Prairie Provinces, especially Saskatchewan, were doing least.

Figure 323, also on the basis of the 1947 statistics, shows the distribution of building investment by types of construction. It is seen that engineering works and residential building makes up slightly more than half of the total. Figure 324 illustrates the expansion of construction of various types from 1942 to 1949.

Employment in the construction industry in Canada is notoriously seasonal but, as the years go on, more and more work is being done in the winter months. During the post-war years, monthly employment has varied from a low of 153,000 to a high of 490,000 workers. The census of 1951 reported 350,000 persons in the construction industry, thus making it about one-fourth as important as the manufacturing industries.

## Housing

Canada emerged from the war with a critical lack of housing. This was the result of three factors: the almost complete lack of house-building during the depression period of the 1930's, the violent population shifts during the war period because of demands for labour in war industries, and a phenomenal increase in the marriage and birth rates. During the war, of course, many "victory villages" were set up near war-time factories. Many of these are still occupied, but others were not well situated in relation to the expansion of peace-time industries. Hence a major concern has been to provide sufficient housing, particularly in the areas of most rapidly growing cities.

In the seven-year post-war period, about 544,000 new housing units were built, inclusive of conversions by which old units were made into smaller modern suites. (Table Number 31). This is at a rate no greater than proportionate to the increase in population during the past decade, and does not take care of the need which had accumulated during the pre-war years. Not only was there overcrowding, but a great deal of remodelling and replacement of buildings was desirable as well. Available statistics are not complete enough to localize all of this house-building activity, but an approximate division is as follows: Maritime Provinces, 7%; Quebec, 27%; Ontario, 35%; Prairie Provinces, 18%; British Columbia, 13%. Of the two million increase in population during the war and post-war years, the Maritime Provinces has 7.5%; Quebec, 32.5%; Ontario, 36.5%; the Prairies Provinces, 7.5% and British Columbia, 16%. Nearly three-fourths of these units were single houses and nearly two-thirds were of completely wooden construction. About one-third were located in the larger "metropolitan" cities, less than 25% were in rural areas and the remainder were located in other urban places. This suggests that smaller cities are growing even faster, relatively,

### Table 31 Housing Units Completed, by Provinces and Regions 1945-51.

| | 1945 | 1946 | 1947 | 1948 | 1949 | 1950 | 1951 | Totals |
|---|---|---|---|---|---|---|---|---|
| Newfoundland | — | — | — | — | — | 1,716 | 941 | 2,657 |
| Prince Edward Island | 97 | 278 | 209 | 252 | 258 | 393 | 290 | 1,777 |
| Nova Scotia | 1,518 | 3,082 | 2,748 | 2,904 | 3,365 | 2,597 | 2,109 | 18,323 |
| New Brunswick | 1,183 | 3,088 | 3,786 | 2,265 | 1,861 | 2,591 | 1,334 | 16,108 |
| Maritime Provinces | 2,798 | 6,448 | 6,743 | 5,421 | 5,484 | 5,581 | 3,733 | 36,208 |
| Quebec | 14,678 | 14,782 | 17,739 | 21,259 | 23,907 | 28,123 | 27,806 | 148,294 |
| Ontario | 15,163 | 21,202 | 26,960 | 28,664 | 32,704 | 32,496 | 32,705 | 189,894 |
| Manitoba | 2,405 | 4,260 | 6,118 | 4,905 | 4,909 | 4,714 | 3,941 | 31,252 |
| Saskatchewan | 2,219 | 3,678 | 4,533 | 3,431 | 3,621 | 2,839 | 2,041 | 22,362 |
| Alberta | 3,037 | 4,713 | 7,074 | 6,473 | 9,650 | 7,448 | 6,287 | 44,682 |
| Prairie Provinces | 7,661 | 12,651 | 17,725 | 14,809 | 18,180 | 15,001 | 12,269 | 98,296 |
| British Columbia | 8,170 | 12,111 | 10,064 | 11,090 | 10,680 | 8,837 | 7,356 | 68,308 |
| Canada | 48,470 | 67,194 | 79,231 | 81,243 | 90,955 | 91,754 | 84,810 | 543,657 |

Data from D.B.S.

than the metropolitan cities. While house building has not been equal to the official declaration of the need, nevertheless, from a journey across the country, one gets the impression of vast new areas of small wooden houses.

The Canadian government has assisted the housing program by direct building in defence areas and by mortgage loans under the National Housing Act and Veterans Land Act.

### Engineering Projects

Engineering projects include all work done to improve the navigability of rivers and harbours, the building of docks, bridges, railways, highways, airports and the like. During the war, such public works projects were kept to a minimum, in keeping with defence needs (See figure 324). Since then the values of contracts awarded and of work done have mounted constantly.

Prominent in this class have been the post-war development programs of various hydro-electric systems, particularly those of Ontario and Quebec. The highway systems of the larger provinces have also expended huge sums to resurface old highways and to build new super-highways, such as the Barrie Highway in Ontario and the Montreal—St. Hyacinthe Highway in Quebec.

The new rapid transit system in Toronto is also a major engineering project of the post-war period.

Another noteworthy development is the building of pipe lines to speed the delivery of petroleum from the Alberta oilfields to refineries in Eastern Canada and on the Pacific coast. Pipe lines for petroleum products have also been built in Ontario. In the near future it is expected that a pipe line will be laid to carry natural gas from Alberta to Toronto and Montreal.

Not completed at the time of writing, but certain to be one of the major engineering feats of the century will be the St. Lawrence Seaway and power development, which will cost several hundred millions of dollars and will have a profound effect upon the economic geography of the whole Great Lakes region.

A project for the immediate future, and one which will have great geographical significance ultimately, is the Trans-Canada Highway which will link the ten provinces from Atlantic to Pacific coasts. In the improvement of existing highways and the creation of new ones, the Federal and Provincial governments expect to spend between $300,000,000 and $500,000,000 before the date of completion which is tentatively set for 1956.

In a very real way Canadians have built Canada. Against great odds in the space relations of the economic regions of the country, skilful engineers and hardy workmen have fashioned a national structure which does credit to the nation planning genius of the Fathers of Confederation. The vanished civilizations of the past are judged in considerable measure by the nature of the enduring structures which they created. The future student will undoubtedly regard Canadians of this century as intensely practical people. Their greatest monuments are all functional structures. Moreover,

there remains much to be done before creative genius may be encouraged to construct architectural ornaments. Within the limits set by the environment, a stable national economy must be evolved, which will be able to weather any adversity. Political and economic planning of a high order are necessary, but they function largely through the efforts of the construction industry which thus has an influence far beyond its measure in dollars and cents.

## Regional Aspects of Production

The regions of Canada vary greatly in their productive capacities, just as they do, also, in their physical features and population patterns. Table 32 sets forth the net values of production for the year 1951 for each province and region. Two-thirds of the annual net value is produced in Quebec and Ontario, less than one-fifth in the Prairie Provinces, less than one-tenth in British Columbia, one-twentieth in the

## Table 32    Distribution of Net Value of Commodity Production 1951

| Provinces and Regions | Net Value of Commodity Production $000 | Per Cent of Total Net Value | Net Value Per Capita $ | Production Workers | | Net Value per Worker $ |
|---|---|---|---|---|---|---|
| | | | | 000 | % | |
| Newfoundland | 130,773 | 1.01 | 362 | 69 | 2.4 | 1,890 |
| Prince Edward Island | 34,416 | .27 | 350 | 20 | .7 | 1,700 |
| Nova Scotia | 299,366 | 2.31 | 465 | 110 | 3.8 | 2,660 |
| New Brunswick | 258,265 | 2.00 | 500 | 92 | 3.2 | 2,800 |
| Maritime Provinces | 592,047 | 4.58 | 472 | 222 | 7.7 | 2,660 |
| Quebec | 3,285,040 | 25.40 | 815 | 833 | 28.8 | 3,950 |
| Ontario | 5,320,040 | 41.15 | 1,160 | 1,031 | 35.4 | 5,150 |
| Manitoba | 558,174 | 4.31 | 715 | 150 | 5.2 | 3,720 |
| Saskatchewan | 872,549 | 6.75 | 1,050 | 185 | 6.4 | 4,700 |
| Alberta | 945,439 | 7.30 | 1,005 | 198 | 6.8 | 4,775 |
| Prairie Provinces | 2,376,162 | 18.36 | 935 | 533 | 18.4 | 4,455 |
| British Columbia | 1,212,254 | 9.35 | 1,040 | 207 | 7.1 | 5,855 |
| Yukon and N.W.T. | 18,114 | .15 | 725 | 6 | .2 | 3,000 |
| Canada | 12,934,430 | 100.00 | 924 | 2,901 | 100.0 | 4,460 |

Data from D.B.S.

## Table 33 Net Production by Industries in Provinces and Regions—1951.

### (Per cent of Total Net Value)

| | Newfoundland | Prince Edward Island | Nova Scotia | New Brunswick | Maritime Provinces | Quebec | Ontario | Manitoba | Saskatchewan | Alberta | Prairie Provinces | British Columbia | North West Territories | Canada |
|---|---|---|---|---|---|---|---|---|---|---|---|---|---|---|
| Agriculture | – | 62.2 | 12.8 | 17.1 | 17.5 | 11.4 | 12.6 | 43.1 | 80.8 | 53.8 | 61.3 | 6.7 | – | 20.8 |
| Forestry | 13.1 | 0.1 | 3.3 | 14.1 | 7.8 | 4.6 | 1.7 | 1.2 | 0.4 | 1.0 | .8 | 13.5 | – | 3.7 |
| Fisheries | 10.3 | 6.5 | 7.2 | 2.9 | 5.3 | 0.1 | 0.1 | 0.8 | 0.1 | 0.1 | .2 | 3.3 | 3.0 | 0.8 |
| Trapping | – | – | 0.1 | – | – | 0.1 | 0.1 | 0.6 | 0.2 | 0.3 | .3 | 0.1 | 13.2 | 0.1 |
| Mining | 19.3 | – | 15.7 | 2.9 | 9.2 | 5.0 | 3.3 | 3.7 | 4.4 | 16.0 | 8.9 | 10.1 | 74.7 | 6.0 |
| Electric Power | 2.0 | 2.5 | 3.9 | 3.3 | 3.6 | 3.9 | 2.4 | 3.3 | 1.3 | 1.7 | 2.0 | 3.0 | 4.9 | 2.8 |
| Primary Prod. | 44.7 | 71.3 | 43.0 | 40.3 | 43.4 | 25.1 | 20.2 | 52.7 | 87.2 | 72.9 | 73.5 | 36.7 | 95.8 | 34.2 |
| Manufacturers | 41.2 | 14.7 | 39.9 | 46.7 | 41.5 | 63.4 | 67.1 | 34.5 | 7.0 | 15.0 | 16.6 | 48.9 | 4.2 | 53.7 |
| Construction | 14.1 | 14.0 | 17.1 | 13.0 | 15.1 | 11.5 | 12.7 | 12.8 | 5.8 | 12.1 | 9.9 | 14.4 | – | 12.1 |
| Secondary Prod. | 55.3 | 28.7 | 57.0 | 59.7 | 56.6 | 74.9 | 79.8 | 47.3 | 12.8 | 27.1 | 26.5 | 63.3 | 4.2 | 65.8 |
| Grand Total | 100.0 | 100.0 | 100.0 | 100.0 | 100.0 | 100.0 | 100.0 | 100.0 | 100.0 | 100.0 | 100.0 | 100.0 | 100.0 | 100.0 |

Data from D.B.S.

## Table 34 Provincial and Regional Net Production 1951.

### (Per cent of total Canadian Net Values)

| | Newfoundland | Prince Edward Island | Nova Scotia | New Brunswick | Maritime Provinces | Quebec | Ontario | Manitoba | Saskatchewan | Alberta | Prairie Provinces | British Columbia | North West Territories | Canada |
|---|---|---|---|---|---|---|---|---|---|---|---|---|---|---|
| Agriculture | – | .8 | 1.5 | 1.6 | 3.9 | 14.0 | 25.0 | 8.9 | 26.3 | 18.9 | 54.1 | 3.0 | – | 100.0 |
| Forestry | 3.5 | – | 2.1 | 7.5 | 9.6 | 31.0 | 18.3 | 1.4 | .6 | 2.0 | 4.0 | 33.6 | – | 100.0 |
| Fisheries | 13.2 | 2.2 | 21.1 | 7.4 | 29.7 | 3.3 | 6.8 | 4.2 | .9 | .5 | 5.6 | 39.8 | .6 | 100.0 |
| Trapping | – | .3 | 1.4 | – | 1.7 | 11.9 | 26.4 | 17.5 | 10.0 | 12.7 | 40.2 | 8.3 | 12.0 | 100.0 |
| Mining | 3.3 | – | 6.1 | 1.0 | 7.1 | 21.4 | 23.2 | 2.7 | 5.1 | 19.7 | 27.5 | 15.8 | 1.7 | 100.0 |
| Electric Power | .7 | .2 | 3.2 | 2.4 | 5.8 | 35.6 | 35.1 | 5.1 | 3.0 | 4.6 | 12.7 | 9.9 | .2 | 100.0 |
| Primary Prod. | 1.3 | .5 | 2.9 | 2.4 | 5.8 | 18.6 | 24.4 | 6.6 | 17.3 | 15.6 | 39.5 | 10.0 | .4 | 100.0 |
| Manufacturers | .7 | .1 | 1.7 | 1.7 | 3.5 | 30.1 | 51.4 | 2.8 | .9 | 2.0 | 5.7 | 8.6 | – | 100.0 |
| Construction | 1.2 | .3 | 3.3 | 2.1 | 5.7 | 24.0 | 42.8 | 4.5 | 3.2 | 7.3 | 15.0 | 11.2 | – | 100.0 |
| Secondary Prod. | .9 | .1 | 2.0 | 1.8 | 3.9 | 29.0 | 49.9 | 3.1 | 1.3 | 3.0 | 7.4 | 8.9 | – | 100.0 |
| Total Production | 1.0 | .3 | 2.3 | 2.0 | 4.6 | 25.4 | 41.2 | 4.3 | 6.7 | 7.3 | 18.3 | 9.3 | .2 | 100.0 |

Data from D.B.S.

Maritime Provinces and one per cent in Newfoundland. There are other broad regional contrasts. Ontario and British Columbia are the most productive, both on a *per capita* basis and on the more realistic standard of net value of output per industrial worker. Quebec and Manitoba occupy intermediate positions which are slightly below the average for the whole country. Alberta and Saskatchewan, on the other hand, are slightly above it. The Maritime Provinces and Newfoundland have the lowest productivity per worker. This difference in efficiency is the key to regional economic contrasts.

Regional economies differ greatly and it is worth while to remember the important industries in each region. Table 33, drawn up on the basis of 1951 statistics, gives the percentages of the total production for each industrial group in each province and region. Table 34, on the other hand, shows the percentage share of each province and region in each of the industrial group values. Thus we find that agriculture is outstandingly important in the Prairie Provinces, for not only is 54% of the agricultural wealth of Canada produced there, but it constitutes 61% of the wealth of the region. Ontario and manufacturing are linked in the same fashion, for 63.4% of Ontario's net production comes from these industries, and it constitutes 51.4%

of the net value of manufacturing in Canada. Forestry is about equally important to New Brunswick, Newfoundland and British Columbia, providing 13-14% of their total production and, normally, constituting the greatest primary industry. Quebec and Ontario, however, produce half of Canada's forest products, although they depend upon them to a much lesser extent. Least diversified of all the provinces is Saskatchewan which depends upon agriculture for more than 80% of its commodity income and, within that industry, it relies largely on a single commodity, wheat. This, of course, is well known to be the reason for the fluctuations in its economic history. More secondary industries are definitely needed. On the other hand, in spite of their much greater diversification, the Atlantic Provinces have not attained high levels of production.

Ontario and Quebec and, to a lesser degree, British Columbia seem to be specialized toward manufacturing. Within this industrial group, however, there is great diversification. In six of the ten provinces, manufacturing ranks as the greatest producer, while in the others it ranks second to agriculture. It seems inevitable that the future will see an increase in the importance of manufacturing, even in those provinces in which it has been slow to develop heretofore.

# Selected References

Bladen, V. W. *An Introduction to Political Economy.* (Chapters V and VI). The University of Toronto Press. Toronto. 1946.

Buckley, K. A. H. *Urban Building and Real Estate Fluctuations in Canada.* Can. Jour. of Econ. and Pol. Sci. 18:41-62. 1952.

*Canada Year Book.* Ottawa. Annual.

*Census of Newfoundland.* 1945.

Currie, A. W. *Economic Geography of Canada.* The Macmillan Company of Canada. Toronto. 1945.

Drummond, W. M. *The Canadian Agricultural Economy.* Journal of Farm Economics. XXXIII pp. 637-48. 1951.

*Eighth Census of Canada.* 1941.

Innis, H. A. *Problems of Staple Production in Canada.* The Ryerson Press. Toronto. 1933.

*Ninth Census of Canada.* 1951.

Taylor, G. *Canada.* Methuen & Co. Limited. London. 1947.

# CHAPTER 24

# The Patterns of Commercial Activity

THE function of commercial activity is to satisfy the needs and desires of mankind. Goods must be bought from those who produce them, and be carried and sold to those who use them. This may be a very local transaction or, even if distant, still within the same country, or it may involve areas outside the country. All the phases and services of commerce enter into these distribution patterns. We have, in the previous chapter, discussed the location and magnitude of the various productive industrial groups in Canada; in this chapter, the importance of external and domestic trade, transportation and communications, and other services will be discussed.

## External Trade

### Growth of External Trade

External trade has always been important to Canada but has grown enormously in recent decades (see figure 325). In the early periods furs, fish and timber were exchanged for a wide variety of European manufactured goods, foods and beverages. The chief exports of 1890 were lumber, cheese, fish, cattle, squared timber and grain. By 1910, wheat had become the leading commodity, followed by lumber, metals, cheese, fish and cattle. In the 1930's, the three most important items were wheat, newsprint and metals, followed by lumber, woodpulp, meats, wheat flour, automobiles, whiskey and raw furs. During World War II, munitions and war supplies, which included much motorized equipment,

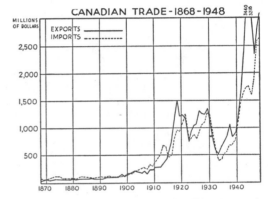

Figure 325 *The Growth of Canadian External Trade. 1868-1948.* Within four decades Canada has become one of the greatest trading nations in the world. (Data from D. B. S.)

comprised more than one-third of the greatly expanded volume of exports. The leading exports in 1948 were newsprint, wheat, woodpulp, lumber, flour, aluminum, fish, ships, copper, grains other than wheat, cattle, nickel, farm machinery, bacon and hams, other meats, seeds, pulpwood, zinc, asbestos, machinery and automobiles.

The leading imports of 1890 were woolen goods, coal, sugar, steel, cotton goods, raw cotton, tea, silk and fruits. In 1910 the list was headed by coal, woolen goods, cotton goods, steel, sugar and machinery. One of the largest items was "settlers effects," brought in by the multitude of immigrants who came in at that time. During the 1930's, the leading classes of imports were petroleum, coal, steel, machinery, automobile parts, fruits, sugar, cotton, woolens, grain products and rubber. The post-war list (1948) is practically the same, but in this order: petroleum, machinery, coal, farm implements, automobile parts, steel, cotton, sugar, wool, electrical apparatus and fruits. The most striking change in the half century has been the demand for petroleum, automobile parts and electrical supplies.

## Important Trade Relations

Ever since Confederation, and indeed long before, Canada has had two important customers, the United States and the United Kingdom, which for many years

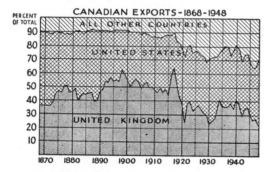

Figure 326. *The Trends in Canadian Export Trade. 1868-1948.* In recent years other countries have been taking an increasing amount of Canadian business away from the British market. (Data from D. B. S.)

absorbed about 90% of all Canadian exports. (See figure 326). Since 1905 and especially since 1917, other world markets have taken a larger share, amounting to 30% in the 1940's. In most cases, these foreign sales have replaced previous transactions with the United Kingdom. The United States has, also, gradually and steadily, replaced the United Kingdom as a source of goods imported into Canada. Imports from other countries have varied between ten and twenty per cent of the total. (See figure 327)

Apart from the United States and the United Kingdom, Canada's exports go largely to France, South Africa, Belgium, India, Netherlands, Australia and Italy. Imports originate in India, Venezuela, Australia, Mexico, Cuba, Malaya, Brazil, Do-

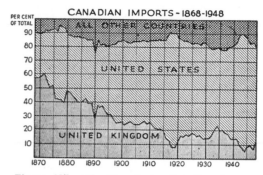

Figure 327. *The Trends in Canadian Import Trade. 1868-1948.* For three-quarters of a century the United States has steadily been replacing the United Kingdom as the source of goods imported into Canada. (Data from D. B. S.)

minican Republic and British Guiana. A few examples will illustrate the special nature of some of these trade relations. Australia takes Canadian automobiles and parts, newsprint, lumber, cotton and artificial silk fabrics, and aluminum, in exchange for wool, raisins, rabbit skins and wines. India buys flour, automobiles and parts, locomotives and railway cars, paper, aluminum and copper while, in return, Canada receives jute fabrics, tea and rugs. Mexico is a market for newsprint, machinery, leather,

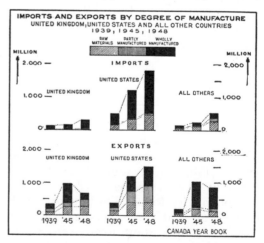

Figure 328. *Imports and Exports Classified by Degree of Manufacture.* (Canada Year Book). Canada has always been an exporter of raw materials and an importer of manufactured goods, but now manufactured goods are beginning to take a leading place in the list of exports.

agricultural machinery, railway cars and fountain pens; in return, Canada imports raw cotton, henequin fibres, and tomatoes. Venezuela is one of Canada's chief sources of petroleum and is, also, a market for flour, newsprint, automobiles and motor trucks, rubber tires and machinery. Canada carries on trade with almost every country in the world, including Abyssinia and Afghanistan.

Goods traded on the international market may be raw materials, partly processed, or completely manufactured consumer's goods. Figure 328 is an analysis of Canadian trade on this basis. Practically all of the imports from the United Kingdom are manufactured goods. From the United States, the completely manufactured goods are most important, but there is a fair proportion of raw materials as well. From other countries, raw materials and partly processed goods are becoming more important than fully manufactured articles. Among the exports, on the other hand, there has been a tendency for processed goods and fully manufactured articles to increase, at the expense of raw materials. While some of the trends, shown in the diagram, are to be ascribed to abnormal war-time demands, they are, nonetheless, in line with the development of Canadian manufacturing industries.

## Balance of Trade

Before World War I, Canada usually had an adverse balance of trade, caused, largely, by heavy investments in railways and producer's equipment. Since that time, except for brief periods during world wide recessions, there have been favorable trade balances, which have transformed Canada from a debtor nation into one of the great creditor nations of the world. This credit balance is owed by the United Kingdom and the rest of the world, while Canada continues to have an adverse balance in her trade with the United States. This may be considered a rather natural result of the Canadian preference for American consumer's goods, reading matter and entertainment, concurrent with a lessened demand for similar products of British and European origins.

Canada is one of the greatest trading nations in the world. In 1955 the per capita value of exports was $280, while that of imported goods was $300. Only Hong Kong and New Zealand have a greater value of trade per capita. The total value of exports was $4,351,284,000 while the imports were valued at $4,712,370,000. Almost one-quarter of the net national income was derived from export trade and expended for imported goods. In total value of foreign trade Canada stood fourth, outranked by the United States, the United Kingdom and France, all of which have much greater populations.

The phenomenal rise in the dollar value of trade is in part to be explained by inflation, nevertheless a comparison of the physical indices for the periods 1935-39 and

D. F. Putnam.

Plate 109. Unloading coal at Little Current, Ontario. The coal used in the mining districts of Northern Ontario is brought across the Great Lakes from mines in the United States. Coal is an important item in Canadian import trade.

1948-52 show that the volume of exports was 1.65 times as great and the volume of imports over twice as great in the former period.

An invisible item in the national income is the money spent by travellers in Canada for transportation, maintenance and recreation. In 1954 this amounted to $305,000,-000, but was offset by $389,000,000 spent by Canadians travelling outside the country. By reason of geographic contiguity the major portion of this exchange is between Canada and the United States.

## Domestic Trade

Domestic trade is the economic life-blood of the nation. It is carried on by almost countless types of business organizations, large and small. Goods must get from producer to consumer and, while these may themselves do much of the buying and selling, a great deal of this work is done by the middleman. He is not concerned with production or ultimate use but, either as an individual or as an organization, undertakes to bring the goods within reach of those who wish to use them. The structures created and used by this business form a significant part of the landscape, es-

pecially in towns and cities and the employment provided is equally important to the working population.

### The Trade in Farm Products

During the period of agricultural development in Canada, farm products constituted the most important group of commodities in commerce and important divisions of domestic trade developed about them. Thus we have strong organizations in the grain trade, the livestock trade and the fruit and vegetable trade. Each of them may be thought of as engaged in buying and accumulating commodities which may either be exported or sold eventually to domestic consumers. Closely allied and, indeed, usually an integrated part of these trades is the business of warehousing and cold storage.

*The Grain Trade.* The grain trade of Canada is practically a government monopoly carried on by the Wheat Board. The Wheat Board was established in 1935 to assist in marketing the surplus grain which had accumulated during the depression. Under war conditions in 1943, all trading in wheat futures on the Winnipeg Grain Exchange was discontinued and the Board

| Table 35 | Permanent and Temporary Grain Storage — 1944 | | |
|---|---|---|---|
| | Permanent 000 bu. | Temporary 000 bu. | Total 000 bu. |
| Western country elevators | 193,643 | 111,070 | 304,713 |
| Private and mill elevators | 15,826 | 225 | 16,051 |
| Semi-public terminal elevators | 18,100 | nil | 18,100 |
| Pacific Port elevators | 21,725 | nil | 21,725 |
| Churchill | 2,500 | nil | 2,500 |
| Fort-William — Port Arthur | 90,467 | 53,263 | 143,730 |
| Totals, Western Division | 342,261 | 164,558 | 506,819 |
| Georgian Bay—Lake Huron Ports | 34,250 | 3,072 | 37,322 |
| Lower Lake Ports | 19,100 | nil | 19,100 |
| St. Lawrence Ports | 24,912 | 3,000 | 27,912 |
| Maritime Ports | 5,277 | nil | 5,277 |
| Totals, Eastern Division | 83,539 | 6,072 | 89,611 |
| Grand Totals | 425,890 | 170,630 | 596,430 |

Canada Year Book 1945.

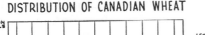

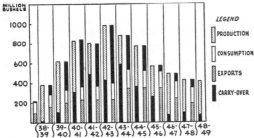

Figure 329. *Production and Distribution of Canadian Wheat. 1938-1948.* The early years of World War II were characterized by high production and disruption of the market, with a consequently very high carry-over of Canadian wheat. (Data from D. B. S.)

was made the sole buying agency. During World War II, crops were good and, while exports to Britain continued at a high level, a very large surplus of wheat accumulated (figure 329) which taxed the permanent elevator storage to capacity and forced the building or conversion of large temporary storage places. Permanent elevator capacity in Canada has remained practically steady at 420 to 425 million bushels, but under these conditions it had to be increased by about 40%. The location of this storage in 1944 is given in Table 35, while the changing relations of stored grain to storage capacity are shown in figure 330. It should be noted that most of the temporary capacity was added to the western country elevators and to those at the head of the lakes.

Domestic requirements of wheat have averaged about 154,000,000 bushels annually over the ten year period shown. Of this only about 50,000,000 were milled for human consumption, while the rest is accounted for by seed requirements, animal feed, industrial use and waste. An average of 100,000,000 bushels per year is actually milled in Canada, but about half of the flour is exported.

*The Livestock Trade.* The livestock trade is organized into a major pattern of stockyards in the large cities such as Edmonton, Calgary, Winnipeg, Toronto and

Montreal. To these yards, cattle, sheep and hogs, etc. are consigned by stockraisers or by drovers who buy from them. From the stockyards, the animals are sold to the large packing plants. Although most of the business is done in this way, there are also local butchers who slaughter and prepare meat directly for retail. They usually buy directly from the producer. The meat packing business, usually, ranks as one of the three largest manufacturing industries in Canada, but it owes its importance to the value of the livestock bought from the farmer. In 1952, the value of the livestock trade was about four-fifths that of the grain trade, returning over $800,000,000 as cash income to the farmer.

*The Fruit and Vegetable Trade.* In recent years, the annual value of fruits, potatoes and other vegetables, grown and marketed in Canada, has had an average value of $150,000,000. Canada imports an average of $100,000,000 per year in vegetables and fruits, including the dried, preserved and canned products. Exports range from $20,000,000 to $30,000,000, hence domestic distribution of this type of goods averages about $225,000,000 per year. Canned, dried or otherwise processed goods do

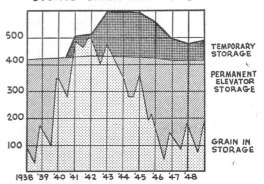

Figure 330. *Storage Capacity and Stored Grain. 1938-1948.* Permanent elevator storage in Canada stands at about 420,000,000 bushels, while total grain requiring storage in 1942 was over 500,000,000 bushels necessitating the creation of temporary facilities, some of which have since been removed. (Data from D. B. S.)

not differ in their manner of distribution from other packaged foods, but the trade in fresh fruits and vegetables entails road-side stands, city market places, packing and cold storage plants and special wholesale and retail establishments. They form a noticeable feature of the geographic pattern of commerce, right from their production in a specialized type of agriculture to their sale in a special type of grocery business.

## Storage

Storage facilities are becoming more and more important features of Canadian business geography, and storage and warehousing statistics are important measurements of business activity. The extent of grain storage facilities and stocks of stored grain have already been discussed, but there are other important storage services, including cold storage of foods, petroleum storage, general warehousing and bonded warehousing.

Cold storage facilities are extensive in Canada. There are large public and private bulk storages, locker storages where the entire space is divided into small units for family use, creamery, cheese factory and grading station storages. The general locations of these facilities are indicated in table 36.

| Table 36 | Cold Storage | 1952 |
|---|---|---|
| | Number of Warehouses | Refrigerated Space Cu. ft. |
| Newfoundland | 52 | 1,606,968 |
| Maritime Provinces | 148 | 8,169,711 |
| Quebec | 248 | 15,511,462 |
| Ontario | 883 | 30,369,266 |
| Prairie Provinces | 612 | 20,710,047 |
| British Columbia | 174 | 29,492,738 |
| Totals | 2,117 | 105,869,192 |

Canada Year Book

Large amounts of food stuffs are continually kept in storage. Some 12-month averages are: butter, 32,000,000 lbs.; cheese, 36,000,000 lbs.; eggs, 12,000,000 dozen;

poultry, 18,000,000 lbs.; pork (including bacon), 60,000,000 lbs.; beef, 30,000,000 lbs.; and fish, 35,000,000 lbs. Available supplies may run much higher at peak seasons, but the extensive system of cold storage makes it possible to maintain an even flow to the retail market, eliminating periods of glut and scarcity which used to characterize the marketing of perishable foodstuffs.

Petroleum storage tanks are located at producing fields, refining centres and main distribution points. The largest of these are at or near Turner Valley, Calgary, Edmonton, Vancouver, Regina, Fort William, Sarnia, Toronto, Ottawa, Montreal, Quebec and Halifax. There are, also, many smaller tanks, located in small ports or at railway points, which serve the surrounding neighborhood.

Bonded warehouses are licensed to store tobacco, and raw materials used to produce beer or spirits, and are under the supervision of the Excise Duty Branch of the Department of National Revenue.

## Wholesale Trade

Canada has certain well defined wholesale centres, which are, for the most part, located in the larger cities; although their rank, as such, is not necessarily that of size of population. The census of 1941 disclosed a volume of wholesale trade of $5,290,000,-000. Two-thirds of this was concentrated in ten cities, ranking as follows: Montreal, Toronto, Winnipeg, Vancouver, Quebec, Calgary, Halifax, Hamilton, Edmonton and Ottawa. The first two accounted for $2,585,-000,000, or 49% of the total. The dollar value of trade in 1951 was more than twice that of 1941, standing at $12,700,000,000. Inasmuch as the general wholesale price index rose from 123 in 1941 to 240 in 1951, the increase in the physical volume of goods was about 23% in ten years.

The regional volumes of wholesale trade are shown in Table 37. There are, also, regional differences in types of business; wholesalers proper and manufacturer's agents are concentrated in Quebec and On-

**Table 37**          **Regional Distribution of Wholesale Trade**

| | Gainfully Employed | | Value of Sales | | | |
| | 1941 | 1951 | 1941 | | 1951 | |
| | Number | Number | $000,000 | % | $000,000 | % |
|---|---|---|---|---|---|---|
| Newfoundland | ‑‑‑‑‑‑‑ | 3,835 | ‑‑‑‑‑‑‑ | -- | 278.5 | 2.2 |
| Maritime Provinces | 7,538 | 15,531 | 254.0 | 4.8 | 533.2 | 4.2 |
| Quebec | 32,634 | 49,653 | 1,726.5 | 32.5 | 3,636.8 | 28.4 |
| Ontario | 40,450 | 64,829 | 1,744.7 | 33.1 | 4,333.0 | 33.8 |
| Prairie Provinces | 25,854 | 39,227 | 1,186.3 | 22.4 | 3,026.9 | 23.7 |
| British Columbia | 10,994 | 22,248 | 379.1 | 7.2 | 989.4 | 7.7 |
| Totals | 117,470 | 195,323 | 5,290.6 | 100.0 | 12,797.8 | 100.0 |

tario, whereas agents and brokers and assemblers of farm produce are more important in the Prairie Provinces.

## Retail Trade

The total retail trade of Canada, disclosed by the Census of 1941, amounted to $3,668,000,000. This had increased to an estimated $8,110,000,000 in 1948, an increase of 122%. The general cost-of-living index advanced by about 40% in the same period so that the actual volume of goods must have increased by 58%. This average must be accepted with some reserve, since price advances have not been uniform, and the cost-of-living index is not based entirely upon the prices of goods sold in the retail trade. There is no doubt, however, that the supply of consumers goods increased rapidly after World War II. Table 38 compares the values of retail trade by selected groups, according to the census returns for 1930 and 1941 and the official estimates for 1948 and 1952.

## Food

The outstanding item of retail trade is the amount of money which Canadians pay for food, usually amounting to about 25% of the consumer's dollar. Most of this is bought through the stores of the food group, or eaten in restaurants, but there are substantial amounts secured from other sources also. It is perhaps of some interest to examine the Canadian diet; Table 39

gives a comparison of the average annual amounts consumed per capita for two five year periods. 1935-39 and 1943-47.

## Regional Distribution

The regional distribution of retail trade, according to the census of 1951, is shown in Table 40. It is pretty well in accord with the distribution of population, except that Ontario and Western Canada have higher average sales per capita while eastern provinces have somewhat less.

Retail trade gives employment to more than 514,000 persons, including proprietors, thus accounting for about 10% of the total gainfully employed in the country.

Retail trade is very closely related to city populations which, as a rule, have greater buying power than rural populations. Table 41 gives the retail trade for the largest retail markets in Canada in 1951. They are the most populous cities, but their trade is related to their economic pulse as well as to their population. One measure of this, the crude rate of sales per capita shows a variation from $1,780 in Victoria to $990 in Quebec. Toronto, with $1,480, is well ahead of Montreal with $990. If, however, the per capita sales of the city be compared with those of the region which it serves, a sales ratio is obtained, which is an even better indicator of trading activity. On this basis, Halifax, St. John's and Moncton would appear to have been the best regional markets among the larger cities in 1951.

**Table 38    Changes in Volume of Retail Trade by Selected Groups 1930-1952***

|  | 1930 $000,000 | 1941 $000,000 | 1948 $000,000 | 1952 $000,000 |
|---|---|---|---|---|
| 1. Grocery and meat stores | 615 | 784 | 1,460 | 2,020 |
| 2. Restaurants | 76 | 131 | 303 | 396 |
| 3. Country general stores | 208 | 215 | 479 | 534 |
| 4. Department and variety stores | 473 | 526 | 961 | 1,184 |
| 5. Clothing and shoe stores | 220 | 295 | 595 | 705 |
| 6. Automobile dealers, garages and filling stations | 381 | 595 | 1,393 | 2,691 |
| 7. Hardware and building materials | 164 | 174 | 448 | 580 |
| 8. Furniture, radios and household appliances | 100 | 118 | 265 | 377 |
| 9. Drug, tobacco and jewellery stores | 134 | 182 | 341 | 439 |
| 10. All other retailers | 386 | 424 | 1,865 | 2,378 |
| Total retail trade | 2,756 | 3,441 | 8,110 | 11,304 |

\* Some retail trade through other than regular retail outlets is not included.

Dominion Bureau of Statistics.

**Table 39      Average Canadian Diet 1935-39, 1943-47 and 1954**

| Food Groups | | 1935-39 | 1943-47 | 1954 |
|---|---|---|---|---|
| Dairy Products (except butter, milk solids) | lbs. | 55.8 | 68.4 | 64.2 |
| Meats (carcass weight) | lbs. | 118.4 | 144.4 | 146.4 |
| Poultry and game | lbs. | 22.7 | 29.6 | 28.6 |
| Fish | lbs. | 11.9 | 10.6 | 13.8 |
| Eggs (fresh weight) | lbs. | 30.7 | 36.0 | 36.6 |
| Fats and oils (butter etc.) | lbs. | 41.9 | 38.2 | 44.3 |
| Pulses and nuts | lbs. | 12.7 | 12.5 | 9.9 |
| Sugar | lbs. | 104.0 | 88.3 | 101.5 |
| Potatoes (retail weight) | lbs. | 192.9 | 197.3 | 146.2 |
| Fruits (fresh weight) | lbs. | 138.7 | 183.1 | 216.8 |
| Vegetables (fresh weight) | lbs. | 78.4 | 90.1 | 91.9 |
| Grain products | lbs. | 208.2 | 198.3 | 165.5 |
| Tea, coffee, cocoa | lbs. | 10.9 | 11.6 | 9.1 |
| Fluid milk (included above) | qts. | 175.0 | 210.0 | 405.2 |

Data from D. B. S.

**Table 40     Regional Distribution of Retail Trade 1951**

|  | Number of Stores | Personnel Number | Sales $000,000 | % of Can. Sales | Per Cap. $ |
|---|---|---|---|---|---|
| Newfoundland | 4,085 | 10,416 | 159.4 | 1.50 | 441 |
| Maritime Provinces | 13,578 | 40,476 | 732.5 | 6.88 | 585 |
| Quebec | 43,539 | 123,417 | 2,438.1 | 22.90 | 604 |
| Ontario | 50,117 | 202,438 | 4,114.2 | 38.65 | 895 |
| Prairie Provinces | 26,958 | 89,361 | 2,110.1 | 19.82 | 825 |
| British Columbia | 13,149 | 48,337 | 1,087.9 | 10.25 | 934 |
| Canada | 151,426 | 514,445 | 10,642.2 | 100.00 | 760 |

Data from Census of Canada, 1951.

## Table 41      City Retail Trade 1951

| | Sales $000,000 | Population 000 | Sales per Capita $ | Regional Sales Ratio | Gainfully Employed | | |
|---|---|---|---|---|---|---|---|
| | | | | | Total 000 | In Retail 000 | % |
| 1. Montreal | 1,011 | 1,022 | 990 | 1.64 | 444.7 | 46.5 | 10.4 |
| 2. Toronto | 1,001 | 676 | 1,480 | 1.65 | 338.6 | 44.9 | 13.2 |
| 3. Vancouver | 462 | 345 | 1,350 | 1.44 | 148.5 | 20.2 | 13.7 |
| 4. Winnipeg | 309 | 236 | 1,310 | 1.59 | 109.2 | 15.9 | 14.6 |
| 5. Hamilton | 228 | 208 | 1,090 | 1.22 | 95.1 | 10.1 | 10.6 |
| 6. Edmonton | 211 | 160 | 1,320 | 1.60 | 67.7 | 8.6 | 12.7 |
| 7. Ottawa | 208 | 202 | 1,030 | 1.15 | 87.6 | 9.4 | 10.7 |
| 8. Calgary | 180 | 129 | 1,400 | 1.70 | 56.4 | 7.8 | 13.8 |
| 9. Quebec | 162 | 164 | 990 | 1.64 | 65.6 | 8.0 | 12.2 |
| 10. Windsor | 130 | 120 | 1,080 | 1.21 | 51.9 | 5.8 | 11.2 |
| 11. London | 126 | 95 | 1,330 | 1.49 | 43.2 | 5.6 | 13.0 |
| 12. Regina | 104 | 71 | 1,470 | 1.78 | 31.8 | 5.1 | 15.9 |
| 13. Halifax | 100 | 85 | 1,175 | 2.01 | 37.6 | 4.8 | 12.8 |
| 14. Victoria | 91 | 51 | 1,780 | 1.91 | 21.1 | 3.1 | 14.8 |
| 15. St. John's | 63 | 53 | 1,190 | 2.70 | 19.2 | 3.1 | 16.4 |
| 16. Saskatoon | 62 | 53 | 1,170 | 1.42 | 21.5 | 3.0 | 13.8 |
| 17. Sudbury | 60 | 42 | 1,425 | 1.59 | 17.2 | 1.7 | 10.0 |
| 18. St. Catharines | 57 | 38 | 1,500 | 1.67 | 16.3 | 1.9 | 11.5 |
| 19. Kitchener | 56 | 45 | 1,250 | 1.40 | 21.8 | 2.3 | 10.7 |
| 20. Saint John | 56 | 51 | 1,100 | 1.88 | 19.9 | 2.5 | 12.7 |
| 21. New Westminster | 49 | 29 | 1,690 | 1.81 | 11.5 | 1.3 | 11.5 |
| 22. Brantford | 49 | 37 | 1,320 | 1.47 | 16.2 | 1.9 | 11.7 |
| 23. Kingston | 44 | 33 | 1,330 | 1.49 | 14.7 | 1.9 | 13.2 |
| 24. Moncton | 43 | 27 | 1,590 | 2.72 | 11.4 | 2.2 | 19.4 |
| 25. Niagara Falls | 39 | 23 | 1,700 | 1.90 | 10.7 | 1.2 | 11.0 |
| Twenty-five cities | 4,901 | 3,993 | 1,225 | 1.61 | 1,779.4 | 218.9 | 12.3 |

Data from D.B.S.

Places of less than 1,000 inhabitants have about 38% of the population but only one-sixth of the sales occur in such places. Obviously the rural people spend considerable money in the nearby cities. The city serving a large area in which there is no serious rival will have a higher sales ratio than one which faces active competition near at hand.

Some comparatively small cities apparently, have more active trade relations with their umlands than the larger ones. Moncton, St. John's and Halifax are outstanding examples. Truro, Kentville and Digby are important trading towns in Nova Scotia as are Barrie, New Liskeard and Tillsonburg in Ontario, Yorkton and Melfort in Saskatchewan, Camrose and Wetaskiwin in Alberta and Prince George in British Columbia. Urban places with weaker retail facilities include some suburbs of large metropolitan cities such as St. Boni-face, V e r d u n , Westmount, Outremont, Cap-de-la-Madeleine, Forest Hill, Swansea and Mimico. Windsor has lower per capita sales than other Ontario cities because of its proximity to Detroit.

*Distribution of outlets.* Most numerous and widely scattered of the retail outlets is the grocery store, with almost 22,000 establishments. Country general stores, which, of course, do grocery business, are even more widely scattered and number about 12,000. Butcher shops, either alone or in combination with groceries, total about 11,000; confectionery stores, 11,500; clothing stores, 12,000; filling stations, 10,000; and restaurants, about 9,000. Department stores, mail order houses and offices, are a small group, maintaining 500 outlets in 1941, but they got 11% of the retail business. There were 533 chain companies, with over 8,000 stores, which did 18.7% of the retail business. Chains operate in the grocery, drug, cloth-

Plate 110. The super-market on a strategic corner, and with plenty of parking space, represents the modern trend in the retail trade.

ing, shoe, tobacco, restaurant, filling station and variety store groups.

### The Hotel Trade

The Canadian hotel usually performs a triple function, providing the traveller with lodging, purveying meals, and dispensing liquid refreshments. In these functions it is closely related to the retail trade and, indeed, most hotels carry other lines of small merchandise for the convenience of their patrons. In a small town, the hotel, or hotels, may add considerable prestige to the business centre. In the larger cities, also, the more important hotels are in the "down-town" areas.

Including both full time and seasonal establishments, there were, in 1954, 5,200 hotels in Canada. They did a gross business of $406,000,000 50% of which represents the sale of alcoholic beverages, 22.5%, revenue from rooms, 18.2%, from meals, and the remainder from small merchandise, such as tobacco. Approximately 70,000 are

employed in the hotel business. Although small hotels are widely scattered, the major part of the business is in the large cities. Four metropolitan cities, Toronto, Montreal, Vancouver and Winnipeg account for about 25% of the total business.

The hotels of Canada are closely related to the transportation systems, both the great railway companies maintaining chains of first-class hotels. These perform a great and efficient service in ministering to the comfort of business people visiting the larger centres. There are also first-class resort hotels, such as those at Banff and Jasper. Only a few smaller towns have been able to maintain good hotels, the change in travelling habits brought about by the automobile having put many of the older "railway station hotels" out of business. Their places were taken, between the wars, by cabins along the highways, often rather flimsily constructed for summer use. In the post-war period, numerous new stopping places have been built. They are more

*Courtesy Canadian National Railways.*

Plate 111. "The Charlottetown", the Canadian National Hotel in the capital city of Prince Edward Island. Both large railway systems operate extensive hotel chains.

permanent and pleasing structures of the *motel* type, fully equipped to offer complete and comfortable lodging, summer and winter. Located outside the cities they help to keep traffic out of the crowded down-town areas.

## Railways

Despite the growth of other means of transportation, the railways remain the most important factor in the economic geography of Canada, and constitute the greatest effort to adjust the somewhat adverse space relations of the economic regions of the country. From the formation of the Dominion, the railways have been, and still are, both a geographic and a political necessity while, at the same time, placing upon the country one of its heaviest financial burdens. Canadian railways were built partly by the government and partly by private enterprise, but always with the help of government subsidies and guaranties. In recent decades, somewhat more than half the total mileage has been under government operation and, except for brief periods of abnormal activity, has not been

able to show a surplus over its cost of operation. This is another way of stating that railway transportation is regarded as a national service, which must be subsidized by the public purse.

The Canadian railways are more than mere systems of land transportation. Both the C.N.R. and C.P.R. have chains of hotels, while the Canadian Pacific is also interested in steamships, airlines, land and irrigation projects.

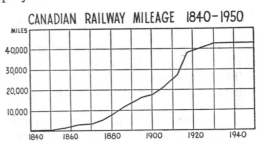

CANADIAN RAILWAY MILEAGE 1840–1950

Figure 331. *Growth of Canadian Railway Mileage. 1840-1950.* The Canadian railways reached their maximum extent about 1930 and have receded slightly since then. (Data from Canada Year Book)

The first railway was begun in 1835. It was only 16 miles in length, connecting La Prairie and St. Johns, Quebec, in order to expedite travel between Montreal and New York. It was opened in 1836. At about the same time, a railway was built to haul coal from Stellarton to Pictou Harbour in Nova Scotia. At first it used horse drawn cars, but became a steam railway in 1839. The "Sampson", the first locomotive on this line, is on display in Halifax. By 1850, however, there were only 66 miles of railway in Canada.

The first through route was the Grand Trunk, begun in 1852 and completed between Montreal and Toronto in 1856. It was extended westward to Sarnia in 1859, and eastward to Riviere du Loup in 1860. It also had a winter outlet to the Atlantic in Portland, Maine.

The Intercolonial was proposed in the 1830's, to link Canada with New Brunswick and Nova Scotia. It was begun near Halifax in 1854, and completed to Riviere

Plate 112.  Canadian railways are being equipped with Diesel locomotives.

du Loup in 1876. Later, over other lines, it ran its trains to Montreal.

The Canadian Pacific was the first transcontinental railway. Advocated in 1849, it was begun as a public work in 1874 and completed by the C.P.R. company in 1885. It received a cash subsidy of $25,000,000, a land grant of 25,000,000 acres and a guarantee of protection against competing lines for twenty years. By 1913, two other transcontinental routes had come into being, through the completion of the Canadian Northern, Grand Trunk Pacific and National Transcontinental. During the period 1900-1915, railway mileage doubled, rising from 17,000 miles to 34,000 miles.

Thereafter, only a few branch lines were built, and there has even been some abandonment. The record of railway mileage is given in graphic form in Figure 331. The totals for 1951 are given in Table 42.

The mileage of Canadian railroads has not changed significantly since 1930, while the available rolling stock actually declined. The low point in railway activity was reached in 1933, when freight and passenger traffic had sunk to half the records for 1928. From a low of 19,000,000 passengers and 57,000,000 tons of freight, railway business reached a peak, in 1944, of 60,000,000 passengers and 155,300,000 tons of freight. (See figure 332) Since the aver-

| Table 42 | Railway Mileage | 1951 |
|---|---|---|
| Newfoundland | | 705 |
| Prince Edward Island | | 285 |
| Nova Scotia | | 1,396 |
| New Brunswick | | 1,835 |
| Quebec | | 4,789 |
| Ontario | | 10,440 |
| Manitoba | | 4,834 |
| Saskatchewan | | 8,739 |
| Alberta | | 5,647 |
| British Columbia | | 3,889 |
| Yukon | | 58 |
| In the United States | | 339 |
| Total single track | | 42,956 |
| Second track | | 2,487 |
| Industrial | | 2,068 |
| Yards and sidings | | 10,639 |
| Grand Total | | 58,150 |

Canada Year Book.

## TONNAGE OF RAILWAY FREIGHT 1932-48

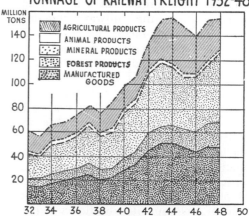

Figure 332. *Tonnage of Railway Freight.* Mineral products and manufactured goods lead in giving work to the railways. Note that in recent years the volume of freight has been nearly two and one half times as large as it was in the depression years. (Data from D. B. S.)

age length of freight haul was 424 miles, the ton-mileage total in 1944 was 66,000,-000,000. Compared with the United States, Canada has about one-eighth as many miles of track, but carries only about one-twelfth as much freight. Of the freight tonnage originating in Canada in 1948, 14% was loaded in the Maritime Provinces, 18% in Quebec, 35% in Ontario, 25% in the Prairie Provinces and 8% in British Columbia. Of 154,900,000 tons of freight in 1948, agricultural products furnished 18%, animal products 2%, mine products 36%, forest products 12% and manufactured and miscellaneous goods 32%.

Railway income in 1952 amounted to $1,162,000,000, or approximately 5.1% of the gross national product. The railways employed 202,000 persons, paying $640,-000,000 in wages, an average of $3,200 per person. This was 3.8% of the total labour force and 6.0% of the total labour income. As well as being an essential factor in the conduct of the nation's business, the railways, themselves, also constitute one of the largest enterprises. Not only in the wages which they pay, and thus increase the public buying power, but also by reason of direct purchases of steel, rolling stock, fuel and numerous other materials, the railways support the industries which they also serve.

Courtesy Canadian National Railways.

Plate 113. The "Abegweit", largest ice-breaking car ferry in the world, connects the railway and highway systems of Prince Edward Island with those of the Canadian mainland.

## Road and Highway Transportation

The development of motor vehicles, since World War I, has led to a parallel development of roads and highways. There have been roads, of course, since the early days of settlement, but the rise of railway trans-

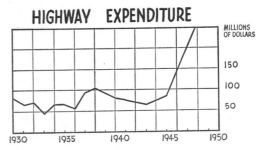

Figure 333. Highway Expenditure. Post war expenditure on highway construction and maintenance has grown enormously. (Data from D. B. S.)

portation prevented the development of through highway routes, and converted existing road nets into railway feeders. In the west, and in other areas of new settlement, the railway arrived first and all road building was considered subsidiary. Nevertheless, in terms of total population, Canada had a rather extended road mileage. Maintenance was usually under local control, and the condition of the travelled surface was far from uniform or satisfactory.

In 30 years the provincial departments of highways have performed miracles. Total expenditure has been very heavy (See figure 333) and most of the construction has been financed by adding to provincial funded debt. The emphasis has been upon the construction of through highways in the various provinces, but roads are continually being opened in new areas for settlement, mining and forestry needs.

At the end of 1954, there were 524,000 miles of rural road in Canada, of which 193,000 miles were surfaced. Of the surfaced road, 159,000 miles were gravel, 32,-000 miles were bituminous surfaced and 1,500 miles were concrete. Hard surfaced roads thus constituted only 6.1% of the

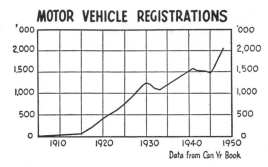

Figure 334. *Motor Vehicle Registration.* Since the end of the war number of motor vehicles has risen at a more rapid rate than ever before.

total. To this may be added about 16,000 miles of urban streets, of which 8,600 miles were paved and 3,700 miles surfaced with gravel and crushed stone.

Although discussed for many years, the Trans-Canada Highway has been slow to materialize. Since 1945, Halifax has been linked to Vancouver by an all-Canadian road, some 4,200 miles in length. About 60% of this distance is paved, but much of the pavement is below standard. At a Trans-Canada Highway Conference in Ottawa in December, 1948, plans for a first-class, hard-surfaced, two-lane highway were drawn up. This road will have an approximate length of 5,000 miles, extending from Newfoundland, Cape Breton and Prince Edward Island to Vancouver Island. It will have a minimum right of way of 100 feet, a paved surface of 22 or 24 feet, minimum curvature of 8° and maximum gradients of 6%. It was estimated that this road would cost about $300,000,000, of which Federal Government agreed to provide $150,000,000 within seven years.

A notable link in the North American highway network is the Alaska highway, extending for 1,600 miles from Fort St. John, B.C. to Fairbanks, Alaska. About 10,000 United States engineer troops and 4,000 civilians, half of whom were Canadians,

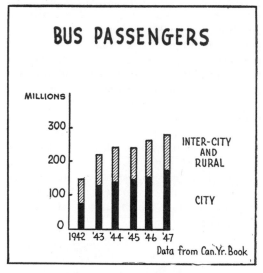

Figure 336. *Numbers of Bus Passengers.*

built the road in the summer of 1942. At the end of the war, the Canadian section of the road was taken over by the Canadian Government. It opens up a vast and practically untouched territory in Northern British Columbia and Yukon.

Canada has a greater concentration of motor vehicles, in relation to its population, than any other country except the United States. In 1954, there were 3,644,589 motor vehicles registered, of which 2,688,465 were passenger cars, 908,-599 were commercial vehicles, 9,860 were

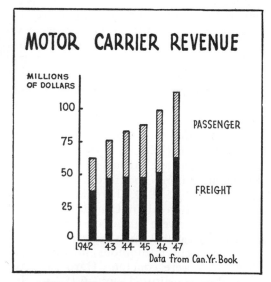

Figure 335. *Motor Carrier Revenues.*

buses and 43,189 were motorcycles. In 1905, there were only 565 motor vehicles registered in Canada; by 1915, there were about 95,000 and, by 1920, over 400,000. There has been a steady increase since then, as shown in Figure 334, except during the periods of 1931-33 and 1941-45. In 1954, Canada had one motor vehicle for each four inhabitants, 6.8 for each mile of road and 110 for each mile of paved highway. Provincial revenues from gasoline tax, motor vehicle registration and the like totalled $325,000,000, each vehicle averaging $21.00 for license and $65.00 gasoline tax.

Commercial motor carrier traffic has assumed considerable proportions but, until 1941, no attempt was made to measure its

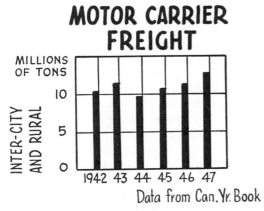

Figure 337. *Growth of Motor Carrier Freight.*

volume. Since then, the Federal Bureau of Statistics has made an annual census covering most commercial enterprises. Passenger traffic statistics are fairly complete, because tickets are sold and accounted for, but it is impossible to get statistics on the operation of thousands of individual trucks. The reported revenues of motor carriers rose from $60,000,000 in 1942 to $179,000,000 in 1950, the number of passengers carried rose from 147,000,000 to 363,000,000 while freight tonnage varied from 10,000,000 to 17,500,000. (See figures 335, 336, 337). In 1950, this business employed over 27,000 persons and paid over $62,000,000 in wages.

## Waterways and Shipping

Canada has 60,000 miles of sea coast fronting on three oceans, as well as the St. Lawrence-Great Lakes artery, the busiest inland waterway on earth. In spite of the fact that many stretches of rugged and inaccessible coastline have no improved harbours, water carriage is very important

### Shipping

Canadian shipping may be divided into three classes: sea going, inland or river and lake international, and coastwise. The first mentioned class plies between the ocean ports on either the Atlantic or the Pacific and foreign ports; the second is between Canadian and United States' ports on the St. Lawrence, Great Lakes or any of the connecting lakes and rivers; the third class is composed of shipping which plies in and out of Canadian ports exclusively, whether on the Great Lakes or the oceans.

Canadian contact with ocean shipping dates back to the days of discovery. European fishing ships made landings in Newfoundland and the Maritime Provinces. Shipyards were early established in New France. Later many ships were built in Quebec and the Maritime Provinces, making this one of the greatest ship owning regions on earth. The *Royal William*, built in Quebec, is credited with the first crossing of the Atlantic entirely by steam power, making the run from Pictou, N.S., to London, England, in 1833. With the passing of wooden ships, Canadian shipbuilding declined, except for the construction of fishing schooners of the Bluenose pattern. During both World Wars, however, ships of all sorts were built in Canadian yards at Halifax, Pictou, Lauzon, Sorel, Montreal, Toronto, Collingwood, the Lakehead and Vancouver.

The total sea-going tonnage entered at Canadian ports in 1911 was about 12,000,000 tons, increasing to 23,000,000 in 1923 and gradually thereafter as shown in Figure 338 to 33,000,000 in 1940. During the

## SHIPPING ENTERED AT CANADIAN PORTS

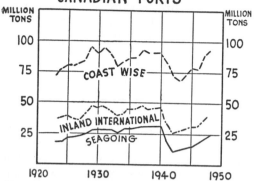

Figure 338. *Shipping Entered at Canadian Ports, 1923-1948*. (Data from Canada Year Book)

war, ocean shipping fell off rather badly but has been on the increase since 1945. Figure 339 shows the activity of the more important ports in 1947.

Sailing vessels were used on the Great Lakes in the early days of settlement and, during the War of 1812, a considerable fleet of war vessels was built and used. The first Canadian steamship was a river boat, the *Accommodation,* built in 1809 to run between Montreal and Quebec. The *Fron-*

*tenac,* in 1817, began a weekly service on Lake Ontario, between York and Prescott. The *Gore,* in 1845, was the first Canadian steamer on the upper Lakes. Although there was little Canadian traffic, Canadian shipping shared in the trade between Buffalo and the Western States. A fleet of several hundred carriers, of which a fair number are Canadian, now operate on the Great Lakes, vessels of large size being able to pass through the New Welland and Sault Ste. Marie canals. In general, wheat and iron ore are carried down the lakes, while coal is carried up. Wheat, pulp and paper and wood are carried to the United States, while coal and iron ore cross the lakes from United States to Canada. A few small, sea-going ships are able to enter the Great Lakes through the St. Lawrence canals, forerunners of much larger carriers which will be able to navigate the proposed St. Lawrence Deep Waterway. In 1948, a total of 392,000 tons of shipping was registered in Ontario. New ships, of 20,000 tons and more than 600 feet in length, have been built in Canadian yards. Among them were the world's largest lake tankers which were used to transport Alberta oil to Ontario refineries.

Lake shipping is classified as international if it plies between Canada and the United States. It has varied from 19,000,000 down to about 14,000,000 tons, since 1903.

Coastwise shipping includes all trade between Canadian ports, whether lake or ocean. It includes the great wheat shipments of the Great Lakes, the coal trade of the Gulf and St. Lawrence River, and the host of small boats and packets in all coastal areas. It, of course, bulks largest in the statistics, varying from 40,000,000 to 50,000,000 tons per year. The prospects of increased production of iron ore in Newfoundland, Labrador and Northern Ontario, and increased oil production in Western Canada, together with increased steel production and petroleum refining

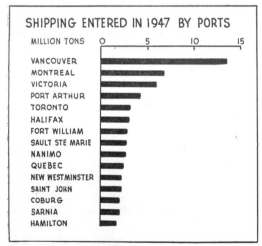

Figure 339. *Shipping Entered at Leading Canadian Ports in 1947*. Note that if the combined Lakehead waterfront be considered as one port, its activity is slightly greater than that of Montreal. (Data from Canada Year Book)

capacity in Ontario, point toward a considerable future increase in Canadian coastwise shipping.

## Canal Systems

There are nearly 500 miles of canals in Canada. They may be divided into two classes: (1) primary canals on the St. Lawrence River and Great Lakes, including the Lachine, Soulanges, Cornwall and Williamsburg canals of the St. Lawrence River, the Welland Ship Canal between Lake Ontario and Lake Erie and the Sault St. Marie canal on the St. Mary River between Lake Huron and Lake Superior; (2) secondary canals, including the St.

Peters Canal between the Bras d'Or Lakes and the Atlantic Ocean, the St. Ours and Chambly Canals on the Richelieu River, the Ste. Anne, Carillon and Grenville Canals on the Ottawa River, the Rideau Canal from Ottawa to Kingston, the Murray Canal from Lake Ontario to the Bay of Quinte and the Trent Canal from the Bay of Quinte to Lake Simcoe and Georgian Bay. The Rideau and Trent Canal systems have a length of over 400 miles, but they are of little commercial significance, having a depth of only 5.5 to 6.0 feet. The particulars of the St. Lawrence and Great Lakes Canals are given in Table 43.

### Table 43          Dimensions of the St. Lawrence—Great Lakes Canals

| Name | Location | Length in Miles | No. | Locks Minimum Dimensions Length ft. | Width ft. | Depth ft. |
|------|----------|-----------------|-----|-------------|-----------|-----------|
| Lachine | Montreal to Lachine | 8.74 | 5 | 270 | 45 | 14 |
| Soulanges | Cascades Point to Coteau Landing | 14.67 | 5 | 280 | 46 | 15 |
| Cornwall | Cornwall to Dickinsons Landing | 11.00 | 6 | 270 | 43.6 | 14 |
| Farran Point | Farran Point Rapids | 1.28 | 1 | 800 | 50 | 16 |
| Rapide Plat | Morrisburg | 3.89 | 2 | 270 | 45 | 15 |
| Galop | Iroquois to Cardinal | 7.36 | 3 | 270 | 45 | 14 |
| St. Lawrence | | 46.94 | 22 | 270 | 43.6 | 14 |
| Welland | Port Weller to Port Colborne | 27.60 | 8 | 859 | 80 | 30 |
| Sault Ste. Marie | Sault Ste. Marie | 1.38 | 1 | 900 | 60 | 18.25 |
| Grand Totals | | 75.92 | 31 | | | |

### Table 44          Nature of Canal Freight in 1951

| Canal | Agricultural Products tons | Animal Products tons | Manuf. and Misc. tons | Forest Products tons | Mineral Products tons | Total tons |
|-------|---------------------------|---------------------|----------------------|---------------------|----------------------|------------|
| Sault Ste. Marie | 1,202,951 | 159 | 1,091,682 | 189,904 | 320,696 | 2,805,392 |
| Welland Ship | 4,118,184 | 300 | 4,075,498 | 613,961 | 7,389,981 | 16,197,924 |
| St. Lawrence | 2,693,613 | 1,612 | 3,391,336 | 794,515 | 3,035,781 | 9,916,857 |
| Other Canals | 2,532 | 4,288 | 112,274 | 8,002 | 277,745 | 414,861 |
| Totals | 8,017,280 | 6,359 | 8,670,790 | 1,606,402 | 11,024,203 | 29,325,034 |

**Table 45**        **Direction and Origin of the Traffic on the St. Lawrence—**
**Great Lakes Canal System—1951**

| Canal | Direction | | Origin | | Total Cargo Tons |
|---|---|---|---|---|---|
| | Up | Down | Canada | U.S.A. | |
| | tons | tons | tons | tons | Tons |
| Sault Ste. Marie | 1,010,371 | 1,795,021 | 2,262,735 | 542,657 | 2,805,392 |
| Welland Ship | 2,752,439 | 13,445,485 | 6,290,487 | 9,907,437 | 16,197,924 |
| St. Lawrence | 4,046,551 | 5,870,306 | 7,065,836 | 2,852,021 | 9,916,857 |
| Totals | 7,809,361 | 21,110,812 | 15,619,058 | 13,302,115 | 28,920,173 |
| Per cent | 26.0 | 74.0 | 54.0 | 46.0 | 100.0 |

The lock at Sault Ste. Marie is paralleled on the American side by several very much larger locks which handle the bulk of the traffic.

The greatest tonnage is that of mineral products, including iron ore, coal, sand and gravel and oil. Agricultural products, largely wheat and other grains, however, have been the most valuable cargo.

Down bound traffic is about three times as great as up bound traffic. American and Canadian freight tonnages are about equal. This is largely made up of iron ore, coal and oil moving to Southern Ontario ports,

# TRAFFIC ON THE GREAT LAKES-
## ST. LAWRENCE CANALS

Figure 340. *Traffic on the Canadian Great Lakes — St. Lawrence Canals. 1920-1948.* Traffic reached a peak of 29,000,000 tons of shipping in the year 1951. (Data from Canada Year Book)

and to New York State ports on Lake Ontario and the St. Lawrence. The total of 29,000,000 tons, given in the table, involves some duplication, however; for part of the of which over 33% used the Welland canal alone. Canadian canals handle about 15% as much freight as Canadian railways. The twenty-eight-year record of canal traffic is shown in Figure 340. The peak reached in 1938 (24.8 million tons) is a long way below the 52,000,000 tons carried in 1913, before the American locks at the "Soo" were completed.

In 1951, the traffic through the American locks at Sault Ste. Marie was over 117,000,000 tons. A record of 120,200,000 tons was reached in 1942, of which over 94,000,000 tons was iron ore for the war effort. In 1951, the Panama canal carried 30,000,000 tons, of which 3,000,000 tons was Canadian freight.

## The St. Lawrence Seaway

The small capacity of the St. Lawrence canals constitutes a traffic bottleneck, and plans for a deep water route from tidewater to the head of the lakes have been made for more than half a century. The section of the river, which is most in need freight uses all three canals, part uses two only, and some, only one canal. Eliminating this duplication, leaves a net total of 23,300,000 tons using Canadian canals, of improvement, is largely on the international boundary, and United States' co-

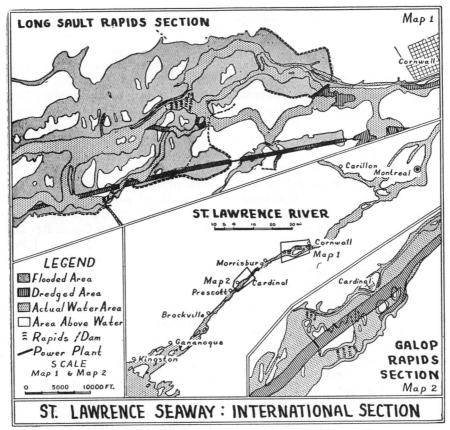

Figure 341. *The St. Lawrence Seaway, International Section.* The most important construction projects in the International section will be at the Long Sault Rapids and the Galop Rapids. The construction of the dams near Cornwall will impound a large volume of water, inundating considerable areas along the river, including portions of towns and villages. In addition to the deep waterway, over 2,000,000 H.P. of electric energy will be made available to the industries of Ontario and New York State.

operation and consent is needed for its development. Until recently, powerful interests were successful in having this agreement delayed. However, in May, 1954, consent was given by the United States' government.

The plans, which were agreed upon by the unratified treaty between the two nations, called for a 27 foot canal with locks equal in capacity to those of the Welland Ship Canal. The great cost of construction could, in part, be paid for by the development of the potential 2,200,000 h.p. of the rapids, a block of power which is urgently needed in both Ontario and New York State. The completion of this project will effect a profound change in both the physical and economic aspects of the St. Lawrence frontier region.

## Airways

At Baddeck, N.S., in 1909, Jack McCurdy in the *Silver Dart* made the first airplane flight by a British subject in the British Empire. Canadians were active in the R.A.F. during World War I and, on their return to Canada, many of them became pioneers in civil aviation. The great expanse of northern Canada, almost inaccessible to ground transportation, was a challenge to aviation, while the thousands of lakes made it the natural habitat of the pontoon plane. Forest patrol, bush flying, air photography and, eventually, inter-city and transcontinental air service came into being.

Trans-Canada Air Lines came into being in 1937, a government controlled air service, set up to pioneer the transcontinental route which, at first, could not be expected to pay its way.

The second World War saw Canada take a leading part in the Commonwealth Air Training Plan, when many airdromes and airports were set up. Transatlantic air services were inaugurated by the Department of Transport and turned over to Trans-Canada Air Lines for operation at the end of the war.

Canadian Pacific Air Lines was formed after the war by the almalgamation of a number of small lines servicing the north and, in 1949, began to operate a trans-Pacific service.

In 1951, T.C.A. operated 18,000 miles of routes, carried 900,000 passengers and nearly 8,000,000 ton-miles of mail and commodity traffic. C.P.A. operated almost 25,-000 miles of routes and carried 184,000 passengers. There were four other domestic airlines maintaining scheduled air services and a number of others operating charter and non-scheduled specific services. Fourteen Commonwealth and foreign air services were authorized to operate in Canada. The growth of civil air traffic in Canada from 1936 to 1948 is shown in figure 342. In 1951 the totals were 610,000,000 passenger miles and 15,000,000 ton-miles of mail and commodity freight. The industry had a payroll of $25,000,000 and employed 7,000.

In 1951, there were 275 land airports and 71 seaplane bases licensed in Canada. The busiest airports were at Malton, a few miles west of Toronto, and Dorval on the island of Montreal, which is the terminus for most transatlantic services. Other important airports are located at Goose Bay and Gander in Newfoundland, Moncton, Rimouski, Ottawa, Winnipeg, Edmonton, Calgary and Vancouver.

## Postal Service

Closely allied with all forms of transportation is the postal service, the oldest as well as the major means of communication. As early as 1703, a courier service was established from Quebec to Three Rivers and Montreal and, in 1734, a "post road" was built complete with post houses, horse and vehicle service. In other provinces, also, early roads were built as "post roads". Since Confederation in 1867, the postal service has been a Federal responsibility, administered by the Canada Post Office Department.

There are approximately 12,000 post offices in Canada. Letter carrier delivery is given in 126 cities and towns by over 5,000 carriers. There are nearly 5,200 rural routes covering 120,000 miles of road and serving 400,000 rural mail boxes. The railway postal services cover 40,000 miles of track with an annual mileage of over 45,000,000 miles, employing a staff of 1,300 mail clerks who sort the mail en route. There are 24,000 miles of air-mail routes. The post office handled an estimated 3,000,-000,000 items of mail in 1952, and received a gross revenue of $122,000,000. In so far as possible, all first class letter mail, up to one ounce in weight, is carried by air. More than 18,000 postal workers are em-

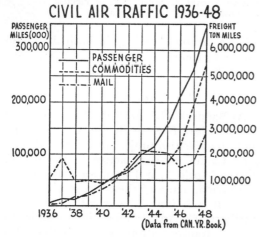

## CIVIL AIR TRAFFIC 1936-48

PASSENGER MILES(000) — FREIGHT TON MILES

1936 '38 '40 '42 '44 '46 '48
(Data from CAN. YR. Book)

Figure 342. *The Growth of Civil Air Traffic. 1936-1948.* Air traffic has grown very rapidly during the war and post-war years.

ployed. These figures indicate the extensiveness of Canada's postal service, one of the most up-to-date in the world.

## Electrical Communications

There are six telegraph systems in Canada, with over 53,000 miles of pole lines, 435,000 miles of wire, 5,200 offices and 10,000 employees. Four systems are operated by the railways, one by the Federal Government, and one is operated independently. Three cable companies, in addition to the telegraph companies, operate submarine cables. Newfoundland, Nova Scotia, and British Columbia have cable connections with Britain, the Azores, Bermuda, Australia and New Zealand. Newfoundland, Cape Breton, Prince Edward Island and Vancouver Island are all connected to the mainland by cables.

The telephone was invented by Alexander Graham Bell in 1876. Teaching in Boston, U.S.A., and spending his vacations at the Bell homestead near Brantford, Ontario, Bell carried on his research in both places. The first long distance phone conversation took place between Brantford and Paris. Since that time, the development of this type of communication has developed tremendously in all parts of the world, but most extensively in North America.

In Canada there are about 3,000 telephone systems with 250,000 miles of line, 10,500,000 miles of wire and 3,100,000 phones in use. There is, thus, a telephone for each five or six inhabitants. Each phone is used, on the average, more than 1,700 times per year. Telephone systems employed over 47,000 persons in 1951, an increase of almost 100% since 1945.

Radio has become almost a universal means of communication within twenty-five years. More than 2,000,000 radio licenses were issued each year in Canada and, since many of them cover more than one set, it is estimated that there are at least 3,000,000 receivers in operation.

There were, in 1950, 148 broadcasting stations operating on the standard broadcast bands, as well as a large number of commercial short wave and frequency-modulation stations. Television stations at Montreal and Toronto were put into operation in Sepember 1952.

The Canadian Broadcasting Corporation was set up in 1936, in order to achieve a national coverage. It owns and operates 19 stations, of which seven have 50,000 watt transmitters. These are: CBA, Sackville, N.B., CBF and CBM, Montreal; CBL, Toronto; CBW, Winnipeg; CBK, Watrous, Saskatchewan; and CBX, Edmonton. The CBC operates three program networks, Trans-Canada and Dominion for English speaking people and the French network for those of that language. These networks include 58 basic stations and 46 supplementary stations. Because of time differences four regional schedules are maintained: Atlantic, Mid-Eastern, Prairie and Pacific. The CBC International Service transmitters are located at Sackville, N.B. Using 50,000 watts they can operate in any of the international short-wave bands and carry programs in twelve languages to Europe, Africa, and Latin America.

Privately owned broadcasting stations began operation in the early 1920's and, since 1929, have offered regular service to many parts of Canada. The majority are low power stations, serving specific localities. CFRB and CJBC, Toronto, and CKLW, Windsor are 50,000 watt stations. There are about 135 privately owned A.M. stations, eight shortwave stations and 30 F.M. stations. Privately owned stations involve an investment of at least $27,000,000 and employ more than 3,700 persons.

The Canadian Government operates extensive wireless telegraph and telephone systems, in connection with various departments such as Defence, Transport, Mines and Technical Surveys, Revenue and Public Works. The Canadian Marconi Company operates long distance radio telegraph and telephone communica-

tions from Drummondville, Quebec, to Newfoundland, Great Britain and Australia.
Radio-telephone services are also operated in British Columbia, northeastern
Quebec and northwestern Ontario in
areas not otherwise served. Most provincial
governments, the Royal Canadian Mounted
Police and many other police units also
operate radio-communications. There are
approximately 6,000 amateur experimental stations in Canada.

## The Press

In spite of the radio, the press is still
the most important mass-medium of communication in Canada. There are (1951)
about 80 daily newspapers, 740 weeklies
and 500 magazines and periodicals of all
sorts. The reported circulations were 2,-
900,000 dailies, 2,500,000 weeklies, and 10,-
000,000 copies of all other types. The printing and publishing business is treated
statistically, as a manufacturing industry.
In 1950, it employed 26,700 people; its gross
product was valued at $181,000,000, and
the net value was $129,000,000. Newspapers
are published in English, French, and
fourteen other languages including Ukrainian, German, Yiddish and Polish. While
many periodicals, and a few weeklies, are
national in coverage, most daily and weekly
newspapers are local and regional, even
though they carry national and world news.
Newspaper coverage, both in news content and in reader patronage, gives strong
indications of the geographic relations of
regional capitals with their umlands. The
daily circulations of city newspapers are
sometimes seven to eight times as great
as the total number of urban households.

## The Importance of Transportation and Communication

Transportation and communication facilities are the means by which mankind
overcomes adverse space relations and are
enabled to exchange goods and ideas. Without such facilities large nations would be
an impossibility. Canada places a great

value upon these systems for her dependence upon them is great. This is, in part,
shown by the extent to which these services are government operated, controlled
and regulated. Much of the necessary effort could not have been made without
government funds. A further indication of
the importance of these services is the fact
that about 8% of all Canadian workers
find employment in these industries.

## Institutions and Services

As a civilization progresses, a substantial body of citizens become segregated
from the main group of producers and
distributors of goods, in order to perform
specialized, essential services. Among these
are the services of banking and finance,
law making, public administration, justice,
health and medical services and education.
They become segregated geographically,
also, according to the needs of the territory which they serve, which means that
they are found more abundantly in larger
population centers and, particularly, in
those cities which have been designated as
political capitals. These range all the way
from the national capital at Ottawa,
through the provincial capitals and county
towns, to the cross roads hamlets where
township offices are located. The city hall
is the civic service centre of the city and
usually occupies a geographically central
location.

Among financial institutions, the chartered banks of Canada can claim to exert
a strong geographic influence. There are
ten chartered banks, with more than 2,900
branches in all parts of the country, as
well as some in foreign countries. About
three-fourths of all the business is done
by four institutions: the Bank of Montreal, Canadian Bank of Commerce, the
Bank of Nova Scotia and the Royal Bank
of Canada. The head offices of Canadian
Banks are among the most imposing structures of Canadian cities — the Bank of
Commerce building in Toronto being the
highest in the country. The "bank corner"

in any small town is a close approach to a "hundred per cent location" and over the years usually becomes the centre of its business and professional district. The presence of a bank in a village gives it an advantage over all competing centres which lack this facility. The Canadian banking system, by providing a country-wide service, ensures a financial stability which crop or business failures in any one area cannot seriously damage. Buildings and service, then, are the contributions of Canadian financial institutions, rather than

ous parts of the cities or towns in which they are located, and they exert an appreciable influence upon its trade and social life.

Elementary schools are found everywhere, even in open country, but secondary schools, usually, only in centres of village status or greater. The consequence of this geographical differential has been a lower average educational attainment for rural citizens. This pattern is being gradually replaced by one of consolidated rural elementary schools and rural high

D. F. Putnam.

Plate 114. King's College, Halifax, Nova Scotia. Founded at Windsor, N. S., in 1779 it is the oldest college in Canada using English as the language of instruction.

the provision of employment. Finance, insurance and real estate, together, account for less than 3% of the gainfully employed.

In 1951, 2,800,000 persons or 20% of the population of Canada attended schools or other educational institutions, where they were taught by about 100,000 instructors. Education is, thus, by far the greatest service industry in the country. Its imprint upon the landscape varies considerably. The great universities, such as Laval, McGill, Montreal, Toronto, and British Columbia, are almost cities in themselves. All universities are conspicu-

schools, which is as yet far from complete.

Religion exerts a geographic influence far beyond the size of the group dispensing its services. This is especially true in Quebec, and in the parts of other provinces, peopled by French-speaking Roman Catholics.

In the past, the church has been the centre of the social life, as well as of religion. The parish centre was also the educational centre. About it developed the rural village, the market town and eventually the manufacturing city. In Quebec, the church spire is the dominant landmark of the village or small town, and the parish is also the unit of civil government. The church has served to crystallize a geographic pattern, which is followed by all the other services and to which commercial activities are obliged to adapt themselves, as well.

Persons in service occupations comprise 20% of the total active population, discounting those engaged in domestic service, and unstated occupations, about 17% of the gainfully employed are to be found in service industries and in the service of the various levels of government. This is, numerically, the second largest group in the country, being exceeded only by the staff in manufacturing. In keeping with this importance is the magnitude of the ensemble of structures in which their activities are housed and the centralizing influence which they exercise on the geographic patterns of the country.

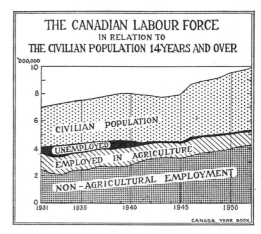

Figure 343. *The Canadian Labour Force.* More than 5,200,000 Canadians were gainfully employed in 1951.

## Employment and Income

During and since World War II, employment has been at a high level in Can-

## Table 46    Employment and Income 1951

| Industrial Groups | Labour Force | | Labour Income | | National Income | |
|---|---|---|---|---|---|---|
| | 000 | % | $000,000 | % | $000,000 | % |
| Agriculture | 827 | 15.8 | 171 | 1.7 | 2,330 | 13.3 |
| Forestry | 130 | 2.5 | 335 | 3.4 | 377 | 2.2 |
| Fishing and Trapping | 51 | 1.0 | 15 | .1 | 92 | .5 |
| Mining | 104 | 2.0 | 356 | 3.6 | 688 | 3.9 |
| Electric Power | 62 | 1.2 | 165 | 1.7 | 365 | 2.1 |
| Primary Industries | 1,174 | 22.5 | 1,042 | 10.5 | 3,852 | 22.0 |
| Construction | 351 | 6.7 | 640 | 6.4 | 857 | 4.9 |
| Manufacturing | 1,361 | 26.1 | 3,344 | 34.0 | 5,127 | 29.4 |
| Secondary Industries | 1,712 | 32.8 | 3,984 | 40.4 | 5,984 | 33.3 |
| Transportation, Storage and Communications | 403 | 7.7 | 1,100 | 11.1 | 1,384 | 8.0 |
| Trade | 710 | 13.6 | 1,383 | 14.0 | 2,374 | 13.6 |
| Finance, Insurance, and Real Estate | 144 | 2.8 | 365 | 3.7 | 1,189 | 6.8 |
| Services | 1,077 | 20.6 | 2,003 | 21.3 | 2,680 | 15.3 |
| Trade and Service Group | 2,334 | 44.7 | 4,851 | 49.1 | 7,628 | 44.7 |
| Grand Totals | 5,220 | 100.0 | 9,877 | 100.0 | 17,463* | 100.0 |

*Includes $335,000,000 to non-residents.                    Data from D. B. S.

ada. Whereas, in 1939, almost 1,000,000 persons were listed as unemployed, less than 200,000 were so listed at the peak of seasonal lay-offs in the years 1945-52. This is shown graphically in figure 343. The census reports of 1941 and 1951, together with the system of labour surveys begun in 1945, give us a very good knowledge of the trend of employment. From 1941-45 there were several hundred thousand on active service, but by 1947 most of them were back in civilian occupations. At the census of 1951 the gainfully employed numbered 5,220,000, about 37% of the total population.

Canadian workers may be classified into three main groups: (a) those engaged in primary industries or the production of raw materials, (b) those engaged in secondary industries, and (c) those engaged in trading the goods produced by the primary and secondary groups, or in providing all sorts of services for the whole population. Since 1941, so many people have withdrawn from agriculture that, in spite of increased employment in other primary industries, the whole group has declined

about 10% in importance. The other groups, and in particular the service industries, have gained greatly in numbers and in relative importance as well.

In 1951, the gross national product or total value of all goods and services at market prices was $21,200,000,000. Deducting indirect taxes and depreciation left a national income of over $17,000,000,000, of which the larger share, almost $9,900,000,000 was earned by the labour force. Primary industries, employing 22.5% of the workers, gained 22% of the national income but distributed only 10.5% of the labour income. Secondary industries with 38.2% of the labour, earned 33.3% of the national income and 40.4% of the labour income. The third group, comprising transportation, trade, finance and services (including government) employed 44.7% of the labour, gained 44.7% of the national income and dispensed 49.1% of the labour income. Application of the principles of human geography will bring to light many significant relationships of all of these activities in each Canadian region.

## Selected References

Bladen, V. W. *An Introduction to Political Economy.* (Chapters V and VI). The University of Toronto Press. Toronto. 1946.

Britnell, G. E. *The Wheat Economy.* University of Chicago Press. Chicago. 1939.

*Canada Year Book.* Ottawa. Annual.

Coats, R. H. (ed.) *Features of Present Day Canada.* The Annals of the American Academy of Political and Social Science. Vol. 253, pp. 1-266. 1947.

Currie, A. W. *Canadian Economic Development.* Thos. Nelson and Sons, Limited. Toronto. 1942.

Currie, A. W. *Economic Geography of Canada.*

The Macmillan Company of Canada. Toronto. 1945.

Currie, A. W. *The St. Lawrence Waterway.* Queens Quarterly. Winter. 1951-2. pp. 558-72. 1952.

Gibson, J. D. (ed). *Canada's Economy in a Changing World.* The Macmillan Company of Canada Limited. Toronto. 1948.

Glazebrook, G. P. deT. *History of Transportation in Canada.* Yale University Press. New Haven. 1938.

Hedges, J. B. *Building the Canadian West.* The MacMillan Company. New York. 1939.

Innis, M. Q. *An Economic History of Canada.* The Ryerson Press. Toronto. 1935.

# CHAPTER 25

# Problems and Trends in National Development

T HE development of Canada has been a fertile field for researchers in history and political economy but, for the most part, events and trends have been interpreted against rather sketchy geographical backgrounds. It might, perhaps, be better to say that geographic factors and the value of the geographic approach have been minimized while the emphasis has been placed upon personal biography and the growth of economic and political institutions. No detailed studies have been made in the fields of either historical or political geography and hence two of the most important volumes on Canadian national development remain to be written. The writing of this book would have been much easier if comprehensive historical and political geographies had been in existence. Each author in dealing with his own region, however, has attempted to show, in some slight degree, the effects of these factors upon the geographical ensemble.

It has been stated that a major function of geography is to provide a sound basis for nation planning. In such a role it is, of course, much more than a mere catalogue of resources. It must be analytical and interpretive, assessing each resource in relation to its location and region as well as to its importance in the economy of the whole country. A major resource will naturally receive adequate attention at all levels but some which are relatively unimportant at

the national level may have major roles in local and regional planning. It may, for instance, be advisable to foster certain industrial developments on the Prairies and in the Maritimes, even though the central manufacturing region is able to supply all demands. It is necessary, also, to maintain communications through hundreds of miles of relatively unoccupied territory which provides little paying traffic. Canada has its problems of national unity as well as those of rate and character of economic development. Canadians must look outside their borders also and consider their location and the role which they must play in the community of nations.

## Canadian Unity

Canada is one of the largest countries on earth. Reasonably compact in shape, it has fairly regular land frontiers. It shares the continent of North America with a friendly nation with whom it enjoys the most cordial relations, making the boundary of little more significance than an ordinary line fence. The frayed and discontinuous northern border is separated from the landmass of Eurasia by the frozen wastes of the Arctic Ocean. The navigable approaches have, during the whole period of development, been under the watchful eyes of friendly, protective navies. Space relations such as these are powerful geographical advantages which have permitted rather small groups of active people to consolidate their hold upon an immense territory. Relieved of the continuous necessity of directing too much of their energy into the organization of defence against outside enemies, Canadians have concentrated upon the solution of internal problems.

Canada is a land of many contrasts, some of them so sharp and so obvious that, to the casual observer, they have always appeared as insurmountable barriers to the achievement of national unity. It is not out of place to remind ourselves of some of them.

Canada is a land of dual culture. There are two official languages, English and French. Through each of these, Canadians are linked to great, historic European civilizations and to modern European currents of thought. To a very large measure this duality of language is paralleled and reinforced by a religious cleavage; French speaking Canadians belong to the Roman Catholic faith while the majority of English speaking Canadians adhere to the various Protestant denominations. When we note, also, that those of French culture are strongly centralized in a single strategic region and in possession of a very considerable block of resources, we realize that this duality is a permanent characteristic of the country. There can be no rapid fusion, no "melting-pot" as in the United States of America. People of other cultures who come to Canada must adhere to one or other of these groups. For the most part they have joined the English culture group and this has tended to preserve the French group although helping to keep it a minority.

"Minority" is a potent word in Canadian history. English settlers who came to Canada in the early years after the conquest were definitely in the minority. Later they were followed by such a flood of immigrants from the British Isles that the French majority was overcome, despite its high birth-rate. In this century, by reason of large-scale immigration from continental Europe and emigration to the United States of native-born Canadians, those of British descent now find themselves in the minority. It is still, however, the largest of the many minorities of which the population of Canada is composed.

Canada is a "new" country, but some of its parts are much newer than others. The contrast between the Prairie Provinces and the older eastern areas was a prime cause of political friction, the contrasts between the new pioneer districts of any province and its older more densely settled area always cause administrative problems.

The interests of rural and urban dwellers have often run counter to one another. Rural dwellers have been primary producers whose staple products sought export markets. The growing towns produced manufactures which, for the most part, sought the domestic market. Hence no single trade policy could satisfy both groups. Since most of the cities were in Quebec and Ontario, increasing sectional tensions were bound to occur.

What then holds the nation together in the face of these contrasts and despite these tensions? According to McInnis [1], "The initial basis of the Canadian community has unquestionably been a determination to remain independent of the United States". Though they may regard them as friendly protectors, Canadians do not desire to have the Americans as political overlords. Historical evidence may indicate that this was, and it still may be, a potent factor in the thinking of all factions of the population but a nation needs a more positive cement.

For some this has been provided by their British connection and by their loyalty to the British Crown. For the country as a whole, however, there is no doubt that, despite the pageantry of Royal visits, these are minor factors and their effects upon Canadians have been very unequal. Moreover, Canada has slowly and quietly wrested her independence from Britain just as ef-

[1] McInnis, Edgar. *The People*, Chapter 1, page 25, in *Canada*, edited by George W. Brown. University of Toronto Press. 1950.

fectively as she has resisted engulfment by the United States. Canadian independence has come gradually and the consequent tradition of evolution rather than revolution is, in itself, a pervading characteristic of Canadian thinking and behaviour.

Most important is a strong sense of achievement. Having inherited the leftovers of a continent they have knit together one of the largest countries on earth and have built a community with a material prosperity and a standard of living unequalled by any other country except that of their great neighbour to the south. This, also, has been achieved slowly and, except in wartime, in a rather unspectacular fashion, but Canadians have been able to convince themselves that they are capable of greater achievements. Canadians do not expect ever to rival Americans in numbers, wealth or power but they have confidence in their ability to build a great nation adapted to its resource base and in conformity with its geographic framework.

It is less than accurate to say that Canada has been built in defiance of geography. It is true, of course, that most of the productive natural regions of the country are northern extensions of regions of the United States. It is true also that those huge Canadian regions, the Shield and the Northland, are largely unproductive. It is even true that, in many instances, north-south communications appear to be easier than east-west. Yet Canada has been consolidated and continues to develop by utilizing the favourable factors in its geographical situation. Unfortunately these have not always been fully realized, however.

The St. Lawrence gateway to the continent was not fully exploited by either its French or English masters. Had either, in their day, recognized the full significance of the territory beyond the rapids, the "Empire of the St. Lawrence" would have been more than an historical legend. Canada would have been larger, the United States would have been smaller and the border would, perhaps, have been less

peaceful. Geography was not defied during colonial days, it was ignored. Had this not been the case, a St. Lawrence Seaway would have come into being very early, to be rebuilt and enlarged with each new development in navigation. Montreal would have become a more formidable rival of New York and the Erie Barge Canal might not have been built. It is to the Erie Canal that New York owes much of its head start, allowing that port to surpass Montreal in the pre-railway era. Early railroads in the Mohawk corridor were also important but other routes now carry much more freight to New York.

The Canadian railway pattern has borne much criticism. Observed from the viewpoint of physical geography alone, it does appear, perhaps, to be sheer defiance. In the realization that international boundaries, however illogical they may seem, are also potent geographical factors, the east-west railway systems become logical geographical correctives. At any rate the Great Lakes route had to be supplemented by a winter land route. Trans-Canada Airlines and the Trans-Canada Highway are justified for the same reasons. It is illogical to expect them to pay the costs of their development after the manner of capitalistic industrial enterprises. They are part of the price which Canada pays for the series of historical accidents which fixed the international boundary, and which must continue to be paid as long as North America accepts the geographical validity of separate national areas.

Canadian control of the Northland and the extension of communications and transportation routes in that direction are also uneconomic. However, they must be considered in the light of political geography rather than judged by the criteria of physical geography and economics. An uncontrolled northern frontier would be a threat, not only to Canada, but to the safety of the whole North American civilization.

Despite all ethnic and sectional tensions, the solution must be found in a united

Canada. No section is either populous enough, or sufficiently self-contained, to be capable of a separate political existence; while the removal of any section which might approach that condition would destroy the balance of the whole and most certainly make it impossible to exert effective control over the empty areas. Future increases in population and productive capacity will tend to increase the internal economic relations and thus to enhance Canadian unity.

## Future Population

Compared with many other countries, there is no doubt that Canada is underpopulated. There have been many estimates of the total carrying capacity of the country. Many people look at the map of Canada and the United States and predict for the northern half of the continent a population as great as that of the southern. It is considered merely a matter of time; Canada is just a century behind, that's all! Such a view is geographically unsound.

Canada and the United States are two nations but they constitute one cluster of human population. The international boundary has never been an effective bar to migration. People of Canadian origin constitute one of the larger groups in the United States of America and Americans are similarly numerous in Canada. It is far less of a cultural barrier. Newspapers, periodicals, moving pictures, radio programs and educational ideas cross the border freely. The Canadian standard of living is almost the same as the American.

The commercial and economic relations of Canada and the United States are very close. Canadian prices follow the same pattern as those of the United States, except for certain differences enforced by tariff walls. There are branches of American firms and much American money invested in Canada and the converse is also true. Canada and the United States are each other's best customers. The developments of the two countries have been parallel in most things and are likely to continue this trend, at least until a considerably higher density of population is reached in both countries.

This is abundantly clear from a study of population growth during the past century. In 1860, the colonies now comprising Canada had a little over 3,000,000 people, the United States had something over 30,000,000. Ninety years later, Canada has 14,000,000 and the U. S. A. has 150,000,000.

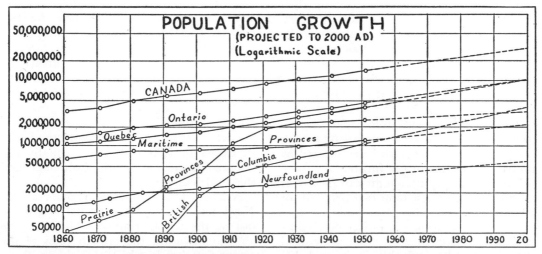

Figure 344.  *Trends of Population Growth in Canada.* By the end of this century Canada will have a population of more than 30,000,000 if the present trends continue.

The average upward trend of population growth is just a little steeper in the United States, but the rate of growth in later decades is slightly lower.

Glancing at Figure 344, we see that, in spite of slight deviations, the trend of population growth in Canada has been remarkably steady. The slump of the 1890's was more than compensated by the expansion in the first years of this century. The effects of the depression of the 1930's, also, have been cancelled by recent growth which is just a little better than the average.

There seems little reason to doubt that the average trend of the past century will continue for some time. It is true that most of the good agricultural land is already in use and the number of people in agricultural occupations has apparently passed its peak. Any further land settlement, and there will undoubtedly be some, will be offset by mechanization and enlargement of farms. Canada may expect a continuing forest activity of large proportions if due care is taken of the resources. In 70 years the value of mineral output has increased one hundred fold and certainly has not yet reached its full expansion. In 60 years the turbine installations for utilization of water power have expanded from 71,000 h.p. to 12,000,000 h.p., more than that of any other country in the world except the United States, and with much the highest rating per capita. Based on this, Canada is developing rapidly as an industrial country, having in only two decades expanded its factory labour force from 500,-000 to about 1,200,000 and the gross value of manufactured goods from $2,500,000,000 to $12,000,000,000. To an increasing extent, the people of Canada will be supported by industrial activity in the future.

The rate of population growth from year to year is a little less than two per cent, or 20% per decade. This means that we may expect to see a population of 20,000,000 by 1975 and of over 30,000,000 by the end of the century. Beyond this it is probably fruitless to speculate. In fact only slight changes in the average annual growth would be sufficient to vary the total by 5,000,000, either up or down, by the end of the fifty year period.

While it is much easier to forecast the growth of the whole population than that of any of the constituent regions, nevertheless we have indications of such trends also. They are not, however, all simple long term trends. There is a great difference between the older eastern provinces and the younger Prairie Provinces and British Columbia.

Ontario and Quebec, which have 60% of the total population, will continue in the lead. Urban and industrial growth, the development of water power and the completion of the St. Lawrence Seaway will keep this part of Canada growing a little faster than the rest for at least another half century. Quebec, which has been slowly but steadily catching up to Ontario, should have done so by the year 2000 when both will have populations of about 11,000,000.

British Columbia, which has for several decades been the most rapidly growing region, may be expected to continue as such for some time. The southwestern corner of that province seems certain to become one of the most densely inhabited and highly industrialized regions in Canada. The Prairie Provinces have, for two decades, had the slowest population growth of any region. While certain sections of Alberta will certainly increase greatly in the next fifty years because of urban and industrial expansion, the agricultural areas of the Great Plains must be regarded as almost saturated. By the end of the century, Western Canada should have a population in excess of 7,000,000, fairly equally distributed between British Columbia and the Prairies.

Neither the Maritime Provinces nor Newfoundland can be expected to grow as fast as the whole country. They may be able to maintain the growth rates of the recent decades; in which case they will, together, have a population of 3,000,000 while the Maritime Provinces will still be the most densely populated region of Canada on the basis of total area. The development of Northern Canada is extremely hard to predict. If mining prospects develop sufficiently there may be a population of a quarter of a million at the close of the century.

Canada must continue to have a moderate and well selected stream of immigrants. This will be necessary in order to maintain the desired rate of growth, for natural increase does so only in the best of years. There will always be a certain number of emigrants who must also be replaced. It would seem that Canada could well assimilate an annual average of about one-fifth as many new-comers as there are added to the population by natural increase.

After two or three centuries of rural expansion, Canada is becoming a land of cities. At the census of 1956, urban places of more than 1,000 persons were found to contain 10,714,855 inhabitants or about 67% of the total population. (See table 47). Seven metropolitan cities of more than 300,000 held 5,036,000 or 31%, seven urban areas of second rank, with 100,000 to 300,000 each, held 1,190,000 or 7½%, while

twenty-five third rank cities, with populations between 30,000 and 100,000, held over 1,580,000 or 9½%, thus bringing the "big city" population to 7,807,000 or 48%. However, the two largest cities, Montreal and Toronto, together contain 18% of Canada's people.

Such concentration of population, industry, commerce and other activities is unwise from several points of view. Foremost in our minds in these days, perhaps, is the matter of defence, for such large cities are extremely vulnerable to air attack. The time-space factor must also be considered. It now takes longer to cross Toronto than it does to go from its outskirts to Hamilton. The rapid transit system, opened in 1954, has improved matters along a north-south axis, but it will be years before east-west traffic is improved. Physical inertia is bound to keep the buildings, streets and parking lots of both Montreal and Toronto well behind the needs of the day, if they continue to expand at the present rate. On the other hand, if the growth of each could be checked when a population of 2,000,000 is reached, there might be some possibility that they could provide themselves with adequate facilities. Every effort should be made to direct additional population to

## Table 47     Urban Populations.     1956.

| Urban Area | Population | Urban Area | Population |
|---|---|---|---|
| Greater Montreal | 1,620,758 | Kitchener-Waterloo | 79,886 |
| Metropolitan Toronto | 1,358,028 | Greater Trois-Rivières | 78,212 |
| Greater Vancouver | 665,017 | Greater St. John's | 77,991 |
| Greater Winnipeg | 409,121 | Saskatoon | 72,858 |
| Greater Ottawa | 345,460 | Greater Oshawa | 64,792 |
| Greater Hamilton | 327,831 | Greater Sherbrooke | 63,866 |
| Greater Quebec | 309,959 | Greater Shawinigan Falls | 58,698 |
| **First Rank Cities** | **5,036,174** | Greater Kingston | 58,290 |
| | | Greater Brantford | 56,089 |
| Greater Edmonton | 251,004 | Greater Sarnia | 52,856 |
| Greater Calgary | 200,449 | Greater Niagara Falls | 51,411 |
| Greater Windsor | 185,865 | Greater Sault Ste. Marie | 50,704 |
| Greater Halifax | 164,200 | Greater Moncton | 50,018 |
| Greater London | 154,453 | Greater Peterborough | 45,848 |
| Greater Victoria | 125,447 | Greater Cornwall | 44,000 |
| Sydney-Glace Bay | 108,347 | Greater Timmins | 39,234 |
| **Second Rank Cities** | **1,189,765** | Greater Guelph | 36,891 |
| | | Greater Drummondville | 34,000 |
| Greater Sudbury | 95,582 | Greater Welland | 31,506 |
| Chicoutimi-Jonquiere | 92,780 | **Third Rank Cities** | **1,580,946** |
| Regina | 89,755 | | |
| Greater Saint John | 86,015 | Greater Cities Total | 7,806,885 |
| Greater Saint Catharines | 85,055 | Other Urban Areas | 2,907,970 |
| Lakehead Cities | 84,609 | Grand Total | 10,714,855 |

other cities. It would be preferable to have six new cities of half a million each, than to add three millions to Montreal and Toronto.

Other existing cities are expanding enormously. Quebec, Ottawa, Hamilton, Windsor, Winnipeg and Vancouver appear to be pointed toward the million mark and it would be well if they were planned so as not to go beyond it. Calgary and Edmonton are also destined to become large cities. If the growth of these larger centres be carefully kept in check, other cities which now have populations of 30,000 or over may hope to have 100,000 to 500,000 by 2000 A.D.

The smaller the city at the present time, the easier it will be to plan and to develop for its role fifty years hence. Indeed, there are certain obvious advantages in creating new cities, free from the shackles of the past. Since there is now no difficulty in providing transportation, these cities may be located away from the crowded areas. The Ottawa Valley, with its abundant water supply, electric power and direct transcontinental routes, would seem to be an obvious place for one such city.

An example of a proposed new city is Ajax. Founded during World War II as the site of a great munition factory, it housed the overflow of the University of Toronto during the post-war years. In 1951, its wartime houses sheltered 4,100 people, organized as an Improvement District. Here, on the shore of Lake Ontario, midway between Toronto and Oshawa and astride the major transportation routes of the province, it is proposed to build an industrial city of 30,000 people.

Ajax, however, is not destined to continue long as an isolated city. It will be part of a conurbation extending from Oshawa to the Niagara River, which by the end of the century will contain several million people and be the greatest concentration of population in Canada. Such an agglomeration will have many nuclei and Ajax will be one of them. It is to be hoped,

therefore, that the foundations will be laid for a community of 100,000.

Between Toronto and Hamilton the conurbation is rapidly taking form. Just west of the Toronto Metropolitan region is Toronto Township which has 50,000 people living under village and rural types of government. Oakville and Trafalgar Township, with an urban and suburban population of 22,000, are due for great expansion because of the location of the new Ford assembly plant. Further developments are bound to follow.

Other areas also are destined for future growth. The Lakehead, for instance, will, at its present rate of growth, be a city of 200,000 by the end of the century. The establishment of a primary steel industry, and the secondary industries which would be attracted by it, might well support double the population in spite of the fact that there is not, and never can be, a great agricultural hinterland. Even a future population of half a million, however, would hardly justify the setting up of a separate province of the Lakehead as is sometimes advocated.

The population of Canada is two and one-half times as large as it was at the beginning of the century; it will most certainly double itself again in the next half century. The resources of the country appear to be ample to support such an increase but some rather bold planning will be required to make sure that they are properly utilized. It will be even more difficult to avoid overcrowding in the more favourable areas, for the greater part of the country will always remain sparsely populated.

## Canada and the World

The maps of the Western Hemisphere, so commonly used in the past, foster the idea of Canadian isolation. Bounded by three oceans, one of which is completely frozen for most of the year and ice-choked for the remainder, Canada seems well removed from contact with other continents. And, so long as all contact depended upon sea transport, the physical isolation was real enough.

When we look at the northern half of a globe, or a polar projection, we see that Canada is much nearer to the centre of things. (Figure 345) Canada's northern frontier forms a considerable portion of the almost complete land ring around the Arctic Ocean. The great circle routes from North America to most parts of the Old World cross or touch upon Canadian territory. Over the eastern and western margins of the country these routes are used by the world's great airlines, two of which are based in Canada itself. There is little likelihood and little use for trans-polar flight in peace time, but it would be impossible to close this door completely against long range bombing or guided missiles in the event of war.

Canada is, and always has been, vitally interested in the Atlantic. Her people and her cultures have trans-Atlantic origins. The early trade of the country was mainly across the Atlantic and much of today's commerce follows Atlantic routes. Outlets to the Atlantic are therefore important. In common with the United States, Canada has a major portion of her population and her industrial development within 500 miles of the Atlantic. During two world wars this Atlantic frontier did not prove to be particularly vulnerable to invasion, but ships in the Atlantic approaches operated under extreme hazard. Much of the Canadian war effort was therefore expended upon Atlantic sea and air patrol for which Canadian bases are strategically located. Geography, in rather simple terms, dictates an interest in the North Atlantic Treaty Organization, much more compelling than that in the United Nations. Even if the United Nations will not work, the North Atlantic Treaty must.

The Pacific is a larger ocean and Canada's Pacific affairs are not so great; nevertheless they are vital. The southwestern corner of British Columbia is attracting an important concentration of population and industry while the foreign trade of Vancouver is second only to that of Montreal among Canadian ports. Canadians may not often remember that in World War I the Japanese navy helped to protect their Pacific commerce but they are not likely to forget the menace of those same Asiatic neighbors during World War II. Canada is desirous of increasing her trans-Pacific trade and, along with the United States, is alert for hostile manifestations from the same direction.

On the south, Canada adjoins the wealthiest and most powerful country on earth. The geographical realities of this relationship have already been discussed. Beyond the United States, however, there are other Americas in which Canada has considerable interest. From them are obtained important raw materials, such as bauxite, sugar and petroleum, to feed Canadian industries. Eastern Canada has a long history of trade relations with the Caribbean regions while, since the opening of the Panama canal, all Latin America is accessible from both Canadian coasts. Development of trade along a north-south axis will continue to be a major concern in Canadian external relations but there seems to be little need for defence against aggression from the south.

Historically, politically, and for a long time commercially, Canada was part of a world system centred upon the British Isles. She is an important member of the British Commonwealth of Nations and thus maintains world-wide relations. Physically and, to a large extent, commercially and culturally, she is also part of an American block with which her future is inseparably connected. Canada is therefore a nation "in the middle" whose political function is to provide a direct link between Britain and the United States, or, better still, between America and Western Europe. If she succeeds in this difficult role it will be because of her unique geographical position and the interplay of rather complex geographical factors. Not yet a "Great Power," but certainly not a minor one, she has reached the stage where her influence is felt throughout the world.

## Selected References

Brown, George W. (Editor) *Canada.* United Nations Series. University of Toronto Press. 1950.

Coats, R. H. (Editor) *Features of Present Day Canada. Annals,* American Academy of Political and Social Science. (Philadelphia) vol. CCLII 1947.

Charles, Enid, N. Keyfitz and H. Roseborough. *The Future Population of Canada.* Bulletin No. F-4. Dominion Bureau of Statistics, Ottawa. 1946.

Keyfits Nathan. *The Growth of Canadian Population.* Population Studies, vol. IV, pp. 47-63. 1950.

Taylor, Griffith. *Canada.* Methuen and Company Limited. London. 1947.

Timlin, Mabel F. *Does Canada Need More People?* Oxford University Press. Toronto. 1951.

Figure 345. *Canada in the World.*

# INDEX